ELEMENTS OF

Linear Algebra

ELEMENTS OF
Linear Algebra

LOWELL J. PAIGE

J. DEAN SWIFT

University of California, Los Angeles

Ginn and Company

BOSTON NEW YORK CHICAGO ATLANTA
DALLAS PALO ALTO TORONTO

TO

Peggy and Rosemary

Preface

This book owes its origin to intensive discussions between the authors and their colleagues concerning the content of the initial university course in algebra for majors in mathematics and mathematically inclined students in the sciences and engineering.

Until quite recently, the almost universal answer to this problem was a course in classical Theory of Equations. A number of factors have contributed to a widespread abandonment of this course. Perhaps the most compelling among these has been the increasing separation of the subject matter from the main stream of modern mathematics. This, in turn, has given rise to a number of courses in the easier parts of abstract algebra. We feel that, unless considerable attention is given to motivation, these courses are likely to create the impression that algebra is an exercise in abstraction for the sake of abstraction.

Our conclusions have been that linear algebra provides a core around which a desirable course can be constructed. This course can (and should) retain sufficient contact with experience and with applications to supply the motivation while permitting the introduction of important features from abstract algebra. Many desirable parts of Theory of Equations may be retained, and the relationship between linear algebra and coordinate geometry will provide a useful example of the interdependence of different branches of mathematics.

We consider our primary audience to be undergraduate mathematics majors, physics majors, or engineers. With these students in mind, we seek to present in this text basic ideas from linear algebra with sufficient rigor to statisfy mathematical tastes and to nurture an understanding of the meaning and nature of proofs in algebra. A serious attempt has been made to accomplish these aims without hampering the exposition by excessive formalism or unnecessary pedantry.

The number of new concepts to be introduced at the outset is kept to a minimum by concentrating on the real number field. However, when complex numbers become necessary we introduce them together with a brief exposition of the theory. The situation for abstract fields is not explicitly covered, but methods which lend themselves readily to generalization have been chosen whenever feasible. Thus the instructor (or the student) may, if he chooses, proceed much of the time at a more abstract level without significant changes in wording.

The basic theory of finite-dimensional vector spaces, of linear transformations over them, and of the associated matrix algebra is presented in Chapters 3, 6, 7, 8, 10, and 11. The discussion often deals with the vector space of real n-tuples, $V_n(R)$, and its subspaces. The concept of isomorphism is introduced initially to establish the equivalence of this theory to the general theory of real finite-dimensional vector spaces.

Matrices are introduced in their proper place as representations of linear transformations. The resulting emphasis on linear transformations avoids the use of clumsy matrix methods where the simpler and more elegant procedures of the algebra of linear transformations are available. However, we recognize that matrices have a definite place, particularly in applications, and we have provided the essential results of matrix algebra. In addition, Chapter 7 contains a discussion of the principal special classes of matrices. There are frequent reminders to the student of the matrix content of theorems when they are presented in terms of linear transformations, and many exercises provide practice in matrix manipulation.

The concept of an equivalence relation provides the algebraic background for our discussion of similarity, congruence, and equivalence of matrices. Geometric interpretations are utilized in the introduction of the orthogonal group of linear transformations and in the reduction of quadratic forms.

Finally, the concept of invariant subspaces, and in particular, of cyclic subspaces relative to a linear transformation, makes possible a development of the theory of canonical forms for matrices and a proof of such results as the Hamilton-Cayley theorem by methods which suggest the power and substance of modern algebra.

The chapters which are not concerned with the basic theory are auxiliary and may, to some extent, be considered as peripheral to the main development.

Chapters 1 and 2 may be used in varying ways in the development of the main topics. The list of field postulates in §2 of Chapter 1 is referred to throughout the text. It serves as a standard of comparison for the laws governing other algebraic structures as they are introduced. Hence, even though the instructor may not wish to discuss properties of general fields in detail at the outset, it would be well to ensure that some understanding of these postulates exists before proceeding. The other material in Chapter 1 on set notation, mappings, and methods of proof can either be covered at the beginning or be used to supplement the discussion in the text at the time the relevant topics are employed in the main development.

Chapter 2 introduces three-dimensional analytic geometry in vector language; many instructors will find it possible to omit the chapter or to use it as supplemental reading to Chapter 3, which it parallels in structure.

A geometrical interpretation of the vector algebra of Chapter 3 is developed in Chapter 4. Although this geometry is not essential to the further development of the theory, it provides a basis for interpretation and visualization that is of particular advantage to those interested in the application of the theory to other areas of mathematics and to physics.

Chapter 5 develops determinants from the point of view of a linear function on a set of vectors.

In Chapter 9, as a means of developing the essentials of the theory of equations, we have taken advantage of the need for some polynomial algebra in the discussion of characteristic and minimal polynomials and of characteristic values of matrices. The proof that the complex numbers are essentially the only two-dimensional division algebra over the real field is believed to be the only one to be found in an elementary text.

The text includes considerably more material than can be covered satisfactorily in a single three-semester-hour course. Indeed, experience has shown that six or seven chapters are sufficient. Thus a choice can be made for a number of courses depending on the preparation of the class and the wishes of the instructor. For a well-prepared class, the six chapters comprising the basic theory, with some supplemental material chosen from the other chapters, will comprise a semester course. A class with less preparation will find that Chapters 1 through 7 provide the basic algebraic and geometric theory of vector spaces, linear transformations, and matrices. This sequence would be particularly suitable for a freshman course given concurrently with calculus.

The cross-reference notation is fairly simple. Figures, theorems, definitions, and formulas within a chapter are numbered in decimal notation with the section number on the left and the number of the individual item on the right. A chapter designation is included only when the item referred to is not in the same chapter as the reference.

Illustrative examples are used abundantly throughout the text. The exercises are problems which either supplement the examples or carry out the simpler and more direct portions of the theory. No attempt has been made to provide a large number of abstractly identical drill problems. With a few exceptions, where provision for some practice is clearly necessary, each problem covers a distinct point. A reasonably large percentage of the problems should be solved by the student. A few exceptionally difficult problems have been starred, as have some sections on which the remainder of the text does not depend.

Answers are provided for those problems whose answers are unique or for which a particular answer will not create confusion even though it may differ from the one found by the student.

We wish to acknowledge our indebtedness to a number of our colleagues who have made valuable suggestions as to the content of this text. Particular thanks in this respect are due to Professors K. Rogers, R. S. Steinberg, and C. B. Tompkins. Professors R. A. Dean and G. Seligman carefully read both the initial draft and the final manuscript, and their critical appraisals were of great assistance. We also wish to thank Mrs. Elaine Barth and Mr. Earl Lusk for their invaluable help in the preparation of the manuscript and, finally, the editorial staff of Ginn and Company for their patience, counsel, and encouragement.

LOWELL J. PAIGE
J. DEAN SWIFT

Contents

Chapter 5 · Determinants

Chapter 6 · Linear Transformations and Matrices

Chapter 7 · Sets of Linear Transformations and Matrices

Chapter 8 · Bilinear and Quadratic Forms

Symbols Frequently Used

1. Set theory:

		PAGE
$\{a, b\}$	a set whose elements are a and b	2
$\in$ ($\notin$)	is (is not) an element of	1
$\subseteq$ ($\subset$)	is (properly) contained in	2
$\supseteq$ ($\supset$)	(properly) contains	2
$\cap$	intersection	2
$\cup$	union	2

2. Fields:

R	real field	4–5
Ra	rational field	5
C; F	complex field; subfield of complex field	243, 245
$F[x]$	polynomials over the field F	258
GCD	greatest common divisor	260

3. Vector spaces:

$[x_1, x_2, \cdots, x_n]$, $\mathbf{X}$	vector	26, 48
$\mathbf{E}_i$	ith natural basis vector	54, 68
$\lvert\mathbf{X}\rvert$	length of $\mathbf{X}$	38, 77
$(\mathbf{X}, \mathbf{Y})$	inner product of $\mathbf{X}$ and $\mathbf{Y}$	42, 76
$\{\mathbf{X}_i\}$	abbreviation for $\{\mathbf{X}_1, \mathbf{X}_2, \cdots, \mathbf{X}_n\}$	88, 142
$L\{\mathbf{X}_1, \mathbf{X}_2, \cdots, \mathbf{X}_n\}$	space generated by $\{\mathbf{X}_1, \mathbf{X}_2, \cdots, \mathbf{X}_n\}$	54
$V_n(R)$, $V_n(C)$, $V_n(F)$	space of n-tuples of designated field	48, 295
$V \oplus W$	direct sum of V and W	74
M_λ	subspace characteristic of λ	276
$L\{\mathbf{X}\mathrm{T}^i\}$, $L\{\mathbf{X}A^i\}$	cyclic subspace generated by $\mathbf{X}$ under T or A	301

4. Geometry:

E_n	Euclidean n-space	48
$(x_1, x_2, \cdots, x_n)$	coordinates of points of E_n	21, 48
$(d_Q(X, Y))$, $d(X, Y)$	(generalized) distance from X to Y	20, 96, 239

5. Transformations and matrices:

		PAGE
$T(a) = b$, $a \xrightarrow{T} b$	the image of a under T is b	9
$\mathbf{X}T = \mathbf{Y}$	the image of **X** under T is **Y**	137
$[a_{ij}]$, A	matrix	154
I; I	identity transformation; identity matrix	163
T^{-1}; A^{-1}	inverse of T; inverse of A	166, 168
A^{T}	transpose of A	115
A^*	conjugate transpose of A	296
det A	determinant of the matrix A	114, 115
Diagonal $[a_1, a_2, \cdots, a_n]$	diagonal matrix	189
$A \sim B$	A and B are in the same equivalence class	184
B(**X**, **Y**)	bilinear mapping or form	217
Q(**X**)	quadratic form	222
$C(p(x))$	companion matrix of $p(x)$	318

ELEMENTS OF

Linear Algebra

CHAPTER 1

Introduction

The purpose of this chapter is manyfold. Briefly, however, it will serve to establish a notation, review the concepts of functions and real numbers, and indicate some of the types of proof that may be found throughout the text. These introductory remarks should be particularly valuable to those students whose previous courses in algebra have been primarily computational in nature. The concept of a set of elements, the extension of the idea of a function on the real numbers to mappings of arbitrary sets, and a knowledge of the nature of various proofs are fundamental to all higher courses in mathematics. At the same time, a review of the real numbers permits us to emphasize an algebraic point of view.

1. Set Notation

We will have many occasions throughout this book to consider an aggregate or collection of objects. These objects will vary considerably both as to description and as to the properties possessed by the individual objects. We shall refer to such an aggregate or collection as a *set of elements.* The individual objects are elements (or members) of the set. For example, 3 is an element of the set of all positive integers; the letter "p" is an element of the set of letters of the alphabet; the set of all integers t such that $t^3 = 11$ contains no elements.

In view of the last example, we see that a set, defined as consisting of those elements which have certain properties, may, in fact, contain no elements. We call such a set the *empty*, or *null*, set. The use of the definite article is justified by the definition of *equality of sets:*

The sets A and B are equal if every element of A is an element of B and every element of B is an element of A.

We write $A = B$ and note that A and B contain the same elements. Hence any two empty sets are equal.

We write $s \in S$ to denote that s is an element of S; the contrary case is written $s \notin S$. If A and B are two sets and each element of A is an element of B, we write $A \subseteq B$ and say that A *is contained in* B or A is a *subset* of B or B *contains* A. If $A \subseteq B$ and $B \subseteq A$, $A = B$ by the definition of equality of sets. If $A \subseteq B$ and $A \neq B$, we say that A is a proper subset of B and write $A \subset B$. The notations $B \supseteq A$ and $B \supset A$ are also used with the same meanings as $A \subseteq B$ and $A \subset B$ respectively. Note that the empty set is a subset of every set.

The student should be sure to distinguish clearly between "element" and "subset." Occasionally, to avoid difficulties of logic, a distinction must be made between an element $a \in A$ and the subset of A whose only element is a. The latter is written $\{a\}$ and we have $\{a\} \subseteq A$. More generally, we often denote a set or subset by specifying each element. For example, $S = \{a, b, x, y, z\}$ or $S = \{1, 2, 3, 4, 5, 6\}$.

The *intersection* of two sets A and B is the set of all elements belonging to both A and B; it is written $A \cap B$. Of course, if the sets have no element in common their intersection is the empty set. In this case we say that A and B are *disjoint.*

The *union* of two sets A and B is the set of all elements belonging either to A or to B or to both A and B. It is denoted by $A \cup B$.

Example 1. We can illustrate many of our definitions with sets of points in a plane. For example, let the sets A_1, A_2, A_3 be the points of a plane bounded by the three circles c_1, c_2, c_3 respectively, as in Figure 1.1. The

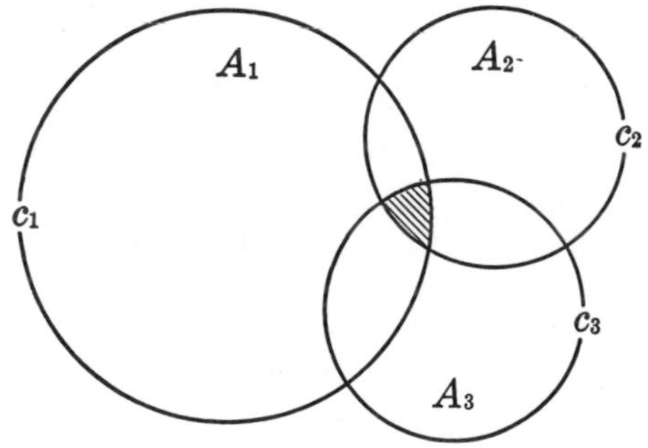

Figure 1.1

shaded portion is the set $A_1 \cap (A_2 \cap A_3) = (A_1 \cap A_2) \cap A_3$. This relation is valid for arbitrary sets, and the proof is typical of arguments demonstrating the equality of sets. We proceed with the proof by letting x be an arbitrary element of $(A_1 \cap A_2) \cap A_3$. Then, because of the definition of intersection, $x \in (A_1 \cap A_2)$ and $x \in A_3$. Similarly, since $x \in A_1 \cap A_2$, $x \in A_1$ and $x \in A_2$. On the other hand $x \in A_2$ and $x \in A_3$ means $x \in A_2 \cap A_3$. Moreover $x \in A_1$ and $x \in A_2 \cap A_3$ means $x \in A_1 \cap (A_2 \cap A_3)$. Therefore an arbitrary element x of $(A_1 \cap A_2) \cap A_3$ is an element of $A_1 \cap (A_2 \cap A_3)$ or

$$(A_1 \cap A_2) \cap A_3 \subseteq A_1 \cap (A_2 \cap A_3).$$

We now essentially repeat the arguments beginning with an arbitrary element y of $A_1 \cap (A_2 \cap A_3)$ to show that

$$A_1 \cap (A_2 \cap A_3) \subseteq (A_1 \cap A_2) \cap A_3,$$

and consequently we have the equality of the sets as desired.

Note that no reference to our diagram has been made in the proof so that the relation $(A_1 \cap A_2) \cap A_3 = A_1 \cap (A_2 \cap A_3)$ is valid for arbitrary sets. Therefore the parentheses are unnecessary and the set may be denoted unambiguously by $A_1 \cap A_2 \cap A_3$. A similar result is true for unions. These facts are expressed by saying that the operations of set union and set intersection are *associative.*

Example 2. Let A be the set of positive even integers, let B be the set of positive integers divisible by 3, and let C be the set of positive odd integers. The set $A \cup C$ is the set of all positive integers, $A \cap C$ is the null set, $A \cap B$ consists of positive integers which are multiples of 6.

EXERCISES

1. In Example 1, indicate the following sets by cross-hatching a redrawing of the original diagram in each case:
(a) $A_1 \cap A_2$ (b) $A_2 \cap A_3$ (c) $(A_1 \cap A_2) \cup A_3$
(d) $A_1 \cap (A_2 \cup A_3)$ (e) $(A_1 \cup A_2) \cap A_3$ (f) $(A_1 \cap A_3) \cup (A_2 \cap A_3)$

2. In Example 2, describe the following sets:
(a) $B \cap C$ (b) $A \cup B$ (c) $(A \cup B) \cap C$ (d) $A \cup (B \cap C)$

3. Prove the statement made in Example 1 that $A_1 \cup (A_2 \cup A_3) = (A_1 \cup A_2) \cup A_3$ for arbitrary sets A_1, A_2, A_3.

4. Let A be the set whose elements are 1, 2, 3, and 4, denoted by $A = \{1, 2, 3, 4\}$, and let $B = \{2, 4, 6, 8\}$. Let C be the set of symbols (a, b), where $a \in A$, $b \in B$.
(a) Is (2, 3) in C? (1, 8)? (6, 3)? (3, 6)?
(b) How many elements are in C?

5. Let $A = \{1, 2, 3\}$. List eight subsets of A. Determine a relation between the number of elements of a set with n elements and the number of subsets.

6. In Example 2 delete "positive" from the descriptions of A and C. Show that now $A \cup C$ is the set of all integers, positive, negative, and zero.

7. Prove that $(A \cap B) \cup C \supseteq A \cap (B \cup C)$ for arbitrary sets A, B, C. Note that these sets are unequal in both Example 1 and Example 2. The inequalities indicate the necessity for caution in dealing with parentheses.

8. Prove that $(A \cup B) \cap C = (A \cap C) \cup (B \cap C)$ for arbitrary sets A, B, C.

9. Prove that equality will always occur in the relation of Exercise 7 if $C \subseteq A$. Illustrate by a diagram.

10. Is there any necessary set-subset relation between $(A \cup B) \cap C$ and $A \cup (B \cap C)$ for arbitrary sets A, B, C? Illustrate possible equality with a diagram.

2. Real Numbers, Fields

The student is undoubtedly familiar with the basic properties of the set of real numbers R, and with those of some of its subsets such as the rational numbers and the integers; for example, the associative property for the addition of real numbers $(a + b) + c = a + (b + c)$. We have seen that a similar property is valid for set intersection $(A \cap B) \cap C = A \cap (B \cap C)$. In like manner, other properties of the real numbers will have analogous applications to sets which we shall consider in this text.

It would be possible to list a few basic properties of the natural numbers $1, 2, 3, \cdots$ and, on the basis of these alone, to construct the systems of the integers (positive, negative, and zero), the rationals (numbers of the form p/q where p and q are integers), and the real numbers in turn. In doing so, we would determine properties of the real numbers of interest to us. This is done, for example, in the book *Foundations of Analysis* by E. Landau (New York, Chelsea Publishing Company). Such a procedure, while admittedly a logical choice, would carry us too far from our goal. We will confine ourselves primarily to preparing a short catalogue of properties or laws possibly satisfied by elements of a set S, while including a few side remarks.

Suppose we have a set S. For the elements of S suppose further that an addition of elements, denoted by $+$, and a multiplication of elements, denoted by $\cdot$ or simply by juxtaposition, are defined. We shall assume for the elements of S that one or more of the following laws may hold:

A1. If $a \in S$, $b \in S$, then $a + b \in S$.

A2. If $a \in S$, $b \in S$, $c \in S$, then

$$(a + b) + c = a + (b + c). \qquad \textit{(Associative law)}$$

A3. There is an element $0 \in S$ such that

$$a + 0 = 0 + a = a \qquad \text{for every } a \in S.$$

A4. For every $a \in S$ there is an element $-a \in S$ such that

$$a + (-a) = (-a) + a = 0.$$

A5. If $a \in S$, $b \in S$, $a + b = b + a$. *(Commutative law)*

M1. If $a \in S$, $b \in S$, then $a \cdot b \in S$.

M2. If $a \in S$, $b \in S$, $c \in S$, then

$$(a \cdot b) \cdot c = a \cdot (b \cdot c). \qquad \textit{(Associative law)}$$

M3. There is an element $1 \in S$ such that $1 \neq 0$ and

$$a \cdot 1 = 1 \cdot a = a \qquad \text{for every } a \in S.$$

M4. For every $a \in S$ such that $a \neq 0$, there is an element $a^{-1} \in S$ such that

$$a \cdot a^{-1} = a^{-1} \cdot a = 1.$$

M5. If $a \in S$, $b \in S$, $a \cdot b = b \cdot a$. (*Commutative law*)

D1. If $a \in S$, $b \in S$, $c \in S$,

$$a(b + c) = ab + ac; \qquad \textit{(Left distributive law)}$$
$$(b + c)a = ba + ca. \qquad \textit{(Right distributive law)}$$

Note that the A-laws deal with properties of addition and the M-laws with properties of multiplication, and that the distributive laws are concerned with the relation between addition and multiplication.

If *all* the above laws apply to S, S is called a *field*. The set of real numbers forms a field; so does the set of rational numbers. These will be called the *real number field* and the *rational number field* respectively. They will be denoted by R and Ra.

There are many other examples of fields, some of which we have deferred to the exercises. At this time there are several remarks which are worthy of note concerning the laws defining a field.

Remark 1. Since we shall be using these laws individually or in small groups, no attempt was made to use the results of one law in stating another. For example, if M5 is assumed, the right distributive law in D1 would follow from the left distributive law and vice versa. However, in Chapter 6, we shall have occasion to consider sets where M5 does not apply but D1 does.

Remark 2. The statement $1 \neq 0$ in M3 is inserted to prevent the set consisting of the number 0 alone from being a field. If this set were a field it would make a number of our statements awkward. Without the requirement $1 \neq 0$, the student can easily verify that the set $\{0\}$ would logically satisfy all eleven laws.

Remark 3. The laws A3 and M3 are distinguished from the rest in that they call two particular elements, 0 and 1, to our attention. These elements appear again in A4 and M4, where they are used to define the *negative* $-a$ and the *inverse* a^{-1} respectively. In terms of the negative and inverse elements we may in turn define the familiar processes of *subtraction* and *division* by the formulas $a - b = a + (-b)$ and $a/b = ab^{-1}$.

Remark 4. The laws selected for our catalogue were not chosen by whim nor even on strictly utilitarian grounds for our needs in the remainder of the book. The assumption of various subsets of these laws for the elements of S is the basis of practically all areas of study in algebra. Moreover, properties of the real numbers that depend only upon addition and multiplication are direct consequences of these laws, and similar results are consequently valid for any field. For example, let us prove that $a \cdot 0 = 0$ for any real number a. Now, $0 + 0 = 0$ by A3; to this equality we apply the left distributive law after multiplying by a,

$$a \cdot (0 + 0) = a \cdot 0,$$
$$a \cdot 0 + a \cdot 0 = a \cdot 0.$$

Now to both sides add $-(a \cdot 0)$, whose existence is assured by A4. Then,

$$[(a \cdot 0) + (a \cdot 0)] + [-(a \cdot 0)] = a \cdot 0 + [-(a \cdot 0)].$$

An application of A2 to the left member and A4 to the right member of the previous equation yields $a \cdot 0 + \{(a \cdot 0) + [-(a \cdot 0)]\} = 0$; then $a \cdot 0 + 0 = 0$ by A4. Finally $a \cdot 0 = 0$ by A3.

No property of real numbers other than those listed has been used in this proof. Therefore $a \cdot 0 = 0$ is valid for any field.

Remark 5. We shall have occasion to mention sets in which only one operation, addition *or* multiplication, is defined. Naturally in these cases we shall consider only laws A1–A5 or M1–M5 respectively. In the latter case we shall delete the restrictions $1 \neq 0$ in M3 and $a \neq 0$ in M4 since an element 0 would not have previously occurred.

The properties of the real numbers that justify our saying that 6 is larger than $\sqrt{2}$ have found no expression in the laws we have listed. In remedying this, four more laws, concerning "order," will now be offered.

Let the set of elements S considered previously have defined for its elements a relation "greater than," written $>$, holding between pairs of elements. Then we consider the applicability of the following laws to S:

O1. If $a \in S$, $b \in S$, precisely one of the following three possibilities is true: $a > b$, $a = b$, $b > a$.

O2. If $a \in S$, $b \in S$, $c \in S$ and $a > b$, $b > c$, then $a > c$.

O3. If $a \in S$, $b \in S$, $c \in S$ and $a > b$, then $a + c > b + c$.

O4. If $a \in S$, $b \in S$, $c \in S$ and $a > b$, $c > 0$, then $ac > bc$.

If all fifteen laws so far written apply to S, S is called an *ordered field*. The real number field R and the rational number field Ra are ordered fields.

Remark 6. In an ordered field or, in general, a set which contains a zero element satisfying the laws A3 and O1–O4, elements a such that $a > 0$ are called *positive;* elements a such that $0 > a$ are called *negative*. The symbol $<$ may be defined by interpreting $a < b$ as $b > a$. Similarly "$a \leq b$" and "$b \geq a$" may be defined to include the possible equality of a and b.

Remark 7. The laws so far listed suffice to establish all purely algebraic properties of the real numbers. (There is room to quibble here, as "purely algebraic" has not been defined and, indeed, might be defined by applying the term solely to consequences of the fifteen laws. We are assuming an intuitive concept which might best be expressed negatively as "not depending on continuity or limits.") As an illustration, let us prove: If $a > b$, then $-b > -a$. To do this, begin with $a > b$ and use O3 twice; adding first $-a$, then $-b$: $a + (-a) > b + (-a)$; $[a + (-a)] + (-b) > [b + (-a)] + (-b)$. Now applying the laws of addition, we obtain $-b > -a$. The student is advised to carry out each step individually and note the particular law of addition used. Proofs of the following additional rules involving order as well as addition and multiplication are left for the exercises:

(i) If $a > b$ and $ab > 0$, then $1/b > 1/a$.
(ii) If $a > b$ and $c > d$, $a + c > b + d$.
(iii) If $a > b > 0$ and $c > d > 0$, $ac > bd$.

Remark 8. We may define the concept of *absolute value* of an element a of an ordered field in a manner similar to that for real numbers. Define $|a|$ to be a if $a \geq 0$ and $|a|$ to be $-a$ if $a < 0$. In the exercises, proofs of the following properties will be required:

(iv) $|ab| = |a||b|$;
(v) $|a + b| \leq |a| + |b|$.

Since we have at least two examples of ordered fields, the real numbers and the rational numbers (there are others; one is mentioned in the exercises), it is clear that we have not listed enough laws applicable to the real numbers to completely describe or characterize the real number field R. The key point in which the real number field differs from the rational field and other ordered fields that contain the rationals is in the property of continuity. To phrase it in colloquial terms, "There are no holes in the reals." This concept of continuity belongs primarily to analysis rather than algebra. Therefore any prolonged discussion would be inappropriate here. The problem affects the subject matter of this book only in our need for a particular relationship between the real field R and the set of points of a line. This relation will be discussed at the beginning of the next chapter. Rather than make any attempt at a complete development of continuity, we will content ourselves with a single example and a statement of the general result.

Let A be a subset of the rational numbers such that $a \in A$ if and only if $a^2 < 2$. There are rational numbers b (indeed infinitely many of them) such that $a \leq b$ for all $a \in A$. Such a number b is *at least as large* as any element of A. These rational numbers b are called *upper bounds* for the set A. In this particular case some upper bounds are 5, 17, 132, $\frac{3}{2}$. Now we ask: "Among all the rational upper bounds for A, is there a least?" The answer is No. We have restricted our attention to just the rational numbers, and if p/q is an upper bound, it is easy to prove that $(3p + 4q)/(2p + 3q)$ is a smaller upper bound. That is, if $p^2/q^2 > 2$, then $[(3p + 4q)/(2p + 3q)]^2 > 2$ and $p/q > (3p + 4q)/(2p + 3q)$. The case $p^2/q^2 = 2$ *does not arise* since $\sqrt{2}$ is irrational. Now if, in the definition of A, the word "rational" is changed to "real," it is easy to see that A has a real *least upper bound*, namely, $\sqrt{2}$. This is characteristic of the real number field: Every subset of the *real* field which has an upper bound has a *real least* upper bound. Furthermore the real field is *the* ordered field that contains the integers and is such that every subset with an upper bound has a least upper bound.

EXERCISES

1. How many of the fifteen basic laws are satisfied by:

(a) The positive integers?

(b) The integers?

(c) The subset of the reals consisting of numbers of the form $a + b\sqrt{2}$ where a and b are rational?

2. Prove that the right distributive law follows from the other laws of a field. Justify each step.

3. Prove: If a and b are real numbers such that $a \neq 0$ and $ab = 0$, then $b = 0$.

4. Prove that $(-a)(-b) = ab$ by associating in two ways the expression $ab + a(-b) + (-a)(-b)$.

5. Prove properties (i), (ii), and (iii) in Remark 7.

6. Prove properties (iv) and (v) in Remark 8.

7. Show that the numbers $a + bi$, where $i^2 = -1$ and a and b are real, form a field. These numbers form the *complex number field.*

8. For the complex number i, show that neither $i > 0$ nor $-i > 0$ by using property O4 after assuming either case. Now show that the complex field is not ordered.

9. Consider the set $S = \{a, b\}$ with addition and multiplication defined by:

$$a + a = b + b = a,\ a + b = b + a = b;$$
$$aa = ab = ba = a,\ bb = b.$$

How many of the first eleven laws are satisfied by S? Is S a field?

10. Prove the statements made in the last paragraph of this section regarding the relations of p/q and $(3p + 4q)/(2p + 3q)$.

11. Prove that no proper subset of the rationals is a field when addition and multiplication are the customary operations.

3. Single-valued Mappings

The concept of a function which has occurred in earlier courses in mathematics must now be reformulated and generalized to conform with modern algebraic usage and to provide a convenient notation. The student is probably most familiar with functions which involve two subsets, X and Y, of the real numbers and are determined by a rule assigning to each element $x \in X$ a particular element $y \in Y$. For example, X may consist of the numbers x such that $-1 \leq x \leq 1$, Y may consist of the numbers y such that $0 \leq y \leq 1$, and the rule could be $y = \sqrt{1 - x^2}$, that is, to each $x \in X$ we assign the real number $\sqrt{1 - x^2}$ in Y. There are clearly three components in the definition of a function: a *domain of definition* X, an *image set* Y, and a rule which assigns to each element $x \in X$ a unique element $y \in Y$. The type of function first described in which X and Y are restricted to be subsets of the real numbers is a special case of what we shall call single-valued mappings.

DEFINITION 3.1. *Let A and B be two arbitrary sets. Let* T *be a rule which assigns to each element $a \in A$ a unique element $b \in B$. Then* T *is called a* SINGLE-VALUED MAPPING *of the set A into the set B.*

The set A is called the *domain of definition* for the mapping T, and the element $b \in B$ assigned by T to a, denoted by $b = \mathrm{T}(a)$, is called the *image* of the element a.

The set $\mathrm{T}(A)$ consisting of all those elements of B which are images of elements in A will be called the *image set* or *range of values*. When $\mathrm{T}(A) = B$ we say that T is a single-valued mapping of A *upon* or *onto* B. When $\mathrm{T}(A)$ is a subset of B we say that T is a single-valued mapping of A *into* B. In any case T is always a single-valued mapping of A *onto* $\mathrm{T}(A)$.

DEFINITION 3.2. *Let* T *be a single-valued mapping of the set A onto the set B. If every element in B is the image of a unique element $a \in A$, then* T *is called a* ONE-TO-ONE *or* BIUNIQUE *mapping of the set A onto the set B.*

The following diagrams may be useful in clarifying these definitions. To simplify matters, we let A and B denote sets of points in the plane. The single-valued mapping T is indicated by drawing an arrow from the element $a \in A$ to the element $b \in B$ to represent the relationship $b = \mathrm{T}(a)$.

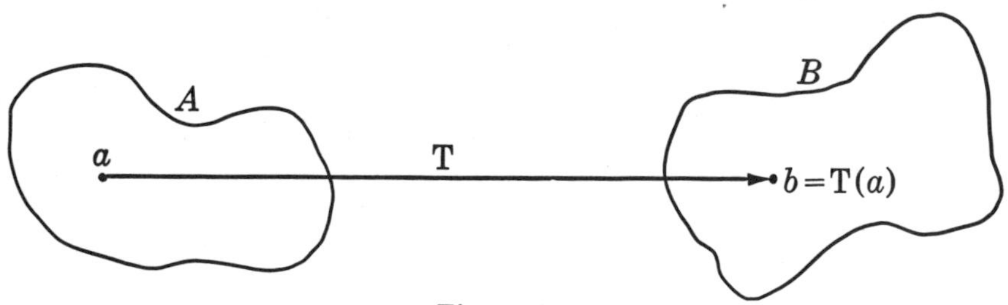

Figure 3.1

The entire mapping of A by T might be indicated by Figure 3.2. Somewhat crudely, if the image set $T(A)$ covers all of B, the mapping T is

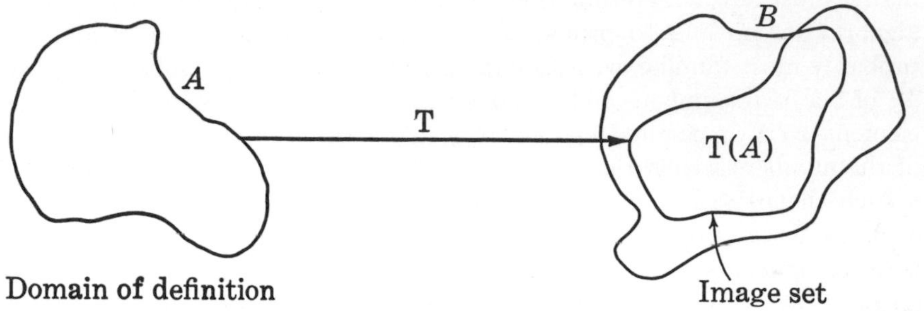

Figure 3.2

upon or *onto* B; on the other hand, if $T(A)$ is not necessarily all of B, the mapping T is *into* B. Again we point out that the mapping T is always *onto* $T(A)$.

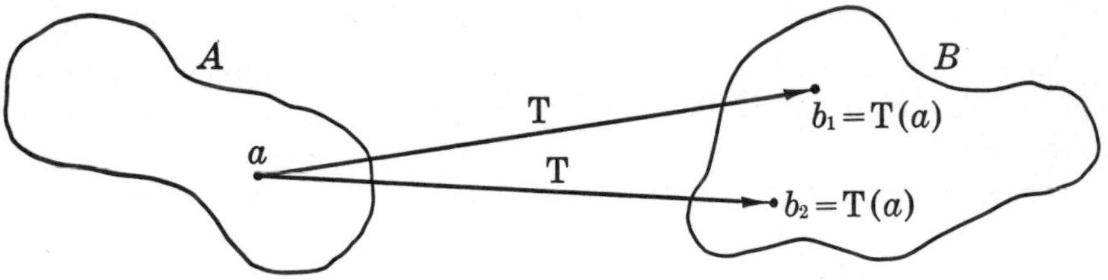

Figure 3.3

The situation illustrated in Figure 3.3 can *never* occur for a single-valued mapping; that is, in such a mapping a unique b is assigned to each $a \in A$. However, we can have the situation illustrated in Figure 3.4 for a single-valued mapping. This would merely indicate that the mapping T is *not*

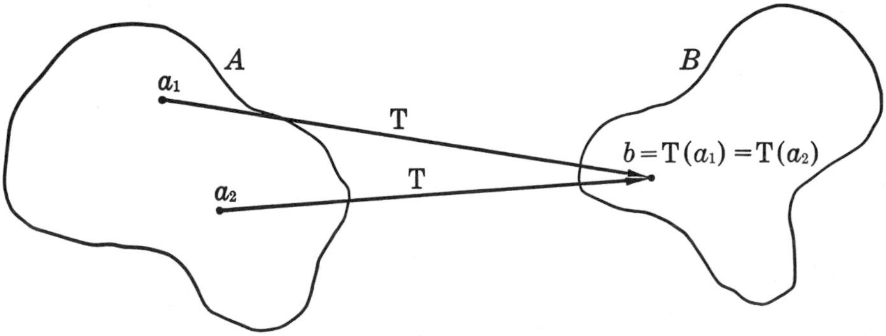

Figure 3.4

one-to-one, or biunique. Thus, in order to prove that a mapping T is one-to-one it is necessary to show that $T(a_1) = T(a_2)$ implies $a_1 = a_2$.

It is possible for a mapping to be one-to-one *into* a set B. Usually in this case the subset $T(A)$ of B is of the most importance, and this is why Definition 3.2 was worded in terms of an onto mapping T.

Even when one is considering mappings of a set onto or into itself, a useful diagram can be made by merely repeating the set A; thus we have the situation shown in Figure 3.5, and again $T(a)$ is in A.

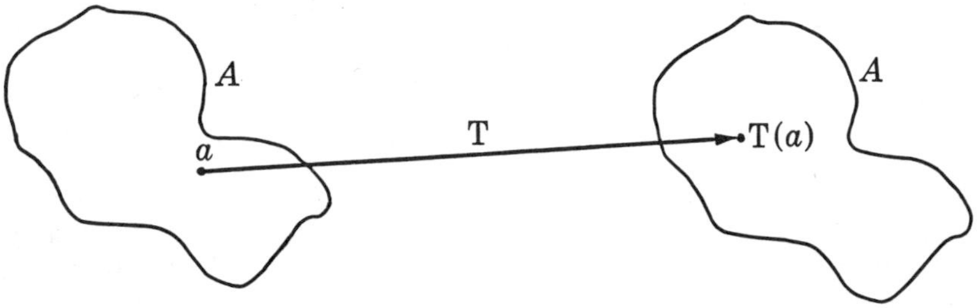

Figure 3.5

Example 1. Let A be the set whose elements are words in a dictionary. Let B be the set whose elements are the letters of the alphabet. A rule T assigns to each element of A the first letter of its spelling. If there were a letter which was never used initially, T would be a single-valued mapping of A into B but not onto B (such letters exist in some alphabets, Russian for example). Certainly T is not one-to-one since many words begin with the same letter.

Example 2. Let A be the set whose elements are the people of a given city. Let B consist of the non-negative integers. A rule T assigns to every person in the city the number of books that person has read during his life. Clearly T is a single-valued mapping of A into B. The image set $T(A)$ cannot coincide with all of B (Why?); hence the mapping T is not of A onto B.

We now give some examples which are mathematical in nature:

Example 3. Let A be the set whose elements are triangles in a plane. Let B consist of the positive real numbers. A rule T assigns to each triangle the area of this triangle. T is a single-valued mapping of A onto B. Clearly T is not a one-to-one mapping of A onto B since many different triangles have the same area.

Example 4. Let A be the set whose elements are the ordered pairs of real numbers (x, y). Let B consist of the real numbers. A rule T assigns to each pair (x, y) of A the number y of B. T is a single-valued mapping of A onto B. (Why?)

EXERCISES

1. Let the set A consist of the people listed in a telephone directory. Let B consist of the integers $0, 1, 2, \cdots, 9$. Define a single-valued mapping of A onto B.

2. Let A be a set of students in a lecture room and let T be a rule assigning to each student his age. Is T a single-valued mapping of A into the set of positive integers? Can one use the set of all integers for B? If so, is the mapping into or onto?

3. Let both A and B be the set of positive integers. Let T assign to n the value n^2. Describe the situation in the terminology of this section.

4. Let A be a finite set of integers $1, 2, \cdots, n$. Let T be a single-valued mapping of A onto A. Prove that T is a one-to-one mapping of A onto A.

5. Let A be the set of positive integers and let B be the set of positive even integers. Let T assign to n the value $2n$. Is T a one-to-one mapping of A onto B? Consider the fact that $B \subset A$. When is such a one-to-one mapping of a set onto a proper subset possible?

6. Let both A and B be the set of positive integers. Let T be a rule which assigns the value n in B to the odd integer $2n - 1$ in A and also the value n to the even integer $2n$ in A. Is T a single-valued mapping of A onto B? Is it one-to-one? Compare with Problem 4.

7. How many different one-to-one mappings of the set $\{1, 2, 3\}$ onto itself are there? Generalize to the set of Problem 4.

8. Is the mapping described in Exercise 3 onto B or into B? Justify your answer.

9. If T_1 and T_2 are single-valued mappings of a set A onto itself, we can define a "product" mapping $T_1 \circ T_2$ by $[T_1 \circ T_2](a) = T_1(T_2(a))$. Is $T_1 \circ T_2$ a single-valued mapping of A onto A? How would you indicate the situation in terms of diagrams?

10. If T is a one-to-one mapping of a set A onto a set B, define the *inverse* mapping T^{-1} to be the mapping from B to A that assigns to an arbitrary element $b \in B$ the element $a \in A$ that maps onto b under the mapping T. Show that $[T^{-1} \circ T](a) = a$ for all $a \in A$.

11. Let A be the set of integers, positive, negative, and zero. Let T_1 be the mapping of A into A that assigns to n the integer $2n + 1$. Let T_2 be the mapping that assigns to n the value $2n - 1$.

(a) What is $(T_1 \circ T_2)(n)$?
What is $(T_2 \circ T_1)(n)$?

(b) Is $T_1 \circ T_2$ a biunique mapping of A onto A?

(c) Does T_1 have an inverse?

(d) Does there exist a mapping T of A into A such that $T \circ T_1(n) = n$ for all n?

4. Proofs

As a final introductory topic we will make a few comments on some of the methods of proof used in mathematics. We assume that the student already has a basic understanding of the meaning of mathematical proof as a logical process of reaching a definite conclusion from definite assumptions. Our purpose here is merely to provide a guide to some of the types of argument which frequently cause difficulty for students inexperienced in rigorous mathematics.

For example, let us turn back to Exercise 3 in §2: "Prove: If a and b are real numbers such that $a \neq 0$ and $ab = 0$, then $b = 0$."

Here the permitted assumptions may be divided into four simple statements:

(i) a is a real number;
(ii) b is a real number;
(iii) $a \neq 0$;
(iv) $ab = 0$.

The desired conclusion to be obtained is that $b = 0$. If we study the assumptions we see that (i) and (ii) simply tell us what set of elements we are dealing with and what rules we can use; (iii) and (iv) offer specific evidence to work with. Indeed, thinking of the laws concerning the real numbers, we recall that (iii) guarantees the existence of an inverse a^{-1} of a such that $a^{-1}a = 1$ (M4). We may multiply equation (iv) by a^{-1} to obtain $a^{-1}(ab) = a^{-1} \cdot 0$ and, by the associative law M2, $(a^{-1}a)b = a^{-1} \cdot 0$. Then $1 \cdot b = a^{-1} \cdot 0$, or $b = a^{-1} \cdot 0 = 0$ by the result proved in Remark 4, §2. We would speak of such a proof as a *direct* proof, as we have reached the desired conclusion without further assumptions.

The operations of the preceding proof can be summarized in a few sentences as follows: Since $a \neq 0$, a has an inverse a^{-1}. Then $a^{-1}(ab) = (a^{-1}a)b = 1 \cdot b = b$. But since $ab = 0$, $a^{-1}(ab) = a^{-1} \cdot 0 = 0$. Therefore $b = 0$. These sentences would constitute a satisfactory solution to the exercise as we have merely suppressed the detailed reason for each step. There are, of course, other satisfactory solutions. We might, for example, decide to investigate what would result if all the assumptions held and the conclusion were false. That is, suppose a and b are real, $a \neq 0$, $ab = 0$ *and* $b \neq 0$. Since we are now assuming $b \neq 0$, b^{-1} exists. Hence $(ab)b^{-1} = 0 \cdot b^{-1}$ or $a \cdot 1 = 0$, $a = 0$. This contradicts the assumption that $a \neq 0$. Thus we see that if we assume a and b real, $a \neq 0$, and $ab = 0$, we cannot simultaneously have $b \neq 0$. Hence we must conclude that $b = 0$.

The method last used is called an *indirect proof*. The assumptions or hypotheses are taken unchanged but the conclusion is denied and we show that the result produces a contradiction (the old name is *reductio ad absurdum*). When, as here, there is no advantage in briefness or clarity to be gained by an indirect proof, the direct method is to be preferred.

Now let us look at a problem in which the indirect method is advantageous. Consider Exercise 4 of §3:

"Let A be a finite set of integers $1, 2, \cdots, n$. Let T be a single-valued mapping of A onto A. Prove that T is a one-to-one mapping of A onto A."

We must show that each element of A is the image of a unique element $a \in A$. Suppose this is false. Then some element of A is the image of at least two elements i and j of A. Since i and j have only one image between them and there are only $n - 2$ other elements in A, the total number of images cannot exceed $(n - 2) + 1 = n - 1$. But the mapping T is onto A by hypothesis, so the total number of images is the number of elements of A, namely n. This is the desired contradiction, and hence each element of A is the image of a unique element of A. The student might question whether this is better than a direct proof of the same problem; he is encouraged to produce a direct proof along similar lines.

It sometimes happens that we prove one result when, by the expenditure of essentially the same amount of effort, we could prove a better, more inclusive result. This process may be illustrated by the last example. Suppose we change the statement to: "Let A be a finite set with n elements, $a_1, a_2, \cdots, a_n$. Let B also be a set with n elements, $b_1, b_2, \cdots, b_n$. Let T be a single-valued mapping of A onto B. Prove that T is a one-to-one mapping of A onto B." If the student will go through the preceding paragraph and change the first, third, sixth, seventh, and eighth occurrences of A to B, the i's to a_i, and the j's to a_j, he will find that he has a proof of the new result which is clearly more general.

Precisely where a generalization is to be preferred over a simpler result is a difficult question to answer. It would of course depend upon the particular objectives in mind. For example, a great deal of the present text could be generalized with little additional effort, but we prefer to maintain a certain amount of simplicity as this will be the first time that the student has met many of the concepts to be considered. The generalizations are often left for the exercises.

Another method of proof often encountered uses *mathematical induction*. There are really two types of induction. In either case the statement to be proved involves a positive integer n and is to be proved for all such integers — for example, the statement $1 + 2 + \cdots + n = n(n + 1)/2$. Also in either case the statement is first proved for $n = 1$. In "weak," or "first-case," induction, the statement is next proved for $n = k$ on the assumption that it is true for $n = k - 1$. Here k is an arbitrary positive integer greater than 1. In "strong," or "second-case," induction, the statement is proved for an arbitrary positive integer k on the assumption that it is true for *all* positive integers less than k. When, in either case, the two parts are successively concluded we assert that the statement is true of all positive integers.

The justification for the last assertion rests on a postulate or law concerning the positive integers:

WELL-ORDERING PRINCIPLE. *Any non-empty set of positive integers contains a least element.*

Now if the statement to which we have applied induction is to fail at all, the set of positive integers for which it fails is not empty and contains a *least* integer k. We know $k \neq 1$ since we prove the statement true for $k = 1$. Hence there are positive integers smaller than k for *all* of which the statement is true. But we prove in strong induction that, if the statement is true for all integers less than k, it is true for k; or, in weak induction, that, if the statement is true for $k - 1$ it is true for k. In either case the statement is true for k. This is a contradiction. Hence the set of positive integers for which the statement fails cannot be non-empty; it must be empty.

To illustrate, we will prove by weak induction that the answer to the second part of Exercise 7 of §3 is $n!$. This is the number of single-valued mappings of the set $\{1, 2, \cdots, n\}$ onto itself. To do this we find it *easier* to do a more general problem — one suggested by the observation made earlier in this section. Let A be the set $\{a_1, a_2, \cdots, a_n\}$ and let $B = \{b_1, b_2, \cdots, b_n\}$. We prove that the number of single-valued mappings of A onto B is $n!$.

First, for $n = 1$, it is obvious that the only single-valued mapping of $\{a_1\}$ onto $\{b_1\}$ is that given by the correspondence $a_1 \longrightarrow b_1$.

Now, assume that the number of single-valued mappings of any set of $k - 1$ elements onto another set of the same number of elements is $(k - 1)!$ and consider the possible mappings of $\{a_1, a_2, \cdots, a_k\}$ upon $\{b_1, b_2, \cdots, b_k\}$. We may take the image of a_1 to be any of the k elements $b_1, b_2, \cdots, b_k$; having made a choice, it is left to determine a single-valued mapping of the subset $\{a_2, \cdots, a_k\}$ upon the set of the remaining $k - 1$ elements of B. By assumption there are $(k - 1)!$ such mappings. Hence the total number is $k \cdot (k - 1)! = k!$.

It is not absolutely necessary that the initial value of an induction process be 1. Any *definite* integer will do, but there must be some place to begin. Thus we might prove the statement for $n = 7$, and the statement would next be proved for k on the assumption that it is true for $k - 1$. Here k is an arbitrary integer greater than 7. Our conclusion would be that the statement is true for all values of $n \geq 7$. Again the well-ordering principle justifies this conclusion, and the proof is left for the student.

We think it desirable to include a remark about exercises or theorems that have the form: "P is true if and only if Q is true." Students often fail to note that two statements are involved and that both must be verified for a complete proof. The two statements to be verified are briefly: (1) If Q is true, then P is true. (2) If P is true, then Q is true. With this word of caution, we hope that the student may find that any difficulty in a particular exercise is in the mathematics and not in a misunderstanding of what he has to prove.

EXERCISES

1. In the argument given on the validity of the induction method, state specifically what was the hypothesis, or basic assumptions; what was the conclusion. Was the proof direct or indirect? If indirect, how was the conclusion assumed false and what contradiction resulted?

2. Give a direct proof by induction of the generalized statement that any single-valued mapping of a set with n elements onto another such set is a one-to-one mapping. Could such a proof be given for the original statement of Exercise 4, §3?

3. Why was it easier in the induction proof illustrated in the text to prove the more general statement?

4. Prove by induction:

(a) $1 + 2 + \cdots + n = n(n + 1)/2$

(b) $1^3 + 2^3 + \cdots + n^3 = \left[\frac{n(n+1)}{2}\right]^2$

5. Using the well-ordering principle, prove that there is no integer between 0 and 1.

Hint: If m is an integer such that $0 < m < 1$, $0 < m^2 < m < 1$.

6. What is wrong with the following "proof" that all elements of any finite non-empty set are identical?

First the statement is certainly true for any set with just one element. Now suppose the statement true for any set with $k - 1$ elements and consider a set $A = \{a_1, a_2, \cdots, a_k\}$. If we remove the first element, a_1, of A, the rest are the same by assumption. If we remove the last, a_k, the rest are again the same. That is, $a_2 = a_3 = \cdots = a_k$ and $a_1 = a_2 = \cdots = a_{k-1}$. Combining the two sets of equalities, $a_1 = a_2 = \cdots = a_k$.

7. Prove by induction that the number of subsets of a set with n elements is 2^n.

8. If A and B are finite sets with m and n elements respectively, prove that the number of single-valued mappings of A into B is n^m. Show how Exercise 7 may be obtained as a special case of this exercise.

9. Let P and Q stand for two statements. Suppose that the compound statement, "If P then Q" is true. Prove that the compound statement, "If not Q then not P" is true.

CHAPTER 2

Vectors and Analytic Geometry of Space

The introduction of a linear coordinate system in space enables us to investigate many geometrical properties by analytic methods. Of particular interest are relations between points, lines, and planes; for example, at what point P might a line L intersect a plane π? The concepts of vectors and of their rules of operation are introduced to provide a convenient and useful tool in answering this and other geometrical questions.

The study of vectors and the application of vectors to the geometry of space will involve a certain amount of duplication of the work of the next chapter, where a more general account of vector spaces will be presented. However, the geometry of space is unique in that it offers an opportunity for visualization in the application of vectors to geometrical properties while permitting sufficient freedom to illustrate many features of vector spaces in general. Accordingly, many students will find this material a helpful illustration of the concepts in future chapters.

1. Coordinate Systems in Space

We shall assume in this section that we are dealing with the points, lines, and planes of familiar Euclidean space. Inherent in this assumption is the concept of distance between two points. A student's previously acquired intuitions and notions concerning distance will be sufficient to introduce coordinate systems in space which will generalize Cartesian coordinate systems.

A *coordinate system* for the points on a line L is established in the following manner: Choose two distinct points P_0 and P_1 on L and call the distance from P_0 to P_1 the unit distance. P_0 is called the origin and P_1 the unit point on L. For each point P on L, denote by p the ratio of the dis-

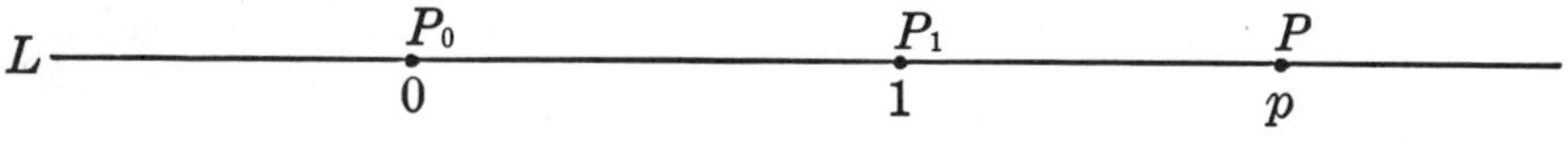

Figure 1.1

tances from P_0 to P and P_0 to P_1. Assign to P the coordinate p if P_0 is not between P and P_1 and $-p$ if P_0 separates P and P_1. This rule of assignment is a single-valued mapping T of the set of points on L into the real numbers. The mapping T is a coordinate system for L.

If we assume that the points on a line L have an existence independent of any coordinate system, it is not obvious that every real number x is the coordinate (image) of some point. In order to make the real number system an effective concept in interpreting our intuitive geometry of space we must make the assumption that the mapping T establishing a coordinate system on a line is a one-to-one mapping of the points of L *onto* the real number system.

It should be clear from the manner of construction of a coordinate system that the ratio of the distance from P_x to P_y, whose coordinates are x and y, to the unit distance is $| x - y |$.

The half line from P_0 which contains P_1 is called the positive coordinate axis, and the other half line is called the negative axis.

Many different coordinate systems may be established on a line L. Thus for P_0 fixed and different choices of P_1, we obtain different coordinates for a particular point P and, consequently, different coordinate systems.

Linear coordinate systems for planes. In order to establish a linear coordinate system for a plane π, take any two intersecting lines L_1 and L_2 in the plane π and, using the point of intersection of L_1 and L_2 as P_0, establish a coordinate system on each of L_1 and L_2. It is not necessary to make the unit distance on L_1 equal to the unit distance on L_2. In Figure 1.2 we have purposely avoided this equality.

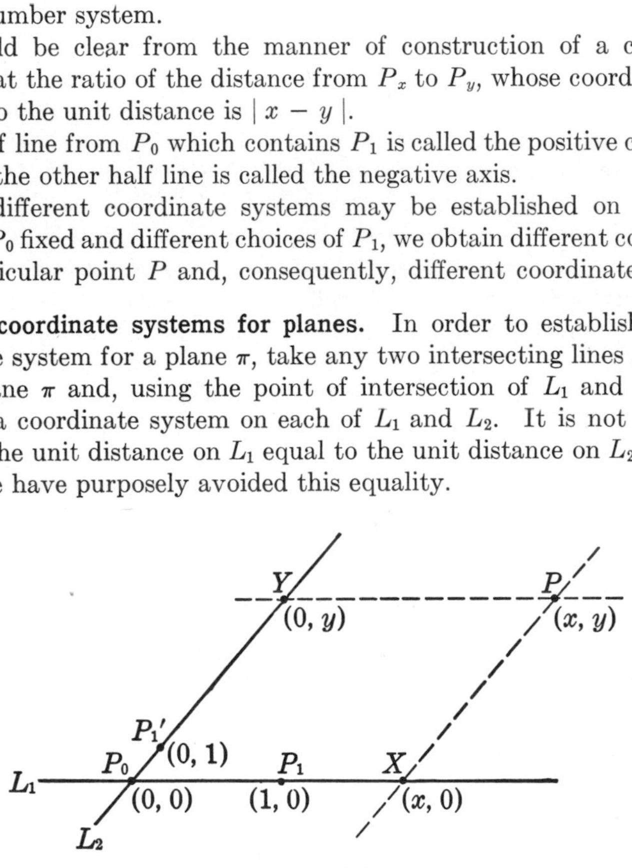

Figure 1.2

A point X on L_1 has a coordinate x in the coordinate system for L_1. In our coordinate system for the plane, we assign to this point the ordered pair of real numbers $(x, 0)$. Similarly, a point Y on L_2 has a coordinate y in the coordinate system for L_2, and we assign to this point the ordered pair $(0, y)$. Hence to P_0 the ordered pair $(0, 0)$ is assigned.

If P is any point in the plane not on L_1 or L_2, we construct lines through P parallel to L_2 and L_1. Let the points of intersection with L_1 and L_2 respectively be X and Y. Then we assign to P the ordered pair (x, y), where x is the coordinate of X on L_1 and y is the coordinate of Y on L_2.

We have now assigned to every point P in the plane an ordered pair of real numbers (x, y). These real numbers are designated as the coordinates of the point P. We have thus established a one-to-one mapping T between all points in the plane and all ordered pairs of real numbers (x, y). This mapping will be called a *linear coordinate system* for the plane π.

If the distances from P_0 to P_1' and P_0 to P_1 are equal and L_1 is perpendicular to L_2, we have a familiar Cartesian coordinate system. In this case the first number in the ordered pair (x, y) is called the *abscissa* and the second number the *ordinate* of the point P.

Example 1. Let us take a Cartesian coordinate system as reference and establish a new linear coordinate system in the plane by the use of the x-axis as L_1 and the line through the origin at an angle of 45° with the x-axis as L_2. Choose the unit point on L_1 to be the point whose Cartesian coordinates are $(2, 0)$. Choose the unit point on L_2 to be the point whose Cartesian coordinates are $(1, 1)$.

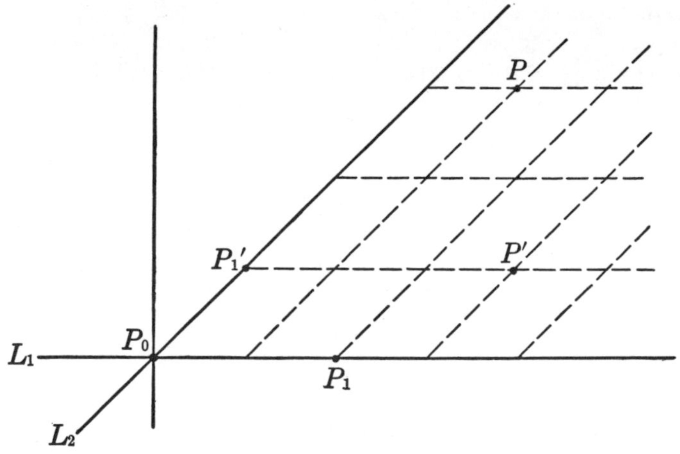

Figure 1.3

We will determine the linear coordinates of the points P and P' whose Cartesian coordinates are $(4, 3)$ and $(4, 1)$.

First, the lines through the point $(4, 3)$ and parallel to L_2 and L_1 intersect L_1 and L_2 at points whose Cartesian coordinates are $(1, 0)$ and $(3, 3)$. Thus, the coordinates of P with respect to L_1 and L_2 are the ordered pair $(\frac{1}{2}, 3)$. Similarly the coordinates of P' are $(\frac{3}{2}, 1)$.

In a Cartesian coordinate system, one of the most useful formulas is the one which gives the distance between any two points. We recall that the distance between a point $P(x_1, y_1)$ and a point $P'(x_2, y_2)$ is given by the formula

$$d(P, P') = [(x_2 - x_1)^2 + (y_2 - y_1)^2]^{1/2}. \tag{1.1}$$

If we apply the same formula to the linear coordinates of Example 1 we obtain the distance from P to P' as $[(\frac{3}{2} - \frac{1}{2})^2 + (1 - 3)^2]^{1/2} = \sqrt{5}$. This is clearly not correct; the formula cannot be taken over into general linear coordinate systems.

It is not our purpose to develop an analytic geometry for linear coordinate systems. However the student will find it interesting to determine the distance formula for an arbitrary system of this type. We indicate the final result here and leave the derivation to the student. Let the distance from P_0 to P_1 be r_1 and from P_0 to P_1' be r_2 and let α be the angle between the positive axis on L_1 and the positive axis on L_2 (measured in a counterclockwise direction). The distance formula is then:

$$\begin{aligned} d(P, P') &\\ &= [r_1^2(x_2 - x_1)^2 + r_2^2(y_2 - y_1)^2 + 2r_1r_2(x_2 - x_1)(y_2 - y_1)\cos\alpha]^{1/2}. \end{aligned} \tag{1.2}$$

An application of formula (1.2) to the linear coordinates of Example 1 gives the distance:

$$d(P, P') = \left[2^2\left(\frac{3}{2} - \frac{1}{2}\right)^2 + \sqrt{2}^2(1 - 3)^2 + 2 \cdot 2\sqrt{2}\left(\frac{3}{2} - \frac{1}{2}\right)(1 - 3)\frac{\sqrt{2}}{2}\right]^{1/2} = 2.$$

This is the correct answer.

Linear coordinate systems for space. In order to establish a linear coordinate system in space, take three lines L_1, L_2, L_3 which intersect in a point P_0, and such that they do not lie in a plane (Figure 1.4). Establish on L_1, L_2, and L_3 coordinate systems with P_1, P_1', P_1'' as unit points.

We assign to points X on L_1, Y on L_2, and Z on L_3 the ordered triples of real numbers $(x, 0, 0)$, $(0, y, 0)$, and $(0, 0, z)$, where x, y, and z are the coordinates of X, Y, and Z on their respective lines; $(0, 0, 0)$ is assigned to P_0. Frequently the letter O is used to designate the origin P_0.

For any point P not on one of L_1, L_2, L_3, we construct planes parallel to the plane of L_2 and L_3, L_3 and L_1, L_1 and L_2, denoting the points of intersection of these planes with the lines L_1, L_2, and L_3 respectively by X, Y, and Z. We assign the ordered triple of real numbers (x, y, z) to the point P.

The real numbers of the ordered triple (x, y, z) thus assigned to each point P in space are the coordinates of the point P. The one-to-one mapping T thus established between the points in space and the ordered triples of real numbers (x, y, z) will be called a *linear coordinate system* in space.

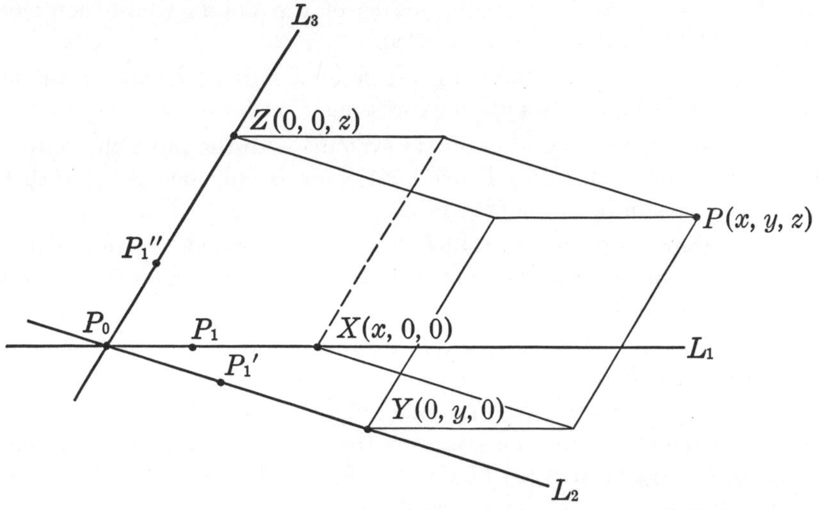

Figure 1.4

If the distances from P_0 to P_1, P_0 to P_1', P_0 to P_1'' are equal and the lines L_1, L_2, L_3 are mutually perpendicular, we have a Cartesian coordinate system for space.

In any coordinate system a line segment will be determined by giving the coordinates of the end points. In those cases where attention is to be drawn to the order of presenting the end points, the line segment will be called a *directed line segment,* the direction being from the end point first presented to the second. Thus XY will be used to indicate the directed line segment from X to Y. We shall also use XY to denote the length of the line segment from X to Y. The meaning should be clear from the context of the discussion. In a diagram, when it is desirable to emphasize the direction of a line segment, an arrowhead will be indicated on the terminal (second) point of the segment.

No essential importance attaches to the use of the letters x, y, z in the first, second, and third places of the coordinate triples. Any letters will serve as well, and, to prepare for future generalizations, we will customarily use notations of the type (x_1, x_2, x_3).

EXERCISES

1. Let a new coordinate system be assigned to an existing coordinate system on a line by taking the point whose coordinate is -3 to be P_0 and the point whose coordinate is $+5$ to be P_1.

(a) Determine the new coordinates of the points whose old coordinates are (i) -3; (ii) 5; (iii) 2; (iv) 16; (v) -24; (vi) $\frac{3}{7}$.

(b) Determine the former coordinates of the points whose new coordinates are (i) 0; (ii) 1; (iii) $\frac{3}{8}$; (iv) 8; (v) -2.

2. In Problem 1, if x is the old coordinate of a point P, and x' the new coordinate of P, find an equation expressing x' in terms of x.

3. Let a line L have two coordinate systems with the same choice for P_0 and different choices for P_1. Prove that there is only one point with the same coordinate in both systems.

4. Show that the result of Problem 3 may be extended to prove that any two distinct coordinate systems for a line L yield the same coordinate for at most one point P.

5. In the linear coordinate system established in Example 1, what are the coordinates of the following points whose Cartesian coordinates are (a) (6, 7); (b) (9, 3); (c) (6, 4); (d) (1, 0); (e) (0, 1)?

What are the Cartesian coordinates of the points whose linear coordinates are (f) (0, 1); (g) (1, 0); (h) (3, 4); (i) (8, 7); (j) $(-1, 3)$?

6. In Example 1, let (x, y) be the Cartesian coordinates and (x', y') the linear coordinates of a point P. Find expressions for x' and y' in terms of x and y.

7. In Example 1, what is the distance between the points whose linear coordinates are (3, 1) and $(5, -1)$?

8. Derive formula (1.2).

9. How is our assumption that a linear coordinate system on a line is a one-to-one mapping of the points of a line onto the real number system used in justifying our statement that the linear coordinate system of a plane π is a one-to-one mapping of points in π onto all ordered pairs of real numbers (x, y)?

2. Line Segments in Space

In order to provide a basis for an analytic geometry of space, we begin by introducing in space a linear coordinate system. The origin O (or P_0) and the three noncoplanar lines L_1, L_2, and L_3 through P_0, as well as the unit points P_1, P_1', P_1'' on these lines, may be chosen arbitrarily. However, having made a definite choice, we will agree to keep this coordinate system fixed for the discussion to follow.

Perhaps the first thing to consider should be an expression for the points lying on a line. Let L be a line joining two points X and Y (Figure 2.1) and let R be an arbitrary point on L.

Through X, Y, and R we pass lines parallel to L_3 intersecting the plane determined by L_1 and L_2 at K, M, and N. The lines through K, M, N parallel to L_1 and L_2 intersect the coordinate lines as indicated. The similarity of the triangles KPN to KQM and KTN to KSM implies

$$\frac{KP}{KQ} = \frac{KN}{KM} = \frac{KT}{KS} \quad \text{or} \quad \frac{r_1 - x_1}{y_1 - x_1} = \frac{r_2 - x_2}{y_2 - x_2}.$$

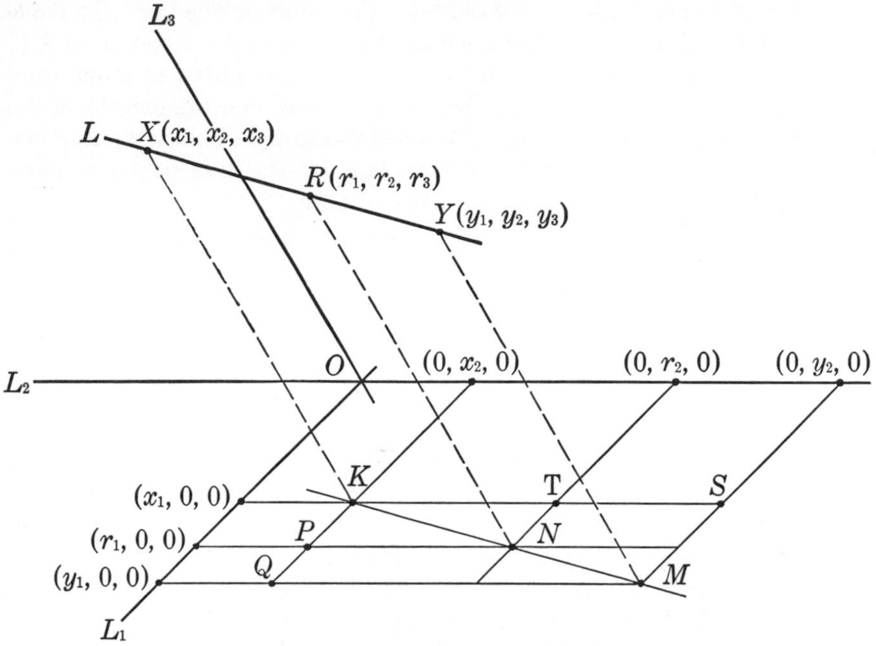

Figure 2.1

A similar consideration in the plane determined by L_2 and L_3, combined with the result above, yields the following relations for the coordinates of the points X, Y, and R:

$$\frac{r_1 - x_1}{y_1 - x_1} = \frac{r_2 - x_2}{y_2 - x_2} = \frac{r_3 - x_3}{y_3 - x_3}. \tag{2.1}$$

If the common ratio in (2.1) is denoted by t, these relations may be expressed by the equations

$$\begin{aligned} r_1 &= x_1 + t(y_1 - x_1) \\ r_2 &= x_2 + t(y_2 - x_2) \\ r_3 &= x_3 + t(y_3 - x_3). \end{aligned} \tag{2.2}$$

The value of t depends upon the position of R with respect to X and Y; t is positive if R and Y are on the same side of X; $t = 0$ if R coincides with X; and t is negative if X separates R and Y. The absolute value of t is the ratio of the lengths XR and XY.

We see that the coordinates of any point on a line are given in terms of the coordinates of a fixed point X, a triple of real numbers

$$[y_1 - x_1, y_2 - x_2, y_3 - x_3]$$

determined by a directed segment XY on the line, and a real number t. The function of these various quantities may be summarized as follows:

The coordinates of X give us a fixed reference point on the line; the triple determined by XY provides a numerical reference to the direction of XY, that is, it specifies the change in each coordinate required to move from X to Y; the real number t expresses the ratio between the lengths of the segments XR and XY with a sign attached to signify a choice of direction.

Let us investigate the triples determined by the line segments more closely. There are several points worthy of note:

1. The assignment of the triple $[y_1 - x_1, y_2 - x_2, y_3 - x_3]$ to the directed line segment from $X(x_1, x_2, x_3)$ to $Y(y_1, y_2, y_3)$ determines a single-valued mapping from the set of directed line segments in space to the set of triples of real numbers. For example, if the coordinates of X and Y are $(3, 1, 1)$ and $(2, -1, 3)$, the triple $[-1, -2, 2]$ is assigned to XY and $[1, 2, -2]$ is assigned to YX. We shall say that the directed segment XY is *associated with* the triple $[-1, -2, 2]$. YX is associated with the triple $[1, 2, -2]$.

2. The mapping just indicated is *not* one-to-one. If P and Q have coordinates $(1, 4, 2)$ and $(0, 2, 4)$, the triple assigned to PQ is again $[-1, -2, 2]$. It is intuitively clear that PQ is parallel to and equal in length to XY. In fact it may be shown that if two segments are associated with the same triple they are equal in length and either collinear or parallel. The student is urged to devise a formal proof of this fact. Every triple of real numbers $[a_1, a_2, a_3]$ is associated with at least one segment (in fact, an infinite number of segments) except that the triple $[0, 0, 0]$ has no associated segment. The triple $[a_1, a_2, a_3]$ is, for example, associated with the segment OA where A has coordinates (a_1, a_2, a_3) and O is the origin.

3. If $X'(x_1', x_2', x_3')$ and $Y'(y_1', y_2', y_3')$ are points on the line XY, the corresponding elements of the triples associated with $X'Y'$ and XY are proportional. To see this, apply (2.2) to the points Y' and X':

$$\begin{aligned} y_1' &= x_1 + t_1(y_1 - x_1) \qquad & x_1' &= x_1 + t_2(y_1 - x_1) \\ y_2' &= x_2 + t_1(y_2 - x_2) & x_2' &= x_2 + t_2(y_2 - x_2) \\ y_3' &= x_3 + t_1(y_3 - x_3) & x_3' &= x_3 + t_2(y_3 - x_3). \end{aligned} \tag{2.3}$$

Now subtract the two sets of equations, and let $t_3 = t_1 - t_2$:

$$\begin{aligned} y_1' - x_1' &= t_3(y_1 - x_1) \\ y_2' - x_2' &= t_3(y_2 - x_2) \\ y_3' - x_3' &= t_3(y_3 - x_3). \end{aligned} \tag{2.4}$$

4. If $X(x_1, x_2, x_3)$, $Y(y_1, y_2, y_3)$, and $Z(z_1, z_2, z_3)$ are any three points in space, the triple associated with XZ can be obtained by *adding* the corresponding elements of the triples associated with XY and YZ. That is,

$$\begin{aligned} z_1 - x_1 &= (z_1 - y_1) + (y_1 - x_1) \\ z_2 - x_2 &= (z_2 - y_2) + (y_2 - x_2) \\ z_3 - x_3 &= (z_3 - y_3) + (z_3 - x_3). \end{aligned} \tag{2.5}$$

In Figure 2.2 the associated triples are indicated beside the corresponding segments.

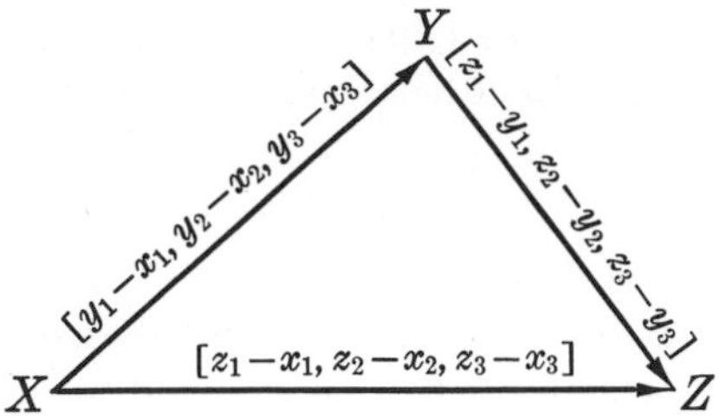

Figure 2.2

5. The remarks made so far suggest that a further study of triples as quantities in their own right may be useful. This is correct; in the next section we shall turn our attention to creating an algebraic system of triples, and the remainder of this chapter will be devoted to an exposition of some of their uses in space geometry. However, it turns out that this algebraic system is not limited to geometry in its applications. In its wider uses, there is no need to confine ourselves to triples; the structure can be extended to n-tuples, that is, to ordered arrangements of n real numbers. Most of the text beyond this chapter will be devoted to results of this generalization.

EXERCISES

In these problems, assume that space has been coordinatized by some fixed coordinate system.

1. Find equations for a point $R(r_1, r_2, r_3)$ on the line joining (1, 1, 1) and (2, − 1, 3). What is the triple associated with the line segment OR? with the line segment RO?

2. Find equations for a point $R(r_1, r_2, r_3)$ on the line joining (2, 3, − 4) and (5, − 2, 0). What is the triple associated with the line segment from (2, 3, − 4) to R? with the line segment from R to (2, 3, − 4)?

3. Find coordinates of a point P on the line joining $X(1, -2, 3)$ and $Y(2, 4, -1)$ which is

(a) The midpoint of XY.
(b) Such that $XP/PY = \frac{1}{3}$.
(c) Such that Y is the midpoint of XP.
(d) Such that X is the midpoint of PY.

4. Let X, Y, Z be points whose coordinates are (1, − 1, 2), (3, 1, 4), (2, 0, 2) respectively. Find the triples associated with the directed line segments XY, YZ, XZ. Verify that the relations corresponding to (2.5) are satisfied.

5. Show that the points $P(1, -1, 4)$ and $Q(5, 3, 0)$ are collinear with the points $X(2, 0, 3)$ and $Y(-2, -4, 7)$.

6. Give a complete proof for the statement: If XY and $X'Y'$ are segments associated with the same triple, either XY is collinear with $X'Y'$ or the segments are parallel. In either case, the segments are equal in length.

3. Vectors

The student will have noted that we used square brackets [ ] to distinguish the triples associated with line segments from triples which were being used as coordinates of points. In this and future sections we retain the square brackets to denote the quantities of a new algebraic system. The student must now adjust to the idea that a triple of real numbers in square brackets is not *necessarily* associated with any segment. Our algebraic system will stand on its own feet although the definitions used are suggested originally by geometric considerations. When the system is to be applied to a geometric problem, as at the end of the present section, it is necessary first to introduce a linear coordinate system in order that line segments may be designated by the coordinates of their end points.

We begin our development by choosing a name and notation to distinguish the triples of our algebraic system and by defining the operations that are to be carried out on these triples.

A triple of real numbers $[x_1, x_2, x_3]$ will be called a *vector*. To clarify the notation, lower-case italic letters will be used to designate real numbers, and boldface roman capitals will denote vectors. Thus $[x_1, x_2, x_3]$ may also be denoted by $\mathbf{X}$. The first, second, and third elements (real numbers) in the triple constituting a vector will be designated the first, second, and third *components* respectively. Two vectors are equal if and only if the corresponding components are equal. Thus $[2, 3, 1] = [\sqrt{4}, \frac{6}{2}, (-1)^2]$ but $[2, 3, 1] \neq [1, 2, 3]$.

If t is an arbitrary real number and $\mathbf{A} = [a_1, a_2, a_3]$, we define:

$$(3.1) \qquad t\mathbf{A} = t[a_1, a_2, a_3] = [ta_1, ta_2, ta_3].$$

This definition which permits a vector to be multiplied by a real number to produce a new vector is called *scalar* multiplication. The definition of scalar multiplication was suggested by point 3 of the previous section. If $\mathbf{A}$ is regarded as associated with some line segment, $t\mathbf{A}$ may be thought of as associated with another segment on the same line.

If $\mathbf{A} = [a_1, a_2, a_3]$ and $\mathbf{B} = [b_1, b_2, b_3]$, we define $\mathbf{A} + \mathbf{B}$ as follows:

$$(3.2) \qquad \mathbf{A} + \mathbf{B} = [a_1, a_2, a_3] + [b_1, b_2, b_3] = [a_1 + b_1, a_2 + b_2, a_3 + b_3].$$

This definition which permits the addition of two vectors to yield a third vector is suggested by point 4 of the previous section. If $\mathbf{A}$ is associated with a line segment XY and $\mathbf{B}$ with YZ, $\mathbf{A} + \mathbf{B}$ is associated with XZ.

We define the negative of a vector **A** by

(3.3) $$-\mathbf{A} = -[a_1, a_2, a_3] = [-a_1, -a_2, -a_3] = (-1)\mathbf{A}.$$

Note that $\mathbf{A} + (-\mathbf{A}) = [0, 0, 0]$. The special vector [0, 0, 0] is designated by **0**; as already noted, it is the only vector which can never be associated with a line segment in geometric applications. Note also that

$$0\mathbf{A} = 0[a_1, a_2, a_3] = [0, 0, 0] = \mathbf{0}.$$

Finally, we define the subtraction of two vectors by:

(3.4) $$\mathbf{A} - \mathbf{B} = \mathbf{A} + (-\mathbf{B}).$$

We wish to emphasize that this set of definitions, while simple, reasonable, and grounded in geometric analogy, was in no sense inevitable. Vector addition, subtraction, and scalar multiplication exist by an act of choice. This choice was guided by our intent to apply the theory as well as by the algebraic properties of the relations involved. To illustrate the point being made, it might appear algebraically inevitable to define a product of two vectors $\mathbf{A} = [a_1, a_2, a_3]$ and $\mathbf{B} = [b_1, b_2, b_3]$ as $[a_1b_1, a_2b_2, a_3b_3]$. Actually there is no geometric use for such a product and we do not make the definition. Later in this chapter we shall have two quite different "products" defined. We shall never mention the "algebraically inevitable" product again.

There are several results which are direct consequences of our definitions and the properties of real numbers. We list these in the form of a theorem and leave the proof as an exercise for the student.

THEOREM 3.1. *Let* **X**, **Y**, **Z** *be arbitrary vectors and let s, t be real numbers. Then*

(i) $$(\mathbf{X} + \mathbf{Y}) + \mathbf{Z} = \mathbf{X} + (\mathbf{Y} + \mathbf{Z}),$$
(ii) $$\mathbf{X} + \mathbf{Y} = \mathbf{Y} + \mathbf{X},$$
(iii) $$(st)\mathbf{X} = s(t\mathbf{X}),$$
(iv) $$(s + t)\mathbf{X} = s\mathbf{X} + t\mathbf{X},$$
(v) $$s(\mathbf{X} + \mathbf{Y}) = s\mathbf{X} + s\mathbf{Y},$$
(vi) $$1\mathbf{X} = \mathbf{X}.$$

The student will notice the similarity of properties (i)–(v) to the laws for real numbers or fields set down in Chapter 1. Indeed (i) is the associative law for vector addition, and (ii) the commutative law for vector addition. However, (iii), (iv), and (v) differ from the associative and distributive laws which they resemble by involving two distinct types of quantities, vectors and real numbers.

Now we are ready to use vectors to simplify geometric statements. At this time we confine ourselves to a single illustration.

Consider the equations for a line (2.2). If we set

$$\mathbf{R} = [r_1, r_2, r_3], \quad \mathbf{X} = [x_1, x_2, x_3], \quad \mathbf{Y} = [y_1, y_2, y_3],$$

equations (2.2) may be replaced by the vector equation

$$\mathbf{R} = \mathbf{X} + t(\mathbf{Y} - \mathbf{X}), \tag{3.5}$$

or

$$\mathbf{R} = (1 - t)\mathbf{X} + t\mathbf{Y}. \tag{3.6}$$

From (3.5) and (3.6) we see that the vector associated with OR is given in terms of the vectors associated with OX and XY or in terms of the vectors associated with OX and OY.

Example 1. The vector equation of the line through (1, 2, − 2) and (2, 3, 1) is

$$\mathbf{R} = (1 - t)[1, 2, -2] + t[2, 3, 1].$$

If $t = \frac{1}{2}$, $\mathbf{R} = \frac{1}{2}[1, 2, -2] + \frac{1}{2}[2, 3, 1] = [\frac{3}{2}, \frac{5}{2}, -\frac{1}{2}]$. If the vector $\mathbf{R}$ is interpreted as being associated with the line segment OR, we see that the point $(\frac{3}{2}, \frac{5}{2}, -\frac{1}{2})$ is the midpoint of the line segment from (1, 2, − 2) to (2, 3, 1). Here, we have associated the vectors [1, 2, − 2] and [2, 3, 1] with the line segments from the origin to the points (1, 2, − 2) and (2, 3, 1).

EXERCISES

1. Perform the indicated operations and obtain the resulting vector:

(a) $2[1, 3, -1] + [1, 0, 2] = ?$

(b) $4[1, 0, -2] - 3[1, -1, -3] = ?$

(c) $a[1, 2, -1] + b[1, 3, 1] = ?$

2. Provide proofs for the six properties of vectors listed in Theorem 3.1.

3. What are the vector equations of the lines joining the following pairs of points?

(a) (2, 3, − 4), (5, − 2, 0)

(b) (1, 1, 1), (2, − 1, 3)

(c) (1, − 2, 3), (2, 4, − 1)

4. Choose two sides XY and XZ of a triangle XYZ as the coordinate lines in a linear coordinate system and let the unit point on each line be chosen at a vertex; take the third coordinate line as any line through X not in the plane of the triangle. What is the vector associated with YZ? What is the vector associated with the line segment from the origin to the midpoint of YZ?

5. Do the following points form the vertices of a parallelogram: (3, 7, − 2), (5, 5, 1), (4, 0, − 1), (6, − 2, 2)?

6. What is the vector associated with the line segment OR, where R is a point $\frac{1}{3}$ of the distance from (2, 6, − 4) to (5, 3, − 1)?

4. Dependence of Vectors

In the previous section we noted that the definition of scalar multiplication was so chosen that if two vectors **X** and **Y** are associated with collinear segments a real number t exists such that $\mathbf{Y} = t\mathbf{X}$. Conversely, suppose we have two nonzero vectors **A** and **B** and a real number $t \neq 0$ such that $\mathbf{B} = t\mathbf{A}$. Then in any coordinate system which may be given, it is easy to find collinear segments associated with **A** and **B**. For example, find any segment associated with **A**, then, using the same initial point, consider the segment on the same line which is $|t|$ times the length of the first segment selected, and choose the direction as indicated in the discussion following equations (2.2).

Briefly then: *Two nonzero vectors are associated with collinear segments if and only if one vector is a nonzero real multiple of the other.*

Now, what about vectors associated with *coplanar* segments? The basic situation is illustrated in Figure 4.1. The segments AB, CD, and EF are coplanar. Initially we assume that no two of these are parallel or collinear. Let **X** be associated with AB, **Y** with CD, and **Z** with EF. Draw BD' parallel to and equal in length to CD, and AF' parallel to and equal in length to EF. Then **Y** is also associated with BD' and **Z** with AF'. Next,

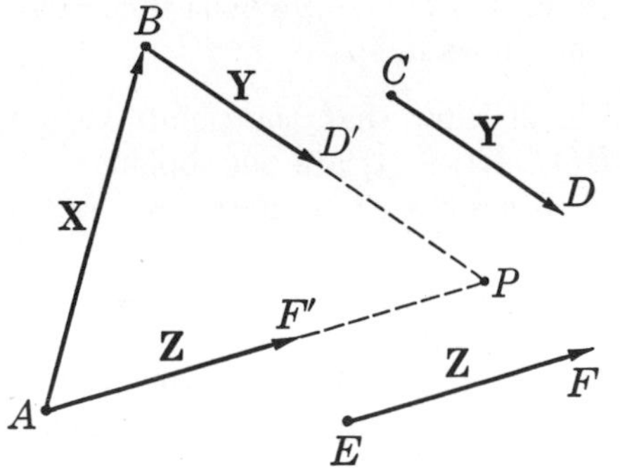

Figure 4.1

if necessary, extend BD' or AF' (or both) until the resulting lines intersect in some point P. Then there are real numbers s and t such that BP is associated with $s\mathbf{Y}$ and AP with $t\mathbf{Z}$. Finally, we have from the agreement as to the definition of vector addition

$$(4.1) \qquad \mathbf{X} + s\mathbf{Y} = t\mathbf{Z}, \quad \text{or} \quad \mathbf{X} = -s\mathbf{Y} + t\mathbf{Z}.$$

We can now partially remove the restrictions made on collinearity and parallelism of the segments. If AB is collinear with or parallel to CD, we can still write $\mathbf{X} = -s\mathbf{Y} + t\mathbf{Z}$, where $t = 0$, since **X** will be a real multiple of **Y** from our answer to the first question raised. If AB and EF are collinear or parallel, then s will be zero in (4.1). If CD and EF are parallel to each other and not to AB, then (4.1) cannot be valid. However, in such a case $\mathbf{Y} = r\mathbf{Z}$ for some r and we write

$$\mathbf{Y} = r\mathbf{Z} + 0\mathbf{X}. \tag{4.1$'$}$$

To express the conclusions of the preceding paragraphs as simply as possible, we resort to a definition.

DEFINITION 4.1. *A vector of the form* $a\mathbf{X} + b\mathbf{Y}$ *is called a* LINEAR COMBINATION *of vectors* $\mathbf{X}$ *and* $\mathbf{Y}$.

We have then proved:

THEOREM 4.1. *If three line segments are coplanar, the vector associated with one of them is a linear combination of the vectors associated with the other two.*

Conversely, if $\mathbf{X}$ is a linear combination of $\mathbf{Y}$ and $\mathbf{Z}$, it is a simple matter to construct a triangle with sides which contain segments associated with $\mathbf{X}$, $\mathbf{Y}$, and $\mathbf{Z}$. The construction is essentially the same as in Figure 4.1.

THEOREM 4.2. *If three vectors are related so that one is a linear combination of the other two, they can be associated with coplanar line segments.*

We may apply the results of the previous theorems to prove geometric properties of points and lines in space.

Example 1. We shall show that the points $A(1, 1, 2)$, $B(3, -2, 3)$, $C(2, -3, 5)$, and $D(4, -1, -1)$ are not coplanar.

The vectors $\mathbf{X}$, $\mathbf{Y}$, $\mathbf{Z}$ associated with the line segments AB, BC, and AD are

$$\mathbf{X} = [2, -3, 1], \quad \mathbf{Y} = [-1, -1, 2], \quad \mathbf{Z} = [3, -2, -3].$$

No two of the segments AB, BC, AD are collinear or parallel. Therefore, if A, B, C, D are coplanar, real numbers r, s must exist such that $\mathbf{X}$, $\mathbf{Y}$, $\mathbf{Z}$ satisfy an equation of the form

$$\mathbf{X} = r\mathbf{Y} + s\mathbf{Z},$$

or

$$\begin{aligned}[2, -3, 1] &= r[-1, -1, 2] + s[3, -2, -3] \\ &= [-r + 3s, -r - 2s, 2r - 3s].\end{aligned}$$

Hence, from the equality of vectors,

$$\begin{aligned} 2 &= -r + 3s \\ -3 &= -r - 2s \\ 1 &= 2r - 3s. \end{aligned} \tag{4.2}$$

The first two equations yield $r = s = 1$. These values do not satisfy the third equation and so $\mathbf{X}$ is not a linear combination of $\mathbf{Y}$ and $\mathbf{Z}$. Hence the four points are not coplanar.

If we were to replace D by the point $E(4, 1, -1)$, we could show that **X**, **Y**, and the vector associated with AE, $[3, 0, -3]$, satisfy the relation

$$[2, -3, 1] = 3[-1, -1, 2] + \tfrac{5}{3}[3, 0, -3].$$

Now Theorem 4.2 and a simple geometric argument prove that A, B, C, and E are coplanar.

Example 2. We shall prove the familiar geometric property of triangles that the medians intersect in a point $\frac{2}{3}$ of the distance along each median.

Let **A** and **B** represent the vectors associated with the sides XY and YZ of the triangle XYZ. Then $\mathbf{A} + \frac{\mathbf{B}}{2}$ is associated with XM, and $s\left(\mathbf{A} + \frac{\mathbf{B}}{2}\right)$ will be associated with XO, where s is the ratio $\frac{XO}{XM}$. We note that $\frac{\mathbf{A}}{2}$ is

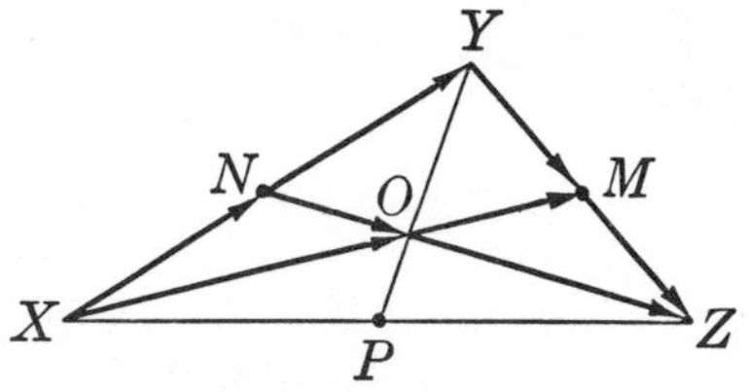

Figure 4.2

associated with both XN and NY so that a consideration of the triangle NYZ shows that $\left(\frac{\mathbf{A}}{2} + \mathbf{B}\right)$ is associated with NZ. Considering the triangle XNO, we see that $\frac{\mathbf{A}}{2} + r\left(\frac{\mathbf{A}}{2} + \mathbf{B}\right)$ is associated with XO, where r is the ratio $\frac{NO}{NZ}$. Thus, equating the two expressions for the vector associated with XO, we have

$$s\left(\mathbf{A} + \frac{\mathbf{B}}{2}\right) = \frac{\mathbf{A}}{2} + r\left(\frac{\mathbf{A}}{2} + \mathbf{B}\right),$$

or

$$\left(\frac{1}{2} + \frac{r}{2} - s\right)\mathbf{A} + \left(r - \frac{s}{2}\right)\mathbf{B} = \mathbf{0}.$$

Since **A** and **B** are not zero or associated with collinear segments, we must have

$$(4.3) \qquad \begin{aligned} \frac{1}{2} + \frac{r}{2} - s &= 0 \\ r - \frac{s}{2} &= 0. \end{aligned}$$

Equations (4.3) have the unique solution $r = \frac{1}{3}$, $s = \frac{2}{3}$. The proof that

YP passes through O follows similarly by expressing the vector associated with the segment from X to the intersection of YP with XM in terms of $\mathbf{A}$ and the vector associated with YP.

We now determine a vector equation for a plane as we did for a line in §3. If R is an arbitrary point in a plane determined by three (noncollinear) points A, B, C, we wish to express the vector $\mathbf{R}$ associated with the line segment OR in terms of the vectors $\mathbf{A}$, $\mathbf{B}$, and $\mathbf{C}$ associated with the line segments OA, OB, and OC. The vectors $\mathbf{R} - \mathbf{A}$, $\mathbf{B} - \mathbf{A}$, $\mathbf{C} - \mathbf{A}$ are

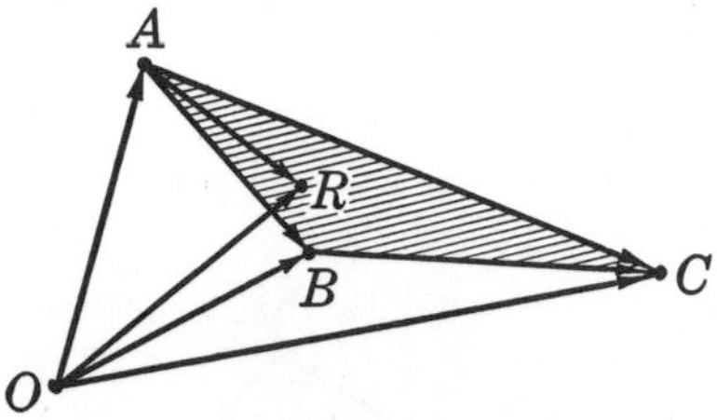

Figure 4.3

associated with the line segments AR, AB, AC respectively, and these segments are coplanar. Finally, AB and AC are not collinear, so there exist real numbers p and q such that

$$\mathbf{R} - \mathbf{A} = p(\mathbf{B} - \mathbf{A}) + q(\mathbf{C} - \mathbf{A}) \tag{4.4}$$

or

$$\mathbf{R} = (1 - p - q)\mathbf{A} + p\mathbf{B} + q\mathbf{C}. \tag{4.5}$$

Compare (4.5) with (3.6).

Example 3. Let us find the vector equation of the plane through the points A, B, C, E of Example 1. We use only A, B, and C; then

$$\mathbf{R} = (1 - p - q)[1, 1, 2] + p[3, -2, 3] + q[2, -3, 5];$$

or

$$\mathbf{R} = [1 + 2p + q, 1 - 3p - 4q, 2 + p + 3q].$$

We may find the vector associated with OE by setting $p = \frac{12}{5}$, $q = -\frac{9}{5}$.

We have not shown that, if one vector is a multiple of another, all segments associated with the vectors are collinear, nor is it true that if one vector is a linear combination of two others, associated line segments *must* be coplanar. In the first case, the segments are either collinear or parallel, and, in the second, the segments are at least parallel to some plane π. Finally, we noticed that it was not always possible to write a specific one of the vectors associated with three coplanar segments as a linear combination of the vectors associated with the other two. The exception occurred when the other segments were parallel or collinear; that is, when the associated vectors were real multiples of each other.

We avoid these special cases as follows:

THEOREM 4.3. *The nonzero vectors* **X**, **Y**, **Z** *are associated with coplanar segments if and only if real numbers* p, q, r *(not all zero) exist such that*

$$p\mathbf{X} + q\mathbf{Y} + r\mathbf{Z} = \mathbf{0}. \tag{4.6}$$

Proof. Choose a nonzero coefficient. Transpose the other terms and then divide by the nonzero coefficient; for example,

$$\mathbf{Y} = -\,p/q\mathbf{X} - r/q\mathbf{Z} \quad \text{if} \quad q \neq 0. \tag{4.7}$$

The relation (4.7) is now of the form of a linear combination and fits Theorems 4.1 and 4.2.

The relation (4.6) is an example of a general class of vector relations that will be of great importance in the sequel.

DEFINITION 4.2. *The vectors* $\mathbf{X}_1$, $\mathbf{X}_2$, $\mathbf{X}_3$, $\cdots$, $\mathbf{X}_n$ *are said to be linearly dependent if real numbers* a_1, a_2, $\cdots$, a_n *(not all zero) exist such that*

$$a_1\mathbf{X}_1 + a_2\mathbf{X}_2 + \cdots + a_n\mathbf{X}_n = \mathbf{0}.$$

In this section we have studied the linear dependence of two and three vectors; in § 5 it will be shown that any four vectors are linearly dependent. Note that Theorem 4.3 states that any three vectors associated with coplanar line segments are linearly dependent.

EXERCISES

1. Are the points (1, 1, − 1), (2, 1, 1), (3, − 1, 2), (0, 3, − 2) coplanar?

2. Find the vector equation of the plane through the points (0, 1, − 1), (1, − 1, 1), (3, − 2, 4).

3. Find the vector equation of the plane through the points (1, − 1, 2) and (3, 1, 1) which is parallel to the line segment joining (− 1, 2, 3) and (4, − 1, 1).

4. In the general vector equation for the plane, what is the locus of the points for which $p = 0$? for which $q = 0$?

5. Express the collinearity of line segments in terms of a dependence relation.

6. Can one vector be linearly dependent?

7. In Example 2, complete the proof that YP passes through the point O.

8. Prove that the diagonals of a parallelogram bisect each other. Use a method suggested by Example 2.

5. Linear Dependence and Simultaneous Linear Equations

Without regard to the geometrical interpretation, how do we determine whether three vectors **A**, **B**, **C** are linearly dependent? The definition requires the existence of three real numbers, x, y, z, *not all zero*, such that $x\mathbf{A} + y\mathbf{B} + z\mathbf{C} = \mathbf{0}$. If $\mathbf{A} = [a_1, a_2, a_3]$, $\mathbf{B} = [b_1, b_2, b_3]$, $\mathbf{C} = [c_1, c_2, c_3]$, the condition for dependence yields the system of linear equations

$$\begin{aligned} a_1x + b_1y + c_1z &= 0 \\ a_2x + b_2y + c_2z &= 0 \\ a_3x + b_3y + c_3z &= 0. \end{aligned} \tag{5.1}$$

These equations clearly have a common solution $x = y = z = 0$, but for dependence we seek another solution. We can say: *The vectors* **A**, **B**, **C** *are linearly dependent if and only if the system of linear equations* (5.1) *does not have a unique solution.*

Let us take a more general problem, the case of three simultaneous linear equations in three unknowns. Thus let

$$\begin{aligned} a_1x + b_1y + c_1z &= d_1 \\ a_2x + b_2y + c_2z &= d_2 \\ a_3x + b_3y + c_3z &= d_3, \end{aligned} \tag{5.2}$$

where we may assume that at least one of a_1, a_2, a_3 is not zero (for otherwise the unknown x would not be involved). We assume that $a_1 \neq 0$ without loss of generality.

One method of solution for the equations (5.2) is a simple extension of the method of elimination for two equations in two unknowns.

We assume that the equations (5.2) have a solution. Then, dividing the first equation by a_1, we have,

$$x + \frac{b_1}{a_1}y + \frac{c_1}{a_1}z = \frac{d_1}{a_1}. \tag{5.3}$$

We now multiply (5.3) by $-a_2$ and add the result to the second equation of (5.2); similarly we multiply (5.3) by $-a_3$ and add the result to the last equation of (5.2). In this manner we obtain the equations

$$\begin{aligned} x + \frac{b_1}{a_1}y + \frac{c_1}{a_1}z &= \frac{d_1}{a_1} \\ \left(b_2 - \frac{a_2b_1}{a_1}\right)y + \left(c_2 - \frac{a_2c_1}{a_1}\right)z &= d_2 - \frac{a_2d_1}{a_1} \\ \left(b_3 - \frac{a_3b_1}{a_1}\right)y + \left(c_3 - \frac{a_3c_1}{a_1}\right)z &= d_3 - \frac{a_3d_1}{a_1}. \end{aligned} \tag{5.4}$$

The equations (5.4) will also have a solution.

Conversely if the equations (5.4) have a solution, equations (5.2) will have a solution. (Why?) Now note, however, that equations (5.4) will have a solution if and only if the last two equations have a solution. (Why?) In this manner we have essentially reduced the number of unknowns by one. If necessary, another application of elimination will lead to one equation involving one unknown.

A number of special cases may arise. These will be illustrated by an example.

Example 1. Let us consider the system of equations

$$\begin{aligned} 3x + 2y + 3z &= 2 \\ x + y - z &= 5 \\ 2x + y + bz &= a, \end{aligned}$$

where a and b are real numbers, for the moment unspecified.

In this example, we indicate that it is sometimes advantageous to permute the equations before carrying out the process leading to the equations of the form of (5.4). This is especially true if one of the coefficients of x is ± 1. Therefore, we interchange the first and second equations to obtain

$$\begin{aligned} x + y - z &= 5 \\ 3x + 2y + 3z &= 2 \\ 2x + y + bz &= a. \end{aligned}$$

We now follow the method described for obtaining equations (5.4): multiply the first equation by (-3) and add it to the second equation; multiply the first equation by (-2) and add it to the third equation. In this manner, we obtain the equations

$$\begin{aligned} x + y - z &= 5 \\ -y + 6z &= -13 \\ -y + (b+2)z &= a - 10. \end{aligned}$$

We continue by multiplying the second equation above by (-1) and adding it to the last equation. Thus, finally, we have the system of equations

$$\begin{aligned} x + y - z &= 5 \\ -y + 6z &= -13 \\ (b-4)z &= a + 3, \end{aligned}$$

and the solutions of these equations are the same as those of our original system of equations.

If $b - 4 \neq 0$, we can solve the last equation for z and successively obtain

y from the second equation and then x from the first equation. In this case, there will be a unique solution for x, y, and z.

If $b - 4 = 0$ and $a + 3 \neq 0$, the last equation becomes

$$0 \cdot z = a + 3,$$

and there will be no solution since $0 \cdot z = 0$ for any value of z.

Finally, if $b - 4 = 0$ and $a + 3 = 0$, the last equation becomes

$$0 \cdot z = 0,$$

and this imposes no restriction on z. Therefore, in this case, z may be chosen arbitrarily and y and x will be determined in terms of z.

Now let us return to the problem of determining whether or not a set of vectors is dependent. The equations (5.1) have at least one solution, $x = y = z = 0$. Either we have many solutions or just this one. In the first case the vectors **A**, **B**, and **C** are dependent, and a relation of dependence is found by choosing for x, y, z any solution of equations (5.1) other than $x = y = z = 0$. If the only set of values which satisfy (5.1) is $x = y = z = 0$, the vectors are not dependent since no dependence relation can be found.

Further, we can now prove that any four vectors must be dependent. Let **A**, **B**, **C**, **D** be $[a_1, a_2, a_3]$, $[b_1, b_2, b_3]$, $[c_1, c_2, c_3]$, $[d_1, d_2, d_3]$ respectively. The problem then is to find values x, y, z, and t, not all 0, such that: $x\mathbf{A} + y\mathbf{B} + z\mathbf{C} + t\mathbf{D} = \mathbf{0}$, or

$$\begin{aligned} a_1x + b_1y + c_1z + d_1t &= 0 \\ a_2x + b_2y + c_2z + d_2t &= 0 \\ a_3x + b_3y + c_3z + d_3t &= 0. \end{aligned} \tag{5.5}$$

If **A**, **B**, and **C** are already dependent we need go no further. That is, if x, y, z, not all zero, exist so that $x\mathbf{A} + y\mathbf{B} + z\mathbf{C} = \mathbf{0}$, then

$$x\mathbf{A} + y\mathbf{B} + z\mathbf{C} + 0\mathbf{D} = \mathbf{0}$$

and we have a relation of dependence for **A**, **B**, **C**, **D**.

If **A**, **B**, **C** are *not* dependent, then if t is set equal to zero in equations (5.5) the only solution for x, y, and z will be $x = y = z = 0$. When the elimination procedure is carried out, none of the resulting equations will be $0 = 0$ since this would allow many solutions as in Example 1 when $b - 4 = 0$, $a + 3 = 0$.

Now, instead of setting $t = 0$, set $t = -1$ in equations (5.5) and transpose the resulting column of d's, so that the equations have the form of equations (5.2). If the elimination is again carried out, the left-hand sides behave just as they did with $t = 0$. We thus get precisely one value for each of x, y, and z, but this time it is not zero unless $\mathbf{D} = \mathbf{0}$, since the right-hand sides of the equations are changed. The situation is that illustrated in Example 1 when $b - 4 \neq 0$. The values obtained for x, y, z, together with $t = -1$, now give a relation of dependence.

EXERCISES

1. Determine which of the following sets of vectors are dependent. If dependent, give a system of coefficients of a linear combination which is zero.

(a) [1, 1, 1], [0, 1, − 1], [1, 4, − 2]
(b) [0, 0, 1], [1, 1, − 2], [3, 4, 1]
(c) [1, 1, − 2], [1, 2, 3], [4, 5, − 3]
(d) [1, 1, 1], [1, 2, 3], [2, 2, 3]
(e) [1, − 1, 3], [1, 4, 5], [2, − 3, 7]

2. In the following systems of equations, determine whether the solutions are unique, non-unique, or nonexistent. In the former two cases indicate the solutions:

(a)
$$\begin{aligned} x + y + z &= 3 \\ x - y - z &= -1 \\ x + 3y + 3z &= 1 \end{aligned}$$

(b)
$$\begin{aligned} x - y + z &= 1 \\ x - 2y + z &= 0 \\ 3x - 4y + z &= 3 \end{aligned}$$

(c)
$$\begin{aligned} y + z &= 3 \\ x - y + z &= 2 \\ x + 2y + z &= 4 \end{aligned}$$

(d)
$$\begin{aligned} y + z &= 0 \\ x + z &= 0 \\ x - y &= 0 \end{aligned}$$

(e)
$$\begin{aligned} 3x - y + z &= 5 \\ x + 2y + z &= 4 \\ -x + 5y + z &= 3 \end{aligned}$$

(f)
$$\begin{aligned} x + 2y + z &= 2 \\ x - y + z &= -1 \\ 2x - y + 3z &= -2 \\ 3x + y - z &= 5 \end{aligned}$$

(g)
$$\begin{aligned} x + y + z + t &= 0 \\ x - y - z + t &= 0 \\ x + 3y + 2z + t &= 0 \end{aligned}$$

3. Show that the vectors

[1, 2, − 1], [2, 1, − 3], [1, 0, 1], and [4, 4, − 8]

are linearly dependent by expressing the vector [4, 4, − 8] as a linear combination of the other three vectors.

4. A solution of the system of equations

$$\begin{aligned} 2x + y - z &= 2 \\ x - y + 2z &= 2 \\ 3x + 2y - 4z &= 1 \end{aligned}$$

is equivalent to a relation of dependence for what set of four vectors?

6. Cartesian Coordinate Systems; Length and Inner Products of Vectors

In §3 we defined the algebraic operations of scalar multiplication and vector addition in a way that would have potential usefulness for geometrical interpretations in an arbitrary linear coordinate system. We shall define in this section and the following section further algebraic operations for vectors that have for their motivation the consequences of selecting a Cartesian coordinate system.

We now assume that space has been coordinatized by three mutually perpendicular lines and that the selected unit distance is the same along all three coordinate directions; that is, we are assuming a Cartesian coordinate system.

The first consequence of this choice is that we may appeal directly to the Pythagorean theorem and obtain the length of any line segment in terms of the coordinates of the end points. From Figure 6.1, we see that the length of the line segment from $X(x_1, x_2, x_3)$ to $Y(y_1, y_2, y_3)$ is

$$[(y_1 - x_1)^2 + (y_2 - x_2)^2 + (y_3 - x_3)^2]^{1/2}.$$

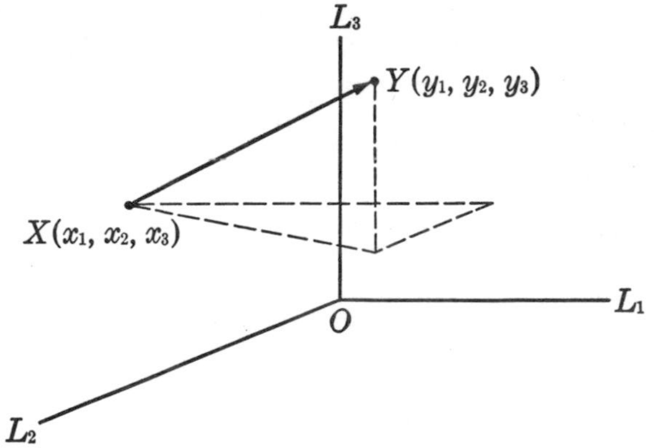

Figure 6.1

If $\mathbf{Z}$ is the vector associated with XY, $\mathbf{Z} = [y_1 - x_1, y_2 - x_2, y_3 - x_3]$ and we are led to an immediate definition of length for a vector.

DEFINITION 6.1. *The length of a vector* $\mathbf{A} = [a_1, a_2, a_3]$ *is defined to be* $(a_1^2 + a_2^2 + a_3^2)^{1/2}$ *and will be denoted by* $|\mathbf{A}|$.

Thus, the length of a vector is the length of any associated line segment in a Cartesian coordinate system. The length of the zero vector $\mathbf{0}$ is zero.

It should be pointed out that Definition 6.1 is imposed upon vectors without regard for any geometrical interpretation. The geometrical motivation merely suggests the definition as was the case with previous definitions.

A second consequence of our choice of a Cartesian coordinate system is the simplicity of expression for the perpendicular projections of a line segment on the coordinate lines. To define the perpendicular projection of XY on L_1, we take planes π_1 and π_2 perpendicular to L_1 and passing through X and Y. L_1 intersects π_1 and π_2 at X' and Y' respectively; and the line segment $X'Y'$ is the perpendicular projection of XY on L_1. If $\mathbf{Z} = [z_1, z_2, z_3]$ is the vector associated with the directed line segment XY, we see that the component $z_1 = y_1 - x_1$ of $\mathbf{Z}$ gives the length and direction

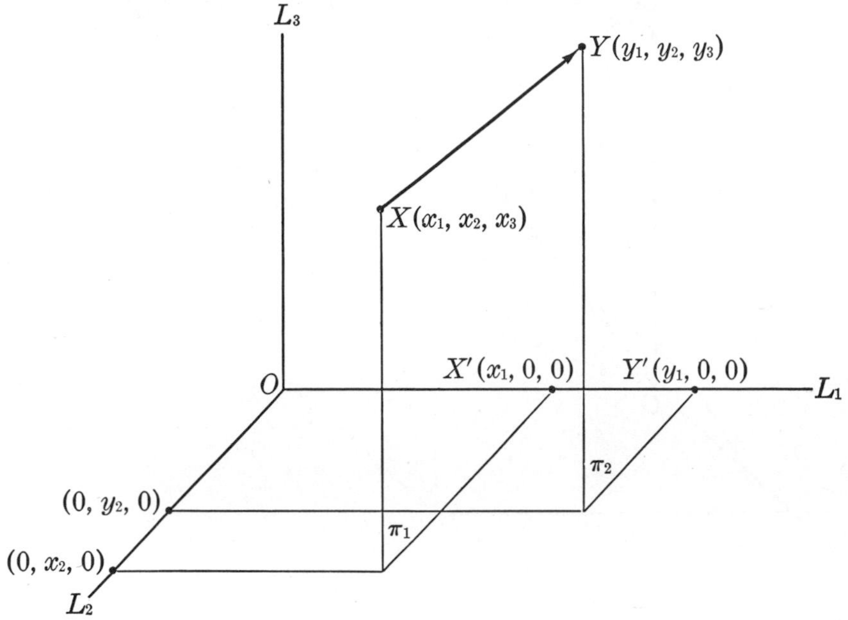

Figure 6.2

of the perpendicular projection of XY on the coordinate line L_1. Similarly, we see that the components z_2 and z_3 of $\mathbf{Z}$ give the length and direction of the perpendicular projections of XY on the coordinate lines L_2 and L_3.

In a Cartesian coordinate system there is a simple expression for the angles that a line joining the points $X(x_1, x_2, x_3)$ and $Y(y_1, y_2, y_3)$ makes with the coordinate axes in terms of the perpendicular projections of XY on the coordinate axes.

We recall briefly that the angle between two skew lines is defined to be the angle between lines parallel to the original lines and passing through the origin. Unless otherwise specified, the angle and the sense of measurement are chosen so that the angle lies in the interval $0 \leq \theta \leq \pi/2$. If we are dealing with directed segments the angle is chosen from positive direction to positive direction and the measurement of angle is expressed in the interval $0 \leq \theta \leq \pi$.

Now if $X(x_1, x_2, x_3)$ and $Y(y_1, y_2, y_3)$ are two distinct points in space, we let $\mathbf{Z} = [z_1, z_2, z_3] = [y_1 - x_1, y_2 - x_2, y_3 - x_3]$ be the vector associated with the directed line segment XY. In Figure 6.3, the line joining the origin and the point $Z(z_1, z_2, z_3)$ is parallel to and equal in length to the directed line segment XY as both OZ and XY are associated with the vector $\mathbf{Z} = [z_1, z_2, z_3]$. We denote the angles made by OZ and the coordinate axes L_1, L_2, L_3 by α, β, γ respectively.

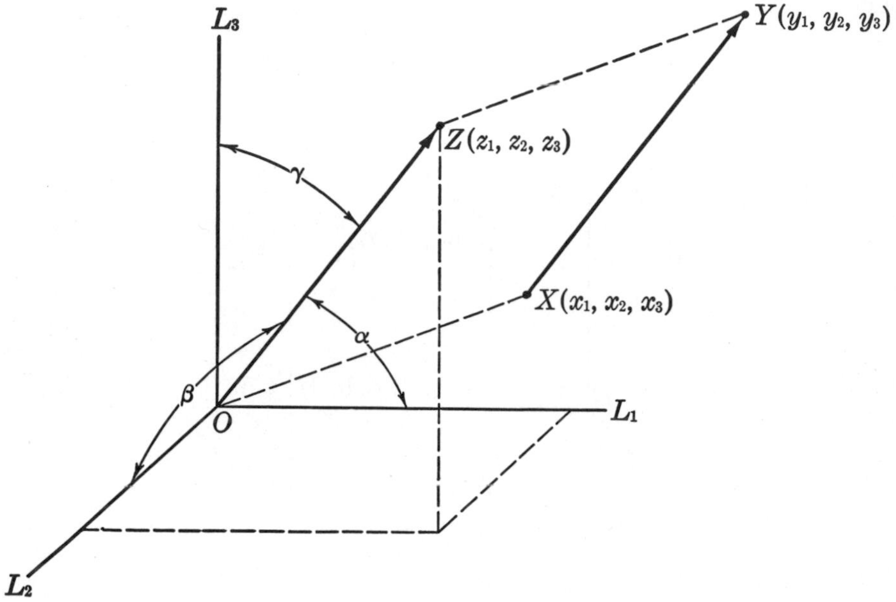

Figure 6.3

From the definition of $|\mathbf{Z}|$ and Figure 6.3 we see that

$$(6.1)\qquad \begin{aligned} \cos\alpha &= \frac{z_1}{|\mathbf{Z}|} = \frac{y_1 - x_1}{\{(y_1 - x_1)^2 + (y_2 - x_2)^2 + (y_3 - x_3)^2\}^{1/2}} \\ \cos\beta &= \frac{z_2}{|\mathbf{Z}|} = \frac{y_2 - x_2}{\{(y_1 - x_1)^2 + (y_2 - x_2)^2 + (y_3 - x_3)^2\}^{1/2}} \\ \cos\gamma &= \frac{z_3}{|\mathbf{Z}|} = \frac{y_3 - x_3}{\{(y_1 - x_1)^2 + (y_2 - x_2)^2 + (y_3 - x_3)^2\}^{1/2}}. \end{aligned}$$

The cosines in (6.1) are called the *direction cosines* of the line containing OZ (or XY) with a positive direction assigned from O toward Z (or from X toward Y). Moreover, we note that

$$(6.2)\qquad \cos^2\alpha + \cos^2\beta + \cos^2\gamma = 1.$$

In a similar manner we determine the angle between two directed lines.

Let the line L join $R(r_1, r_2, r_3)$ and $S(s_1, s_2, s_3)$, the line L^* join $P(p_1, p_2, p_3)$ and $Q(q_1, q_2, q_3)$, with the positive directions being from R to S and from P to Q. We denote by $\mathbf{X} = [x_1, x_2, x_3] = [s_1 - r_1, s_2 - r_2, s_3 - r_3]$ and $\mathbf{Z} = [z_1, z_2, z_3] = [q_1 - p_1, q_2 - p_2, q_3 - p_3]$ the vectors associated with the directed line segments RS and PQ. We associate the line segments OX and OZ in Figure 6.4 with the vectors $\mathbf{X}$ and $\mathbf{Z}$, and the angle between

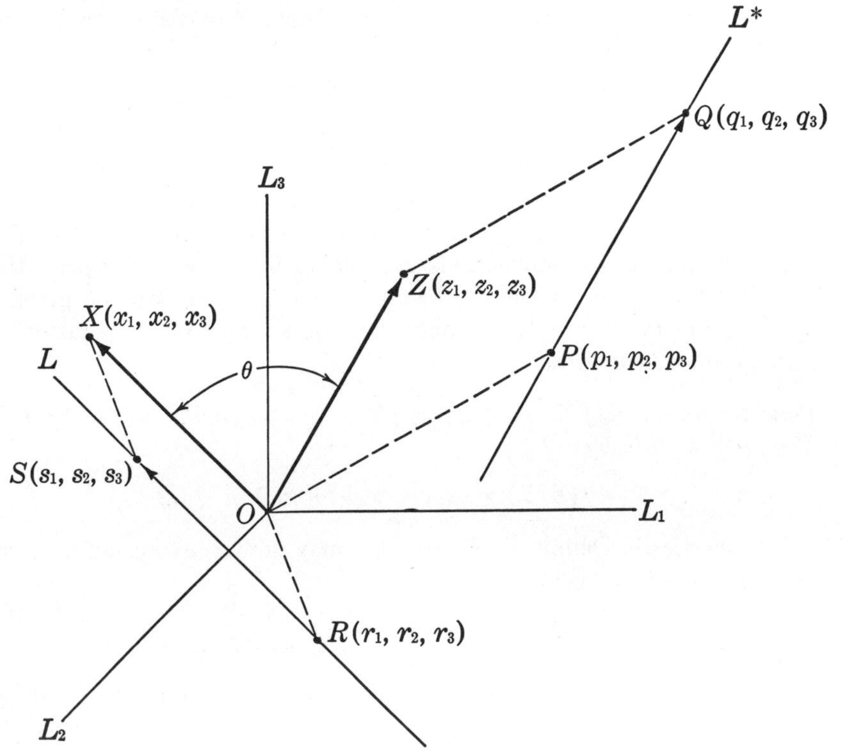

Figure 6.4

L and L^* is defined to be the angle between OX and OZ. We apply the law of cosines to the triangle OXZ to obtain

$$(z_1 - x_1)^2 + (z_2 - x_2)^2 + (z_3 - x_3)^2 = |\mathbf{Z}|^2 + |\mathbf{X}|^2 - 2|\mathbf{Z}||\mathbf{X}|\cos\theta.$$

Expansion of the left side yields

$$|\mathbf{Z}|^2 + |\mathbf{X}|^2 - 2(z_1x_1 + z_2x_2 + z_3x_3) = |\mathbf{Z}|^2 + |\mathbf{X}|^2 - 2|\mathbf{Z}||\mathbf{X}|\cos\theta,$$

or

$$\cos\theta = \frac{x_1z_1 + x_2z_2 + x_3z_3}{|\mathbf{X}||\mathbf{Z}|}.$$

Let $\alpha_1, \beta_1, \gamma_1$ and $\alpha_2, \beta_2, \gamma_2$ denote the angles that OX and OZ make with the coordinate lines. Then, using (6.1), the preceding result may be formulated as

$$\cos\theta = \cos\alpha_1 \cos\alpha_2 + \cos\beta_1 \cos\beta_2 + \cos\gamma_1 \cos\gamma_2 = \frac{x_1z_1 + x_2z_2 + x_3z_3}{|\mathbf{X}|\,|\mathbf{Z}|}.$$

These results lead us to make the following definition:

DEFINITION 6.2. *Let* $\mathbf{X} = [x_1, x_2, x_3]$ *and* $\mathbf{Z} = [z_1, z_2, z_3]$ *be arbitrary nonzero vectors. The cosine of the angle* θ *between* $\mathbf{X}$ *and* $\mathbf{Z}$ *is given by the expression*

$$\cos\theta = \frac{x_1z_1 + x_2z_2 + x_3z_3}{|\mathbf{X}|\,|\mathbf{Z}|}.$$

It should be pointed out that Definition 6.2 is imposed upon vectors without regard for any geometrical interpretation. The previous geometrical considerations certainly motivated the definition and in a Cartesian coordinate system the applications are plentiful. However, before this fact is illustrated, the preceding results and definitions will be given a simpler expression through the definition of an algebraic operation of "inner product" for vectors.

DEFINITION 6.3. *If* $\mathbf{X} = [x_1, x_2, x_3]$, $\mathbf{Y} = [y_1, y_2, y_3]$, *the* INNER PRODUCT *of* $\mathbf{X}$ *and* $\mathbf{Y}$ *is given by*

$$(\mathbf{X}, \mathbf{Y}) = x_1y_1 + x_2y_2 + x_3y_3.$$

The properties in Definitions 6.1 and 6.2 may now be expressed in terms of the inner product by

$$|\mathbf{A}| = (\mathbf{A}, \mathbf{A})^{1/2}, \quad \cos\theta = \frac{(\mathbf{X}, \mathbf{Z})}{(\mathbf{X}, \mathbf{X})^{1/2}(\mathbf{Z}, \mathbf{Z})^{1/2}}.$$

The inner product of vectors is a single-valued mapping from ordered vector pairs to the real numbers, and it is a simple matter to verify the following properties:

(i) $$(\mathbf{X}, \mathbf{Y}) = (\mathbf{Y}, \mathbf{X}).$$

(ii) $$a(\mathbf{X}, \mathbf{Y}) = (a\mathbf{X}, \mathbf{Y}).$$

(iii) $$(\mathbf{X} + \mathbf{Y}, \mathbf{Z}) = (\mathbf{X}, \mathbf{Z}) + (\mathbf{Y}, \mathbf{Z}).$$

In view of the expression for $\cos\theta$, we call two nonzero vectors $\mathbf{X} = [x_1, x_2, x_3]$ and $\mathbf{Z} = [z_1, z_2, z_3]$ *orthogonal* if and only if $(\mathbf{X}, \mathbf{Z}) = 0$.

To illustrate the usefulness of inner products and the geometric interpretation of $(\mathbf{X}, \mathbf{Y}) = 0$ in a Cartesian coordinate system, we will find a vector expression for a plane through a point $P(a_1, a_2, a_3)$ and perpendicular to a given vector $\mathbf{Y} = [y_1, y_2, y_3]$. Let OQ be a segment such that Q is in the plane π whose equation is sought and such that OQ is associated with a vector that is a real nonzero multiple of $\mathbf{Y}$, say $t\mathbf{Y}$. If $R(x_1, x_2, x_3)$ is an arbitrary point in the plane, the segments PR and OQ are orthogonal.

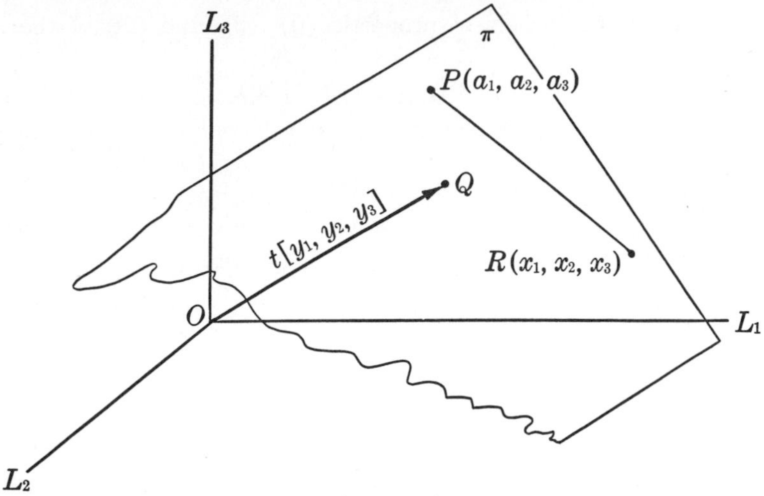

Figure 6.5

Hence the vectors $[x_1 - a_1, x_2 - a_2, x_3 - a_3]$ and **Y** are orthogonal,

$$([x_1 - a_1, x_2 - a_2, x_3 - a_3], [y_1, y_2, y_3]) = 0,$$

or
$$x_1y_1 + x_2y_2 + x_3y_3 = a_1y_1 + a_2y_2 + a_3y_3.$$

If we denote by **R** the vector associated with OR and by **P** the vector associated with OP, these equations can be written $(\mathbf{R} - \mathbf{P}, \mathbf{Y}) = 0$, $(\mathbf{R}, \mathbf{Y}) = (\mathbf{P}, \mathbf{Y})$, and we have vector expressions for the equation of a plane.

Another application is the following: Suppose we have given a plane in which we wish to establish a Cartesian coordinate system. Let A, B, C be noncollinear points in the plane and let **X** and **Y** be associated with AB and AC respectively. Now every nonzero vector $\mathbf{Z} = a\mathbf{X} + b\mathbf{Y}$ is associated with a segment in the plane having A for its initial point. If we choose a and b so that $(\mathbf{Z}, \mathbf{X}) = (a\mathbf{X} + b\mathbf{Y}, \mathbf{X}) = a(\mathbf{X}, \mathbf{X}) + b(\mathbf{Y}, \mathbf{X}) = 0$, the segment associated with **Z** is perpendicular to AB and the lines thus determined may be used for axes of the new system. In particular, we may choose $b = 1$ and $a = -(\mathbf{X}, \mathbf{Y})/(\mathbf{X}, \mathbf{X})$.

Example 1. Let the plane π be determined by $A(1, 2, 3)$, $B(2, 5, -1)$, $C(1, -4, 2)$. Then $\mathbf{X} = [1, 3, -4]$, $\mathbf{Y} = [0, -6, -1]$, $\mathbf{Z} = \frac{14}{26}\mathbf{X} + \mathbf{Y} = [\frac{7}{13}, -\frac{57}{13}, -\frac{41}{13}]$. Then $(\mathbf{X}, \mathbf{Z}) = 0$, so that if D is $(\frac{20}{13}, -\frac{31}{13}, -\frac{2}{13})$, AD is associated with **Z** and AD is perpendicular to AB.

EXERCISES

1. Find the length of the vectors $[2, 1, -1]$, $[3, 0, 1]$, $[a, a + 1, a - 1]$.

2. Find the angle between the lines joining the points $(0, 1, -1)$, $(2, 3, 5)$ and the points $(2, 1, -3)$, $(5, 4, 1)$ of a Cartesian coordinate system.

3. Carry out the proofs of properties (i), (ii), and (iii) of the inner product of two vectors.

4. Find ([1, 3, 2], [2, − 1, 3]); ([1, − 1, 5], 3[1, 2, − 1] + 2[− 1, 1, 3]).

5. Find the equation of the plane through the point (1, 1, 1) orthogonal to the vector [1, − 1, 2]:

(a) In vector form.

(b) As a linear equation in x_1, x_2, x_3.

6. Find the equation of a plane perpendicular to the line through (− 1, 1, 5) and (3, − 1, 1) through the midpoint of that segment.

7. Find the equation of a plane through the point (2, 3, 4) and parallel to the plane (**R**, [− 1, 1, 2]) = 5.

8. Find a pair of perpendicular vectors dependent on [1, − 3, 2] and [4, 2, − 3].

9. Find a pair of orthogonal vectors associated with segments in the plane $3x_1 + 4x_2 + 5x_3 = 7$.

10. Given vectors [1, 1, 1], [2, 0, − 1].

(a) Find two vectors dependent on them that are orthogonal.

(b) Find a third vector orthogonal to both those found in (a).

(c) Find unit vectors (vectors of length 1) in the directions of the vector found in (a) and (b).

7. The Outer Product of Vectors

The material presented so far in this chapter is, in its basic content, not limited to ordered triples. The next chapter will show how readily the concepts may be extended to ordered n-tuples of real numbers $[x_1, x_2, \cdots, x_n]$. There is however one concept that, as far as this course is concerned, is definable only in space. A generalization, while possible, would take us far afield from our present purpose.

DEFINITION 7.1. *If* $\mathbf{X} = [x_1, x_2, x_3]$ *and* $\mathbf{Y} = [y_1, y_2, y_3]$ *are two vectors, the* OUTER PRODUCT, *written* $[\mathbf{X}, \mathbf{Y}]$ *or* $\mathbf{X} \times \mathbf{Y}$, *is the vector*

$$[x_2y_3 - x_3y_2, x_3y_1 - x_1y_3, x_1y_2 - x_2y_1].$$

Before proceeding to a geometrical interpretation of the outer product, observe that the outer product is a single-valued mapping of all ordered pairs of vectors into the set of vectors. Moreover, the following properties of the outer product are immediate consequences of the definition:

(i) $$[\mathbf{X}, \mathbf{Y}] = - [\mathbf{Y}, \mathbf{X}].$$

(ii) $$(\mathbf{X}, [\mathbf{X}, \mathbf{Y}]) = (\mathbf{Y}, [\mathbf{X}, \mathbf{Y}]) = 0.$$

Property (ii) states that the vector $[\mathbf{X}, \mathbf{Y}]$ is orthogonal to the vectors $\mathbf{X}$ and $\mathbf{Y}$. Moreover, we can compute the length of $[\mathbf{X}, \mathbf{Y}]$ to be

$$
\begin{aligned}
([\mathbf{X}, \mathbf{Y}], [\mathbf{X}, \mathbf{Y}])^{1/2} &= [(x_2y_3 - x_3y_2)^2 + (x_3y_1 - x_1y_3)^2 + (x_1y_2 - x_2y_1)^2]^{1/2} \\
&= [(x_1^2+x_2^2+x_3^2)(y_1^2+y_2^2+y_3^2) - (x_1y_1+x_2y_2+x_3y_3)^2]^{1/2} \\
&= [(\mathbf{X}, \mathbf{X})(\mathbf{Y}, \mathbf{Y}) - (\mathbf{X}, \mathbf{Y})^2]^{1/2} \\
&= (\mathbf{X}, \mathbf{X})^{1/2}(\mathbf{Y}, \mathbf{Y})^{1/2}\left\{1 - \left[\frac{(\mathbf{X}, \mathbf{Y})^2}{(\mathbf{X}, \mathbf{X})(\mathbf{Y}, \mathbf{Y})}\right]\right\}^{1/2} \\
&= |\mathbf{X}|\,|\mathbf{Y}|\,(1 - \cos^2\theta)^{1/2} = |\mathbf{X}|\,|\mathbf{Y}|\sin\theta,
\end{aligned}
$$

where θ is the acute angle between **X** and **Y**. Hence, in a Cartesian coordinate system the length of [**X**, **Y**] is the area of a parallelogram whose sides are associated with **X** and **Y**.

Perhaps the most useful application of the outer product of two vectors is in the determination of a vector perpendicular to two given vectors. This in turn simplifies other problems which we will illustrate in detail for a Cartesian coordinate system.

Example 1. The plane determined by three points: Let the points be A, B, C. Let the vector associated with AB be $\mathbf{D} = [d_1, d_2, d_3]$ and that associated with AC be $\mathbf{E} = [e_1, e_2, e_3]$. A vector orthogonal to the plane is $[\mathbf{D}, \mathbf{E}]$. If $\mathbf{X} = [x_1, x_2, x_3]$ is associated with OX, where $X(x_1, x_2, x_3)$ is an arbitrary point of the plane, and $\mathbf{A} = [a_1, a_2, a_3]$ is associated with the point $A(a_1, a_2, a_3)$, then $\mathbf{X} - \mathbf{A}$ is associated with AX. Hence,

$$(\mathbf{X} - \mathbf{A}, [\mathbf{D}, \mathbf{E}]) = 0.$$

This is a new form of a vector equation of a plane.

Example 2. The perpendicular distance between two nonparallel lines: This problem is computationally tedious without vectors but now becomes quite easy. Let the lines be determined by the points A, B and C, G respectively (Figure 7.1). We wish to find the length of the mutual perpendicular QP. It would be difficult to find P and Q, but we can find the length of AH (Figure 7.1), a line segment parallel to and equal in length to PQ. This will give the prescribed answer. If **D** is associated with AB

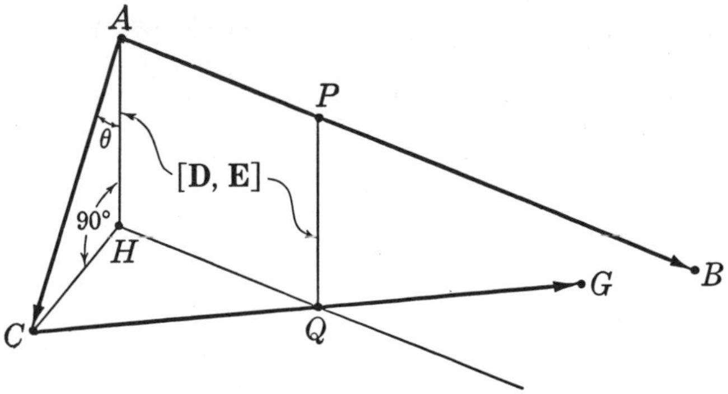

Figure 7.1

and **E** with CG, [**D**, **E**] is in the direction of PQ or QP. Let **F** be associated with AC. Then consider

$$\frac{(\mathbf{F}, [\mathbf{D}, \mathbf{E}])}{|\,[\mathbf{D}, \mathbf{E}]\,|} = |\,\mathbf{F}\,| \cdot \frac{|\,[\mathbf{D}, \mathbf{E}]\,|}{|\,[\mathbf{D}, \mathbf{E}]\,|} \cos\theta = |\,\mathbf{F}\,| \cos\theta, \tag{7.1}$$

where θ is the angle between the line segments AC and AH. Clearly (7.1) gives the desired length of AH or PQ.

Example 3. The scalar triple product of three vectors: Let A, B, C, P be four points which, at the outset, are assumed to be noncoplanar. Let **D**, **E**, **F** be associated with the segments AB, AC, AP. There is a parallelepiped whose sides are these three segments (Figure 7.2). The area of the base is $|\,[\mathbf{D}, \mathbf{E}]\,|$ since the area is equal to the product of the lengths of adjoining sides and the sine of the included angle. The altitude PQ is $AP \cos\theta$, where θ is the angle between AP and PQ, and PQ is in the direction of [**D**, **E**]. Hence, the volume of the parallelepiped is ([**D**, **E**], **F**) or its negative, depending on the sign. The expression ([**D**, **E**], **F**) is called the

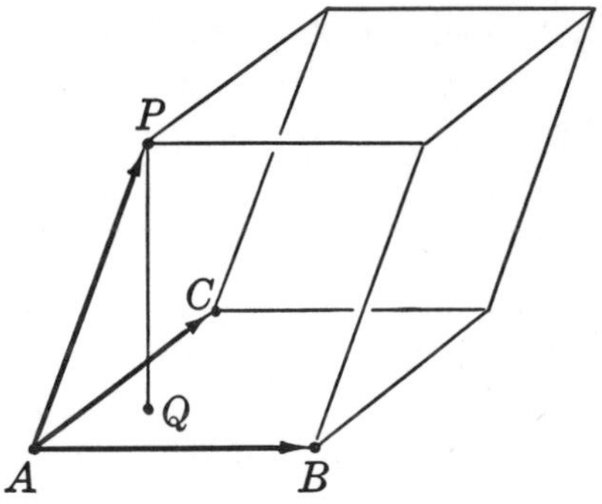

Figure 7.2

scalar triple product of **D**, **E**, and **F**. Special interest is attached to the case in which A, B, C, P are coplanar. Then ([**D**, **E**], **F**) = 0. (Why?) On the other hand, for any three nonzero vectors there exist associated segments with a given initial point. If these segments lie in a plane, the vectors are dependent, and conversely.

Thus,

Theorem 7.1. *Three vectors are dependent if and only if the scalar triple product is zero.*

The last theorem makes the verification of dependence or independence perfectly straightforward. It will be generalized by means of determinants in later chapters.

EXERCISES

1. Prove $[\mathbf{X}, \mathbf{Y}] = -[\mathbf{Y}, \mathbf{X}]$.

2. Find $[\mathbf{A}, \mathbf{B}]$ if $\mathbf{A} = [1, -3, 5]$, $\mathbf{B} = [-2, 4, 1]$.

3. If $[\mathbf{A}, \mathbf{B}] = \mathbf{0}$, what can be said about $\mathbf{A}$ and $\mathbf{B}$?

4. Prove property (ii) for the outer product.

5. Given three arbitrary vectors $\mathbf{A}$, $\mathbf{B}$, $\mathbf{C}$ there are twelve ways to make a formally different scalar triple product: $([\mathbf{A}, \mathbf{B}], \mathbf{C})$, $(\mathbf{A}, [\mathbf{B}, \mathbf{C}])$, $([\mathbf{B}, \mathbf{A}], \mathbf{C})$, etc. Show that only two values may occur. How are these values related?

6. Give the equation of the plane determined by $A(1, -2, 4)$, $B(2, -1, 7)$, $C(3, -5, 1)$.

7. If D is $(4, -1, 3)$ and A, B, C are as given in Problem 6, find the perpendicular distance from AB to CD.

8. Investigate the following sets of vectors for linear dependence:

(a) $[1, 1, 2]$, $[1, 2, 3]$, $[3, 0, 2]$

(b) $[1, -1, 2]$, $[1, 2, 3]$, $[3, 0, 7]$

(c) $[-1, 1, -2]$, $[1, 2, 3]$, $[4, 1, 7]$

9. Show that the associative law for multiplication does not apply to the outer product. That is $[\mathbf{A}, [\mathbf{B}, \mathbf{C}]] \neq [[\mathbf{A}, \mathbf{B}], \mathbf{C}]$ for some vectors $\mathbf{A}$, $\mathbf{B}$, $\mathbf{C}$.

CHAPTER 3

Vector Spaces

We have seen in the previous chapter how the points and line segments of space give rise to ordered triples of real numbers with the introduction of a linear coordinate system. Our physical experience makes it difficult or impossible to conceive of a space in which the ordered n-tuple of real numbers $(x_1, x_2, \cdots, x_n)$ arises as the coordinates of a point P_x in a linear coordinate system. Nevertheless, a generalization of the concept of ordered triples to ordered n-tuples of real numbers will confront us with a choice of either a geometric or an algebraic structure for these n-tuples. In order to provide a basis for a geometrical interpretation, we define the points of the space E_n to consist of all ordered n-tuples of real numbers $(x_1, x_2, \cdots, x_n)$.

It would now be possible to define a distance between points of E_n and develop an analytic geometry for the resulting geometrical system. However, we have seen that an algebraic system of vectors provides a convenient tool for the interpretation of many geometrical results in space. With this in mind, we turn in this chapter to the development of an algebraic system of vectors for n-tuples and return to the geometry of E_n later.

1. The Vector Space $V_n(R)$ and Real Vector Spaces

Different symbols (x_1, x_2, x_3) and $[x_1, x_2, x_3]$ were used to distinguish between the coordinates of points and vectors associated with line segments in space. Although the distinction is perhaps unnecessary, we prefer to retain a similar visual difference between ordered n-tuples of real numbers when considered as points of E_n and when considered as elements of a set for which we shall prescribe algebraic operations. We begin by generalizing the algebraic concepts of Chapter 2. The *real vector space* $V_n(R)$ will be defined in terms of its elements, a rule of equality, and two rules of operation.

DEFINITION 1.1. *The set of elements of $V_n(R)$ is the set of ordered n-tuples of real numbers $\{[x_1, x_2, \cdots, x_n]\}$. These elements are called* VECTORS, *and we will write* $\mathbf{X} = [x_1, x_2, \cdots, x_n]$, $\mathbf{X} \in V_n(R)$.

EQUALITY OF VECTORS. *If* $\mathbf{X} = [x_1, x_2, \cdots, x_n]$ *and* $\mathbf{Y} = [y_1, y_2, \cdots, y_n]$, *then* $\mathbf{X} = \mathbf{Y}$ *if and only if* $x_1 = y_1, x_2 = y_2, \cdots, x_n = y_n$.

ADDITION OF VECTORS.

$$[x_1, x_2, \cdots, x_n] + [y_1, y_2, \cdots, y_n] = [x_1 + y_1, x_2 + y_2, \cdots, x_n + y_n].$$

SCALAR MULTIPLICATION. *For all real numbers* $r \in R$, *and any vector* $\mathbf{X} \in V_n(R)$,

$$r[x_1, x_2, \cdots, x_n] = [rx_1, rx_2, \cdots, rx_n].$$

The real number x_i in the vector $\mathbf{X} = [x_1, x_2, \cdots, x_i, \cdots, x_n]$ is called the *i*th component of $\mathbf{X}$. In terms of components, the definitions and rules of operation for vectors of $V_n(R)$ state that $\mathbf{X} = \mathbf{Y}$ if corresponding components are equal; to add $\mathbf{X}$ and $\mathbf{Y}$, add corresponding components; to multiply $\mathbf{X}$ by a number r, multiply each component by r.

Example 1. Let $\mathbf{X} = [0, -1, 2, 3]$ and $\mathbf{Y} = [5, 1, 2, -3]$. Then

$$\begin{aligned} \mathbf{X} + \mathbf{Y} &= [0, -1, 2, 3] + [5, 1, 2, -3] \\ &= [0 + 5, -1 + 1, 2 + 2, 3 + (-3)] = [5, 0, 4, 0]. \\ 3\mathbf{X} &= 3[0, -1, 2, 3] = [3 \cdot 0, 3(-1), 3 \cdot 2, 3 \cdot 3] = [0, -3, 6, 9]. \end{aligned}$$

Both $\mathbf{X} + \mathbf{Y}$ and $3\mathbf{X}$ are vectors of $V_4(R)$.

The rules of operation for the vectors of $V_n(R)$ are the same as for $V_3(R)$ of Chapter 2 and have similar implications. For example, we let the *zero vector* $[0, 0, \cdots, 0]$ be denoted by $\mathbf{0}$ and see that

$$[x_1, x_2, \cdots, x_n] + [0, \cdots, 0] = [0, \cdots, 0] + [x_1, \cdots, x_n] = [x_1, \cdots, x_n];$$

or $\mathbf{X} + \mathbf{0} = \mathbf{0} + \mathbf{X} = \mathbf{X}$ for all vectors $\mathbf{X}$ of $V_n(R)$.

The *negative* of the vector $\mathbf{X} = [x_1, x_2, \cdots, x_n]$ is defined to be the vector $-\mathbf{X} = [-x_1, -x_2, \cdots, -x_n]$, and we see that

$$\begin{aligned} [x_1, \cdots, x_n] + [-x_1, \cdots, -x_n] &= [-x_1, \cdots, -x_n] + [x_1, \cdots, x_n] \\ &= [0, 0, \cdots, 0]; \end{aligned}$$

or $\mathbf{X} + (-\mathbf{X}) = (-\mathbf{X}) + \mathbf{X} = \mathbf{0}$ for all $\mathbf{X}$ of $V_n(R)$.

Using the procedure suggested by real numbers, we define the subtraction of vectors by the equation

$$\mathbf{X} - \mathbf{Y} = \mathbf{X} + (-\mathbf{Y}).$$

In terms of components, when subtracting vectors we subtract corresponding components.

Example 2. Let $\mathbf{X} = [1, 2, 3, -4, 5]$ and $\mathbf{Y} = [1, 1, 2, -1, 3]$ be vectors of $V_5(R)$. Then,

$$\begin{aligned} \mathbf{X} - \mathbf{Y} &= [1, 2, 3, -4, 5] - [1, 1, 2, -1, 3] \\ &= [1 - 1, 2 - 1, 3 - 2, -4 - (-1), 5 - 3] = [0, 1, 1, -3, 2]. \end{aligned}$$

The student will find that, for vectors **X**, **Y**, **Z** of $V_n(R)$, the rules

$$(\mathbf{X} + \mathbf{Y}) + \mathbf{Z} = \mathbf{X} + (\mathbf{Y} + \mathbf{Z})$$
$$\mathbf{X} + \mathbf{Y} = \mathbf{Y} + \mathbf{X}$$

follow from the corresponding associative and commutative laws for real numbers.

Briefly, the vectors of $V_n(R)$ may be added together or multiplied by any real number to yield again a vector of $V_n(R)$, and these vectors satisfy the following algebraic laws:

A1. If $\mathbf{X}, \mathbf{Y} \in V_n(R)$, then $\mathbf{X} + \mathbf{Y} \in V_n(R)$.

A2. For vectors $\mathbf{X}, \mathbf{Y}, \mathbf{Z} \in V_n(R)$,

$$(\mathbf{X} + \mathbf{Y}) + \mathbf{Z} = \mathbf{X} + (\mathbf{Y} + \mathbf{Z}). \qquad \textit{(Associative law)}$$

A3. There is a vector $\mathbf{0} \in V_n(R)$, such that

$$\mathbf{0} + \mathbf{X} = \mathbf{X} + \mathbf{0} = \mathbf{X} \quad \text{for all } \mathbf{X} \in V_n(R).$$

A4. For every $\mathbf{X} \in V_n(R)$, there is a vector $-\mathbf{X} \in V_n(R)$ such that

$$\mathbf{X} + (-\mathbf{X}) = (-\mathbf{X}) + \mathbf{X} = \mathbf{0}.$$

A5. For vectors $\mathbf{X}, \mathbf{Y} \in V_n(R)$,

$$\mathbf{X} + \mathbf{Y} = \mathbf{Y} + \mathbf{X}. \qquad \textit{(Commutative law)}$$

S1. If $\mathbf{X} \in V_n(R)$ and a is any real number, $a\mathbf{X} \in V_n(R)$.

S2. For real numbers $a, b \in R$, vectors $\mathbf{X} \in V_n(R)$,

$$(ab)\mathbf{X} = a(b\mathbf{X}).$$

S3. For real numbers $a, b \in R$, vectors $\mathbf{X} \in V_n(R)$,

$$(a + b)\mathbf{X} = a\mathbf{X} + b\mathbf{X}.$$

S4. For real numbers $a \in R$, vectors $\mathbf{X}, \mathbf{Y} \in V_n(R)$,

$$a(\mathbf{X} + \mathbf{Y}) = a\mathbf{X} + a\mathbf{Y}.$$

S5. $1 \cdot \mathbf{X} = \mathbf{X}$, for all $\mathbf{X} \in V_n(R)$.

The verification of laws S1, S2, S3, S4, and S5 will be left to the student. The laws satisfied by $V_n(R)$ should be compared with the results stated in Theorem 3.1 of Chapter 2.

There are many subsets V of $V_n(R)$, the vectors of which may be added, subtracted, or multiplied by scalars to give again a vector of V. The vectors of these subsets satisfy laws A1–A5 and S1–S5 with $V_n(R)$ replaced by V. Most of the laws are trivially verified because the elements of V are, at the same time, elements of $V_n(R)$.

Example 3. Let V consist of all vectors of $V_4(R)$ whose third component is 0. The vectors of V are of the form $[x_1, x_2, 0, x_4]$. Then,

$$[x_1, x_2, 0, x_4] + [y_1, y_2, 0, y_4] = [x_1 + y_1, x_2 + y_2, 0, x_4 + y_4]$$

and
$$r[x_1, x_2, 0, x_4] = [rx_1, rx_2, 0, rx_4],$$

so that the sum of two vectors and the scalar multiples of vectors in V are again in V. Moreover, all the laws satisfied by $V_4(R)$ are satisfied by V.

Example 4. Let V consist of all vectors of the form

$$a[1, 3, -2, 1] + b[2, 1, 0, 0],$$

where a and b are arbitrary real numbers. Certainly,

$$\begin{aligned}(a_1[1, 3, -2, 1] + b_1[2, 1, 0, 0]) + (a_2[1, 3, -2, 1] + b_2[2, 1, 0, 0]) \\ = (a_1 + a_2)[1, 3, -2, 1] + (b_1 + b_2)[2, 1, 0, 0];\end{aligned}$$

and

$$t(a[1, 3, -2, 1] + b[2, 1, 0, 0]) = (ta)[1, 3, -2, 1] + (tb)[2, 1, 0, 0].$$

Hence, sums and scalar multiples of vectors in V are again in V. Again, all the laws satisfied by $V_4(R)$ are satisfied by V.

These examples lead us to make the more general definition:

DEFINITION 1.2. *Let R be the field of real numbers and let V be a set of elements together with an operation of addition (+), a scalar multiplication of elements of V by elements of R yielding again elements of V and satisfying (with $V_n(R)$ replaced by V) the laws* A1–A5 *and* S1–S5. *Then V will be called a* REAL VECTOR SPACE *or a* VECTOR SPACE OVER R.

Clearly, $V_n(R)$ is a vector space over R and so are the subsets of vectors V of $V_n(R)$ given in Examples 3 and 4. Example 4 is a special case of the following general observation: Let $\mathbf{X}_1, \mathbf{X}_2, \cdots, \mathbf{X}_r$ be an arbitrary finite set of vectors of $V_n(R)$. The set V of all vectors of the form

$$a_1\mathbf{X}_1 + a_2\mathbf{X}_2 + \cdots + a_r\mathbf{X}_r,$$

where a_i are arbitrary real numbers, is a vector space over R. The proof that V is a vector space over R is a straightforward generalization of Example 4.

The space V just defined is the *smallest* vector space that contains $\mathbf{X}_1, \mathbf{X}_2, \cdots, \mathbf{X}_r$ in the sense that any vector space W which contains $\mathbf{X}_1, \mathbf{X}_2, \cdots, \mathbf{X}_r$ must, in view of A1 and S1, contain all vectors

$$a_1\mathbf{X}_1 + a_2\mathbf{X}_2 + \cdots + a_r\mathbf{X}_r.$$

That is, W must contain V.

The definition of a real vector space enables us to consider as vector spaces sets of elements that are not n-tuples of real numbers. For example, let the elements of V be polynomials $p(x)$ with real coefficients and such that $p(0) = 0$. For vector addition we take ordinary addition of polynomials, and for scalar multiplication, the multiplication of a polynomial by a real number. All the laws for a vector space over R are easily verified; as an illustration, if $p(x)$ and $q(x)$ are elements of V, $p(0) + q(0) = 0 + 0 = 0$ so that $p(x) + q(x) \in V$.

Actually, while in the process of generalizing, we could have defined a vector space over an arbitrary field F. In this case, V would again be a set of elements for which an addition is defined satisfying A1–A5. However, scalar multiplication would be between vectors and elements of F again yielding vectors such that S1–S5 are satisfied. For example, n-tuples of complex numbers $[c_1, c_2, \cdots, c_n]$ with definitions similar to Definition 1.1 would form a vector space over the complex numbers. Similarly the set of n-tuples of rational numbers would be a vector space over the rational numbers. For most purposes, real vector spaces will be quite general enough to demonstrate the concepts that we wish to introduce. We shall make this restriction for the next few chapters.

For convenience, we give at this time the following definition:

DEFINITION 1.3. *A non-empty subset W of a real vector space V is a* SUBSPACE *of V if for every pair of vectors $\mathbf{X}_1$ and $\mathbf{X}_2$ of W, $\mathbf{X}_1 + \mathbf{X}_2$ and $r\mathbf{X}_1$ (for all real numbers r), are also contained in W.*

The student can verify that every subspace of a vector space V is again a vector space.

Except for a few exercises below that indicate the generality of the definition of a vector space over R, we shall normally confine our exercises and examples to subspaces of $V_n(R)$.

EXERCISES

1. Let $\mathbf{X} = [2, 3, -1, 5]$ and $\mathbf{Y} = [1, 2, 0, -1]$. Compute the following: (a) $\mathbf{X} + 2\mathbf{Y}$; (b) $3\mathbf{X} - \mathbf{Y}$; (c) $a\mathbf{X} + b\mathbf{Y}$.

2. Determine whether the following subsets of $V_4(R)$ are subspaces of $V_4(R)$ and hence vector spaces over R:

   (a) The set of all vectors for which $x_1 = x_4$.
   (b) The set of all vectors for which $x_1 + x_2 = 0$.
   (c) The set of all vectors for which $x_1 \cdot x_2 = 0$.

3. Determine the smallest subspaces of $V_4(R)$ containing the sets of vectors:

   (a) $[0, 0, 0, 0]$, $[1, 0, 0, 0]$.
   (b) $[1, 2, 0, 1]$, $[2, 4, 0, 2]$, $[0, 0, 0, 1]$.
   (c) $[a, a, 0, 0]$, $[a, 0, 0, 0]$.

4. Show that the set of all polynomials of degree ≤ 5 with real coefficients is a vector space over R if the operation of vector addition is ordinary polynomial addition and scalar multiplication is the multiplication of a polynomial by a real number.

What is the smallest subspace containing the polynomials $1, x, x^2, x^3, x^4$, and x^5?

5. Using the same operations of vector addition and scalar multiplication as were defined in Exercise 4, determine whether the set of all polynomials in x with real coefficients (without any limitation on the degrees) forms a vector space over R.

6. Let V be the set of all real-valued functions defined on the interval $0 \leq x \leq 1$. Define vector addition and scalar multiplication as usual addition of functions and multiplication of a function by a real number. Show that V is a vector space over R.

Determine which of the following subsets of V are subspaces of V:

(a) The set of all functions f for which $f(1) = 0$.
(b) The set of all functions f for which $f(0) = f(1)$.
(c) The set of all functions f for which $f(0) + f(1) = 0$.
(d) The set of all functions f for which $f(x) \geq 0$.
(e) The set of all functions f for which $f(\frac{1}{2}) = \dfrac{f(0) + f(1)}{2}$.

7. Verify that property S2 is valid in $V_n(R)$.

8. Verify that the set of all vectors $a_1\mathbf{X}_1 + \cdots + a_r\mathbf{X}_r$, where the a_i are arbitrary real numbers and the $\mathbf{X}_i$ are fixed vectors of a vector space V over R, is a vector space over R.

9. Prove that a subspace of $V_n(R)$ is a vector space over R.

10. For an arbitrary vector space V over R, show that $0\mathbf{X} = \mathbf{0}$ for all $\mathbf{X}$ of V, where the 0 on the left is the zero element of R and the $\mathbf{0}$ on the right is the zero element of V.

2. Linear Dependence and Generators

We have stated that we were interested in determining the structure of $V_n(R)$ in order to apply the results to E_n. However, many of our concepts will apply to any vector space over R, and we shall permit this generality where convenient. Rather than continually state that we are dealing with a vector space V over R, for the next few chapters we shall always mean by a vector space V, a real vector space.

Let V be a vector space. A vector of the form

$$a_1\mathbf{X}_1 + a_2\mathbf{X}_2 + \cdots + a_r\mathbf{X}_r,$$

where $\mathbf{X}_i \in V$ and $a_1, a_2, \cdots, a_r$ are arbitrary real numbers, is called a *linear combination* of the vectors $\mathbf{X}_1, \cdots, \mathbf{X}_r$. In Exercise 8 of §1 the student was asked to prove that the set of all linear combinations of r vectors selected from a vector space V is again a vector space. We shall assume that this has been done.

Now suppose that a vector space V is given in advance. If it is possible to find r vectors $\mathbf{X}_1, \mathbf{X}_2, \cdots, \mathbf{X}_r$ of V such that every vector $\mathbf{X}$ of V can be written as a linear combination

$$\mathbf{X} = a_1\mathbf{X}_1 + a_2\mathbf{X}_2 + \cdots + a_r\mathbf{X}_r, \tag{2.1}$$

we say that the vectors $\mathbf{X}_1, \mathbf{X}_2, \cdots, \mathbf{X}_r$ are a *set of generators* of V, or that V is *generated* (*spanned*) by the vectors $\mathbf{X}_1, \mathbf{X}_2, \cdots, \mathbf{X}_r$.

We use the notation

$$V = L\{\mathbf{X}_1, \mathbf{X}_2, \cdots, \mathbf{X}_r\}$$

to denote that the vector space V is generated by the vectors $\mathbf{X}_1, \mathbf{X}_2, \cdots, \mathbf{X}_r$. The L should remind the student that V consists of all linear combinations of the vectors $\mathbf{X}_1, \mathbf{X}_2, \cdots, \mathbf{X}_r$.

Example 1. Let V be the subspace of $V_4(R)$ consisting of all vectors whose fourth component is zero. Every vector in V has the form $[a_1, a_2, a_3, 0]$, and by using the rules of vector operations we have

$$[a_1, a_2, a_3, 0] = a_1[1, 0, 0, 0] + a_2[0, 1, 0, 0] + a_3[0, 0, 1, 0].$$

Hence,

$$V = L\{[1, 0, 0, 0], [0, 1, 0, 0], [0, 0, 1, 0]\}.$$

Since $[1, 0, 0, 0] = [1, 1, 1, 0] - [0, 1, 1, 0]$, we may also write

$$[a_1, a_2, a_3, 0] = a_1[1, 1, 1, 0] - a_1[0, 1, 1, 0] + a_2[0, 1, 0, 0] + a_3[0, 0, 1, 0],$$

or
$$V = L\{[1, 1, 1, 0], [0, 1, 1, 0], [0, 1, 0, 0], [0, 0, 1, 0]\}.$$

Example 2. The previous example suggests that the vectors

$$\begin{aligned} \mathbf{E}_1 &= [1, 0, \cdots, 0] \\ \mathbf{E}_2 &= [0, 1, \cdots, 0] \\ &\cdots\cdots \\ \mathbf{E}_n &= [0, 0, \cdots, 1] \end{aligned} \tag{2.2}$$

generate $V_n(R)$. Indeed, for any vector $[x_1, x_2, \cdots, x_n]$ of $V_n(R)$,

$$[x_1, x_2, \cdots, x_n] = x_1\mathbf{E}_1 + x_2\mathbf{E}_2 + \cdots + x_n\mathbf{E}_n.$$

Hence, $V = L\{\mathbf{E}_1, \mathbf{E}_2, \cdots, \mathbf{E}_n\}$, or $\mathbf{E}_1, \mathbf{E}_2, \cdots, \mathbf{E}_n$ are a set of generators for $V_n(R)$.

We see from Example 1 that the number of vectors in a set of generators for a vector space V may vary. This is not surprising, because if

$$V = L\{\mathbf{X}_1, \mathbf{X}_2, \cdots, \mathbf{X}_r\},$$

any vector $\mathbf{X}$ of V has the form

$$\mathbf{X} = a_1\mathbf{X}_1 + a_2\mathbf{X}_2 + \cdots + a_r\mathbf{X}_r;$$

hence, $\mathbf{X} = a_1\mathbf{X}_1 + a_2\mathbf{X}_2 + \cdots + a_r\mathbf{X}_r + 0 \cdot \mathbf{Y}_1 + 0 \cdot \mathbf{Y}_2 + \cdots + 0 \cdot \mathbf{Y}_t$, where $\mathbf{Y}_1, \mathbf{Y}_2, \cdots, \mathbf{Y}_t$ are arbitrary vectors of V. Moreover, any vector $\mathbf{Z}$ such that $\mathbf{Z} = b_1\mathbf{X}_1 + \cdots + b_r\mathbf{X}_r + c_1\mathbf{Y}_1 + \cdots + c_t\mathbf{Y}_t$ is in V for any real numbers $b_1, \cdots, b_r, c_1, \cdots, c_t$. (Why?) Thus,

$$V = L\{\mathbf{X}_1, \mathbf{X}_2, \cdots, \mathbf{X}_r, \mathbf{Y}_1, \mathbf{Y}_2, \cdots, \mathbf{Y}_t\}.$$

If for no other reason than convenience of writing, it seems reasonable to determine whether there is a unique smallest number of vectors in a set of generators that may be used to generate a vector space V. In order to answer questions of this nature, we recall and generalize the concept of *linear dependence* from Chapter 2.

DEFINITION 2.1. *The vectors $\mathbf{X}_1, \mathbf{X}_2, \cdots, \mathbf{X}_r$ of a vector space V are said to be* LINEARLY DEPENDENT *if there exist real numbers $a_1, a_2, \cdots, a_r$, not all zero, such that*

$$a_1\mathbf{X}_1 + a_2\mathbf{X}_2 + \cdots + a_r\mathbf{X}_r = \mathbf{0}.$$

If the vectors $\mathbf{X}_1, \mathbf{X}_2, \cdots, \mathbf{X}_r$ are not linearly dependent, they are said to be *linearly independent.* Equivalently, the vectors $\mathbf{X}_1, \mathbf{X}_2, \cdots, \mathbf{X}_r$ are linearly independent if the only linear combination

$$a_1\mathbf{X}_1 + a_2\mathbf{X}_2 + \cdots + a_r\mathbf{X}_r$$

which is $\mathbf{0}$ is the one in which $a_1 = a_2 = \cdots = a_r = 0$.

Example 3. Let $\mathbf{X}_1 = [1, 0, 0, 0]$, $\mathbf{X}_2 = [0, 1, 0, 0]$, and $\mathbf{X}_3 = [0, 0, 1, 0]$. If $a_1\mathbf{X}_1 + a_2\mathbf{X}_2 + a_3\mathbf{X}_3 = [a_1, a_2, a_3, 0] = \mathbf{0}$, then, by the definition of equality, $a_1 = a_2 = a_3 = 0$. Hence, the vectors $\mathbf{X}_1$, $\mathbf{X}_2$, and $\mathbf{X}_3$ are linearly independent.

Example 4. Let $\mathbf{X}_1 = [1, 1, 1, 0]$, $\mathbf{X}_2 = [0, 1, 1, 0]$, $\mathbf{X}_3 = [0, 1, 0, 0]$, and $\mathbf{X}_4 = [0, 0, 1, 0]$. Then

$$0\mathbf{X}_1 + 1 \cdot \mathbf{X}_2 - 1 \cdot \mathbf{X}_3 - 1 \cdot \mathbf{X}_4 = \mathbf{0},$$

so that the vectors $\mathbf{X}_1, \mathbf{X}_2, \mathbf{X}_3, \mathbf{X}_4$ are linearly dependent. Note that the vectors used in Examples 3 and 4 are the generating sets of Example 1. One set of generators is linearly independent and the other set is linearly dependent.

THEOREM 2.1. *The nonzero vectors* $\mathbf{X}_1, \mathbf{X}_2, \cdots, \mathbf{X}_n$ *of a vector space* V *are linearly dependent if and only if some* $\mathbf{X}_k$, *with* $2 \leq k$, *is a linear combination of the preceding* $\mathbf{X}_i$*'s, that is,* $\mathbf{X}_1, \mathbf{X}_2, \cdots, \mathbf{X}_{k-1}$.

Proof. Let the vector $\mathbf{X}_k$ be a linear combination of the preceding $\mathbf{X}_i$'s. Then,

$$\mathbf{X}_k = a_1\mathbf{X}_1 + a_2\mathbf{X}_2 + \cdots + a_{k-1}\mathbf{X}_{k-1},$$

or

$$a_1\mathbf{X}_1 + a_2\mathbf{X}_2 + \cdots + a_{k-1}\mathbf{X}_{k-1} - 1 \cdot \mathbf{X}_k + 0 \cdot \mathbf{X}_{k+1} + \cdots + 0 \cdot \mathbf{X}_n = \mathbf{0},$$

and consequently the vectors $\mathbf{X}_1, \mathbf{X}_2, \cdots, \mathbf{X}_n$ are linearly dependent because the coefficient -1 is certainly not zero.

In order to prove the "only if" part, we assume that the vectors $\mathbf{X}_1, \mathbf{X}_2, \cdots, \mathbf{X}_n$ are linearly dependent. Hence,

$$a_1\mathbf{X}_1 + a_2\mathbf{X}_2 + \cdots + a_k\mathbf{X}_k + \cdots + a_n\mathbf{X}_n = \mathbf{0}$$

and not all coefficients are zero. Let a_k be the last coefficient that is not zero. Then,

$$\mathbf{X}_k = -\frac{a_1}{a_k}\mathbf{X}_1 - \frac{a_2}{a_k}\mathbf{X}_2 - \cdots - \frac{a_{k-1}}{a_k}\mathbf{X}_{k-1},$$

and the conditions of the theorem are fulfilled as k cannot be 1 since $\mathbf{X}_1 \neq \mathbf{0}$.

Linearly independent generators. We turn now to the problem of determining whether there is a smallest number of vectors that generate a vector space V. Let V be a vector space with generators $\mathbf{X}_1, \mathbf{X}_2, \cdots, \mathbf{X}_r$, or

$$V = L\{\mathbf{X}_1, \mathbf{X}_2, \cdots, \mathbf{X}_r\}.$$

Ignore, for the present, the question of how we determine whether or not $\mathbf{X}_1, \mathbf{X}_2, \cdots, \mathbf{X}_r$ are linearly independent; we assume this determination made for the vector space $V = L\{\mathbf{X}_1, \mathbf{X}_2, \cdots, \mathbf{X}_r\}$. Two situations may occur:

1. The vectors $\mathbf{X}_1, \mathbf{X}_2, \cdots, \mathbf{X}_r$ are linearly independent. In this case, if any vector $\mathbf{X}_i$ is removed, the remaining vectors will not generate V. We know $\mathbf{X}_i \in V$, and if the remaining vectors generate V,

$$\mathbf{X}_i = a_1\mathbf{X}_1 + \cdots + a_{i-1}\mathbf{X}_{i-1} + a_{i+1}\mathbf{X}_{i+1} + \cdots + a_r\mathbf{X}_r,$$

for real numbers $a_1, \cdots, a_r$, or

$$a_1\mathbf{X}_1 + \cdots + (-1)\mathbf{X}_i + \cdots + a_r\mathbf{X}_r = \mathbf{0}.$$

Hence $\mathbf{X}_1, \mathbf{X}_2, \cdots, \mathbf{X}_r$ would be linearly dependent contrary to our assumption. Consequently, if we insist on generating V by $\mathbf{X}_1, \mathbf{X}_2, \cdots, \mathbf{X}_r$ or a subset of these vectors, it cannot be done except by using all of them.

2. The vectors $\mathbf{X}_1, \mathbf{X}_2, \cdots, \mathbf{X}_r$ are linearly dependent. In this case consider the set of vectors

$$\{\mathbf{X}_1, \mathbf{X}_2, \mathbf{X}_3, \cdots, \mathbf{X}_r\}$$

and beginning with $\mathbf{X}_2$ remove a vector if it can be written as a linear combination of the preceding vectors. (We can assume $\mathbf{X}_1 \neq \mathbf{0}$; otherwise, we could remove it.) There remains after this process, by virtue of Theorem 2.1, a set of linearly independent vectors

$$\{\mathbf{X}_1, \mathbf{X}_{i_2}, \cdots, \mathbf{X}_{i_k}\}, \tag{2.3}$$

where $i_2, i_3, \cdots, i_k$ are a subset of the integers $2, 3, \cdots, r$.

Certainly $V = L\{\mathbf{X}_1, \mathbf{X}_{i_2}, \cdots, \mathbf{X}_{i_k}\}$, since, for every $\mathbf{X}$ in V,

$$\mathbf{X} = a_1\mathbf{X}_1 + a_2\mathbf{X}_2 + \cdots + a_r\mathbf{X}_r,$$

and if $\mathbf{X}_i$ is not among the vectors (2.3) it may be replaced by a linear combination of preceding vectors from the set (2.3).

The conclusions of the preceding paragraphs may be put in the form of the following theorem:

THEOREM 2.2. *If $\mathbf{X}_1, \mathbf{X}_2, \cdots, \mathbf{X}_r$ generate a vector space V, then there is a linearly independent subset of these vectors whose elements generate V.*

Example 1 provides an illustration of Theorem 2.2. Thus,

$$V = L\{[1, 1, 1, 0], [0, 1, 1, 0], [0, 1, 0, 0], [0, 0, 1, 0]\};$$

or

$$V = L\{[1, 1, 1, 0], [0, 1, 1, 0], [0, 1, 0, 0]\}$$

since $[0, 0, 1, 0] = [0, 1, 1, 0] - [0, 1, 0, 0]$. The vector $[0, 0, 1, 0]$ is the only generating vector that can be written as a linear combination of the preceding.

Two interesting questions now arise.

1. Does there exist at least one set of linearly independent generators for a given subspace V of $V_n(R)$?

Or, more generally,

1′. Does there exist at least one set of linearly independent generators for a given vector space V over R?

2. If we start with different finite sets of generators of a vector space V and apply Theorem 2.2, is the resulting number of linearly independent vectors the same?

We shall prove that the answer to question 1 is Yes. Although the same answer may be given to question 1′, its proof is beyond the scope of this text. Why the difference? It is this: We have shown that $V_n(R)$ has a finite set of generators $\mathbf{E}_1, \cdots, \mathbf{E}_n$ but we cannot be sure that an *arbitrary* vector space V over R has a *finite* set of generators. For example, what would be a finite set of generators for all polynomials? It is easy to see that none exists. For if there were a finite set of generators, there would be among these generators a polynomial of highest degree. Let this degree be n. How would we write x^{n+1} in terms of the generators? We couldn't.

In this text we shall consider only vector spaces which have a finite set of generators and we therefore add the following assumption to those of Definition 1.2 for a real vector space:

F. FINITENESS: *There exists a finite set of vectors* $\mathbf{X}_1, \mathbf{X}_2, \cdots, \mathbf{X}_m$ *of* V *such that every vector* $\mathbf{X}$ *of* V *may be expressed in the form*

$$\mathbf{X} = a_1\mathbf{X}_1 + a_2\mathbf{X}_2 + \cdots + a_m\mathbf{X}_m,$$

where $a_1, a_2, \cdots, a_m$ *are real numbers.*

Note that in our assumption F we have not assumed a set of linearly independent generators for a vector space V. However, an application of Theorem 2.2 assures us that V will have a finite set of linearly independent generators.

Assumption F is, of course, redundant for $V_n(R)$ in view of the system of generators given by equations (2.2), but we wish to emphasize the fact that *all* spaces under discussion from this section on will have a finite set of generators.

We shall now return to questions 1, 1′, and 2, using a method of proof which will recur several times in the sequel and which may be described as a "replacement process."

THEOREM 2.3. *Let* $V = L\{\mathbf{X}_1, \mathbf{X}_2, \cdots, \mathbf{X}_r\}$, *where* $\mathbf{X}_1, \cdots, \mathbf{X}_r$ *are linearly independent vectors. If* $\mathbf{Y}_1, \mathbf{Y}_2, \cdots, \mathbf{Y}_s$ *are a set of linearly independent vectors of* V, *then* $r \geq s$.

COROLLARY 1. *Let* $V = L\{\mathbf{X}_1, \cdots, \mathbf{X}_r\} = L\{\mathbf{Y}_1, \cdots, \mathbf{Y}_s\}$, *where the sets of vectors* $\{\mathbf{X}_i\}$ *and* $\{\mathbf{Y}_i\}$ *are linearly independent. Then* $r = s$.

COROLLARY 2. *The maximum number of linearly independent vectors in* $V_n(R)$ *is* n. *Stated otherwise, every set of* $n + 1$ *vectors of* $V_n(R)$ *is linearly dependent.*

Proof of Theorem 2.3. We know that $\mathbf{Y}_s \in V$, and that

$$\mathbf{Y}_s = a_1\mathbf{X}_1 + a_2\mathbf{X}_2 + \cdots + a_r\mathbf{X}_r \quad \text{or} \quad (-1)\mathbf{Y}_s + a_1\mathbf{X}_1 + \cdots + a_r\mathbf{X}_r = \mathbf{0}.$$

Thus the vectors $\mathbf{Y}_s, \mathbf{X}_1, \cdots, \mathbf{X}_r$ are linearly dependent because the coefficient (-1) of $\mathbf{Y}_s$ is not zero.

We consider $V = L\{\mathbf{Y}_s, \mathbf{X}_1, \cdots, \mathbf{X}_r\}$ and reduce the generators to a set of linearly independent generators by removing a vector $\mathbf{X}_i$ if it can be written as a linear combination of preceding vectors $\mathbf{Y}_s, \mathbf{X}_1, \cdots, \mathbf{X}_{i-1}$. Certainly $\mathbf{Y}_s$ will be retained and at least one vector $\mathbf{X}_i$ will be removed. Let us assume that $\mathbf{X}_i$ is the first vector removed so that

$$\mathbf{X}_i = a_1\mathbf{Y}_s + a_2\mathbf{X}_1 + \cdots + a_i\mathbf{X}_{i-1}, \tag{2.4}$$

and $a_1 \neq 0$, for otherwise the vectors $\mathbf{X}_1, \cdots, \mathbf{X}_i$ would be linearly dependent.

Then $V = L\{\mathbf{Y}_s, \mathbf{X}_1, \cdots, \mathbf{X}_{i-1}, \mathbf{X}_{i+1}, \cdots, \mathbf{X}_n\}$. Now repeat the process: $V = L\{\mathbf{Y}_{s-1}, \mathbf{Y}_s, \mathbf{X}_1, \cdots, \mathbf{X}_{i-1}, \mathbf{X}_{i+1}, \cdots, \mathbf{X}_n\}$, and these vectors must be linearly dependent by the same argument used to show that the vectors $\{\mathbf{Y}_s, \mathbf{X}_1, \cdots, \mathbf{X}_n\}$ were dependent. Then again we may remove at least one vector which is a linear combination of the preceding ones. This vector must be an $\mathbf{X}_j$ since it cannot be $\mathbf{Y}_{s-1}$ or $\mathbf{Y}_s$ because the vectors $\{\mathbf{Y}_i\}$ are independent.

Continue in this way; at each step one $\mathbf{Y}$ vector is introduced and an $\mathbf{X}$ vector removed. Now it follows that $r \geq s$ since there must be an $\mathbf{X}$ vector to remove each time a $\mathbf{Y}$ vector is added. If the $\mathbf{X}$ vectors were exhausted, the $\mathbf{Y}$ vectors would be linearly dependent since each time the new $\mathbf{Y}$ vector is added the set becomes dependent.

Corollary 1 now follows immediately from the theorem. We first consider the linearly independent vectors $\mathbf{Y}_1, \cdots, \mathbf{Y}_s$ of $L\{\mathbf{X}_1, \cdots, \mathbf{X}_r\}$ and conclude $r \geq s$. Now consider $\mathbf{X}_1, \cdots, \mathbf{X}_r$ as linearly independent vectors of $L\{\mathbf{Y}_1, \cdots, \mathbf{Y}_s\}$; then $s \geq r$. Hence $r = s$.

In order to verify Corollary 2, we recall that $V_n(R) = L\{\mathbf{E}_1, \mathbf{E}_2, \cdots, \mathbf{E}_n\}$ and the vectors $\mathbf{E}_1, \cdots, \mathbf{E}_n$ are linearly independent. A set of $n + 1$ linearly independent vectors of $V_n(R)$ would be impossible because the theorem would imply $n \geq n + 1$; clearly a contradiction.

We are now able to show that every subspace V of $V_n(R)$ possesses a set of linearly independent generators. Consider V and choose a vector $\mathbf{X}_1 \neq \mathbf{0}$ of V. If $V = L\{\mathbf{X}_1\}$, we are through. Otherwise, let $\mathbf{X}_2$ be a vector of V not in $L\{\mathbf{X}_1\}$. Then $\mathbf{X}_1, \mathbf{X}_2$ are linearly independent, for otherwise $\mathbf{X}_2$ would be a multiple of $\mathbf{X}_1$ and would be contained in $L\{\mathbf{X}_1\}$. If $V = L\{\mathbf{X}_1, \mathbf{X}_2\}$, we are through. If $V \neq L\{\mathbf{X}_1, \mathbf{X}_2\}$, choose $\mathbf{X}_3 \in V$ and not in $L\{\mathbf{X}_1, \mathbf{X}_2\}$. Again $\mathbf{X}_1, \mathbf{X}_2, \mathbf{X}_3$ are linearly independent and, continuing in this manner, we reach a point where

$$V = L\{\mathbf{X}_1, \cdots, \mathbf{X}_k\}.$$

We know the process must end with $k \leq n$ because Corollary 2 of Theorem 2.3 states that there is no set of $n + 1$ linearly independent vectors in $V_n(R)$.

We have now provided an affirmative answer to question 1. The modification of the previous discussion to provide an affirmative answer for those vector spaces V over R satisfying assumption F is left to the student in the exercises.

Corollary 1 of Theorem 2.3 shows that every finite set of linearly independent generators of a vector space V contains the same number of vectors. This provides an answer to question 2.

EXERCISES

1. Determine a set of independent generators for $V_4(R)$ of which one is $[1, -1, 1, 2]$.

2. Determine a set of linearly independent generators for the vector space $V = L\{[1, 2, 0], [-1, 1, 0], [1, 1, 0]\}$.

3. Show that the elements of any set of vectors containing the zero vector are linearly dependent.

4. Let $V = L\{\mathbf{X}_1, \mathbf{X}_2, \cdots, \mathbf{X}_k\}$, where $\mathbf{X}_1, \cdots, \mathbf{X}_k$ are linearly independent vectors. Show that if

$$\mathbf{X} = a_1\mathbf{X}_1 + a_2\mathbf{X}_2 + \cdots + a_k\mathbf{X}_k = b_1\mathbf{X}_1 + b_2\mathbf{X}_2 + \cdots + b_k\mathbf{X}_k,$$

then $a_1 = b_1, a_2 = b_2, \cdots, a_k = b_k$.

5. Prove the converse of Problem 4, which may be stated as follows: If every $\mathbf{X}$ of $L\{\mathbf{X}_1, \mathbf{X}_2, \cdots, \mathbf{X}_k\}$ has a unique representation of the form $\mathbf{X} = a_1\mathbf{X}_1 + \cdots + a_r\mathbf{X}_k$, then the vectors $\mathbf{X}_1, \mathbf{X}_2, \cdots, \mathbf{X}_k$ are linearly independent.

6. Are the following spaces identical:

$$V = L\{[1, -1, 2, 0], [2, 1, 1, 1], [3, -1, 2, -1]\},$$

and

$$W = L\{[3, 0, 3, 1], [1, 2, -1, 1], [4, -1, 5, 1]\}?$$

7. If $\mathbf{X}_1, \mathbf{X}_2, \mathbf{X}_3$ are linearly independent vectors of V, then are the vectors $\mathbf{X}_1 + \mathbf{X}_2, \mathbf{X}_2 + \mathbf{X}_3, \mathbf{X}_3 + \mathbf{X}_1$ linearly independent?

8. Prove that any subset of a set of linearly independent vectors is again a set of linearly independent vectors.

9. Prove that in any vector space V satisfying assumption F there are at most m linearly independent vectors.

10. Under the same hypothesis as in Exercise 9, show that every subspace of V has a set of linearly independent generators.

11. In the proof of Theorem 2.3, show that only one vector $\mathbf{X}_i$ can be removed at each step.

3. Linear Dependence of Vectors and Simultaneous Linear Equations

In the theoretical discussion of the preceding section it was frequently assumed that a determination of the linear dependence or independence of a set of vectors $\mathbf{X}_1, \mathbf{X}_2, \mathbf{X}_3, \cdots, \mathbf{X}_k$ could be made. In most cases the generality of the proofs made it unnecessary to require anything other than the knowledge of the existence of real numbers $c_1, c_2, \cdots, c_k$ (not all zero) such that

$$c_1\mathbf{X}_1 + c_2\mathbf{X}_2 + \cdots + c_k\mathbf{X}_k = \mathbf{0}$$

if these vectors were linearly dependent.

When applying this discussion to specific examples of $V_n(R)$, we must provide a way of determining the constants $c_1, c_2, \cdots, c_k$. A quite effective way is the simple generalization of the method of elimination given in §5 of Chapter 2.

Example 1. We desire to determine whether or not the vectors $\mathbf{A}_1=[1, 2, -1, 4]$, $\mathbf{A}_2=[2, 1, 3, 5]$, $\mathbf{A}_3=[1, -1, 3, -1]$, and $\mathbf{A}_4=[3, 0, 4, 0]$ are linearly dependent.

The linear dependence or independence of these vectors is equivalent to the existence or nonexistence of numbers c_1, c_2, c_3, c_4 (not all zero) such that

$$c_1[1, 2, -1, 4]+c_2[2, 1, 3, 5]+c_3[1, -1, 3, -1]+c_4[3, 0, 4, 0]=\mathbf{0}. \tag{3.1}$$

If the vectors of (3.1) are added, the definition of the equality of vectors yields the system of equations

$$\begin{aligned} 1c_1 + 2c_2 + 1c_3 + 3c_4 &= 0\\ 2c_1 + 1c_2 - 1c_3 + 0c_4 &= 0\\ -1c_1 + 3c_2 + 3c_3 + 4c_4 &= 0\\ 4c_1 + 5c_2 - 1c_3 + 0c_4 &= 0 \end{aligned} \tag{3.2}$$

The vectors $\mathbf{A}_1$, $\mathbf{A}_2$, $\mathbf{A}_3$, and $\mathbf{A}_4$ will be linearly dependent if there exist constants c_1, c_2, c_3, c_4 different from $c_1 = c_2 = c_3 = c_4 = 0$ that satisfy the system of linear equations (3.2) simultaneously. Certainly $c_1 = c_2 = c_3 = c_4 = 0$ satisfy (3.2) simultaneously, but we are seeking a solution with at least one $c_i \neq 0$.

At this stage, it appears that we have replaced one problem by an equally difficult, although equivalent, problem. We shall indicate a straightforward manner by which *all* solutions of (3.2) may be obtained.

Multiply the first equation of (3.2) successively by -2, 1, and -4 and add the results to the second, third, and fourth equations respectively. Thus we obtain the equations

$$\begin{aligned} &&1c_1+2c_2+1c_3+3c_4&=0\\ -2(1c_1+2c_2+1c_3+3c_4)+&(2c_1+1c_2-1c_3+0c_4)=&-3c_2-3c_3-6c_4&=0\\ 1(1c_1+2c_2+1c_3+3c_4)+&(-1c_1+3c_2+3c_3+4c_4)=&5c_2+4c_3+7c_4&=0\\ -4(1c_1+2c_2+1c_3+3c_4)+&(4c_1+5c_2-1c_3+0c_4)=&-3c_2-5c_3-12c_4&=0. \end{aligned} \tag{3.2$'$}$$

It should be clear that any solution of (3.2) is a solution of (3.2)′ and conversely. Moreover, there is a solution of (3.2)′ if and only if there is a solution of the last three equations of (3.2)′. In this manner the problem has been simplified in that we have reduced the number of equations that must be solved. Now, using the last three equations of (3.2)′, form the system of equations

$$\begin{aligned} &&-3c_2-3c_3-6c_4&=0\\ \tfrac{5}{3}(-3c_2-3c_3-6c_4)+&(5c_2+4c_3+7c_4)=&-1c_3-3c_4&=0\\ -1(-3c_2-3c_3-6c_4)+&(-3c_2-5c_3-12c_4)=&-2c_3-6c_4&=0. \end{aligned} \tag{3.2$''$}$$

Again, it should be clear that any solution of (3.2)″ is a solution of the last three equations of (3.2)′. Moreover (3.2)″ has a solution if and only if the equations

$$\begin{aligned} -1c_3 - 3c_4 &= 0 \\ -2c_3 - 6c_4 &= 0 \end{aligned}$$

have a solution. The value of c_2 may be determined in the first equation of (3.2)″ after c_3 and c_4 are determined. These equations reduce on multiplying the first by 2 and subtracting it from the second to the system

$$\begin{aligned} -1c_3 - 3c_4 &= 0 \\ 0c_3 + 0c_4 &= 0. \end{aligned} \tag{3.2'''}$$

Combining (3.2)‴, (3.2)″, and (3.2)′, we see that any solution of (3.2) is a solution of the system

$$\begin{aligned} 1c_1 + 2c_2 + 1c_3 + 3c_4 &= 0 \\ -3c_2 - 3c_3 - 6c_4 &= 0 \\ -1c_3 - 3c_4 &= 0 \\ 0c_4 &= 0, \end{aligned}$$

and conversely.

In this "diagonal" form we obtain all solutions. The last equation leaves c_4 unrestricted; the third determines c_3 in terms of an arbitrary choice of c_4, $c_3 = -3c_4$. Then from the second, by substitution, $c_2 = c_4$; finally the first gives $c_1 = -2c_4$. These values satisfy (3.2) simultaneously, and consequently

$$-2c_4[1, 2, -1, 4] + c_4[2, 1, 3, 5] - 3c_4[1, -1, 3, -1] + c_4[3, 0, 4, 0] = \mathbf{0}. \tag{3.3}$$

Since c_4 was arbitrary, the choice of $c_4 = 1$ gives the vector $[3, 0, 4, 0] = 2[1, 2, -1, 4] - [2, 1, 3, 5] + 3[1, -1, 3, -1]$. Hence, if we were determining a set of linearly independent generators for $L\{\mathbf{A}_1, \mathbf{A}_2, \mathbf{A}_3, \mathbf{A}_4\}$, the vector $\mathbf{A}_4$ could be removed.

The general case illustrated by Example 1 is set forth in the following theorem:

THEOREM 3.1. *Let*

$$\begin{aligned} \mathbf{A}_1 &= [a_{11}, a_{21}, \cdots, a_{n1}] \\ \mathbf{A}_2 &= [a_{12}, a_{22}, \cdots, a_{n2}] \\ &\cdots\cdots\cdots \\ \mathbf{A}_k &= [a_{1k}, a_{2k}, \cdots, a_{nk}] \end{aligned}$$

be k vectors of $V_n(R)$. These vectors are linearly dependent if and only if there exists a solution to the system of linear equations

$$
(3.4)\qquad
\begin{aligned}
a_{11}c_1 + a_{12}c_2 + \cdots + a_{1k}c_k &= 0\\
a_{21}c_1 + a_{22}c_2 + \cdots + a_{2k}c_k &= 0\\
\cdots\cdots\cdots\cdots\cdots\cdots&\cdots\\
a_{n1}c_1 + a_{n2}c_2 + \cdots + a_{nk}c_k &= 0
\end{aligned}
$$

different from $c_1 = c_2 = c_3 = \cdots = c_k = 0$.

Proof. If $\mathbf{A}_1, \cdots, \mathbf{A}_k$ are linearly dependent there exist c's (not all zero) such that

$$
(3.5)\qquad c_1\mathbf{A}_1 + c_2\mathbf{A}_2 + \cdots + c_k\mathbf{A}_k = \mathbf{0}.
$$

Equating components yields the system (3.4). Conversely, if there exist c's (not all zero) satisfying (3.4), these same c's satisfy (3.5).

Rather than discuss the solutions of a system of linear equations (3.4), we will turn to a more general situation.

Let us consider a system of linear equations

$$
(3.6)\qquad
\begin{aligned}
a_{11}c_1 + a_{12}c_2 + \cdots + a_{1k}c_k &= d_1\\
a_{21}c_1 + a_{22}c_2 + \cdots + a_{2k}c_k &= d_2\\
\cdots\cdots\cdots\cdots\cdots\cdots&\cdots\\
a_{n1}c_1 + a_{n2}c_2 + \cdots + a_{nk}c_k &= d_n,
\end{aligned}
$$

where a_{ij} and d_i are real numbers and the d_i are not necessarily all zero.

A *solution* of the system (3.6) is a set of real numbers $c_1, c_2, \cdots, c_k$ which satisfy all the equations simultaneously. If all the d_i are zero, we say that (3.6) is a *homogeneous* system of linear equations; otherwise, (3.6) is called a *nonhomogeneous* system of linear equations.

The method of elimination used in Example 1 for a homogeneous system can be used for the nonhomogeneous system of linear equations (3.6) and is illustrated in § 5 of Chapter 2.

The theory of solutions of systems of linear equations may be phrased in terms of vector spaces.

THEOREM 3.2. *The system of linear equations* (3.6) *has a solution if and only if the vector* $[d_1, d_2, \cdots, d_n]$ *is contained in the vector subspace of* $V_n(R)$ *generated by the vectors* $\mathbf{A}_1 = [a_{11}, a_{21}, \cdots, a_{n1}]$, $\mathbf{A}_2 = [a_{12}, a_{22}, \cdots, a_{n2}]$, $\cdots, \mathbf{A}_k = [a_{1k}, a_{2k}, \cdots, a_{nk}]$.

Proof. If $[d_1, \cdots, d_n] \in L\{\mathbf{A}_1, \mathbf{A}_2, \cdots, \mathbf{A}_k\}$ then $[d_1, d_2, \cdots, d_n] = c_1\mathbf{A}_1 + c_2\mathbf{A}_2 + \cdots + c_k\mathbf{A}_k$ for some set of real numbers $c_1, c_2, \cdots, c_k$. Adding the vectors on the right and applying the definition of equality, we get the system of equations (3.6); that is, the values $c_1, c_2, \cdots, c_k$ are solutions of (3.6).

Conversely, if a solution of (3.6) exists, the values $c_1, c_2, \cdots, c_k$ which determine a solution provide the coefficients in the equation:

$$
(3.7)\qquad [d_1, d_2, \cdots, d_n] = c_1\mathbf{A}_1 + c_2\mathbf{A}_2 + \cdots + c_k\mathbf{A}_k.
$$

That is, $[d_1, d_2, \cdots, d_n] \in L\{\mathbf{A}_1, \mathbf{A}_2, \cdots, \mathbf{A}_k\}$.

If $[d_1, d_2, \cdots, d_n] = [0, 0, \cdots, 0]$, the last theorem asserts that a solution of the following system of homogeneous equations will always exist:

$$(3.8) \qquad \begin{aligned} a_{11}c_1 + a_{12}c_2 + \cdots + a_{1k}c_k &= 0 \\ a_{21}c_1 + a_{22}c_2 + \cdots + a_{2k}c_k &= 0 \\ \cdots\cdots\cdots\cdots &\cdots \\ a_{n1}c_1 + a_{n2}c_2 + \cdots + a_{nk}c_k &= 0. \end{aligned}$$

However, this statement turns out to be trivial since the solution $c_1 = c_2 = \cdots = c_k = 0$ is certainly available. There are some situations in which we can guarantee a nonzero solution. One of these occurs when $k > n$. The number of vectors appearing in the statement of the theorem is then at least $n + 1$, and Theorem 2.3 shows that these vectors are linearly dependent. Consequently a solution exists in which the c_i are not all zero. Another way of stating this result is to remark that a system of homogeneous equations will always have a nonzero solution if the number of unknowns exceeds the number of equations. It is important to note that by "nonzero solution" is meant a set of values $c_1, \cdots, c_k$ not *all* zero.

We may consider the set of all solutions of (3.8) from a slightly different point of view. A solution is a k-tuple of real numbers and may be thought of as an element $[c_1, c_2, \cdots, c_k]$ of $V_k(R)$. Now let $\mathbf{A} = [a_1, a_2, \cdots, a_k]$ and $\mathbf{B} = [b_1, b_2, \cdots, b_k]$ be solutions of (3.8). Then for $i = 1, 2, \cdots, n$,

$$\begin{aligned} a_{i1}(a_1 + b_1) + \cdots + a_{ik}(a_k + b_k) &= (a_{i1}a_1 + a_{i2}a_2 + \cdots + a_{ik}a_k) \\ &\quad + (a_{i1}b_1 + a_{i2}b_2 + \cdots + a_{ik}b_k) \\ &= 0 + 0 = 0. \end{aligned}$$

Thus $\mathbf{A} + \mathbf{B}$ is also a solution of (3.8). Similarly, $r\mathbf{A} = [ra_1, ra_2, \cdots, ra_k]$ is also a solution. Therefore the set of all solutions of (3.8), considered as vectors of $V_k(R)$, forms a subspace V, *the solution space of* (3.8).

It is of interest to determine the number of linearly independent vectors needed to generate V. As we see from Theorem 3.2, any solution of (3.8) is equivalent to a solution of

$$(3.9) \qquad c_1\mathbf{A}_1 + c_2\mathbf{A}_2 + \cdots + c_k\mathbf{A}_k = \mathbf{0},$$

where $\mathbf{A}_i = [a_{1i}, a_{2i}, \cdots, a_{ni}]$ for $i = 1, 2, \cdots, k$; and conversely any solution of (3.9) is a solution of (3.8).

Now let us assume that the maximum number of linearly independent vectors from $\mathbf{A}_1, \cdots, \mathbf{A}_k$ is r and that these are $\mathbf{A}_1, \mathbf{A}_2, \cdots, \mathbf{A}_r$. Then we must have the linear combinations

$$(3.10) \qquad \begin{aligned} \mathbf{A}_{r+1} &= b_{11}\mathbf{A}_1 + \cdots + b_{1r}\mathbf{A}_r \\ \mathbf{A}_{r+2} &= b_{21}\mathbf{A}_1 + \cdots + b_{2r}\mathbf{A}_r \\ \cdots\cdots &\cdots\cdots\cdots \\ \mathbf{A}_k &= b_{k-r,1}\mathbf{A}_1 + \cdots + b_{k-r,r}\mathbf{A}_r. \end{aligned}$$

If we substitute the relations for the vectors $\mathbf{A}_i$, where $r < i \leq k$, into (3.9), we obtain the relation

$$c_1\mathbf{A}_1 + \cdots + c_r\mathbf{A}_r + c_{r+1}(b_{11}\mathbf{A}_1 + \cdots + b_{1r}\mathbf{A}_r) + \cdots + c_k(b_{k-r,1}\mathbf{A}_1 + \cdots + b_{k-r,r}\mathbf{A}_r) = \mathbf{0},$$

or

$$\begin{aligned} &(c_1 + c_{r+1}b_{11} + c_{r+2}b_{21} + \cdots + c_kb_{k-r,1})\mathbf{A}_1 \\ +\ &(c_2 + c_{r+1}b_{12} + c_{r+2}b_{22} + \cdots + c_kb_{k-r,2})\mathbf{A}_2 \\ &\qquad\vdots \\ +\ &(c_r + c_{r+1}b_{1r} + c_{r+2}b_{2r} + \cdots + c_kb_{k-r,r})\mathbf{A}_r = \mathbf{0}. \end{aligned}$$

The vectors $\mathbf{A}_1, \mathbf{A}_2, \cdots, \mathbf{A}_r$ were chosen to be linearly independent so that each coefficient in the previous relation must be zero. We thus obtain the system of equations

$$\begin{aligned} c_1 + c_{r+1}b_{11} + c_{r+2}b_{21} + \cdots + c_kb_{k-r,1} &= 0 \\ c_2 + c_{r+1}b_{12} + c_{r+2}b_{22} + \cdots + c_kb_{k-r,2} &= 0 \\ \cdots\cdots\cdots\cdots\cdots\cdots\cdots\cdots\ & \\ c_r + c_{r+1}b_{1r} + c_{r+2}b_{2r} + \cdots + c_kb_{k-r,r} &= 0. \end{aligned} \tag{3.11}$$

If $c_{r+1}, \cdots, c_k$ are chosen arbitrarily, the values of $c_1, \cdots, c_r$ are uniquely determined for a solution of equations (3.11) and hence of (3.9) or (3.8). Now, choosing successively one of $c_{r+1}, \cdots, c_k$ equal to -1 and the remainder 0, we obtain the solution vectors of (3.8)

$$\begin{matrix} [b_{11}, & b_{12}, & \cdots, b_{1r}, & -1, & 0, 0, \cdots, & 0] \\ [b_{21}, & b_{22}, & \cdots, b_{2r}, & 0, & -1, 0, \cdots, & 0] \\ \cdots & \cdots & \cdots & \cdots & \cdots & \cdots \\ [b_{k-r,1}, & b_{k-r,2}, & \cdots, b_{k-r,r}, & 0, & 0, 0, \cdots, & -1]. \end{matrix} \tag{3.12}$$

We shall leave it to the student in the exercises to show that these vectors are linearly independent and that they generate the solution space of the system of homogeneous linear equations (3.8).

EXERCISES

1. Determine whether or not the following vectors are linearly independent. If not, express $\mathbf{A}_3$ as a linear combination of $\mathbf{A}_1$ and $\mathbf{A}_2$.

(a) $\mathbf{A}_1 = [1, 2, -1]$, $\mathbf{A}_2 = [2, 1, 4]$, $\mathbf{A}_3 = [-1, 7, -17]$.

(b) $\mathbf{A}_1 = [2, 1]$, $\mathbf{A}_2 = [1, 1]$, $\mathbf{A}_3 = [4, 5]$.

(c) $\mathbf{A}_1 = [3, 1, 0, 1]$, $\mathbf{A}_2 = [1, 4, -1, 0]$, $\mathbf{A}_3 = [0, 1, -1, 0]$.

2. Determine all solutions of the system of equations

$$\begin{aligned} 3c_1 + 2c_2 - c_3 &= 0 \\ c_1 + 3c_2 + 2c_3 &= 0 \\ -2c_1 + c_2 + 3c_3 &= 0. \end{aligned}$$

3. The number of solutions of the equations of Problem 2 determines the linear independence or dependence of a set of vectors in $V_3(R)$. List these vectors and state whether they are dependent or independent.

4. Determine all solutions of the system of linear equations

$$\begin{aligned} c_1 + 2c_2 + c_3 + 2c_4 &= 6 \\ 2c_1 - c_2 + 3c_3 + 6c_4 &= 10 \\ 3c_1 + c_2 + 4c_3 + 8c_4 &= 16 \\ c_1 - 3c_2 + 2c_3 + 4c_4 &= 4. \end{aligned}$$

5. Is the vector [6, 10, 16, 4] contained in the vector space

$$V = L\{[1, 2, 3, 1], [2, -1, 1, -3], [1, 3, 4, 2]\}?$$

6. Solve the system of linear equations

$$\begin{aligned} c_1 - 2c_2 + 3c_3 &= 0 \\ 3c_1 + 2c_2 - c_3 &= 0 \\ 2c_1 + c_2 + 5c_3 &= 0 \\ -c_1 + 4c_2 + c_3 &= 0. \end{aligned}$$

What statement can you make concerning the linear independence or linear dependence of the vectors [1, 3, 2, − 1], [− 2, 2, 1, 4], and [3, − 1, 5, 1] from the solution of the linear equations above?

7. Solve the system of linear equations

$$\begin{aligned} c_1 - 2c_2 + 3c_3 + c_4 &= 0 \\ -2c_1 + c_2 + c_3 - 2c_4 &= 0 \\ c_2 - c_3 + 3c_4 &= 0. \end{aligned}$$

8. Follow through the discussion following (3.8) with the system of equations in Exercise 7 and obtain the vectors (3.12) for this exercise.

9. Determine a value of k that makes the following vectors linearly dependent:

$$[1, 2, k], \quad [0, 1, k - 1], \quad [3, 4, 3].$$

10. Prove that the vectors in (3.12) are linearly independent.

11. Prove that every solution vector of (3.9), and hence of (3.8), can be written as a linear combination of the vectors of (3.12).

12. Show that every linear combination of the vectors of (3.12) is a solution of (3.8). Hence show that the set of all solution vectors forms a vector space generated by $k - r$ linearly independent vectors.

13. Let $[c_1, c_2, \cdots, c_k]$ be a solution vector of (3.6). Show that $[c_1, c_2, \cdots, c_k] + [a_1, a_2, \cdots, a_k]$, where $[a_1, a_2, \cdots, a_k]$ is any solution of (3.8), is a solution of (3.6). Next show that all solutions of (3.6) are obtained in this manner.

4. Bases and Dimension of Vector Spaces

We have seen in §2 that the number of linearly independent vectors needed to generate a vector space V is unique. It seems reasonable to expect a set of linearly independent generators to play an important role in any discussion of a vector space. This is indeed the case, and we make the following definition:

DEFINITION 4.1. *A set of vectors* $\mathbf{X}_1, \mathbf{X}_2, \cdots, \mathbf{X}_k$ *of a vector space* V *is called a* BASIS *for* V *if*

(i) $V = L\{\mathbf{X}_1, \mathbf{X}_2, \cdots, \mathbf{X}_k\}$;

(ii) $\mathbf{X}_1, \mathbf{X}_2, \cdots, \mathbf{X}_k$ *are linearly independent.*

We have the following simple theorem:

THEOREM 4.1. *A set of linearly independent vectors* $\mathbf{X}_1, \mathbf{X}_2, \cdots, \mathbf{X}_k$ *of a vector space* V *is a basis for* V *if and only if the maximum number of linearly independent vectors of* V *is* k.

COROLLARY. *If a vector space* V *is generated by* k *linearly independent vectors, then every set of* k *linearly independent vectors of* V *is a basis.*

Proof of Theorem 4.1. First consider the "if" part of the theorem. The vectors $\mathbf{X}_1, \mathbf{X}_2, \cdots, \mathbf{X}_k$ are linearly independent by hypothesis. The set of vectors $\mathbf{X}_1, \cdots, \mathbf{X}_k, \mathbf{X}$ is linearly dependent for any vector $\mathbf{X}$ of V because there are $k + 1$ vectors and the maximum number of linearly independent vectors is k. We now apply Theorem 2.1 to see that

$$\mathbf{X} = a_1\mathbf{X}_1 + a_2\mathbf{X}_2 + \cdots + a_k\mathbf{X}_k.$$

No earlier vector could be a linear combination of the preceding because the vectors $\mathbf{X}_1, \mathbf{X}_2, \cdots, \mathbf{X}_k$ are linearly independent. Hence every vector $\mathbf{X}$ is a linear combination of $\mathbf{X}_1, \cdots, \mathbf{X}_k$ and so $V = L\{\mathbf{X}_1, \mathbf{X}_2, \cdots, \mathbf{X}_k\}$.

For the "only if" part, we assume $V = L\{\mathbf{X}_1, \mathbf{X}_2, \cdots, \mathbf{X}_k\}$, where $\mathbf{X}_1, \cdots, \mathbf{X}_k$ are linearly independent. If $\mathbf{Y}_1, \mathbf{Y}_2, \cdots, \mathbf{Y}_s$ is a maximum set of linearly independent vectors of V, we apply Theorem 2.3 to see that $k \geq s$. Moreover, we know of one set of k vectors that are linearly independent; namely, $\mathbf{X}_1, \mathbf{X}_2, \cdots, \mathbf{X}_k$. Hence the proof is complete.

The Corollary may be verified by noting that Theorem 2.3 assures us that the maximum number of linearly independent vectors of V is k. Now apply the theorem to any set of k linearly independent vectors.

Example 1. Let a vector space V consist of all vectors $[x_1, x_2, x_3, x_4, x_5]$ of $V_5(R)$ such that $x_1 + 2x_2 - x_3 = 0$. It is clear that $[0, 0, 0, 1, 0]$, $[0, 0, 0, 0, 1]$, $[1, 0, 1, 0, 0]$, and $[2, -1, 0, 0, 0]$ are vectors of V. Moreover, these vectors are linearly independent. They must form a basis for V because any set of five linearly independent vectors in V would imply $V_5(R) = V$, which is clearly not the case.

Example 2. In (2.2) it was shown that $\mathbf{E}_1, \mathbf{E}_2, \cdots, \mathbf{E}_n$ generate $V_n(R)$. Since $[x_1, x_2, \cdots, x_n] = x_1\mathbf{E}_1 + x_2\mathbf{E}_2 + \cdots + x_n\mathbf{E}_n = \mathbf{0}$ only if $x_1 = x_2 = \cdots = x_n = 0$, the vectors $\mathbf{E}_1, \mathbf{E}_2, \cdots, \mathbf{E}_n$ are linearly independent. Hence $\mathbf{E}_1, \cdots, \mathbf{E}_n$ form a basis for $V_n(R)$. Henceforth, we will call this basis the *natural basis* of $V_n(R)$.

The concept of a basis for an arbitrary vector space V permits us to make an interesting and useful relation between V and the vector space $V_n(R)$, where n is the number of elements in a basis for V. Let $\{\mathbf{X}_1, \cdots, \mathbf{X}_n\}$ be a basis for V. Then every vector $\mathbf{X}$ of V may be expressed as a linear combination

$$\mathbf{X} = a_1\mathbf{X}_1 + a_2\mathbf{X}_2 + \cdots + a_n\mathbf{X}_n. \tag{4.1}$$

We have previously asked the student to show that this expression for an arbitrary vector $\mathbf{X}$ of V as a linear combination of linearly independent vectors $\mathbf{X}_1, \mathbf{X}_2, \cdots, \mathbf{X}_n$ is unique (Exercise 4, § 2). Therefore, if to each vector $\mathbf{X}$ of V we assign the n-tuple of coefficients $[a_1, a_2, \cdots, a_n]$ in (4.1), we have a single-valued mapping T from V to $V_n(R)$. Moreover, an arbitrary vector $[a_1, a_2, \cdots, a_n]$ of $V_n(R)$ is the image of $a_1\mathbf{X}_1 + a_2\mathbf{X}_2 + \cdots + a_n\mathbf{X}_n$. Hence the mapping T is *onto* $V_n(R)$. The mapping T is one-to-one. To see this, let $\mathrm{T}(\mathbf{X}) = \mathrm{T}(\mathbf{Y}) = [a_1, a_2, \cdots, a_n]$. Then, because of the manner in which T was defined, $\mathbf{X} = \mathbf{Y} = a_1\mathbf{X}_1 + a_2\mathbf{X}_2 + \cdots + a_n\mathbf{X}_n$. This shows that T is a one-to-one mapping of V onto $V_n(R)$.

Let us investigate the mapping T further. If $\mathbf{X}$ and $\mathbf{Y}$ are arbitrary vectors of V, we express them in terms of the basis $\{\mathbf{X}_1, \cdots, \mathbf{X}_n\}$ and have

$$\mathbf{X} = a_1\mathbf{X}_1 + \cdots + a_n\mathbf{X}_n, \quad \mathbf{Y} = b_1\mathbf{X}_1 + \cdots + b_n\mathbf{X}_n;$$

then

$$\begin{aligned} \mathbf{X} + \mathbf{Y} &= (a_1 + b_1)\mathbf{X}_1 + \cdots + (a_n + b_n)\mathbf{X}_n, \\ r\mathbf{X} &= (ra_1)\mathbf{X}_1 + \cdots + (ra_n)\mathbf{X}_n. \end{aligned}$$

In terms of the mapping T, the previous statement can be expressed briefly as follows:

$$\begin{aligned} &\text{If } \mathbf{X} \xrightarrow{\mathrm{T}} [a_1, a_2, \cdots, a_n], \quad \mathbf{Y} \xrightarrow{\mathrm{T}} [b_1, b_2, \cdots, b_n], \qquad \text{then} \\ &\mathbf{X} + \mathbf{Y} \xrightarrow{\mathrm{T}} [a_1 + b_1, a_2 + b_2, \cdots, a_n + b_n] \\ &\qquad\qquad = [a_1, a_2, \cdots, a_n] + [b_1, b_2, \cdots, b_n], \\ &r\mathbf{X} \xrightarrow{\mathrm{T}} [ra_1, ra_2, \cdots, ra_n] = r[a_1, a_2, \cdots, a_n]. \end{aligned} \tag{4.2}$$

Thus, we see that the sum of two vectors (or a scalar multiple of a vector) maps upon the sum (or scalar multiple) of the images. Any property of V that involves only the sums or scalar multiples of vectors in V will be reflected in a similar property in terms of the image vectors in $V_n(R)$.

For example, if the vectors $\mathbf{Y}_1$, $\mathbf{Y}_2$, $\mathbf{Y}_3$ are linearly dependent in V, then $c_1\mathbf{Y}_1 + c_2\mathbf{Y}_2 + c_3\mathbf{Y}_3 = \mathbf{0}$ in V, where the c_i are not all zero. Now if

$$\mathbf{Y}_1 \xrightarrow{\mathrm{T}} [r_1, r_2, \cdots, r_n]$$
$$\mathbf{Y}_2 \xrightarrow{\mathrm{T}} [s_1, s_2, \cdots, s_n]$$
$$\mathbf{Y}_3 \xrightarrow{\mathrm{T}} [t_1, t_2, \cdots, t_n],$$

then from the relations (4.2),

$$c_1\mathbf{Y}_1 + c_2\mathbf{Y}_2 + c_3\mathbf{Y}_3 \xrightarrow{\mathrm{T}} c_1[r_1, r_2, \cdots, r_n] + c_2[s_1, s_2, \cdots, s_n] + c_3[t_1, t_2, \cdots, t_n].$$

However, the left member of the previous relation is $\mathbf{0}$ in V, and

$$\mathbf{0} = 0 \cdot \mathbf{X}_1 + 0 \cdot \mathbf{X}_2 + \cdots + 0 \cdot \mathbf{X}_n$$

so that $\mathbf{0} \xrightarrow{\mathrm{T}} [0, 0, \cdots, 0]$. Hence,

$$c_1[r_1, r_2, \cdots, r_n] + c_2[s_1, s_2, \cdots, s_n] + c_3[t_1, t_2, \cdots, t_n] = [0, 0, \cdots, 0].$$

This says that the image vectors of $\mathbf{Y}_1$, $\mathbf{Y}_2$, $\mathbf{Y}_3$ are linearly dependent in $V_n(R)$.

Algebraically (that is, with respect to vector addition and scalar multiplication), the vector spaces V and $V_n(R)$ are *indistinguishable.* Whether we deal with the vectors $\mathbf{X}$ in V or their images in $V_n(R)$ will be immaterial in determining algebraic properties. We may express the situation in more general terms as follows:

DEFINITION 4.2. *If there exists any one-to-one mapping* T *of V onto $V_n(R)$ for which the relations in* (4.2) *are valid, we say that V is* ISOMORPHIC *to $V_n(R)$.*

In essence, we have shown that every vector space with n basis elements is *isomorphic* to $V_n(R)$.

Example 3. All polynomials with real coefficients of degree $\leq n - 1$ form a vector space V. If we define a mapping T by

$$p(x) = a_0 + a_1x + \cdots + a_{n-1}x^{n-1} \xrightarrow{\mathrm{T}} [a_0, a_1, \cdots, a_{n-1}],$$

it is easy to see that the mapping T satisfies the relations in (4.2). Hence, V is isomorphic to $V_n(R)$.

The student might well ask why we introduced general vector spaces V over R if any such space with n basis vectors is isomorphic to $V_n(R)$. The answer is not apparent. However, it is usually easier to determine whether a set of elements V satisfies the axioms of a vector space over R than to try to see whether it can be expressed in terms of n-tuples. This is particularly true when first dealing with subspaces, even of $V_n(R)$. Moreover, vector spaces without finite bases are permitted. A great deal of the theory does not require a finite basis although, for convenience, we have so limited our discussion.

Geometrically, we have associated the line segments in three-dimensional Euclidean space with vectors of $V_3(R)$. Since any vector space V with n basis elements is isomorphic to $V_n(R)$, an obvious generalization makes it reasonable to define the dimension of an arbitrary vector space V as follows:

DEFINITION 4.3. *The dimension of a vector space V is the number of vectors in a basis for V.*

We note from Theorem 4.1 that the dimension of a vector space could have been defined alternatively as the maximum number of linearly independent vectors of V. In particular, $V_n(R)$ is an n-dimensional vector space.

Example 4. The vectors [1, 1, 0, 0], [0, 0, 1, 0], [0, 0, 0, 1] are easily shown to be linearly independent and they form a basis for the subspace V of $V_4(R)$ consisting of all vectors for which $x_1 = x_2$. Thus the dimension of V is 3.

The following theorem provides a relation between linearly independent vectors, bases, and dimension of a vector space V.

THEOREM 4.2. *If $\mathbf{Y}_1, \mathbf{Y}_2, \cdots, \mathbf{Y}_k$ are linearly independent vectors of V, then either $V = L\{\mathbf{Y}_1, \mathbf{Y}_2, \cdots, \mathbf{Y}_k\}$ or vectors $\mathbf{X}_{k+1}, \cdots, \mathbf{X}_r$ contained in V may be found such that the vectors $\mathbf{Y}_1, \cdots, \mathbf{Y}_k, \mathbf{X}_{k+1}, \cdots, \mathbf{X}_r$ form a basis for V.*

Proof. The method of proof uses the replacement process as in the proof of Theorem 2.3. First, we know that there is a set of linearly independent vectors $\mathbf{X}_1^*, \cdots, \mathbf{X}_r^*$ such that $V = L\{\mathbf{X}_1^*, \cdots, \mathbf{X}_r^*\}$. Now consider $V = L\{\mathbf{Y}_k, \mathbf{X}_1^*, \cdots, \mathbf{X}_r^*\}$ and reduce to a linearly independent basis. As in the previous proof, one $\mathbf{X}_i^*$ will be removed. Repeated application of the process gives a basis

$$V = L\{\mathbf{Y}_1, \cdots, \mathbf{Y}_k, \mathbf{X}_{k+1}, \cdots, \mathbf{X}_r\},$$

where $\mathbf{X}_{k+1}, \cdots, \mathbf{X}_r$ are a subset of the $\mathbf{X}_i^*$ vectors, or it may happen that $k = r$. In this latter case $V = L\{\mathbf{Y}_1, \cdots, \mathbf{Y}_k\}$.

In a few words, we say that any set of linearly independent vectors of V may be *extended* to a basis of V.

EXERCISES

1. Let V be the set of all vectors of $V_4(R)$ such that

$$x_1 + x_2 + x_3 + x_4 = 0.$$

(a) Do the vectors [1, − 1, 0, 0], [1, 1, − 2, 0], [1, 0, − 1, 0] form a basis for V?

(b) Do the vectors [1, 0, 0, − 1], [1, 0, − 1, 0], [4, − 1, − 2, − 1] form a basis for V?

2. Find two bases of $V_4(R)$ that have no elements in common.

3. Find two bases of $V_4(R)$ that have only the vectors [0, 0, 1, 0] and [0, 0, 0, 1] in common.

4. For what values of k will the vectors $[k, 1 - k, k]$, $[2k, 2k - 1, k + 2]$, $[- 2k, k, - k]$ form a basis for $V_3(R)$?

5. Find a basis for the subspace of $V_5(R)$ in which $x_1 = x_2 = - x_3$. It will be necessary to make certain that your basis is complete; that is, that you actually have the maximum number of independent elements.

6. Find a basis of $L\{[1, - 1, 2, 3], [1, 0, 1, 0], [3, - 2, 5, 7]\}$ which includes the vector [1, 1, 0, − 1].

7. Extend the set [1, 1, − 1, 1], [1, 0, 1, 1], [1, 2, 1, 1] to a basis of $V_4(R)$.

8. Consider the subspace V of $V_4(R)$ for which a basis is [1, − 1, 0, 1] and [2, 1, − 1, 0].

(a) What is the form of the general vector of this subspace?

(b) In terms of your answer to the previous part indicate an isomorphic mapping of V onto $V_2(R)$.

9. Prove that every subspace of $V_n(R)$ has no more than n linearly independent vectors. What can you conclude about the dimension of every subspace V of $V_n(R)$ from this fact?

5. Subspaces of Vector Spaces

In previous sections we have used various devices to identify subspaces of a vector space; a set of generators or, better, a basis, may be given. Also, when we are dealing with the vector space $V_n(R)$, a relationship between components such as the set of vectors $[x_1, x_2, \cdots, x_n]$ of $V_n(R)$ for which $x_1 = x_2$ is a satisfactory definition. In this section we wish to define operations for subspaces that do not depend on the particular manner in which they are identified.

If S and T are two arbitrary subspaces of a vector space V, the *intersection* $S \cap T$ and the *union* $S \cup T$ of these spaces are defined as the *intersection* and *union* of the sets S and T. The latter is not usually a subspace in its own right.

DEFINITION 5.1. *If S and T are subspaces of a vector space V, the set of all possible sums of a vector in S with a vector in T is denoted by $S + T$ and is called the* SUM *of the subspaces S and T.*

Note that, since the zero vector at least is in both S and T, $S + T$ will include $S \cup T$. Moreover, any subspace W which includes $S \cup T$ will certainly include $S + T$.

THEOREM 5.1. *The intersection $S \cap T$ and sum $S + T$ of subspaces S and T of a vector space V are again subspaces of V.*

Proof. If $\mathbf{X}$ and $\mathbf{Y}$ are arbitrary vectors of $S \cap T$, then $\mathbf{X}$ and $\mathbf{Y}$ are vectors of S and of T. Then $a\mathbf{X} + b\mathbf{Y}$ is a vector of both S and T so that $a\mathbf{X} + b\mathbf{Y} \in S \cap T$, where a and b are arbitrary real numbers. Consequently $S \cap T$ is a subspace of S and of T as well as of V.

An arbitrary vector of $S + T$ is of the form $\mathbf{X}_1 + \mathbf{Y}_1$ where $\mathbf{X}_1 \in S$ and $\mathbf{Y}_1 \in T$. Given any two elements $\mathbf{X}_1 + \mathbf{Y}_1$ and $\mathbf{X}_2 + \mathbf{Y}_2$ of $S + T$, then $a(\mathbf{X}_1 + \mathbf{Y}_1) + b(\mathbf{X}_2 + \mathbf{Y}_2) = (a\mathbf{X}_1 + b\mathbf{X}_2) + (a\mathbf{Y}_1 + b\mathbf{Y}_2)$, where a and b are arbitrary real numbers. Since $a\mathbf{X}_1 + b\mathbf{X}_2 \in S$, $a\mathbf{Y}_1 + b\mathbf{Y}_2 \in T$, we see that $a(\mathbf{X}_1 + \mathbf{Y}_1) + b(\mathbf{X}_2 + \mathbf{Y}_2)$ is again in $S + T$ and hence that $S + T$ is a subspace of V.

Example 1. Let $S = L\{[1, -1, 0], [1, 0, 2]\}$, $T = L\{[0, 1, 0], [0, 1, 2]\}$. We wish to determine the subspaces $S \cap T$ and $S + T$.

It is relatively easy to determine $S + T$, since

$$S + T = L\{[1, -1, 0], [1, 0, 2], [0, 1, 0], [0, 1, 2]\}.$$

The vectors $[1, 0, 2]$, $[0, 1, 2]$, and $[0, 1, 0]$ are linearly independent because a linear relation $c_1[1, 0, 2] + c_2[0, 1, 2] + c_3[0, 1, 0] = \mathbf{0}$ leads to a system of equations $c_1 = 0$, $c_2 + c_3 = 0$, $2c_1 + 2c_2 = 0$, and the unique solution is $c_1 = c_2 = c_3 = 0$. We now apply the Corollary of Theorem 4.1 and have $S + T = V_3(R)$.

In order to determine $S \cap T$, note that an arbitrary vector $\mathbf{X}$ of $S \cap T$ must have the form $a[1, -1, 0] + b[1, 0, 2]$ since it is contained in S. At the same time $\mathbf{X}$ must have the form $c[0, 1, 0] + d[0, 1, 2]$, as $\mathbf{X}$ is also a vector of T. Thus,

$$a[1, -1, 0] + b[1, 0, 2] = c[0, 1, 0] + d[0, 1, 2],$$

and this vector relation leads to the system of equations

$$\begin{aligned} a + b \qquad\qquad &= 0 \\ -a \qquad - c - d &= 0 \\ 2b \qquad - 2d &= 0. \end{aligned}$$

Consequently, for a solution, a may be arbitrary and then $b = -a$, $d = -a$, $c = 0$. Hence,

$$\mathbf{X} = a[1, -1, 0] + (-a)[1, 0, 2] = a[0, -1, -2],$$

or

$$\mathbf{X} = 0[0, 1, 0] + (-a)[0, 1, 2] = a[0, -1, -2],$$

and $S \cap T = L\{[0, 1, 2]\}$.

For arbitrary subspaces S and T of a vector space V, there is an interesting relation between the dimensions of the subspaces S, T, $S \cap T$, and $S + T$.

THEOREM 5.2. *If S and T are subspaces of a vector space V, then:*

$$\text{dimension } S + \text{dimension } T = \text{dimension } (S \cap T) + \text{dimension } (S + T).$$

Proof. Let a basis for $S \cap T$ be $\mathbf{X}_1, \cdots, \mathbf{X}_k$. By Theorem 4.2 we may extend this linearly independent set of vectors of S to a basis for S. Then let vectors $\mathbf{S}_1, \mathbf{S}_2, \cdots, \mathbf{S}_{m-k}, \mathbf{X}_1, \mathbf{X}_2, \cdots, \mathbf{X}_k$ be a basis for S. Similarly, we may extend $\mathbf{X}_1, \mathbf{X}_2, \cdots, \mathbf{X}_k$ to a basis $\mathbf{X}_1, \cdots, \mathbf{X}_k, \mathbf{T}_1, \cdots, \mathbf{T}_{r-k}$ of T.

We will now show that the vectors

$$\mathbf{S}_1, \mathbf{S}_2, \cdots, \mathbf{S}_{m-k}, \mathbf{X}_1, \cdots, \mathbf{X}_k, \mathbf{T}_1, \mathbf{T}_2, \cdots, \mathbf{T}_{r-k} \tag{5.1}$$

form a basis for $S + T$. Certainly all the vectors of (5.1) are elements of $S + T$; furthermore, any vector of $S + T$ is the sum of a vector of S and a vector of T and may be expressed as a linear combination of the vectors (5.1); the first m are a basis for S, and the last r are a basis for T. Hence

$$S + T = L\{\mathbf{S}_1, \cdots, \mathbf{S}_{m-k}, \mathbf{X}_1, \cdots, \mathbf{X}_k, \mathbf{T}_1, \cdots, \mathbf{T}_{r-k}\}.$$

It remains to be shown that these vectors are linearly independent. Suppose there is a linear relation of the form

$$\begin{aligned} a_1\mathbf{S}_1 + a_2\mathbf{S}_2 + \cdots + a_{m-k}\mathbf{S}_{m-k} \\ + b_1\mathbf{X}_1 + \cdots + b_k\mathbf{X}_k + c_1\mathbf{T}_1 + \cdots + c_{r-k}\mathbf{T}_{r-k} = \mathbf{0}, \end{aligned} \tag{5.2}$$

where not all the a_i, b_i, c_i are 0. Indeed we may assume that not all the a_i are 0 since otherwise the vectors $\mathbf{X}_1, \cdots, \mathbf{X}_k, \mathbf{T}_1, \cdots, \mathbf{T}_{r-k}$ would be dependent, contrary to the assumption that they are a basis of T.

Transposing, we have:

$$\begin{aligned} a_1\mathbf{S}_1 + \cdots + a_{m-k}\mathbf{S}_{m-k} \\ = -(b_1\mathbf{X}_1 + \cdots + b_k\mathbf{X}_k + c_1\mathbf{T}_1 + \cdots + c_{r-k}\mathbf{T}_{r-k}). \end{aligned} \tag{5.3}$$

Now equation (5.3) implies that $a_1\mathbf{S}_1 + \cdots + a_{m-k}\mathbf{S}_{m-k}$ is in T and hence in $S \cap T$. Then it may be expressed as a linear combination of the $\mathbf{X}_i$,

$$a_1\mathbf{S}_1 + \cdots + a_{m-k}\mathbf{S}_{m-k} = d_1\mathbf{X}_1 + d_2\mathbf{X}_2 + \cdots + d_k\mathbf{X}_k.$$

This is impossible unless all a_i and d_i are 0 because $\mathbf{S}_1, \cdots, \mathbf{S}_{m-k}, \mathbf{X}_1, \cdots, \mathbf{X}_k$ are linearly independent. Since the a_i are not all zero we have a contradiction, and the vectors of (5.1) are linearly independent.

Now the theorem results when we note that dimension $S = m$, dimension $T = r$, dimension $S \cap T = k$, and dimension $S + T = m + r - k$.

Example 2. Every pair of two-dimensional subspaces of $V_3(R)$ has a nonzero intersection. To prove this, we note that $S + T$ has dimension at most 3 (and at least 2). Then the equation of the theorem reads:

$$4 = \text{dimension } (S + T) + \text{dimension } (S \cap T),$$

or

$$4 - \text{dimension } (S + T) = \text{dimension } (S \cap T).$$

Hence dimension $(S \cap T)$ is either 1 or 2.

Geometrically, this has a simple interpretation in space. With S, since it is generated by two linearly independent vectors, we can associate a plane passing through the origin. All line segments in this plane will be associated with linear combinations of the two generating vectors. Similarly T can be associated with another plane passing through the origin. These planes will either be identical or intersect in a line. In the latter case, a vector $\mathbf{X}$ associated with a segment of the line of intersection will lie in both S and T and hence be in $S \cap T$. Moreover, $S \cap T = L\{\mathbf{X}\}$ will be one-dimensional.

If S and T are subspaces of a vector space V, we have seen that $S + T$ is a subspace W of V. Let us now change our point of view. Starting with a subspace W of the vector space V, is it possible to express W as the sum of two other subspaces S and T? We let $W = L\{\mathbf{X}_1, \mathbf{X}_2, \cdots, \mathbf{X}_k\}$ be a subspace of dimension $r > 1$ (where, of course, $k \geq r$). Now by letting $S = L\{\mathbf{X}_1, \cdots, \mathbf{X}_t\}$, $T = L\{\mathbf{X}_{t+1}, \cdots, \mathbf{X}_k\}$ for $1 \leq t \leq k - 1$ we obtain a *decomposition* of W into the sum of subspaces S and T; that is, $W = S + T$. It should be clear that W can be expressed as the sum of subspaces in many ways. If the vectors we have used to generate W are linearly independent, then $S \cap T = \mathbf{0}$ and every $\mathbf{X}$ of W can be expressed uniquely in the form

$$\mathbf{X} = \mathbf{Y} + \mathbf{Z}, \tag{5.4}$$

where $\mathbf{Y} \in S$, $\mathbf{Z} \in T$. Otherwise the vectors $\mathbf{X}_1, \cdots, \mathbf{X}_k$ would be linearly dependent. (Why?)

Conversely, if $W = S + T$ and every vector $\mathbf{X}$ of W can be written uniquely in the form (5.4), $S \cap T = \mathbf{0}$. We see this because the assumption that $S \cap T \neq \mathbf{0}$ means that the vectors of this intersection can be expressed as elements either of S or of T and hence not uniquely.

A decomposition of a vector space V into the sum of subspaces $S + T$, where $S \cap T = \mathbf{0}$, will be of importance in the next section.

DEFINITION 5.2. *If $W = S + T$, where S and T are subspaces of a vector space W and $S \cap T = \mathbf{0}$, we write $W = S \oplus T$ and say that W is the* DIRECT SUM *of the subspaces S and T.*

The concept of a direct sum decomposition has a simple geometric interpretation in space. We let W be the vector space $V_3(R)$ and associate the vector $[x_1, x_2, x_3]$ of $V_3(R)$ with the line segment OX. Let S be a two-dimensional subspace of $V_3(R)$ generated by the vectors $\mathbf{Y} = [y_1, y_2, y_3]$ and $\mathbf{Z} = [z_1, z_2, z_3]$. Associate with S the plane π containing the line segments OY and OZ (Figure 5.1). Now if $V_3(R) = S \oplus T$, and T is generated by $\mathbf{X} = [x_1, x_2, x_3]$, the line segment OX cannot lie in the plane π, for then $\mathbf{X}$ would be a linear combination of $\mathbf{Y}$ and $\mathbf{Z}$, and $\mathbf{X}$ would be contained in S contrary to the direct sum requirement. Hence T is associated with a line intersecting π. Now it should be clear that *any* line intersecting

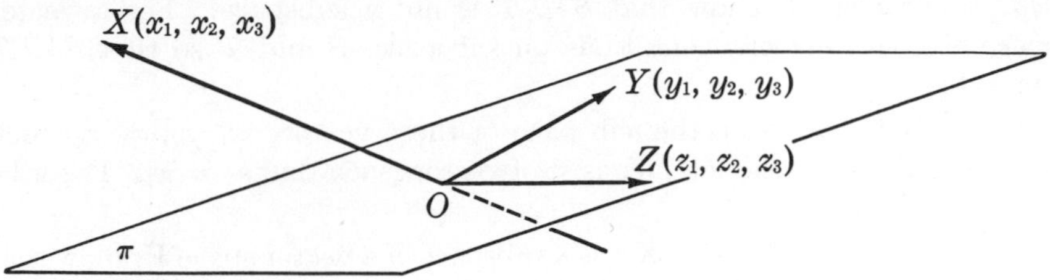

Figure 5.1

π at O could be used to determine a subspace T, such that $V_3(R) = S \oplus T$. Hence a direct sum decomposition is not unique even when S is kept fixed.

We also see why T cannot be two-dimensional. In that case T would be associated with a plane π^*, and the planes π and π^* would have at least a line of intersection so that $S \cap T \neq \mathbf{0}$.

Example 3. Let $V = L\{[1, 0, 1, 0], [1, 0, 1, 1], [1, 0, 0, 0]\}$.
Then $V = L\{[1, 0, 1, 0], [1, 0, 1, 1]\} \oplus L\{[1, 0, 0, 0]\}$;
or $V = L\{[1, 0, 1, 0], [1, 0, 1, 1]\} \oplus L\{[3, 0, 2, 1]\}$.

We note that even though S is the same, T is different for the two decompositions. We have merely selected the first two elements of a basis for V as the basis for S. The second basis for T is the sum of the basis vectors of V as originally presented.

EXERCISES

1. Find the intersection and sum of the subspaces

$$S = L\{[1, 0, 1], [1, 1, 0]\} \quad \text{and} \quad T = L\{[1, 2, 3], [0, 0, 1]\}.$$

2. In $V_4(R)$ let $S = L\{[2, 2, -1, 2], [1, 1, 1, -2], [0, 0, 2, -4]\}$,

and $T = L\{[2, -1, 1, 1], [-2, 1, 3, 3], [3, -6, 0, 0]\}$.

Determine the dimensions of S, T, $S \cap T$, $S + T$ and verify the relation of Theorem 5.2.

3. Prove that every pair of k-dimensional subspaces of a $(2k - 1)$-dimensional vector space must have a nonzero intersection.

4. Let $S = L\{[1, 0, 2], [-1, 1, 0]\}$ and find two subspaces T such that $V_3(R) = S \oplus T$.

5. If $V = S \oplus T$, and $\mathbf{X}$ is a vector of V such that $\mathbf{X} = \mathbf{Y} + \mathbf{Z}$, where $\mathbf{Y} \in S$, $\mathbf{Z} \in T$; then $\mathbf{Y}$ is called the projection of $\mathbf{X}$ on S, $\mathbf{Z}$ the projection of $\mathbf{X}$ on T. Let $V = L\{[1, 2, -1], [1, -1, 0]\} \oplus L\{[1, 0, 1]\}$ (i.e., $V = S \oplus T$); find the projection of $\mathbf{X} = [4, 1, -3]$ on S and on T. Interpret this result geometrically in space.

6. If $V = S \oplus T$, under what conditions will the projection of a vector $\mathbf{X}$ of V on S be $\mathbf{0}$? the projection of $\mathbf{X}$ on T be $\mathbf{0}$?

7. In Problem 1, show that $S \cup T$ is not a subspace. For a vector space V give sufficient conditions on subspaces S and T so that $S \cup T$ is a subspace.

8. In $V_4(R)$, let S be the subspace of those vectors $[x_1, x_2, x_3, x_4]$ such that $x_1 - 2x_3 = 0$, and let T consist of vectors such that $x_2 = x_4$. Describe $S + T$, $S \cap T$.

9. If $W = L\{\mathbf{X}_1, \mathbf{X}_2, \cdots, \mathbf{X}_k\}$ is a subspace of a vector space V, show that W may also be considered as the intersection of all subspaces of V that contain the vectors $\mathbf{X}_1, \mathbf{X}_2, \cdots, \mathbf{X}_k$.

6. Inner Products of Vectors in $V_n(R)$

If we are to capitalize on the algebraic system of vectors $V_n(R)$ in providing a concept of distance for E_n, there should be a "product" of vectors in $V_n(R)$ giving rise to a scalar quantity similar to $(\mathbf{X}, \mathbf{Y})$ in $V_3(R)$. We have available an obvious generalization.

DEFINITION 6.1. *The* INNER (*or scalar*) PRODUCT $(\mathbf{X}, \mathbf{Y})$ *of vectors* $\mathbf{X} = [x_1, x_2, \cdots, x_n]$ *and* $\mathbf{Y} = [y_1, y_2, \cdots, y_n]$ *of* $V_n(R)$ *is defined to be*

$$(\mathbf{X}, \mathbf{Y}) = x_1y_1 + x_2y_2 + \cdots + x_ny_n.$$

The following properties of the inner product $(\mathbf{X}, \mathbf{Y})$ are immediate consequences of the definition and the properties of vectors:

(6.1)
- (i) $(a\mathbf{X} + b\mathbf{Y}, \mathbf{Z}) = a(\mathbf{X}, \mathbf{Z}) + b(\mathbf{Y}, \mathbf{Z})$, where $\mathbf{X}$, $\mathbf{Y}$, and $\mathbf{Z}$ are vectors of $V_n(R)$ and a, b are arbitrary real numbers.
- (ii) $(\mathbf{X}, \mathbf{Y}) = (\mathbf{Y}, \mathbf{X})$ for all $\mathbf{X}$, $\mathbf{Y}$ of $V_n(R)$.
- (iii) $(\mathbf{X}, \mathbf{X}) > 0$ if and only if $\mathbf{X} \neq \mathbf{0}$.

To prove (i), let $\mathbf{X} = [x_1, \cdots, x_n]$, $\mathbf{Y} = [y_1, \cdots, y_n]$, $\mathbf{Z} = [z_1, \cdots, z_n]$; then

$$a\mathbf{X} + b\mathbf{Y} = [ax_1 + by_1, \cdots, ax_n + by_n],$$

and

$$\begin{aligned}(a\mathbf{X} + b\mathbf{Y}, \mathbf{Z}) &= ([ax_1 + by_1, \cdots, ax_n + by_n], [z_1, \cdots, z_n]) \\ &= (ax_1z_1 + by_1z_1) + \cdots + (ax_nz_n + by_nz_n) \\ &= (ax_1z_1 + ax_2z_2 + \cdots + ax_nz_n) \\ &\quad + (by_1z_1 + by_2z_2 + \cdots + by_nz_n) \\ &= a([x_1, \cdots, x_n], [z_1, \cdots, z_n]) \\ &\quad + b([y_1, \cdots, y_n], [z_1, \cdots, z_n]) \\ &= a(\mathbf{X}, \mathbf{Z}) + b(\mathbf{Y}, \mathbf{Z}).\end{aligned}$$

Properties (ii) and (iii) are left for the student to verify.

If we were dealing with vector spaces other than $V_n(R)$ or its subspaces it is possible that a concept of "inner product" might still be available. The inner product is given as a mapping from the set of pairs of vectors of $V_n(R)$ into the real numbers. If for a vector space V, a mapping T from pairs of vectors of V to the real numbers is given such that

$$\text{(i}'\text{)}\quad T(a\mathbf{X} + b\mathbf{Y}, \mathbf{Z}) = aT(\mathbf{X}, \mathbf{Z}) + bT(\mathbf{Y}, \mathbf{Z}),$$
$$\text{(ii}'\text{)}\quad T(\mathbf{X}, \mathbf{Y}) = T(\mathbf{Y}, \mathbf{X}),$$
$$\text{(iii}'\text{)}\quad T(\mathbf{X}, \mathbf{X}) > 0 \quad \text{if and only if } \mathbf{X} \neq \mathbf{0},$$

we could call T an "inner product" mapping for V. The student familiar with the calculus can readily verify that the set of functions continuous on the closed interval $0 \leq x \leq 1$ is a vector space for which the operation given by $\int_0^1 f(x)\, g(x)\, dx$ determines an inner product mapping for the pair (f, g). In terms of this more general concept it is clear that the mapping $(\mathbf{X}, \mathbf{Y})$ of Definition 1.1 is not the only "inner product" available for $V_n(R)$. For example, $T(\mathbf{X}, \mathbf{Y}) = x_1y_1 + 2x_2y_2 + \cdots + nx_ny_n$ satisfies (i′), (ii′), and (iii′). Nevertheless the product $(\mathbf{X}, \mathbf{Y})$ will be the only inner product which will be needed for some chapters to come. We return to a consideration of its properties.

We borrow by analogy from the definitions of Chapter 2 and make the following definitions in $V_n(R)$ in terms of the inner product.

DEFINITION 6.2. *The* LENGTH *of a vector* $\mathbf{X} = [x_1, \cdots, x_n]$ *is defined to be* $|\mathbf{X}| = (\mathbf{X}, \mathbf{X})^{1/2}$.

We note from property (iii) of (6.1) that the zero vector $\mathbf{0}$ is the only vector of length zero. All other vectors have length greater than zero.

DEFINITION 6.3. *Two vectors* $\mathbf{X}$ *and* $\mathbf{Y}$ *are called* ORTHOGONAL *if* $(\mathbf{X}, \mathbf{Y}) = 0$.

Under this definition note that the vector $\mathbf{0}$ is orthogonal to all vectors. For this reason, the property of orthogonality is usually restricted to non-zero vectors although occasionally we must include $\mathbf{0}$ in a discussion.

DEFINITION 6.4. *A set of vectors* $\mathbf{X}_1, \cdots, \mathbf{X}_n$ *is said to be an* ORTHOGONAL SET OF VECTORS *if* $(\mathbf{X}_i, \mathbf{X}_j) = 0$ *for* $i \neq j$.

DEFINITION 6.5. *Two subspaces* S *and* T *of* $V_n(R)$ *are called* ORTHOGONAL SUBSPACES *of* $V_n(R)$ *if* $(\mathbf{X}, \mathbf{Y}) = 0$ *for all vectors* $\mathbf{X}$ *of* S *and* $\mathbf{Y}$ *of* T.

Example 1. Let us find all vectors orthogonal to $[1, -1, 2]$. If $\mathbf{X} = [x_1, x_2, x_3]$ is such a vector, $([1, -1, 2], [x_1, x_2, x_3]) = x_1 - x_2 + 2x_3 = 0$. Thus the set of vectors required will be given by the set of solutions of the homogeneous equation $x_1 - x_2 + 2x_3 = 0$. It is apparent that this solution space has dimension 2 and that a basis is $[1, 1, 0], [2, 0, -1]$. The answer, then, is $L\{[1, 1, 0], [2, 0, -1]\}$.

The example is a special case of the following theorem:

THEOREM 6.1. *The set of all vectors orthogonal to vectors* $\mathbf{X}_1, \mathbf{X}_2, \cdots, \mathbf{X}_k$ *is a vector subspace* T *of* $V_n(R)$.

The proof of Theorem 6.1 is a simple extension of the arguments of Example 1 and will be left as an exercise for the student. Moreover it is easy to show that T is orthogonal to $L\{\mathbf{X}_1, \mathbf{X}_2, \cdots, \mathbf{X}_k\}$.

Orthogonal bases — the Gram-Schmidt process. Suppose a subspace V of $V_n(R)$ is given, can we find an orthogonal basis for it? That is, we want a basis consisting of orthogonal vectors. The question and its affirmative answer are important in a number of applications. In the preceding chapter a method was indicated which obtained (in the language of the present section) an orthogonal basis for any two-dimensional subspace of $V_3(R)$. The method to be given now is simply an extension of the procedure given there. We take any basis of V and choose one of the vectors, $\mathbf{X}_1$, of this basis as the first member, $\mathbf{Y}_1$, of the orthogonal basis. Then we find the second member, $\mathbf{Y}_2$, by determining a vector orthogonal to $\mathbf{Y}_1$ which is a linear combination of $\mathbf{X}_2$ and $\mathbf{Y}_1$; that is, $\mathbf{Y}_2$ is an element of $L\{\mathbf{Y}_1, \mathbf{X}_2\} = L\{\mathbf{X}_1, \mathbf{X}_2\}$. We proceed in this way to get successive vectors $\mathbf{Y}_i$ orthogonal to all the previous ones and belonging to the space V. The whole process may be summarized in the proof of the following theorem:

THEOREM 6.2. *Every subspace V of $V_n(R)$ possesses an orthogonal set of vectors as a basis for V.*

Proof (the Gram-Schmidt process). Let $\mathbf{X}_1, \mathbf{X}_2, \cdots, \mathbf{X}_r$ be a basis for V. We will modify the vectors of this basis in a systematic manner to obtain an orthogonal basis for V. First, let $\mathbf{Y}_1 = \mathbf{X}_1$ and then successively:

$$\mathbf{Y}_i = \mathbf{X}_i - \left\{\frac{(\mathbf{X}_i, \mathbf{Y}_{i-1})}{(\mathbf{Y}_{i-1}, \mathbf{Y}_{i-1})}\right\}\mathbf{Y}_{i-1} - \cdots - \left\{\frac{(\mathbf{X}_i, \mathbf{Y}_1)}{(\mathbf{Y}_1, \mathbf{Y}_1)}\right\}\mathbf{Y}_1 \tag{6.2}$$

for $2 \leq i \leq r$.

The remainder of the proof will now follow by induction. We assume the following properties to be valid for $j < i$:

(i) $L\{\mathbf{Y}_1, \cdots, \mathbf{Y}_j\} = L\{\mathbf{X}_1, \cdots, \mathbf{X}_j\}$.
(ii) $\mathbf{Y}_1, \mathbf{Y}_2, \cdots, \mathbf{Y}_j$ form an orthogonal set of vectors.

We are using strong induction and it is clear that properties (i) and (ii) are valid for $j = 1$. The next step is to show that properties (i) and (ii) are valid for $j = i$ under the assumptions above.

First $\mathbf{Y}_i \neq \mathbf{0}$ or it would follow from (6.2) and the induction assumptions that $\mathbf{X}_1, \cdots, \mathbf{X}_i$ would be linearly dependent. (Why?)

If $j < i$, we take the inner product of both sides of (6.2) with $\mathbf{Y}_j$ and use the induction assumption that $\mathbf{Y}_j$ is orthogonal to all the $\mathbf{Y}_k$ ($k < i$; $k \neq j$). Then,

$$(\mathbf{Y}_i, \mathbf{Y}_j) = (\mathbf{X}_i, \mathbf{Y}_j) - \left\{\frac{(\mathbf{X}_i, \mathbf{Y}_j)}{(\mathbf{Y}_j, \mathbf{Y}_j)}\right\}(\mathbf{Y}_j, \mathbf{Y}_j) = 0.$$

Hence $\mathbf{Y}_1, \mathbf{Y}_2, \cdots, \mathbf{Y}_i$ are mutually orthogonal.

We see from (6.2) and the induction assumption that

$$L\{\mathbf{Y}_1, \cdots, \mathbf{Y}_i\} \subseteq L\{\mathbf{X}_1, \cdots, \mathbf{X}_i\}.$$

Moreover, $\mathbf{X}_i \in L\{\mathbf{Y}_1, \cdots, \mathbf{Y}_i\}$ and $L\{\mathbf{Y}_1, \cdots, \mathbf{Y}_{i-1}\} = L\{\mathbf{X}_1, \cdots, \mathbf{X}_{i-1}\}$ by the induction assumption so that

$$L\{\mathbf{Y}_1, \cdots, \mathbf{Y}_i\} \supseteq L\{\mathbf{X}_1, \cdots, \mathbf{X}_i\}.$$

Hence we have $L\{\mathbf{Y}_1, \cdots, \mathbf{Y}_i\} = L\{\mathbf{X}_1, \cdots, \mathbf{X}_i\}$, and our induction proof is complete.

Example 2. Let $V = L\{[1, 0, 1, 0], [1, 1, 3, 0], [0, 2, 0, 1]\}$ and find an orthogonal basis for V.

Set

$$\mathbf{Y}_1 = [1, 0, 1, 0].$$

Then

$$\mathbf{Y}_2 = [1, 1, 3, 0] - \frac{([1, 1, 3, 0], [1, 0, 1, 0])}{([1, 0, 1, 0], [1, 0, 1, 0])}[1, 0, 1, 0]$$

or

$$\mathbf{Y}_2 = [1, 1, 3, 0] - 2[1, 0, 1, 0] = [-1, 1, 1, 0].$$

Finally,

$$\mathbf{Y}_3 = [0, 2, 0, 1] - \frac{([0, 2, 0, 1], [-1, 1, 1, 0])}{([-1, 1, 1, 0], [-1, 1, 1, 0])}[-1, 1, 1, 0] - \frac{([0, 2, 0, 1], [1, 0, 1, 0])}{([1, 0, 1, 0], [1, 0, 1, 0])}[1, 0, 1, 0]$$

or

$$\mathbf{Y}_3 = [0, 2, 0, 1] - \tfrac{2}{3}[-1, 1, 1, 0] - 0[1, 0, 1, 0] = [\tfrac{2}{3}, \tfrac{4}{3}, -\tfrac{2}{3}, 1].$$

It is easily checked that $(\mathbf{Y}_1, \mathbf{Y}_2) = (\mathbf{Y}_1, \mathbf{Y}_3) = (\mathbf{Y}_2, \mathbf{Y}_3) = 0$.

The vectors of $V_n(R)$ whose length is 1 are called *unit vectors*. If $\mathbf{X}$ is any nonzero vector, then $\mathbf{Y} = \mathbf{X}/(\mathbf{X}, \mathbf{X})^{1/2}$ is a unit vector since

$$(\mathbf{Y}, \mathbf{Y}) = \left(\frac{\mathbf{X}}{(\mathbf{X}, \mathbf{X})^{1/2}}, \frac{\mathbf{X}}{(\mathbf{X}, \mathbf{X})^{1/2}}\right) = \frac{1}{(\mathbf{X}, \mathbf{X})}(\mathbf{X}, \mathbf{X}) = 1.$$

The process of replacing a vector by the corresponding unit vector in a computation is called *normalization*. When it is applied to the determination of an orthogonal basis the result is termed an *orthonormal* basis.

In actual calculations there are two ways to find an orthonormal basis. The first is to follow the method of Example 2 and then to divide each $\mathbf{Y}_i$ by $(\mathbf{Y}_i, \mathbf{Y}_i)^{1/2}$. The second is to normalize at each step (including the first); in this case the denominators in the Gram-Schmidt process may be ignored. (Why?) The student may choose whichever method he prefers; we merely offer the observation that in machine calculation the second method is preferable since fewer divisions are involved. The second method may be illustrated by its application to the problem of Example 2.

$$\mathbf{Y}_1 = \left[\frac{1}{\sqrt{2}}, 0, \frac{1}{\sqrt{2}}, 0\right].$$

$$\mathbf{Y}_2' = [1, 1, 3, 0] - \left([1, 1, 3, 0], \left[\frac{1}{\sqrt{2}}, 0, \frac{1}{\sqrt{2}}, 0\right]\right)\left[\frac{1}{\sqrt{2}}, 0, \frac{1}{\sqrt{2}}, 0\right]$$

$$= [1, 1, 3, 0] - [2, 0, 2, 0] = [-1, 1, 1, 0];$$

$$\mathbf{Y}_2 = \left[-\frac{1}{\sqrt{3}}, \frac{1}{\sqrt{3}}, \frac{1}{\sqrt{3}}, 0\right].$$

$$\mathbf{Y}_3' = [0,2,0,1] - \left([0,2,0,1], \left[-\frac{1}{\sqrt{3}}, \frac{1}{\sqrt{3}}, \frac{1}{\sqrt{3}}, 0\right]\right)\left[-\frac{1}{\sqrt{3}}, \frac{1}{\sqrt{3}}, \frac{1}{\sqrt{3}}, 0\right]$$

$$- \left([0, 2, 0, 1], \left[\frac{1}{\sqrt{2}}, 0, \frac{1}{\sqrt{2}}, 0\right]\right)\left[\frac{1}{\sqrt{2}}, 0, \frac{1}{\sqrt{2}}, 0\right]$$

$$= [0, 2, 0, 1] - \left[-\frac{2}{3}, \frac{2}{3}, \frac{2}{3}, 0\right] - 0\left[\frac{1}{\sqrt{2}}, 0, \frac{1}{\sqrt{2}}, 0\right] = \left[\frac{2}{3}, \frac{4}{3}, -\frac{2}{3}, 1\right];$$

$$\mathbf{Y}_3 = \left[\frac{2}{\sqrt{33}}, \frac{4}{\sqrt{33}}, \frac{-2}{\sqrt{33}}, \frac{3}{\sqrt{33}}\right].$$

Orthogonal complements. At the present time, we shall content ourselves with an application of orthogonal vectors in the identification of subspaces of $V_n(R)$. We shall first prove that for any subspace V of $V_n(R)$ there exists an orthogonal subspace W such that $V_n(R)$ is the direct sum of the subspaces V and W; that is, $V_n(R) = V \oplus W$. Example 3 will illustrate the proof to follow.

Example 3. We seek to find a subspace W of $V_4(R)$ orthogonal to $V = L\{[1, 0, 1, 0], [1, 1, 3, 0]\}$ and such that $V \oplus W = V_4(R)$.

We know from Theorem 4.2 that the vectors [1, 0, 1, 0], [1, 1, 3, 0] can be extended to a basis of $V_4(R)$. This may be done in many ways; we choose

$$[1, 0, 1, 0], [1, 1, 3, 0], [0, 1, 0, 0], [0, 0, 0, 1].$$

Now we apply the Gram-Schmidt process to obtain an orthogonal basis.

$\mathbf{Y}_1 = [1, 0, 1, 0];$
$\mathbf{Y}_2 = [-1, 1, 1, 0]$ from Example 2.

$$\mathbf{Y}_3 = [0, 1, 0, 0] - \frac{([0, 1, 0, 0], [-1, 1, 1, 0])}{([-1, 1, 1, 0], [-1, 1, 1, 0])}[-1, 1, 1, 0] = [\tfrac{1}{3}, \tfrac{2}{3}, -\tfrac{1}{3}, 0];$$

$\mathbf{Y}_4 = [0, 0, 0, 1].$

It is clear that

$$V = L\{[1, 0, 1, 0], [-1, 1, 1, 0]\}$$

and

$$W = L\{[\tfrac{1}{3}, \tfrac{2}{3}, -\tfrac{1}{3}, 0], [0, 0, 0, 1]\}$$

are orthogonal subspaces of $V_4(R)$. Moreover, $V \cap W = \mathbf{0}$, so that $V_4(R) = V \oplus W$.

THEOREM 6.3. *If V is a subspace of $V_n(R)$, there exists a unique subspace W of $V_n(R)$ orthogonal to V such that $V_n(R) = V \oplus W$.*

Proof. Let $\{\mathbf{X}_1, \mathbf{X}_2, \cdots, \mathbf{X}_k\}$ be a basis for V. Extend this set of vectors to a basis for $V_n(R)$. Thus,

$$V_n(R) = L\{\mathbf{X}_1, \cdots, \mathbf{X}_k, \mathbf{Z}_{k+1}, \cdots, \mathbf{Z}_n\}.$$

Now apply the Gram-Schmidt process to this basis to obtain an orthogonal basis for $V_n(R)$. Thus,

$$V_n(R) = L\{\mathbf{Y}_1, \mathbf{Y}_2, \cdots, \mathbf{Y}_k, \mathbf{Y}_{k+1}, \cdots, \mathbf{Y}_n\},$$

and we know from the Gram-Schmidt procedure that $L\{\mathbf{X}_1, \cdots, \mathbf{X}_k\} = L\{\mathbf{Y}_1, \cdots, \mathbf{Y}_k\}$. Set $W = L\{\mathbf{Y}_{k+1}, \cdots, \mathbf{Y}_n\}$. Then $V_n(R) = V \oplus W$, and W is a subspace orthogonal to V.

We must still prove that if W_1 is any subspace orthogonal to V such that $V_n(R) = V \oplus W_1$, then $W_1 = W$. This is left as an exercise (Exercise 10).

The subspace W of Theorem 6.3 is called the *orthogonal complement* of V in $V_n(R)$.

The concept of orthogonal complement provides another method of describing subspaces of $V_n(R)$. Let V be a subspace of $V_n(R)$ and let W be the orthogonal complement of V. Suppose W has a basis,

$$\begin{aligned}
\mathbf{A}_1 &= [a_{11}, a_{12}, \cdots, a_{1n}] \\
\mathbf{A}_2 &= [a_{21}, a_{22}, \cdots, a_{2n}] \\
&\cdots\cdots\cdots \\
\mathbf{A}_k &= [a_{k1}, a_{k2}, \cdots, a_{kn}].
\end{aligned}$$

Every vector $\mathbf{X}$ of V satisfies the conditions: $(\mathbf{X}, \mathbf{A}_1) = (\mathbf{X}, \mathbf{A}_2) = \cdots = (\mathbf{X}, \mathbf{A}_k) = 0$. If we write $\mathbf{X} = [x_1, x_2, \cdots, x_n]$, these conditions are equivalent to:

$$\begin{aligned}
a_{11}x_1 + a_{12}x_2 + \cdots + a_{1n}x_n &= 0 \\
a_{21}x_1 + a_{22}x_2 + \cdots + a_{2n}x_n &= 0 \\
\cdots\cdots\cdots& \\
a_{k1}x_1 + a_{k2}x_2 + \cdots + a_{kn}x_n &= 0,
\end{aligned} \tag{6.3}$$

so that the components of every vector of V satisfy the homogeneous system of equations (6.3). On the other hand, if $[x_1, x_2, \cdots, x_n]$ is any element of the solution space of the system (6.3), it is orthogonal to all members of W. Now we have not actually shown that any vector orthogonal to all elements of W is necessarily in V. The justification of this statement is left to the student (Exercise 10). When this proof is completed, it follows that V may be described as the solution space of the system (6.3).

Example 4. Using the results of Example 3, we may identify the subspace $V = L\{[1, 0, 1, 0], [1, 1, 3, 0]\}$ as the totality of solutions of the system of homogeneous linear equations

$$\begin{aligned} \tfrac{1}{3}x_1 + \tfrac{2}{3}x_2 - \tfrac{1}{3}x_3 + 0 \cdot x_4 &= 0 \\ x_4 &= 0. \end{aligned}$$

EXERCISES

1. Find the value of $(\mathbf{X}, \mathbf{Y})$ for the vectors:
(a) $\mathbf{X} = [1, 2, 3, -1, 2]$, $\mathbf{Y} = [0, 1, 2, 1, -4]$.
(b) $\mathbf{X} = [1, 2, -1, 3]$, $\mathbf{Y} = [4, -1, -1, -1]$.

2. Determine the values of x for which the following vectors are orthogonal:

$$[x, x-1, x, -1], \quad [2x, x, 3, 1].$$

3. Using the Gram-Schmidt process, obtain a basis of orthogonal vectors for the vector space

$$V = L\{[1, 2, -1, 0], [1, 0, -2, 1], [0, 1, 1, 0]\}.$$

4. Prove that any set of nonzero orthogonal vectors is a linearly independent set.

5. Prove that the intersection, $S \cap T$, of two orthogonal spaces S and T consists of the zero vector only.

6. What is the geometrical interpretation of the Gram-Schmidt process in the plane and in space?

7. Prove the "Schwarz inequality"

$$(\mathbf{X}, \mathbf{Y}) \leq |\mathbf{X}|\,|\mathbf{Y}|.$$

Hint: Consider the vector $a\mathbf{X} + \mathbf{Y}$ and determine a condition necessary for $(a\mathbf{X} + \mathbf{Y}, a\mathbf{X} + \mathbf{Y}) \geq 0$.

8. Let $V_n(R) = V \oplus W$, where V and W are orthogonal subspaces. Then for any vector $\mathbf{X}$, $\mathbf{X} = \mathbf{Y} + \mathbf{Z}$, where $\mathbf{Y} \in V$, $\mathbf{Z} \in W$. We call $\mathbf{Y}$ the orthogonal projection of $\mathbf{X}$ on V, $\mathbf{Z}$ the orthogonal projection of $\mathbf{X}$ on W (see Exercise 5, §5). Find the orthogonal projection of $\mathbf{X} = [1, -2, 3, 0]$ on the subspace $L\{[0, 1, -2, 0], [1, 2, 1, 0]\}$.

9. What is the geometric interpretation of the orthogonal projection of a vector on a subspace V in the plane and in space?

10. If V and W are subspaces of $V_n(R)$ such that $V_n(R) = V \oplus W$ and W is orthogonal to V, show that any vector $\mathbf{X}$ orthogonal to all members of V is in W. Hence show that the orthogonal complement of V may be uniquely defined as the set of all vectors orthogonal to all members of V.

Hint: Certainly $\mathbf{X} = \mathbf{Y} + \mathbf{Z}$, $\mathbf{Y} \in V$, $\mathbf{Z} \in W$. Now show $\mathbf{Y} = \mathbf{0}$.

11. Show that the Gram-Schmidt process provides an effective way to determine whether or not the vectors $\mathbf{X}_1, \cdots, \mathbf{X}_k$ are dependent. If they are dependent, one of the $\mathbf{Y}_i$ must be zero.

*7. Dual Spaces

As a concluding topic for this chapter, we wish to describe briefly a concept that may often be used effectively in a discussion of vector spaces.

Consider the mapping from the vectors of $V_n(R)$ to the reals which results when $\mathbf{Y}$ is held fixed but $\mathbf{X}$ is allowed to vary over the vectors of $V_n(R)$ in the inner product $(\mathbf{X}, \mathbf{Y})$. We may indicate the mapping by $\mathrm{T}_\mathbf{Y}$; that is, $\mathrm{T}_\mathbf{Y}(\mathbf{X}) = (\mathbf{X}, \mathbf{Y})$. The properties of inner products applied to the mapping $\mathrm{T}_\mathbf{Y}$ give

$$\begin{aligned} \mathrm{T}_\mathbf{Y}(a\mathbf{X}_1 + b\mathbf{X}_2) &= (a\mathbf{X}_1 + b\mathbf{X}_2, \mathbf{Y}) \\ &= a(\mathbf{X}_1, \mathbf{Y}) + b(\mathbf{X}_2, \mathbf{Y}) = a\mathrm{T}_\mathbf{Y}(\mathbf{X}_1) + b\mathrm{T}_\mathbf{Y}(\mathbf{X}_2). \end{aligned} \tag{7.1}$$

More generally, single-valued mappings from V to the reals (not necessarily those arising from inner products) which have the property expressed by (7.1) are called *linear functionals over* V. Linear functionals may be added by the rule:

$$(\mathrm{T}_1 + \mathrm{T}_2)(\mathbf{X}) = \mathrm{T}_1(\mathbf{X}) + \mathrm{T}_2(\mathbf{X}); \tag{7.2}$$

and multiplied by real numbers:

$$a\mathrm{T}_1(\mathbf{X}) = \mathrm{T}_1(a\mathbf{X}) \tag{7.3}$$

to give again linear functionals. Briefly, *the set of linear functionals over a vector space V is itself a vector space* with respect to the addition and multiplication defined by (7.2) and (7.3). (The details of checking laws A1–A5 and S1–S5 are left to the student.) The resulting vector space of linear functionals is called the *dual space of* V. Let us indicate the situation for $V_2(R)$. Here, if T is an arbitrary linear functional,

$$\begin{aligned} \mathrm{T}([x_1, x_2]) &= \mathrm{T}(x_1[1, 0] + x_2[0, 1]) \\ &= x_1\mathrm{T}([1, 0]) + x_2\mathrm{T}([0, 1]) = x_1\mathrm{T}(\mathbf{E}_1) + x_2\mathrm{T}(\mathbf{E}_2). \end{aligned}$$

Thus any linear functional is determined by its value for $\mathbf{E}_1$ and $\mathbf{E}_2$.

Now let T_1 be defined by:

$$T_1(\mathbf{E}_1) = 1, \quad T_1(\mathbf{E}_2) = 0;$$

and let T_2 be defined by

$$T_2(\mathbf{E}_1) = 0, \quad T_2(\mathbf{E}_2) = 1.$$

If T is any linear functional such that

$$T(\mathbf{E}_1) = a, \quad T(\mathbf{E}_2) = b,$$

then

$$T(\mathbf{X}) = T([x_1, x_2]) = x_1a + x_2b,$$

while

$$T_1(\mathbf{X}) = x_1 \quad \text{and} \quad T_2(\mathbf{X}) = x_2.$$

Thus

$$T(\mathbf{X}) = aT_1(\mathbf{X}) + bT_2(\mathbf{X}).$$

Hence any linear functional T is a linear combination of T_1 and T_2 so that these functionals generate the dual space. Moreover T_1 and T_2 are linearly independent since, if the "zero" functional, $Z(\mathbf{X}) = 0$ for all $\mathbf{X}$, were a linear combination of T_1 and T_2,

$$aT_1(\mathbf{X}) + bT_2(\mathbf{X}) = 0 \qquad \text{for all } \mathbf{X}.$$

Letting $\mathbf{X}$ be $\mathbf{E}_1$ and $\mathbf{E}_2$ in turn we would have

$$aT_1(\mathbf{E}_1) + bT_2(\mathbf{E}_1) = a = 0$$

and

$$aT_1(\mathbf{E}_2) + bT_2(\mathbf{E}_2) = b = 0.$$

Thus T_1 and T_2 are a basis for the dual space, and this result is an illustration of a general theorem to the effect that the dimension of a vector space is equal to the dimension of its dual space. (The theorem depends on condition F, page 58, and is not true otherwise.)

The study of dual spaces is an interesting part of the algebraic theory of vector spaces. However, it is an area whose development would carry us away from the main points which we wish to develop. We must refer the interested reader to such books as *Finite-Dimensional Vector Spaces*, by Paul R. Halmos (Princeton, New Jersey, D. Van Nostrand Company, Inc.), for further information.

CHAPTER 4

Euclidean n-Space

The extension of our concepts of Euclidean space to higher-dimensional analogues would involve axioms for points, lines, planes, and higher-dimensional subspaces as well as discussions of the concepts of distance, parallelism, perpendicularity, and so on. It is not our purpose to give any such detailed axiomatic treatment of Euclidean n-space.

A study of Euclidean n-space may be approached from the point of view of coordinate systems. Therefore, in order to provide a geometrical setting to accompany $V_n(R)$, we shall consider the n-tuples of real numbers $(x_1, x_2, \cdots, x_n)$ as representing the points of a Euclidean space E_n. We seek to generalize some of the geometrical content of Chapter 2 to E_n in order that the student may become familiar with terminology frequently encountered in other courses in mathematics and physics. Since we wish to emphasize applications of the algebraic properties of $V_n(R)$, we will first discuss properties of E_n in which the concept of distance plays a minor role. Later we will examine the concept of distance and discuss this and related geometric concepts.

1. Lines and Coordinate Systems in E_n

The points of Euclidean space E_n are represented by the n-tuples of real numbers $(x_1, x_2, \cdots, x_n)$. Let $X(x_1, x_2, \cdots, x_n)$ and $Y(y_1, y_2, \cdots, y_n)$ be two distinct points of E_n. The set of all points $Z(z_1, z_2, \cdots, z_n)$ of E_n for which

$$
\begin{aligned}
z_1 &= x_1 + t(y_1 - x_1) \\
z_2 &= x_2 + t(y_2 - x_2) \\
&\cdots\cdots \\
z_n &= x_n + t(y_n - x_n),
\end{aligned}
\tag{1.1}
$$

where t is a real number, is defined to be the *line* joining the points X and Y. In (1.1), t represents (in a sense to be made more definite later) a ratio of distances in E_n. These equations should be compared with equations (2.2) of Chapter 2.

The *line segment* from X to Y consists of those points z for which $0 \leq t \leq 1$ in (1.1), and the vector $[y_1 - x_1, y_2 - x_2, \cdots, y_n - x_n]$ of $V_n(R)$ is associated with the directed line segment XY.

If the point $(0, 0, \cdots, 0)$ of E_n is denoted by O, we may pass from a point $Z(z_1, z_2, \cdots, z_n)$ to the vector $\mathbf{Z} = [z_1, z_2, \cdots, z_n]$ by considering the vector associated with the line segment OZ. In particular, we note that the vector associated with the directed line segment XY is $(\mathbf{Y} - \mathbf{X})$. Thus, the relation (1.1) may be written briefly in the vector form

$$\mathbf{Z} = \mathbf{X} + t(\mathbf{Y} - \mathbf{X}), \quad \text{or} \quad \mathbf{Z} = (1 - t)\mathbf{X} + t\mathbf{Y},$$

which corresponds to the relation (2.3) of Chapter 2.

All the previous definitions are simple analogues of the geometric situation in space after a linear coordinate system has been established. The question now arises: "What corresponds in E_n to a linear coordinate system in space?" We proceed to answer this question as follows:

Choose an arbitrary point $P_0(p_1, p_2, \cdots, p_n)$ as origin and select n other points $P_1^{(1)}, P_1^{(2)}, \cdots, P_1^{(n)}$ such that the vectors $\mathbf{X}_i = \mathbf{P}_1^{(i)} - \mathbf{P}_0$ associated with the directed segments $P_0P_1^{(i)}$ (for $i = 1, 2, \cdots, n$) are linearly independent. The point $P_1^{(i)}$ plays the role of the unit point selected on the line joining P_0 and $P_1^{(i)}$.

If $R(r_1, r_2, \cdots, r_n)$ is an arbitrary point of E_n, the vector $\mathbf{R} - \mathbf{P}_0 = [r_1 - p_1, r_2 - p_2, \cdots, r_n - p_n]$ associated with the directed line segment P_0R may be uniquely expressed as a linear combination of the basis vectors $\mathbf{X}_1, \mathbf{X}_2, \cdots, \mathbf{X}_n$ of $V_n(R)$. Thus,

$$(1.2) \quad [r_1 - p_1, r_2 - p_2, \cdots, r_n - p_n] = r_1^*\mathbf{X}_1 + r_2^*\mathbf{X}_2 + \cdots + r_n^*\mathbf{X}_n,$$

and the n real numbers $(r_1^*, r_2^*, \cdots, r_n^*)$ are called the coordinates of the point R with respect to the linear coordinate system determined by $P_0, P_1^{(1)}, \cdots, P_1^{(n)}$.

Again, we note that a linear coordinate system provides a one-to-one mapping of the points of E_n onto all ordered n-tuples of real numbers. In particular, if we take P_0 to be $(0, 0, \cdots, 0)$ and take $P_1^{(1)}, P_1^{(2)}, \cdots, P_1^{(n)}$ to be the points $(1, 0, \cdots, 0), (0, 1, 0, \cdots), \cdots, (0, 0, \cdots, 1)$ respectively, then $\mathbf{X}_i = \mathbf{P}_1^{(i)} - \mathbf{P}_0$ are the natural basis vectors of $V_n(R)$; $\mathbf{X}_i = \mathbf{E}_i$. Thus,

$$(1.3) \quad [r_1, r_2, \cdots, r_n] = r_1\mathbf{E}_1 + r_2\mathbf{E}_2 + \cdots + r_n\mathbf{E}_n,$$

and the point $R(r_1, r_2, \cdots, r_n)$ has coordinates $(r_1, r_2, \cdots, r_n)$ relative to this linear coordinate system.

As in space, it is often desirable to change from one linear coordinate system in E_n to another. Therefore we wish to determine a relationship between the coordinates $(r_1^*, r_2^*, \cdots, r_n^*)$ and $(r_1, r_2, \cdots, r_n)$. The expressions in (1.2) and (1.3) may be written

$$\mathbf{R} = \mathbf{P}_0 + r_1^*\mathbf{X}_1 + r_2^*\mathbf{X}_2 + \cdots + r_n^*\mathbf{X}_n,$$
$$\mathbf{R} = r_1\mathbf{E}_1 + r_2\mathbf{E}_2 + \cdots + r_n\mathbf{E}_n.$$

Equating these expressions for $\mathbf{R}$, we obtain

$$\mathbf{P}_0 + r_1^*\mathbf{X}_1 + r_2^*\mathbf{X}_2 + \cdots + r_n^*\mathbf{X}_n = r_1\mathbf{E}_1 + r_2\mathbf{E}_2 + \cdots + r_n\mathbf{E}_n. \tag{1.4}$$

The vectors $\mathbf{E}_1, \cdots, \mathbf{E}_n$ form an orthonormal set of vectors so that $(\mathbf{E}_i, \mathbf{E}_j) = 0$ for $i \neq j$, $(\mathbf{E}_i, \mathbf{E}_i) = 1$ for $i = 1, 2, \cdots, n$. Hence if we take the inner product of both sides of (1.4) with $\mathbf{E}_1, \mathbf{E}_2, \cdots, \mathbf{E}_n$, we obtain in turn

$$(1.5)\quad \begin{array}{l} (\mathbf{P}_0, \mathbf{E}_1) + r_1^*(\mathbf{X}_1, \mathbf{E}_1) + r_2^*(\mathbf{X}_2, \mathbf{E}_1) + \cdots + r_n^*(\mathbf{X}_n, \mathbf{E}_1) = r_1 \\ (\mathbf{P}_0, \mathbf{E}_2) + r_1^*(\mathbf{X}_1, \mathbf{E}_2) + r_2^*(\mathbf{X}_2, \mathbf{E}_2) + \cdots + r_n^*(\mathbf{X}_n, \mathbf{E}_2) = r_2 \\ \cdots\cdots\cdots\cdots\cdots\cdots\cdots\cdots\cdots \\ (\mathbf{P}_0, \mathbf{E}_n) + r_1^*(\mathbf{X}_1, \mathbf{E}_n) + r_2^*(\mathbf{X}_2, \mathbf{E}_n) + \cdots + r_n^*(\mathbf{X}_n, \mathbf{E}_n) = r_n. \end{array}$$

The equations (1.5) give a straightforward way of finding the coordinates $(r_1, r_2, \cdots, r_n)$ if the coordinates $(r_1^*, r_2^*, \cdots, r_n^*)$ are known.

Is there a similar set of equations to determine the $(r_1^*, r_2^*, \cdots, r_n^*)$ if the $(r_1, r_2, \cdots, r_n)$ are known?

It should be observed that if the coordinates $(r_1, r_2, \cdots, r_n)$ are fixed we could simply treat equations (1.5) as linear simultaneous equations for the unknowns $r_1^*, r_2^*, \cdots, r_n^*$ and solve. However, at least theoretically, we do have the following alternative: Let $\mathbf{A}_1, \mathbf{A}_2, \cdots, \mathbf{A}_n$ be n nonzero vectors such that $\mathbf{A}_i$ is orthogonal to the set of vectors

$$\{\mathbf{X}_1, \mathbf{X}_2, \cdots, \mathbf{X}_{i-1}, \mathbf{X}_{i+1}, \cdots, \mathbf{X}_n\}$$

for $i = 1, 2, \cdots, n$. Now take the inner product of both sides of (1.4) with each $\mathbf{A}_i$. We obtain

$$(\mathbf{P}_0, \mathbf{A}_i) + r_i^*(\mathbf{X}_i, \mathbf{A}_i) = r_1(\mathbf{E}_1, \mathbf{A}_i) + \cdots + r_n(\mathbf{E}_n, \mathbf{A}_i) \tag{1.6}$$

for $i = 1, 2, \cdots, n$, since $(\mathbf{X}_j, \mathbf{A}_i) = 0$ if $i \neq j$.

Thus, formally, we obtain the equations

$$r_i^* = \frac{1}{(\mathbf{X}_i, \mathbf{A}_i)}[r_1(\mathbf{E}_1, \mathbf{A}_i) + \cdots + r_n(\mathbf{E}_n, \mathbf{A}_i) - (\mathbf{P}_0, \mathbf{A}_i)] \tag{1.7}$$

for $i = 1, 2, \cdots, n$. It remains for the student to show that $(\mathbf{X}_i, \mathbf{A}_i) \neq 0$; then we have equations similar to (1.5) for the coordinates $(r_1^*, r_2^*, \cdots, r_n^*)$ in terms of the coordinates $(r_1, r_2, \cdots, r_n)$.

Example 1. In E_4, let us establish a coordinate system by choosing $P_0(0, 1, 2, -1)$, $P_1^{(1)}(1, -1, 0, -1)$, $P_1^{(2)}(0, 1, 0, -3)$, $P_1^{(3)}(1, 1, 1, 0)$, $P_1^{(4)}(0, 0, 1, 0)$. The vectors $\mathbf{X}_i = \mathbf{P}_1^{(i)} - \mathbf{P}_0$ are then

$$\mathbf{X}_1 = [1, -2, -2, 0], \quad \mathbf{X}_2 = [0, 0, -2, -2],$$
$$\mathbf{X}_3 = [1, 0, -1, 1], \quad \mathbf{X}_4 = [0, -1, -1, 1].$$

The coordinates of the point $R(r_1, r_2, r_3, r_4)$ relative to this coordinate system are determined from the relation (1.2) or

$$\begin{aligned}[r_1, r_2 - 1, r_3 - 2, r_4 + 1] &= r_1^*[1, -2, -2, 0] \\ &+ r_2^*[0, 0, -2, -2] + r_3^*[1, 0, -1, 1] + r_4^*[0, -1, -1, 1].\end{aligned}$$

Now a relation between the coordinates $(r_1^*, r_2^*, r_3^*, r_4^*)$ and (r_1, r_2, r_3, r_4) can be obtained directly from this vector relation by adding the vectors on the right and equating components. Thus,

$$\begin{aligned} r_1^* \qquad\qquad + r_3^* \qquad\quad &= r_1 \\ -2r_1^* \qquad\qquad\qquad - r_4^* &= r_2 - 1 \\ -2r_1^* - 2r_2^* - r_3^* - r_4^* &= r_3 - 2 \\ -2r_2^* + r_3^* + r_4^* &= r_4 + 1. \end{aligned}$$

If we wish to obtain a similar expression for the r_i^* in terms of the r_i, we solve the simultaneous linear equations by first reducing to the equivalent "diagonal form":

$$\begin{aligned} r_1^* \qquad + r_3^* \qquad\quad &= r_1 \\ -2r_2^* + r_3^* - r_4^* &= 2r_1 + r_3 - 2 \\ 2r_3^* - r_4^* &= 2r_1 + r_2 - 2 \\ -2r_4^* &= 2r_1 + r_3 - r_4 - 3; \end{aligned}$$

the solution is then

$$\begin{aligned} \tfrac{1}{2}r_1 - \tfrac{1}{2}r_2 + \tfrac{1}{4}r_3 - \tfrac{1}{4}r_4 - \tfrac{1}{4} &= r_1^* \\ -\tfrac{1}{4}r_1 + \tfrac{1}{4}r_2 - \tfrac{3}{8}r_3 - \tfrac{1}{8}r_4 + \tfrac{3}{8} &= r_2^* \\ \tfrac{1}{2}r_1 + \tfrac{1}{2}r_2 - \tfrac{1}{4}r_3 + \tfrac{1}{4}r_4 + \tfrac{1}{4} &= r_3^* \\ -r_1 \qquad\qquad - \tfrac{1}{2}r_3 + \tfrac{1}{2}r_4 + \tfrac{3}{2} &= r_4^*. \end{aligned}$$

The student can easily verify that the vectors

$$\begin{aligned} \mathbf{A}_1 &= [2, -2, 1, -1], \quad \mathbf{A}_2 = [-2, 2, -3, -1], \\ \mathbf{A}_3 &= [2, 2, -1, 1], \qquad \mathbf{A}_4 = [-2, 0, -1, 1] \end{aligned}$$

satisfy the requirements needed in our particular case for the derivation of equations (1.7). These equations then become precisely those given above for expressing the r_i^* in terms of the r_i. The principal difficulty is in determining the vectors $\mathbf{A}_i$.

There remains at least one more way to determine an expression for the r_i^* in terms of r_i. We could, for example, obtain expressions for $\mathbf{P}_0$ and for the $\mathbf{E}_i$ occurring in (1.4) in terms of the basis vectors $\{\mathbf{X}_i\}$ of $V_n(R)$. Thus,

$$\begin{aligned} \mathbf{P}_0 &= p_1^*\mathbf{X}_1 + p_2^*\mathbf{X}_2 + \cdots + p_n^*\mathbf{X}_n, \\ \mathbf{E}_i &= a_{i1}\mathbf{X}_1 + a_{i2}\mathbf{X}_2 + \cdots + a_{in}\mathbf{X}_n. \end{aligned}$$

Now, substituting these expressions in (1.4), we would have two expressions for a single vector as a linear combination of the independent vectors

$\{\mathbf{X}_i\}$. Since these expressions must be identical (see Exercise 2, §2, Chapter 3), we may equate the coefficients of $\mathbf{X}_i$ to obtain:

$$p_i^* + r_i^* = r_1a_{1i} + r_2a_{2i} + \cdots + r_na_{ni}$$

for $i = 1, 2, \cdots, n$. This method involves a consideration of different bases of $V_n(R)$; we shall return to this discussion in Chapter 6.

EXERCISES

1. Determine a set of equations of the line joining the points
(a) $(1, 2, -1, 3), (2, 4, 1, 5)$.
(b) $(1, 4, -1, 3), (0, 3, -3, 1)$.

2. Determine whether the lines of Exercise 1 intersect and if so find their point of intersection.

3. In E_4, obtain the relations between the coordinates (r_1, r_2, r_3, r_4) and $(r_1^*, r_2^*, r_3^*, r_4^*)$ if the *-coordinate system is introduced by the points

$$P_0 = (1, 1, 0, 0), \quad P_1^{(1)} = (2, 1, 1, 1), \quad P_1^{(2)} = (1, 1, 1, 0),$$
$$P_1^{(3)} = (1, 1, 1, 1), \quad P_1^{(4)} = (1, 2, 0, 0).$$

4. (a) For the coordinate system in Exercise 3, what are the new coordinates of the point $P(3, 1, 2, 4)$?
(b) What is the point whose new *-coordinates are $(1, 3, 1, 0)$?

5. Prove that $(\mathbf{X}_i, \mathbf{A}_i)$ which occurs in formula (1.7) is never zero.

6. Discuss the relation between coordinates if the $\{\mathbf{X}_i\}$ form an orthonormal set of vectors in (1.4).

7. Let two coordinate systems be introduced in E_n with points $P_0, P_1^{(i)}$ and $Q_0, Q_1^{(i)}$ such that $\mathbf{X}_i = \mathbf{P}_1^{(i)} - \mathbf{P}_0$ and $\mathbf{Y}_i = \mathbf{Q}_1^{(i)} - \mathbf{Q}_0$ $(i = 1, 2, \cdots, n)$ are two sets of linearly independent vectors. Let $(r_1^*, r_2^*, \cdots, r_n^*)$ be the coordinates of $R(r_1, r_2, \cdots, r_n)$ relative to the P's and $(r_1', r_2', \cdots, r_n')$ be the coordinates of R relative to the Q's. Show how the discussion leading to (1.7) may be extended to obtain a relation between the r_i^* and r_i'.
Hint: (1.4) would be replaced by

$$\mathbf{P}_0 + r_1^*\mathbf{X}_1 + \cdots + r_n^*\mathbf{X}_n = \mathbf{Q}_0 + r_1'\mathbf{Y}_1 + \cdots + r_n'\mathbf{Y}_n.$$

2. Planes in E_n

If a coordinate system is introduced in space, a plane passing through the noncollinear points P_0, P_1, and P_2 can be identified with the totality of points $R(r_1, r_2, r_3)$ satisfying the vector relation

$$\mathbf{R} = \mathbf{P}_0 + t_1(\mathbf{P}_1 - \mathbf{P}_0) + t_2(\mathbf{P}_2 - \mathbf{P}_0),$$

where t_1 and t_2 are arbitrary real numbers (see (4.4), Chapter 2). Note that $(\mathbf{P}_1 - \mathbf{P}_0)$ and $(\mathbf{P}_2 - \mathbf{P}_0)$ are linearly independent vectors of $V_3(R)$.

We generalize this observation to define k-planes of E_n for $k = 1, 2, \cdots, n$.

DEFINITION 2.1. *Let $P_0, P_1, \cdots, P_k$ be $k + 1$ points of E_n such that the vectors $(\mathbf{P}_i - \mathbf{P}_0)$ associated with the line segments P_0P_i (for $i = 1, 2, \cdots, k$) are linearly independent. The set of all points $R(r_1, r_2, \cdots, r_n)$ such that*

$$(2.1) \qquad \mathbf{R} = \mathbf{P}_0 + t_1(\mathbf{P}_1 - \mathbf{P}_0) + t_2(\mathbf{P}_2 - \mathbf{P}_0) + \cdots + t_k(\mathbf{P}_k - \mathbf{P}_0),$$

where $t_1, t_2, \cdots, t_k$ are arbitrary real numbers, is said to be a k-PLANE S_k *of E_n. Clearly S_k contains the points $P_0, P_1, \cdots, P_k$ themselves.*

If R is a point of S_k defined above, the coefficients $t_1, t_2, \cdots, t_k$ are uniquely determined in (2.1); otherwise the vectors $(\mathbf{P}_i - \mathbf{P}_0)$ would be linearly dependent contrary to the hypothesis. Thus, with the choice of P_0 as origin and $P_1, \cdots, P_k$ as unit points on the lines $P_0P_1, \cdots, P_0P_k$, we may coordinatize S_k by means of k-tuples of real numbers $(t_1, t_2, \cdots, t_k)$. Of course, it must be remembered that such a linear coordinate system is valid only for the points of S_k. The corresponding situation in space is essentially: "If you know which plane you are considering, it can in itself be coordinatized by means of ordered pairs."

The points R of a k-plane of E_n may be represented in a more symmetrical form than (2.1), in which no special emphasis is attached to any of the points. We merely combine the vectors of (2.1) to read

$$(2.1)' \qquad \begin{aligned} &\mathbf{R} = (1 - t_1 - t_2 - \cdots - t_k)\mathbf{P}_0 + t_1\mathbf{P}_1 + \cdots + t_k\mathbf{P}_k, \\ \text{or} \quad &\mathbf{R} = t_0\mathbf{P}_0 + t_1\mathbf{P}_1 + \cdots + t_k\mathbf{P}_k, \end{aligned}$$

where $t_0 + t_1 + \cdots + t_k = 1$. Of course, the linear independence of the vectors $(\mathbf{P}_i - \mathbf{P}_0)$ for $i = 1, 2, \cdots, k$ is still assumed, for otherwise the set of all points R satisfying (2.1)′ would form an h-plane of E_n with $h < k$. (Why?)

We now establish the uniqueness of a k-plane containing the points $P_0, P_1, \cdots, P_k$.

THEOREM 2.1. *Let $P_0, \cdots, P_k$ be points of E_n such that the vectors $(\mathbf{P}_i - \mathbf{P}_0)$ for $i = 1, 2, \cdots, k$ are linearly independent. Then there is only one k-plane S_k of E_n containing $P_0, P_1, \cdots, P_k$.*

Proof. By Definition 2.1, the set S_k of all points $R(r_1, r_2, \cdots, r_n)$ such that (2.1) is satisfied is a k-plane of E_n containing $P_0, P_1, \cdots, P_k$.

Assume that $Q_0, Q_1, \cdots, Q_k$ are $k + 1$ points satisfying Definition 2.1 and yielding a second k-plane S_k' containing $P_0, P_1, \cdots, P_k$. We wish to show that $S_k' = S_k$; that is, that every point of S_k is a point of S_k' and conversely.

The points of S_k' satisfy a relation of the form

$$(2.2) \qquad \mathbf{R} = \mathbf{Q}_0 + s_1\mathbf{Y}_1 + \cdots + s_k\mathbf{Y}_k,$$

where $\mathbf{Y}_i = \mathbf{Q}_i - \mathbf{Q}_0$ for $i = 1, 2, \cdots, k$.

Since the points P_i ($i = 0, 1, \cdots, k$) are assumed to be in S_k', we have real numbers c_{ij} such that

$$\mathbf{P}_i = \mathbf{Q}_0 + c_{i1}\mathbf{Y}_1 + \cdots + c_{ik}\mathbf{Y}_k \tag{2.3}$$

for $i = 0, 1, \cdots, k$. Substituting these expressions in (2.1), we see that every point of S_k satisfies a relation

$$\mathbf{R} = \mathbf{Q}_0 + c_1\mathbf{Y}_1 + \cdots + c_k\mathbf{Y}_k \tag{2.4}$$

for some real numbers $c_1, c_2, \cdots, c_k$. Thus $S_k \subseteq S_k'$.

In order to show that $S_k' \subseteq S_k$, we subtract the expression for $\mathbf{P}_0$ from $\mathbf{P}_i$ in (2.3) to obtain

$$\mathbf{P}_i - \mathbf{P}_0 = d_{i1}\mathbf{Y}_1 + d_{i2}\mathbf{Y}_2 + \cdots + d_{ik}\mathbf{Y}_k,$$

where $d_{ij} = (c_{ij} - c_{0j})$ for $i, j = 1, 2, \cdots, k$.

By hypothesis the vectors $(\mathbf{P}_i - \mathbf{P}_0)$ for $i = 1, 2, \cdots, k$ are linearly independent vectors contained in the vector space $L\{\mathbf{Y}_1, \mathbf{Y}_2, \cdots, \mathbf{Y}_k\}$ and so may be used as a basis for this vector space (Corollary to Theorem 4.1, Chapter 3). Hence, we can express each $\mathbf{Y}_i$ as a linear combination of the $(\mathbf{P}_i - \mathbf{P}_0)$. Moreover, $\mathbf{Q}_0 = \mathbf{P}_0 - c_{01}\mathbf{Y}_1 - \cdots - c_{0k}\mathbf{Y}_k$ from (2.3), and consequently we can obtain an expression for vectors of the form $\mathbf{R}$ of (2.2) as a linear combination of $\mathbf{P}_0$ and the vectors $(\mathbf{P}_i - \mathbf{P}_0)$. Then $\mathbf{R}$ will have the form (2.1) and R is a point of S_k. Thus $S_k' \subseteq S_k$. Since we have previously proved $S_k \subseteq S_k'$ we conclude that $S_k = S_k'$.

In view of Theorem 2.1, it now makes sense to speak of *the* 2-plane containing three points not lying on a line or *the* k-plane containing $k + 1$ points $P_0, P_1, \cdots, P_k$ which are not contained in an h-plane with $h < k$.

An $(n - 1)$-plane is called a *hyperplane* of E_n.

Example 1. Let $(0, 1, 2, -1)$, $(4, 1, 0, -1)$, $(2, 1, 1, 1)$, and $(2, -1, 1, 2)$ be points of E_4 and determine the 3-plane (hyperplane) containing these points.

We may choose any of these points for P_0, say $(0, 1, 2, -1)$. Then,

$$\begin{aligned}
[4, 1, 0, -1] - [0, 1, 2, -1] &= [4, 0, -2, 0],\\
[2, 1, 1, 1] \quad - [0, 1, 2, -1] &= [2, 0, -1, 2],\\
[2, -1, 1, 2] - [0, 1, 2, -1] &= [2, -2, -1, 3],
\end{aligned}$$

and it is easily shown that these vectors are linearly independent. S_3 consists of all points $R(r_1, r_2, r_3, r_4)$ such that

$$\begin{aligned}
[r_1, r_2, r_3, r_4] = [0, 1, 2, -1] &+ t_1[4, 0, -2, 0]\\
&+ t_2[2, 0, -1, 2] + t_3[2, -2, -1, 3],
\end{aligned}$$

where t_1, t_2, t_3 are arbitrary real numbers. Thus,

$$S_3 = \{(4t_1 + 2t_2 + 2t_3, 1 - 2t_3, 2 - 2t_1 - t_2 - t_3, -1 + 2t_2 + 3t_3)\}.$$

For $k + 1$ points $P_0, \cdots, P_k$ of E_n such that the vectors $(\mathbf{P}_i - \mathbf{P}_0)$ for $i = 1, 2, \cdots, k$ are linearly independent, we have a k-plane S_k. We can associate with S_k the k-dimensional vector subspace V_k of $V_n(R)$ generated by $\mathbf{P}_i - \mathbf{P}_0$ for $i = 1, 2, \cdots, k$. It should be clear that if $\{\mathbf{X}_1, \mathbf{X}_2, \cdots, \mathbf{X}_k\}$ is *any* basis for V_k, the points R of S_k satisfy the relation

$$\mathbf{R} - \mathbf{P}_0 = c_1\mathbf{X}_1 + c_2\mathbf{X}_2 + \cdots + c_k\mathbf{X}_k, \tag{2.5}$$

where $c_1, c_2, \cdots, c_k$ are real numbers.

In the particular case of a hyperplane S_{n-1}, let $\mathbf{X}_1, \mathbf{X}_2, \cdots, \mathbf{X}_{n-1}$ be a basis for the vector subspace V_{n-1} associated with S_{n-1}. Applying Theorem 6.3, Chapter 3, we take the vector $\mathbf{A}_1 = [a_1, a_2, \cdots, a_n]$ as generator of the orthogonal complement to $L\{\mathbf{X}_1, \cdots, \mathbf{X}_{n-1}\}$; that is, the inner product $(\mathbf{X}_i, \mathbf{A}_i) = 0$ for $i = 1, 2, \cdots, n - 1$. Hence, taking the inner product of both sides of (2.5) with $\mathbf{A}_1$, we have

$$\begin{aligned} &(\mathbf{A}_1, \mathbf{R} - \mathbf{P}_0) = 0, \\ \text{or} \quad &a_1r_1 + a_2r_2 + \cdots + a_nr_n = (\mathbf{A}_1, \mathbf{P}_0) = d_1, \end{aligned} \tag{2.6}$$

for all points R of S_{n-1}. Moreover, if $(r_1, r_2, \cdots, r_n)$ is a solution of (2.6), then $(\mathbf{A}_1, \mathbf{R}) = (\mathbf{A}_1, \mathbf{P}_0)$, $(\mathbf{A}_1, \mathbf{R} - \mathbf{P}_0) = 0$. Using Exercise 10, §6 of Chapter 3, we see that $\mathbf{R} - \mathbf{P}_0$ is a linear combination of the $\mathbf{X}_i$'s and that $(r_1, r_2, \cdots, r_n)$ is a point of S_{n-1}. This argument establishes the following theorem:

THEOREM 2.2. *Every hyperplane S_{n-1} of E_n consists of all those points $(r_1, r_2, \cdots, r_n)$ satisfying an equation of the form*

$$a_1r_1 + a_2r_2 + \cdots + a_nr_n = d_1.$$

We now have the analogue of the situation in space: the hyperplanes of E_n are defined by means of linear equations.

Example 2. To obtain the equation of the hyperplane of Example 1, note that a vector $[x_1, x_2, x_3, x_4]$ orthogonal to $[4, 0, -2, 0]$, $[2, 0, -1, 2]$, and $[2, -2, -1, 3]$ can be obtained by solving the equations

$$\begin{aligned} ([x_1, x_2, x_3, x_4], [4, 0, -2, 0]) &= 4x_1 \phantom{{}- 2x_2} - 2x_3 \phantom{{}+ 3x_4} = 0 \\ ([x_1, x_2, x_3, x_4], [2, 0, -1, 2]) &= 2x_1 \phantom{{}- 2x_2} - x_3 + 2x_4 = 0 \\ ([x_1, x_2, x_3, x_4], [2, -2, -1, 3]) &= 2x_1 - 2x_2 - x_3 + 3x_4 = 0. \end{aligned}$$

These equations have a solution vector $[1, 0, 2, 0]$, and this plays the role of $\mathbf{A}_1$ in the discussion above. Thus, $([1, 0, 2, 0], \mathbf{R} - [0, 1, 2, -1]) = 0$, or

$$r_1 + 2r_3 = 4,$$

is the equation of the hyperplane S_3. This result should be compared with the coordinates of an arbitrary point of S_3 as given in Example 1.

To establish a generalization of the identification of lines in space as the intersection of planes, we prove the following theorem for E_n:

THEOREM 2.3. *Let S_k be a k-plane of E_n. Then S_k is the set of points in the intersection of $n - k$ hyperplanes of E_n.*

Proof. Let V_k be the k-dimensional vector subspace of $V_n(R)$ associated with S_k. By Theorem 6.3 of Chapter 3, there is an $(n - k)$-dimensional orthogonal complement in $V_n(R)$ to V_k. We select the vectors $\mathbf{A}_1 = [a_{11}, \cdots, a_{1n}], \cdots, \mathbf{A}_{n-k} = [a_{n-k,1}, \cdots, a_{n-k,n}]$ as a basis for the orthogonal complement of V_k. If P_0 is a fixed point of S_k and R is any other point of S_k, then

$$(\mathbf{A}_i, \mathbf{R} - \mathbf{P}_0) = 0 \qquad \text{for } i = 1, 2, \cdots, n - k,$$

since $\mathbf{R} - \mathbf{P}_0$ is a vector of V_k. We now obtain from these inner products the following simultaneous system of linear equations satisfied by the points R of S_k:

$$\begin{array}{lllll} a_{11}r_1 & + a_{12}r_2 & + \cdots + a_{1n}r_n & = (\mathbf{A}_1, \mathbf{P}_0) & = d_1 \\ a_{21}r_1 & + a_{22}r_2 & + \cdots + a_{2n}r_n & = (\mathbf{A}_2, \mathbf{P}_0) & = d_2 \\ \cdot\ \cdot\ \cdot & \cdot\ \cdot\ \cdot & \cdot\ \cdot\ \cdot & \cdot\ \cdot\ \cdot & \cdot\ \cdot \\ a_{n-k,1}r_1 & + a_{n-k,2}r_2 & + \cdots + a_{n-k,n}r_n & = (\mathbf{A}_{n-k}, \mathbf{P}_0) & = d_{n-k}. \end{array} \tag{2.7}$$

Conversely, any solution vector $[r_1, r_2, \cdots, r_n]$ of (2.7) satisfies $(\mathbf{A}_i, \mathbf{R}) = (\mathbf{A}_i, \mathbf{P}_0)$ or $(\mathbf{A}_i, \mathbf{R} - \mathbf{P}_0) = 0$ for $i = 1, 2, \cdots, n - k$. Again it follows from Exercise 10, §6 of Chapter 3, that $\mathbf{R} - \mathbf{P}_0$ is in the vector space V_k so that the point R is in S_k.

Each equation of (2.7) can be interpreted as defining a hyperplane, and our proof is complete; $(r_1, r_2, \cdots, r_n)$ must lie in each of the hyperplanes and so in their intersection.

We will illustrate the converse of Theorem 2.3 with an example showing that the set of points lying in the intersection of hyperplanes is a k-plane of E_n.

Example 3. We will determine the points of E_n lying in the intersection of the hyperplanes whose equations are

$$\begin{aligned} r_1 - 2r_2 - 5r_3 + 3r_4 - r_5 &= 6 \\ r_2 + 3r_3 \qquad\quad + r_5 &= 1 \\ 2r_1 - r_2 \qquad + r_4 - 3r_5 &= 4 \\ 3r_1 - 2r_2 - 2r_3 + 4r_4 - 3r_5 &= 11. \end{aligned}$$

We solve these equations in the manner of the previous chapter and obtain an equivalent system:

$$\begin{aligned} r_1 - 2r_2 - 5r_3 + 3r_4 - r_5 &= 6 \\ r_2 + 3r_3 \qquad\quad + r_5 &= 1 \\ r_3 - 5r_4 - 4r_5 &= -11 \\ 0 &= 0. \end{aligned}$$

In this form we see that r_4 and r_5 may be chosen arbitrarily and then

$$\begin{aligned} r_3 &= -11 + 5r_4 + 4r_5 \\ r_2 &= 34 - 15r_4 - 13r_5 \\ r_1 &= 19 - 8r_4 - 5r_5. \end{aligned}$$

Thus, the set of points S of E_n lying in the intersection of these hyperplanes is

$$\{(19 - 8r_4 - 5r_5, 34 - 15r_4 - 13r_5, -11 + 5r_4 + 4r_5, r_4, r_5)\},$$

where r_4 and r_5 are arbitrary.

Every vector $\mathbf{R}$ from the origin to one of the points of S can be written in the form

$$\mathbf{R} = [19, 34, -11, 0, 0] + r_4[-8, -15, 5, 1, 0] + r_5[-5, -13, 4, 0, 1],$$

and since the vectors $[-8, -15, 5, 1, 0]$ and $[-5, -13, 4, 0, 1]$ are linearly independent it follows from Definition 1.1 that S is a 2-plane.

The reason the four hyperplanes determine a 2-plane and not a line (1-plane), as might be expected, is that the last hyperplane contains the intersection of the other three; specifically, the last equation is the sum of the first three. (What is an analogous situation in space?)

The geometric interpretation of the solution of a system of linear equations in three unknowns as a point, line, or plane in space may now be generalized to a simultaneous system of linear equations in n unknowns. We interpret the solution as a t-plane S_t of E_n defined by the intersection of hyperplanes. No solution exists if the hyperplanes do not intersect. For example, in space there is no solution if two of the planes are parallel.

For E_n, the concept of parallelism in space is generalized in the following manner:

Definition 2.2. *Let V_p and V_q be the vector spaces of $V_n(R)$ associated with a p-plane S_p and a q-plane S_q of E_n. The planes S_p and S_q are* PARALLEL *if either $V_p \subseteq V_q$ or $V_q \subseteq V_p$, and S_p and S_q are disjoint.*

The student should compare this definition with his intuitions concerning parallelism in space.

Example 4. Let us show that the hyperplane determined by the equation

$$5r_1 + r_2 - r_3 + 2r_4 = 7$$

is parallel to the line $[r_1, r_2, r_3, r_4] = [1, 0, 1, 1] + t[0, 1, 1, 0]$ in the sense of Definition 2.2. We note that $(1, 2, 0, 0)$, $(1, 0, -2, 0)$, $(1, 0, 0, 1)$, and $(0, 0, -1, 3)$ are points of the hyperplane. Hence, choosing $(1, 2, 0, 0)$ as P_0, we have

$$V_3 = L\{[0, -2, -2, 0], [0, -2, 0, 1], [-1, -2, -1, 3]\}.$$

Of course, $V_1 = L\{[0, 1, 1, 0]\}$, and we see that

$$[0, 1, 1, 0] = -\tfrac{1}{2}[0, -2, -2, 0],$$

so that $V_1 \subseteq V_3$.

If there were a point $(1, t, 1 + t, 1)$ of the line which was on the hyperplane, there would be a number t such that $5 \cdot (1) + t - (1 + t) + 2 \cdot 1 = 7$. Clearly this is impossible, and hence the hyperplane and the line do not intersect. Therefore the hyperplane and the line are parallel.

An n-dimensional *parallelotope*, corresponding to the parallelogram in a plane and the parallelepiped in space, is defined in the following manner: Let $n + 1$ points $P_0, P_1, \cdots, P_n$ be given such that $(P_i - P_0)$ (for $i = 1, 2, \cdots, n$) are linearly independent vectors. The n-dimensional parallelotope whose edges through P_0 are P_0P_i consists of the set of all points R of E_n for which

$$\mathbf{R} = \mathbf{P}_0 + t_1(\mathbf{P}_1 - \mathbf{P}_0) + \cdots + t_n(\mathbf{P}_n - \mathbf{P}_0),$$

where $0 \leq t_i \leq 1$.

By choosing first $t_1 = 0$ and then $t_1 = 1$, we obtain the points of the "parallel" faces passing through the end points P_0 and P_1 of the edge P_0P_1. It is left as an exercise for the student to show that these faces are contained in parallel hyperplanes.

EXERCISES

1. What are the coordinates of the points lying in the 2-plane S_2 of E_4 determined by the points

$$(1, -1, 0, 3), (2, 1, 0, 2), (1, -1, 1, 3)?$$

2. The 2-plane S_2 of Problem 1 is the intersection of two hyperplanes. Determine two hyperplanes whose intersection is S_2.

3. Show that 2-planes of E_4 can intersect

(a) in a point.

(b) in a line.

(c) in a 2-plane.

(d) not at all.

4. Determine the value of k for the k-plane of E_5 defined as the intersection of the following hyperplanes:

$$\begin{aligned} x_1 \quad\quad + 3x_3 - 2x_4 + x_5 &= 4 \\ x_2 - x_3 - x_4 + 5x_5 &= 5 \\ 2x_1 + x_2 + x_3 \quad\quad\quad &= 3 \\ -2x_2 + 6x_3 - 3x_4 - 3x_5 &= 0. \end{aligned}$$

5. Let S_p be a p-plane and S_q a q-plane of E_n. Show how the intersection of S_p and S_q is determined from the equations of hyperplanes defining S_p and S_q.

6. Let S_p and S_q be as in the previous exercise. Show how the k-plane of smallest dimension containing both S_p and S_q may be found.

7. Let S_p be a p-plane and S_q a q-plane of E_n. If $p + q > n$, prove that S_p and S_q contain parallel subplanes.

8. Prove that a line not parallel to a hyperplane either intersects the hyperplane in a unique point or is totally contained in it.

9. Verify that the faces of a parallelotope passing through the end points P_0 and P_1 of the edge P_0P_1 are contained in parallel hyperplanes.

3. Distance in Euclidean n-Space, E_n

The properties of E_n discussed so far did not require the concept of distance between two points for their derivation. Many choices for distance are available; but we desire an expression for distance in E_n that agrees with our previous definitions and intuitions; particularly so when the line, plane, and space are coordinatized by a Cartesian coordinate system and considered as E_1, E_2, and E_3. Moreover, the length of a vector has been defined in the previous chapter, and vectors have been associated with line segments of E_n in §1. In order to conform to these previously discussed ideas, we make the following definition for distance in E_n:

DEFINITION 3.1. *The distance from the point* $X(x_1, x_2, \cdots, x_n)$ *to the point* $Y(y_1, y_2, \cdots, y_n)$ *of* E_n *is a real number* $d(X, Y)$ *given by the formula*

$$d(X, Y) = \{(y_1 - x_1)^2 + (y_2 - x_2)^2 + \cdots + (y_n - x_n)^2\}^{1/2}.$$

As an alternative, the distance from X to Y could be defined as the length of the vector associated with the directed line segment XY, or

$$d(X, Y) = (\mathbf{Y} - \mathbf{X}, \mathbf{Y} - \mathbf{X})^{1/2}. \tag{3.1}$$

These definitions of distance agree with the expressions for distance on a line, in a plane, and in space if we assume that a Cartesian coordinate system has been introduced.

Note that the distance between points of E_n is a real number assigned to ordered pairs of points of E_n. Hence the concept of distance involves a single-valued mapping d from the set of all ordered pairs of points in E_n to the real number field R.

The mapping (function) d possesses the following three properties: For points X, Y, and Z of E_n,

(i) $d(X, Y) \geq 0$, with equality occurring if and only if $X = Y$.
(ii) $d(X, Y) = d(Y, X)$.
(iii) $d(X, Y) + d(Y, Z) \geq d(X, Z)$.

These properties reflect intuitive ideas concerning distance; namely, distance should be non-negative; distance should not depend on the direction traveled on a line segment; the sum of two sides of a triangle should be equal to or larger than the third side ("the shortest distance between two points is a straight line").

Properties (i) and (ii) for $d(X, Y)$ should be verified by the student; they are simple consequences of the definition and of the non-negative character of the square of any real number. Property (iii) is more difficult to verify, and we shall need the following property of real numbers:

SCHWARZ INEQUALITY. *Let* $\mathbf{A} = [a_1, a_2, \cdots, a_n]$ *and* $\mathbf{B} = [b_1, b_2, \cdots, b_n]$ *be vectors of* $V_n(R)$. *Then,*

$$(a_1^2 + a_2^2 + \cdots + a_n^2)(b_1^2 + b_2^2 + \cdots + b_n^2) \geq (a_1b_1 + a_2b_2 + \cdots + a_nb_n)^2;$$

or, in terms of inner products for vectors of $V_n(R)$,

$$(\mathbf{A}, \mathbf{A})(\mathbf{B}, \mathbf{B}) \geq (\mathbf{A}, \mathbf{B})^2.$$

Proof. In order to give a simple proof of this inequality, let us recall that a quadratic polynomial $Ax^2 + Bx + C$ (with real coefficients and $A > 0$) is non-negative for all real values of x if and only if $B^2 - 4AC \leq 0$. Graphically, this condition merely assures us that the parabola whose equation is $y = Ax^2 + Bx + C$ will not cross the x-axis.

Now define a quadratic polynomial in x in the following manner:

$$(3.2) \qquad (x\mathbf{A} + \mathbf{B}, x\mathbf{A} + \mathbf{B}) = (\mathbf{A}, \mathbf{A})x^2 + 2(\mathbf{A}, \mathbf{B})x + (\mathbf{B}, \mathbf{B}).$$

The left member of (3.2) is non-negative for all real values of x since it is a sum of squares, and consequently the right member is non-negative for all real values of x. If the criterion discussed at the beginning of the proof is applied to the right member of (3.2), the Schwarz inequality follows at once.

The verification of property (iii) for $d(X, Y)$ is now an application of the Schwarz inequality. For the points X, Y, and Z, the distances XY, YZ, and XZ are respectively $(\mathbf{Y} - \mathbf{X}, \mathbf{Y} - \mathbf{X})^{1/2}$, $(\mathbf{Z} - \mathbf{Y}, \mathbf{Z} - \mathbf{Y})^{1/2}$, and $(\mathbf{Z} - \mathbf{X}, \mathbf{Z} - \mathbf{X})^{1/2}$. We take $\mathbf{A}$ and $\mathbf{B}$ in the vector form of the Schwarz inequality to be $\mathbf{Y} - \mathbf{X}$ and $\mathbf{Z} - \mathbf{Y}$. Then

$$2(\mathbf{Y} - \mathbf{X}, \mathbf{Y} - \mathbf{X})^{1/2}(\mathbf{Z} - \mathbf{Y}, \mathbf{Z} - \mathbf{Y})^{1/2} \geq 2(\mathbf{Y} - \mathbf{X}, \mathbf{Z} - \mathbf{Y}).$$

If $(\mathbf{Y} - \mathbf{X}, \mathbf{Y} - \mathbf{X}) + (\mathbf{Z} - \mathbf{Y}, \mathbf{Z} - \mathbf{Y})$ is added to both sides of the above inequality, we obtain as the left side

$$(\mathbf{Y} - \mathbf{X}, \mathbf{Y} - \mathbf{X}) + 2(\mathbf{Y} - \mathbf{X}, \mathbf{Y} - \mathbf{X})^{1/2}(\mathbf{Z} - \mathbf{X}, \mathbf{Z} - \mathbf{Y})^{1/2} + (\mathbf{Z} - \mathbf{Y}, \mathbf{Z} - \mathbf{Y}),$$

and the right side becomes

$$(\mathbf{Y} - \mathbf{X}, \mathbf{Y} - \mathbf{X}) + (\mathbf{Y} - \mathbf{X}, \mathbf{Z} - \mathbf{Y}) + (\mathbf{Y} - \mathbf{X}, \mathbf{Z} - \mathbf{Y}) + (\mathbf{Z} - \mathbf{Y}, \mathbf{Z} - \mathbf{Y}).$$

The simplification of these terms yields

$$[(\mathbf{Y}-\mathbf{X},\mathbf{Y}-\mathbf{X})^{1/2}+(\mathbf{Z}-\mathbf{Y},\mathbf{Z}-\mathbf{Y})^{1/2}]^2 \geq (\mathbf{Y}-\mathbf{X}+\mathbf{Z}-\mathbf{Y},\mathbf{Y}-\mathbf{X}+\mathbf{Z}-\mathbf{Y})=(\mathbf{Z}-\mathbf{X},\mathbf{Z}-\mathbf{X}).$$

Then, taking square roots, we obtain

$$(\mathbf{Y}-\mathbf{X},\mathbf{Y}-\mathbf{X})^{1/2}+(\mathbf{Z}-\mathbf{Y},\mathbf{Z}-\mathbf{Y})^{1/2}\geq(\mathbf{Z}-\mathbf{X},\mathbf{Z}-\mathbf{X})^{1/2},$$

or

$$d(X,Y)+d(Y,Z)\geq d(X,Z).$$

The line segment joining the points X and Z is usually defined to be the totality of points Y such that

$$d(X,Y)+d(Y,Z)=d(X,Z).$$

The student will note that in Exercise 4 we are asking him to verify that this definition is consistent with that given for a line segment in § 1.

The next property that will be introduced is the concept of angle between lines of E_n. We let the line L_1 be defined by the points $P(p_1, p_2, \cdots, p_n)$ and $Q(q_1, q_2, \cdots, q_n)$, while the line L_2 is defined by the points $R(r_1, r_2, \cdots, r_n)$ and $S(s_1, s_2, \cdots, s_n)$. The vectors

$$\mathbf{Q}-\mathbf{P}=[q_1-p_1,\cdots,q_n-p_n] \quad\text{and}\quad \mathbf{S}-\mathbf{R}=[s_1-r_1,\cdots,s_n-r_n]$$

are associated with the line segments PQ and RS. As was done in three-dimensional space, we define the angle between L_1 and L_2 to be the angle between the vectors $\mathbf{Q}-\mathbf{P}$ and $\mathbf{S}-\mathbf{R}$. Thus we need only define the angle between vectors in $V_n(R)$.

DEFINITION 3.2. *If* $\mathbf{A}=[a_1, a_2, \cdots, a_n]$ *and* $\mathbf{B}=[b_1, b_2, \cdots, b_n]$ *are nonzero vectors of* $V_n(R)$, *the angle* θ *between the vectors is determined by the expression*

$$\cos\theta=\frac{(\mathbf{A},\mathbf{B})}{(\mathbf{A},\mathbf{A})^{1/2}(\mathbf{B},\mathbf{B})^{1/2}}.$$

If we use the vector form of the Schwarz inequality, we see that

$$1\geq\frac{(\mathbf{A},\mathbf{B})^2}{(\mathbf{A},\mathbf{A})(\mathbf{B},\mathbf{B})}\geq 0 \quad\text{or}\quad -1\leq\frac{(\mathbf{A},\mathbf{B})}{(\mathbf{A},\mathbf{A})^{1/2}(\mathbf{B},\mathbf{B})^{1/2}}\leq 1.$$

Thus there is a unique angle θ, $0\leq\theta\leq\pi$, such that $\cos\theta$ is given by the formula in Definition 3.2.

The definition of orthogonality of vectors in the previous chapter, that is, $(\mathbf{A},\mathbf{B})=0$, agrees with the fact that $\cos\theta=0$ or $\theta=\pi/2$.

Example 1. Let L_1 of E_5 be defined by the points $P(0, 1, -1, -2, 3)$ and $Q(1, 3, -2, 1, 4)$. Let L_2 be defined by the points $R(1, 2, 3, 0, 1)$

and $S(2, 2, 5, 2, 1)$. The vectors $[1, 2, -1, 3, 1]$ and $[1, 0, 2, 2, 0]$ are associated with PQ and RS. Therefore,

$$\cos \angle L_1, L_2 = \cos \theta = \frac{([1, 2, -1, 3, 1], [1, 0, 2, 2, 0])}{4 \cdot 3} = \frac{5}{12},$$

or $\theta = \cos^{-1} \frac{5}{12}$.

We will give at this time a simple illustration of how familiar properties of space generalize to analogous properties for E_n.

If a Cartesian coordinate system has been introduced in a plane, the perpendicular (or minimum) distance from a point $P(p_1, p_2)$ to a line L identified by the equation $ax_1 + bx_2 = c$ is given by the following formula (see any text in analytic geometry):

$$d^2 = \left(\frac{ap_1 + bp_2 - c}{\sqrt{a^2 + b^2}}\right)^2.$$

What is the corresponding formula in E_n? We seek the minimum distance from a point $P(p_1, p_2, \cdots, p_n)$ to a hyperplane defined by the equation

$$a_1r_1 + a_2r_2 + \cdots + a_nr_n = d_1, \quad \text{or} \quad (\mathbf{A}, \mathbf{R}) = d_1,$$

where $\mathbf{A} = [a_1, a_2, \cdots, a_n]$ and $R(r_1, r_2, \cdots, r_n)$ is a point of the hyperplane. Recall that the vector $\mathbf{A} = [a_1, a_2, \cdots, a_n]$ is orthogonal to the vector subspace associated with the hyperplane.

Every line L through the point P has an equation of the form $\mathbf{R} = \mathbf{P} + t\mathbf{B}$, where $\mathbf{B} = [b_1, b_2, \cdots, b_n]$ is a vector essentially specifying the direction of L. If the line L intersects the hyperplane, the point R of intersection is obtained by solving for t from the equation $(\mathbf{A}, \mathbf{P} + t\mathbf{B}) = d_1$, or $(\mathbf{A}, \mathbf{P}) + t(\mathbf{A}, \mathbf{B}) = d_1$. Since L is assumed to intersect the hyperplane, either $(\mathbf{A}, \mathbf{B}) = 0$, in which case it follows that $\mathbf{P}$ lies in the hyperplane, or

$$(\mathbf{A}, \mathbf{B}) \neq 0, \quad t = \frac{d_1 - (\mathbf{A}, \mathbf{P})}{(\mathbf{A}, \mathbf{B})},$$

and the point of intersection is given by

$$\mathbf{R} = \mathbf{P} + \left(\frac{d_1 - (\mathbf{A}, \mathbf{P})}{(\mathbf{A}, \mathbf{B})}\right)\mathbf{B}.$$

The distance from P to R is $(\mathbf{R} - \mathbf{P}, \mathbf{R} - \mathbf{P})^{1/2}$, or

$$d(P, R)^2 = (d_1 - (\mathbf{A}, \mathbf{P}))^2 \frac{(\mathbf{B}, \mathbf{B})}{(\mathbf{A}, \mathbf{B})^2}. \tag{3.3}$$

Let R_0 be the point of intersection of the hyperplane with the line through P in the direction of the vector $\mathbf{A}$. Then, in (3.3), $\mathbf{B} = \mathbf{A}$ and

$$d(P, R_0)^2 = (d_1 - (\mathbf{A}, \mathbf{P}))^2 \frac{1}{(\mathbf{A}, \mathbf{A})}. \tag{3.4}$$

We note that $d(P, R)^2 \geq d(P, R_0)^2$ because of Schwarz's inequality,

$$\frac{(\mathbf{B}, \mathbf{B})}{(\mathbf{A}, \mathbf{B})^2} \geq \frac{1}{(\mathbf{A}, \mathbf{A})}.$$

Hence, the minimum distance from the point P to the hyperplane is given by

$$d(P, R_0)^2 = \left(\frac{a_1p_1 + a_2p_2 + \cdots + a_np_n - d_1}{\sqrt{a_1^2 + a_2^2 + \cdots + a_n^2}}\right)^2,$$

which is the simple generalization of the formula for the plane.

We carry the analogy one step farther. As mentioned previously, the vector $\mathbf{A}$ is orthogonal to the vector space associated with the hyperplane, and hence the minimum distance from a point P to a hyperplane is in a direction orthogonal to the hyperplane.

We will conclude this section with a heuristic discussion of content (volume) of a parallelotope in E_n. The explicit definition will be given in the next chapter. Let the $n + 1$ points $P_0, P_1, \cdots, P_n$ of E_n define a parallelotope whose edges through the point P_0 are P_0P_i $(i = 1, 2, \cdots, n)$ so that $\mathbf{X}_i = \mathbf{P}_i - \mathbf{P}_0$ are the n linearly independent vectors associated with these edges. We proceed by induction to define the content of a parallelotope in E_n. The content (area) in the plane E_2 and the content (volume) in space E_3 are familiar. In each case, we obtain the content by merely multiplying the content of the parallelotope of next lower dimension by the perpendicular distance from the end point of the next edge to the k-plane containing that lower-dimensional parallelotope. Thus, in Figure 3.1, P_2R is orthogonal to P_0P_1, and P_3R is orthogonal to the plane determined by P_0, P_1, and P_2. Moreover the vector associated with P_2R is in

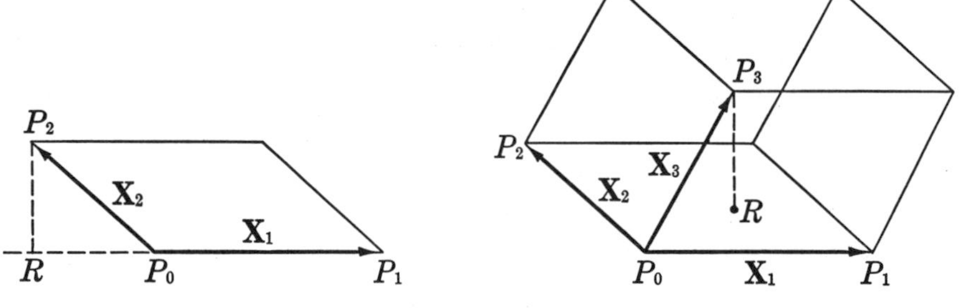

Figure 3.1

the space generated by $\mathbf{X}_1 = \mathbf{P}_1 - \mathbf{P}_0$ and $\mathbf{X}_2 = \mathbf{P}_2 - \mathbf{P}_0$; similarly the vector associated with P_3R is in the space generated by $\mathbf{X}_1$, $\mathbf{X}_2$, and $\mathbf{X}_3 = \mathbf{P}_3 - \mathbf{P}_0$. From our preceding discussion of minimum distances to hyperplanes, we see that the distances P_2R and P_3R are given by $(\mathbf{X}_2, \mathbf{U}_2)$

and $(\mathbf{X}_3, \mathbf{U}_3)$, where $\mathbf{U}_2$ is a unit vector in $L\{\mathbf{X}_1, \mathbf{X}_2\}$ orthogonal to $\mathbf{X}_1$, and $\mathbf{U}_3$ is a unit vector in $L\{\mathbf{X}_1, \mathbf{X}_2, \mathbf{X}_3\}$ orthogonal to $\mathbf{X}_1$ and $\mathbf{X}_2$.

Thus, the volume of the parallelotope defined by P_0, P_1, P_2, P_3 is

$$(\text{Area of parallelogram}) \cdot (\mathbf{X}_3, \mathbf{U}_3).$$

Our inductive step would now be as follows: Assume that the content of the r-dimensional parallelotope defined by the points $P_0, P_1, \cdots, P_r$ has been determined and denote it by $C(P_0, \cdots, P_r)$. Let $\mathbf{U}_{r+1}$ be a unit vector orthogonal to the vectors $\mathbf{X}_1, \mathbf{X}_2, \cdots, \mathbf{X}_r$ and contained in the vector space $L\{\mathbf{X}_1, \mathbf{X}_2, \cdots, \mathbf{X}_{r+1}\}$. Then the $(r + 1)$-dimensional content for the $(r + 1)$-dimensional parallelotope defined by the points $P_0, P_1, \cdots, P_{r+1}$ would be given by

$$C(P_0, P_1, \cdots, P_{r+1}) = C(P_0, P_1, \cdots, P_r) \cdot (\mathbf{X}_{r+1}, \mathbf{U}_{r+1}).$$

This account of a possible definition of volume leaves many questions unanswered. One is, if we rearrange the order in which we selected the vertices in computing the volume, does the same answer result? The definition to be adopted in the next chapter will be less intuitive but more amenable to investigation.

Incidentally, the Gram-Schmidt orthogonalization process (with normalization) provides us automatically with the orthogonal vectors $\mathbf{U}_i$ that are necessary for our computation.

EXERCISES

1. Determine the length of the line segments between the points

(a) $(1, 2, 3, -1), (1, 0, 1, 2)$.
(b) $(1, 0, 1, 2), (3, 4, -1, 1)$.
(c) $(1, 2, 3, -1), (3, 4, -1, 1)$.

2. Determine whether the points $(1, 2, -1, 1, 3)$, $(2, -1, 3, 4, 2)$, and $(0, 5, 3, -2, 4)$ are collinear.

3. Prove that properties (i) and (ii) of a distance function $d(X, Y)$ are valid for Definition 2.1.

4. Show that the triangular equality

$$d(X, Y) + d(Y, Z) = d(X, Z)$$

holds if and only if Y lies on the line segment XZ.

5. Determine the angles between the lines determined by the points $(1, 2, -1, 3)$, $(4, 1, -1, 5)$ and $(2, 3, -1, 1)$, $(4, 1, -2, 3)$.

6. What is the minimum distance from the point $(2, 1, 3, 5, 2)$ to the hyperplane determined by the equation

$$3r_1 + 2r_2 - r_3 + r_5 = 2?$$

7. Find the point of intersection of the line joining $(2, 1, -3, 2)$ and $(4, 0, 1, 3)$ and the hyperplane determined by the equation

$$3r_1 - r_2 + r_3 + 2r_4 = 5.$$

8. Prove that the locus of all points equidistant from two fixed points is a hyperplane.

9. Determine the volume in E_4 of the parallelotope defined by the points $P_0(1, 2, 3, 4)$, $P_1(-1, 2, 1, 3)$, $P_2(1, 0, 2, 1)$, $P_3(3, 1, 2, -1)$, $P_4(0, 1, 0, 2)$.

10. Prove that if the vectors associated with the sides of a parallelotope, $\mathbf{P}_i - \mathbf{P}_0$, are mutually perpendicular, then the content is the product of the lengths of the sides.

CHAPTER 5

Determinants

It often occurs in the discussion of a mathematical topic that a particular solution of a problem is of less importance than the knowledge that a solution does or does not exist. We have a good example of such a situation in the study of linear dependence or independence of vectors. In Chapter 3 we have shown that this question leads to simultaneous linear equations and we have provided a method for obtaining a solution of the equations. However, the more important question is often whether a nonzero solution exists. For this, the method presented was not, perhaps, the most efficient.

In this chapter the concept of nth-order determinants is developed with the thought that its application to other topics in mathematics often provides a compact form for the answer to problems for which one desires only the knowledge of the existence of a solution. This will be particularly true as applied to vector spaces when one is seeking to determine whether or not a set of vectors is linearly independent.

1. Definition of Determinants

In §7 of Chapter 3 we discussed briefly the idea of a linear functional, a mapping from vectors of a vector space to the real numbers. We now wish to look at an extension of this idea. We will consider a particular mapping (function) Δ from ordered sets of n vectors of $V_n(R)$ to the real numbers. There will, of course, be a distinct mapping for each value of n; the context will distinguish the particular case under discussion. The real number assigned to the ordered set of n vectors $\mathbf{X}_1, \mathbf{X}_2, \cdots, \mathbf{X}_n$ will be denoted by the functional notation $\Delta(\mathbf{X}_1, \mathbf{X}_2, \cdots, \mathbf{X}_n)$, and we shall insist that Δ possess the following properties:

(i) Δ is linear in each of its arguments; that is,

$$\begin{aligned}&\Delta(\mathbf{X}_1, \cdots, \mathbf{X}_{i-1}, a\mathbf{X}_i + b\mathbf{Y}_i, \mathbf{X}_{i+1}, \cdots, \mathbf{X}_n)\\ &= a\Delta(\mathbf{X}_1, \cdots, \mathbf{X}_{i-1}, \mathbf{X}_i, \mathbf{X}_{i+1}, \cdots, \mathbf{X}_n) + b\Delta(\mathbf{X}_1, \cdots, \mathbf{X}_{i-1}, \mathbf{Y}_i, \mathbf{X}_{i+1}, \cdots, \mathbf{X}_n),\end{aligned}$$

where we have indicated the linearity of Δ for only the ith argument.

(ii) $\Delta(\mathbf{X}_1, \mathbf{X}_2, \cdots, \mathbf{X}_n) = 0$ if any two of its arguments are equal; that is, when $\mathbf{X}_i = \mathbf{X}_j$ with $i \neq j$.

(iii) $\Delta(\mathbf{X}_1, \mathbf{X}_2, \cdots, \mathbf{X}_n) = 1$ for the particular case $\mathbf{X}_i = \mathbf{E}_i$ $(i = 1, 2, \cdots, n)$; that is, when the ith argument is the natural basis vector of $V_n(R)$ whose ith component is 1 and whose other components are zero.

It is far from obvious that these rules define a unique mapping, Δ, for each n. It may seem quite possible that there might be many such functions or, on the other hand, it may not be clear that there is *any* function with these properties. In the case that $n = 2$ or 3 this last question is readily disposed of. For $n = 2$, let $\mathbf{X} = [x_1, x_2]$, $\mathbf{Y} = [y_1, y_2]$ and define $\Delta(\mathbf{X}, \mathbf{Y}) = x_1y_2 - x_2y_1$. It is a simple matter to check the three basic properties of Δ. Further, the student can readily verify that, in a Cartesian coordinate system, $|\Delta(\mathbf{X}, \mathbf{Y})|$ is the area of the parallelogram defined by segments associated with $\mathbf{X}$ and $\mathbf{Y}$ originating at the origin (Figure 1.1).

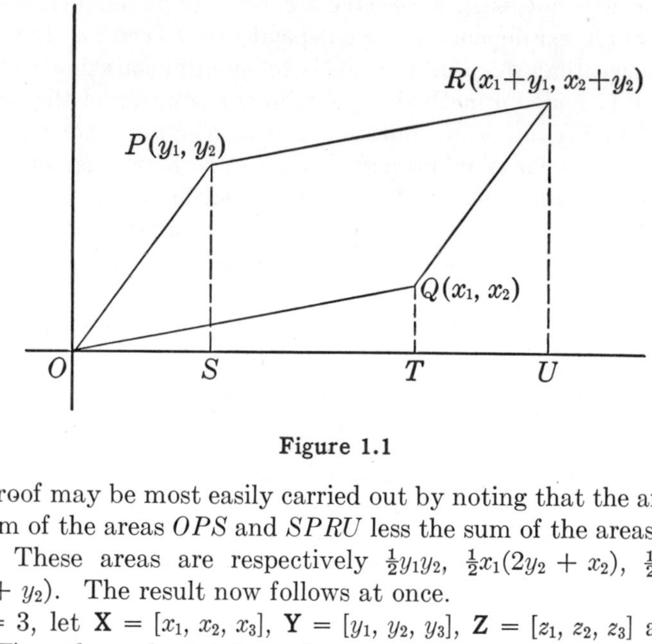

Figure 1.1

The proof may be most easily carried out by noting that the area $OPRQ$ is the sum of the areas OPS and $SPRU$ less the sum of the areas OQT and $TQRU$. These areas are respectively $\frac{1}{2}y_1y_2$, $\frac{1}{2}x_1(2y_2 + x_2)$, $\frac{1}{2}x_1x_2$, and $\frac{1}{2}y_1(2x_2 + y_2)$. The result now follows at once.

If $n = 3$, let $\mathbf{X} = [x_1, x_2, x_3]$, $\mathbf{Y} = [y_1, y_2, y_3]$, $\mathbf{Z} = [z_1, z_2, z_3]$ and define $\Delta(\mathbf{X}, \mathbf{Y}, \mathbf{Z})$ as the scalar triple product

$$([\mathbf{X}, \mathbf{Y}], \mathbf{Z}) = (x_2y_3 - x_3y_2)z_1 + (x_3y_1 - x_1y_3)z_2 + (x_1y_2 - x_2y_1)z_3$$

of §7, Chapter 2. The three properties of Δ again can be easily verified, and the scalar triple product has been related to volume in the section mentioned.

Thus the function Δ appears to exist in the simplest cases and to be related to the content (area, volume) of a geometric figure. We will extend this relation to the content of a parallelotope in E_n when Δ has been proved unique for each value of n. As it happens, for historical reasons, the name *nth-order determinant* rather than *content* has been assigned to the function (mapping) Δ.

In order to obtain more basic information about Δ both toward our immediate goal of establishing its uniqueness and toward eventual applications, we list some immediate consequences of the first three properties:

(iv) If two arguments are permuted, the value of $\Delta(\mathbf{X}_1, \mathbf{X}_2, \cdots, \mathbf{X}_n)$ is changed only in sign. That is,

$$\Delta(\mathbf{X}_1, \cdots, \mathbf{X}_i, \cdots, \mathbf{X}_j, \cdots, \mathbf{X}_n) = -\Delta(\mathbf{X}_1, \cdots, \mathbf{X}_j, \cdots, \mathbf{X}_i, \cdots, \mathbf{X}_n).$$

(v) If the arguments are linearly dependent, $\Delta(\mathbf{X}_1, \mathbf{X}_2, \cdots, \mathbf{X}_n) = 0$.

To prove property (iv), we observe:

$$\begin{aligned}
& \qquad\quad i\text{TH POSITION} \qquad j\text{TH POSITION} \\
0 = {} & \Delta(\mathbf{X}_1, \cdots, \mathbf{X}_i + \mathbf{X}_j, \cdots, \mathbf{X}_i + \mathbf{X}_j, \cdots, \mathbf{X}_n) && \text{[Property (ii)]} \\
= {} & \Delta(\mathbf{X}_1, \cdots, \mathbf{X}_i, \cdots, \mathbf{X}_i + \mathbf{X}_j, \cdots, \mathbf{X}_n) \\
& + \Delta(\mathbf{X}_1, \cdots, \mathbf{X}_j, \cdots, \mathbf{X}_i + \mathbf{X}_j, \cdots, \mathbf{X}_n) && \text{[Property (i)]} \\
= {} & \Delta(\mathbf{X}_1, \cdots, \mathbf{X}_i, \cdots, \mathbf{X}_i, \cdots, \mathbf{X}_n) + \Delta(\mathbf{X}_1, \cdots, \mathbf{X}_i, \cdots, \mathbf{X}_j, \cdots, \mathbf{X}_n) \\
& + \Delta(\mathbf{X}_1, \cdots, \mathbf{X}_j, \cdots, \mathbf{X}_i, \cdots, \mathbf{X}_n) + \Delta(\mathbf{X}_1, \cdots, \mathbf{X}_j, \cdots, \mathbf{X}_j, \cdots, \mathbf{X}_n) \\
& && \text{[Property (i) twice]} \\
= {} & \Delta(\mathbf{X}_1, \cdots, \mathbf{X}_i, \cdots, \mathbf{X}_j, \cdots, \mathbf{X}_n) + \Delta(\mathbf{X}_1, \cdots, \mathbf{X}_j, \cdots, \mathbf{X}_i, \cdots, \mathbf{X}_n). \\
& && \text{[Property (ii) twice]}
\end{aligned}$$

In order to prove property (v), assume that $\mathbf{X}_1, \mathbf{X}_2, \cdots, \mathbf{X}_n$ are linearly dependent. One of them, say $\mathbf{X}_i$, is a linear combination of the preceding vectors (§2, Chapter 3) or

$$\mathbf{X}_i = a_1\mathbf{X}_1 + a_2\mathbf{X}_2 + \cdots + a_{i-1}\mathbf{X}_{i-1}.$$

We substitute this expression for $\mathbf{X}_i$ in Δ to obtain

$$\begin{aligned}
\Delta(\mathbf{X}_1, \cdots, \mathbf{X}_n) = {} & \Delta(\mathbf{X}_1, \cdots, \mathbf{X}_{i-1}, a_1\mathbf{X}_1 + \cdots + a_{i-1}\mathbf{X}_{i-1}, \mathbf{X}_{i+1}, \cdots, \mathbf{X}_n) \\
= {} & a_1\Delta(\mathbf{X}_1, \cdots, \mathbf{X}_{i-1}, \mathbf{X}_1, \cdots, \mathbf{X}_n) \\
& + a_2\Delta(\mathbf{X}_1, \cdots, \mathbf{X}_{i-1}, \mathbf{X}_2, \cdots, \mathbf{X}_n) + \cdots \\
& + a_{i-1}\Delta(\mathbf{X}_1, \cdots, \mathbf{X}_{i-1}, \mathbf{X}_{i-1}, \cdots, \mathbf{X}_n)
\end{aligned}$$

by $i - 2$ applications of property (i). But then all the terms in this expansion of Δ are zero by property (ii).

EXERCISES

1. Show from property (i) that

$$\Delta(\mathbf{X}_1, \cdots, a\mathbf{X}_i, \cdots, \mathbf{X}_n) = a\Delta(\mathbf{X}_1, \cdots, \mathbf{X}_i, \cdots, \mathbf{X}_n).$$

Interpret this result in terms of area for a determinant of order 2.

2. Show that $\Delta(\mathbf{X}_1, \cdots, \mathbf{0}, \cdots, \mathbf{X}_n) = 0$.

2. The Uniqueness of Δ for $n = 2$ and 3

We shall now show that the function Δ, as defined by properties (i), (ii), and (iii) of §1, is unique for the cases $n = 2$ and 3.

Let
$$\mathbf{X}_1 = [x_{11}, x_{12}] = x_{11}\mathbf{E}_1 + x_{12}\mathbf{E}_2,$$
$$\mathbf{X}_2 = [x_{21}, x_{22}] = x_{21}\mathbf{E}_1 + x_{22}\mathbf{E}_2;$$

then
$$\begin{aligned}\Delta(\mathbf{X}_1, \mathbf{X}_2) &= \Delta(x_{11}\mathbf{E}_1 + x_{12}\mathbf{E}_2, x_{21}\mathbf{E}_1 + x_{22}\mathbf{E}_2)\\ &= x_{11}\Delta(\mathbf{E}_1, x_{21}\mathbf{E}_1 + x_{22}\mathbf{E}_2) + x_{12}\Delta(\mathbf{E}_2, x_{21}\mathbf{E}_1 + x_{22}\mathbf{E}_2)\\ &= x_{11}x_{21}\Delta(\mathbf{E}_1, \mathbf{E}_1) + x_{11}x_{22}\Delta(\mathbf{E}_1, \mathbf{E}_2)\\ &\quad + x_{12}x_{21}\Delta(\mathbf{E}_2, \mathbf{E}_1) + x_{12}x_{22}\Delta(\mathbf{E}_2, \mathbf{E}_2),\\ &= x_{11}x_{22}\Delta(\mathbf{E}_1, \mathbf{E}_2) + x_{12}x_{21}\Delta(\mathbf{E}_2, \mathbf{E}_1),\end{aligned}$$

by successive applications of property (i) and two applications of property (ii). We now apply property (iv) and property (iii) to obtain

$$\Delta(\mathbf{X}_1, \mathbf{X}_2) = x_{11}x_{22}\Delta(\mathbf{E}_1, \mathbf{E}_2) - x_{12}x_{21}\Delta(\mathbf{E}_1, \mathbf{E}_2),$$
$$\Delta(\mathbf{X}_1, \mathbf{X}_2) = x_{11}x_{22} - x_{12}x_{21}.$$

We have indicated in §1 that this expression for $\Delta(\mathbf{X}_1, \mathbf{X}_2)$ does actually satisfy properties (i), (ii), and (iii). Hence the determinant function Δ does exist and is unique for $n = 2$.

Now let us turn to the more difficult case of $n = 3$. Let

$$\mathbf{X}_1 = [x_{11}, x_{12}, x_{13}] = x_{11}\mathbf{E}_1 + x_{12}\mathbf{E}_2 + x_{13}\mathbf{E}_3,$$
$$\mathbf{X}_2 = [x_{21}, x_{22}, x_{23}] = x_{21}\mathbf{E}_1 + x_{22}\mathbf{E}_2 + x_{23}\mathbf{E}_3,$$
$$\mathbf{X}_3 = [x_{31}, x_{32}, x_{33}] = x_{31}\mathbf{E}_1 + x_{32}\mathbf{E}_2 + x_{33}\mathbf{E}_3;$$

then

$$\begin{aligned}&\Delta(\mathbf{X}_1, \mathbf{X}_2, \mathbf{X}_3)\\ &\quad = \Delta(x_{11}\mathbf{E}_1 + x_{12}\mathbf{E}_2 + x_{13}\mathbf{E}_3, x_{21}\mathbf{E}_1 + x_{22}\mathbf{E}_2 + x_{23}\mathbf{E}_3, x_{31}\mathbf{E}_1 + x_{32}\mathbf{E}_2 + x_{33}\mathbf{E}_3).\end{aligned}$$

Two applications of property (i) will yield

$$\begin{aligned}\Delta(\mathbf{X}_1, \mathbf{X}_2, \mathbf{X}_3) = &\; x_{11}\Delta(\mathbf{E}_1, x_{21}\mathbf{E}_1 + x_{22}\mathbf{E}_2 + x_{23}\mathbf{E}_3, x_{31}\mathbf{E}_1 + x_{32}\mathbf{E}_2 + x_{33}\mathbf{E}_3)\\ &+ x_{12}\Delta(\mathbf{E}_2, x_{21}\mathbf{E}_1 + x_{22}\mathbf{E}_2 + x_{23}\mathbf{E}_3, x_{31}\mathbf{E}_1 + x_{32}\mathbf{E}_2 + x_{33}\mathbf{E}_3)\\ &+ x_{13}\Delta(\mathbf{E}_3, x_{21}\mathbf{E}_1 + x_{22}\mathbf{E}_2 + x_{23}\mathbf{E}_3, x_{31}\mathbf{E}_1 + x_{32}\mathbf{E}_2 + x_{33}\mathbf{E}_3).\end{aligned}$$

Repeated application of property (i) to bring the real numbers x_{ij} outside of Δ as multipliers will ultimately lead to 27 terms involving, as arguments of Δ, only $\mathbf{E}_1$, $\mathbf{E}_2$, $\mathbf{E}_3$ in some arrangement. Of these 27 terms, the student will find that 21 will have at least two arguments equal, for example, $x_{11}x_{21}x_{32}\Delta(\mathbf{E}_1, \mathbf{E}_1, \mathbf{E}_2)$. The terms having equal arguments will be zero by property (ii). However, six terms will survive:

$$\begin{aligned}\Delta(\mathbf{X}_1, \mathbf{X}_2, \mathbf{X}_3) = &\; x_{11}x_{22}x_{33}\Delta(\mathbf{E}_1, \mathbf{E}_2, \mathbf{E}_3) + x_{11}x_{23}x_{32}\Delta(\mathbf{E}_1, \mathbf{E}_3, \mathbf{E}_2)\\ &+ x_{12}x_{21}x_{33}\Delta(\mathbf{E}_2, \mathbf{E}_1, \mathbf{E}_3) + x_{12}x_{23}x_{31}\Delta(\mathbf{E}_2, \mathbf{E}_3, \mathbf{E}_1)\\ &+ x_{13}x_{21}x_{32}\Delta(\mathbf{E}_3, \mathbf{E}_1, \mathbf{E}_2) + x_{13}x_{22}x_{31}\Delta(\mathbf{E}_3, \mathbf{E}_2, \mathbf{E}_1).\end{aligned}$$

Now $\Delta(\mathbf{E}_1, \mathbf{E}_2, \mathbf{E}_3) = 1$ by property (iii); and by properties (iv) and (iii)

$$\Delta(\mathbf{E}_1, \mathbf{E}_3, \mathbf{E}_2) = -\Delta(\mathbf{E}_1, \mathbf{E}_2, \mathbf{E}_3) = -1.$$

Similarly,

$$\Delta(\mathbf{E}_2, \mathbf{E}_1, \mathbf{E}_3) = -\Delta(\mathbf{E}_1, \mathbf{E}_2, \mathbf{E}_3) = -1,$$
$$\Delta(\mathbf{E}_3, \mathbf{E}_2, \mathbf{E}_1) = -\Delta(\mathbf{E}_1, \mathbf{E}_2, \mathbf{E}_3) = -1.$$

However,

$$\Delta(\mathbf{E}_2, \mathbf{E}_3, \mathbf{E}_1) = -\Delta(\mathbf{E}_1, \mathbf{E}_3, \mathbf{E}_2) = +\Delta(\mathbf{E}_1, \mathbf{E}_2, \mathbf{E}_3) = 1$$

by two applications of property (iv) and then property (iii). Similarly, $\Delta(\mathbf{E}_3, \mathbf{E}_1, \mathbf{E}_2) = 1$. Thus, finally,

$$\Delta(\mathbf{X}_1, \mathbf{X}_2, \mathbf{X}_3) = x_{11}x_{22}x_{33} - x_{11}x_{23}x_{32} - x_{12}x_{21}x_{33} + x_{12}x_{23}x_{31} + x_{13}x_{21}x_{32} - x_{13}x_{22}x_{31}.$$

A simple comparison reveals this result to be equivalent to the determinant of order 3 that we discussed in the last section. Hence Δ is unique for $n = 3$.

It is apparent that this procedure is, in its essentials, perfectly general for a determinant of any order. The basic method proceeds as follows:

Step 1. Beginning with $\Delta(\mathbf{X}_1, \mathbf{X}_2, \cdots, \mathbf{X}_n)$, express each vector $\mathbf{X}_i = [x_{i1}, x_{i2}, \cdots, x_{in}]$ as $\mathbf{X}_i = x_{i1}\mathbf{E}_1 + x_{i2}\mathbf{E}_2 + \cdots + x_{in}\mathbf{E}_n$ for $i = 1, 2, \cdots, n$ and substitute in Δ.

Step 2. Use property (i) repeatedly to expand Δ to a sum of terms that involve only the $\mathbf{E}_i$ in various arrangements as arguments.

Step 3. Use property (ii) to eliminate all terms which have equal arguments. The remaining terms now have each one of the n $\mathbf{E}_j$ as an argument in some arrangement. (Why?) A typical term would now look like

$$x_{1i_1}x_{2i_2} \cdots x_{ni_n}\Delta(\mathbf{E}_{i_1}, \mathbf{E}_{i_2}, \cdots, \mathbf{E}_{i_n}),$$

where $i_1, i_2, \cdots, i_n$ is some arrangement of the numbers $1, 2, \cdots, n$.

Step 4. Now apply property (iv) and, by successive interchanges of arguments, bring $\Delta(\mathbf{E}_{i_1}, \mathbf{E}_{i_2}, \cdots, \mathbf{E}_{i_n})$ to $\pm\,\Delta(\mathbf{E}_1, \mathbf{E}_2, \cdots, \mathbf{E}_n)$, where the $\mathbf{E}_i$ are now in their natural order and the sign will be $+$ or $-$ according as an even or an odd number of changes was used in rearranging the $\mathbf{E}_i$.

Step 5. Apply property (iii) to evaluate the remaining determinants.

The procedures of Steps 1, 2, and 3 should be clear and definite. We can easily see that at the conclusion of Step 2 there are n^n summands. There are n summands in breaking up $\mathbf{X}_1$, and for *each* of these, n more summands are necessary to break up $\mathbf{X}_2$, and so on. At the end of Step 3 there are $n! = n(n-1) \cdots 2 \cdot 1$ summands remaining. (See Exercise 7, §3, and the discussion in §4 of Chapter 1 for this exercise.)

It is only at Step 4 that vagueness occurs. An explicit procedure for making interchanges has not been set out. Indeed, when we try it for $n > 2$, we see that there are usually many different ways in which this can be done. For example, we have shown above that

$$\Delta(\mathbf{E}_2, \mathbf{E}_3, \mathbf{E}_1) = -\Delta(\mathbf{E}_1, \mathbf{E}_3, \mathbf{E}_2) = +\Delta(\mathbf{E}_1, \mathbf{E}_2, \mathbf{E}_3);$$

however,

$$\Delta(\mathbf{E}_2, \mathbf{E}_3, \mathbf{E}_1) = -\Delta(\mathbf{E}_2, \mathbf{E}_1, \mathbf{E}_3) = +\Delta(\mathbf{E}_1, \mathbf{E}_2, \mathbf{E}_3)$$

is another possible method.

There are really two problems for determinants of order n:

(1) It must be shown that the arrangement of the arguments $\mathbf{E}_{i_1}$, $\mathbf{E}_{i_2}, \cdots, \mathbf{E}_{i_n}$ can be brought to the arrangement of arguments $\mathbf{E}_1, \mathbf{E}_2, \cdots, \mathbf{E}_n$ by successive interchanges.

(2) It must be shown that no matter how (1) is accomplished, the same value of the original Δ will arise.

In order to work out these final problems of Step 4, we must consider rearrangements of the integers $1, 2, \cdots, n$ in more detail. This will be done in the following section.

EXERCISES

1. Find $\Delta(\mathbf{X}_1, \mathbf{X}_2)$ in the following cases:

(a) $\mathbf{X}_1 = [1, 2]$, $\mathbf{X}_2 = [3, -1]$.
(b) $\mathbf{X}_1 = [3, 4]$, $\mathbf{X}_2 = [-4, 1]$.
(c) $\mathbf{X}_1 = [a, 0]$, $\mathbf{X}_2 = [0, b]$.

2. Find $\Delta(\mathbf{X}_1, \mathbf{X}_2, \mathbf{X}_3)$ in the following cases:

(a) $\mathbf{X}_1 = [1, 2, 3]$, $\mathbf{X}_2 = [1, 0, -1]$, $\mathbf{X}_3 = [0, 0, 1]$.
(b) $\mathbf{X}_1 = [1, 1, 1]$, $\mathbf{X}_2 = [1, 1, -1]$, $\mathbf{X}_3 = [2, 1, 0]$.
(c) $\mathbf{X}_1 = [2, 1, -1]$, $\mathbf{X}_2 = [1, 2, 2]$, $\mathbf{X}_3 = [0, -1, -3]$.

3. Prove that $\Delta(\mathbf{X}_1 + a\mathbf{X}_2 + b\mathbf{X}_3, \mathbf{X}_2, \mathbf{X}_3) = \Delta(\mathbf{X}_1, \mathbf{X}_2, \mathbf{X}_3)$ where a and b are arbitrary real numbers.

4. What is the determinant function Δ for $V_1(R)$?

5. Prove the statement that a determinant with n vector arguments has $n!$ terms in its expansion.

3. Permutations and the Uniqueness of Δ for Arbitrary n

An arrangement of the integers $1, 2, \cdots, n$ as $i_1, i_2, \cdots, i_n$ (a reordering without duplication or omission) will be called a *permutation* of the integers $1, 2, \cdots, n$. For example, 4312 is a permutation of the integers 1, 2, 3, and 4. Note that a permutation of the integers $1, 2, \cdots, n$ is a one-to-one mapping of the set of integers $1, 2, \cdots, n$ onto itself. The integer i_k is the image of the integer k, and the ordering $i_1, i_2, \cdots, i_n$ is that of the images of $1, 2, \cdots, n$.

The problem raised in the previous section of bringing the arguments $\mathbf{E}_{i_1}, \mathbf{E}_{i_2}, \cdots, \mathbf{E}_{i_n}$ of Δ to the ordering $\mathbf{E}_1, \mathbf{E}_2, \cdots, \mathbf{E}_n$ by successive interchanges of arguments can be looked upon as simply passing from the permutation $i_1, i_2, \cdots, i_n$ to $1, 2, \cdots, n$ by successive interchanges of integers. As an example, consider the permutation 43512. To put this in natural order we may proceed as follows: 43512, 43152, 43125, 34125, 31425, 31245, 13245, 12345. The seven successive permutations follow a pattern: First, the last integer, 5, bypasses those integers which it precedes, then the next-to-the-last integer, 4, is moved into place, and so on. We can count the required number of interchanges of integers at the start. We observe that 5 precedes $\underline{2}$ numbers which it should follow (1 and 2); that 4 precedes $\underline{3}$ numbers which it should follow (3, 1, and 2); and that 3 precedes $\underline{2}$ numbers which it should follow (1 and 2). The total of the underlined numbers is the total number of interchanges of integers required, each interchange corresponding to precisely one correction of an improper order.

It is clear that the method just described may be applied to a permutation $i_1, i_2, \cdots, i_n$ of any size n to bring it into natural order $1, 2, \cdots, n$ by successive interchanges. The improper precedences counted are called *inversions;* the interchanges of two integers are referred to as *transpositions* of the integers. Hence we have:

If a permutation $i_1, i_2, \cdots, i_n$ has K inversions, it may be restored to the natural order $1, 2, \cdots, n$ *by K transpositions.*

Of course the method of restoring a permutation to its natural order by correcting inversions is not the only one available; the following three steps would do for the permutation of the example above: 43512, 13542, 15342, 12345. The method of inversions is useful in that it gives a definite procedure applicable to an arbitrary permutation and, more importantly, gives an easy way of counting the corresponding number of transpositions.

Example 1. The permutation 5671423 has 14 inversions. The restoring steps are: 5617423, 5614723, 5614273, 5614237, 5164237, 5146237, 5142637, 5142367, 1542367, 1452367, 1425367, 1423567, 1243567, 1234567. The student should try other methods aiming at greater economy, counting the steps in each case. Note that, however many steps are required, the number is always even.

The *invariance of parity* of a permutation (the property of a permutation always to require an even number of transpositions to bring it to $1, 2, 3, \cdots, n$ if an even number works at all, or always to require an odd number in the complementary case) must now be proved. The proof unfortunately involves an ingenious trick: a polynomial apparently designed only for this purpose is introduced, used in the proof, and then dismissed. The excuse is that other known proofs are longer and even less satisfactory.

THEOREM 3.1. *If P is the permutation $i_1, i_2, \cdots, i_n$ of the integers $1, 2, \cdots, n$ and if P may be changed to the natural order $1, 2, \cdots, n$ by p and also by q transpositions, then p and q are both even or both odd integers.*

Proof. First we introduce a polynomial $f_I(x_1, x_2, \cdots, x_n)$ in n symbols $x_1, x_2, \cdots, x_n$. Here I stands for the arrangement $1, 2, \cdots, n$, and we define the polynomial as follows:

$$f_I(x_1, x_2, \cdots, x_n) = \prod_{i<j}^{n} (x_i - x_j),$$

where the right-hand side means the product of all possible factors $(x_i - x_j)$ for $i < j$ with i and j restricted to the integers $1, 2, \cdots, n$. In general, f_I has $n(n-1)/2$ factors; for $n = 4$ we have

$$f_I(x_1, x_2, x_3, x_4) = (x_1 - x_2)(x_1 - x_3)(x_1 - x_4)(x_2 - x_3)(x_2 - x_4)(x_3 - x_4).$$

The second step of the proof is to define a similar polynomial $f_P(x_1, x_2, \cdots, x_n)$ for the arbitrary permutation $P = i_1, i_2, \cdots, i_n$ as follows:

$$f_P(x_1, x_2, \cdots, x_n) = \prod_{r<s}^{n} (x_{i_r} - x_{i_s});$$

that is, in each factor of the product, the element of positive sign is the one whose subscript appears first in the permutation P. For example, if P is 2143,

$$f_P(x_1, x_2, x_3, x_4) = (x_2 - x_1)(x_2 - x_4)(x_2 - x_3)(x_1 - x_4)(x_1 - x_3)(x_4 - x_3).$$

Another way of describing $f_P(x_1, x_2, \cdots, x_n)$ is by the equation

$$(3.1) \qquad f_P(x_1, x_2, \cdots, x_n) = f_I(x_{i_1}, x_{i_2}, \cdots, x_{i_n}).$$

That is, f_P is obtained from f_I by replacing x_1 by x_{i_1}, x_2 by x_{i_2}, and so on until x_n is replaced by x_{i_n}. Every factor $(x_r - x_s)$ with $r < s$ in f_I is replaced by $(x_{i_r} - x_{i_s})$. Now, either $(x_{i_r} - x_{i_s})$ of f_P is in f_I or $(x_{i_s} - x_{i_r})$ is a factor of f_I. Since no two factors $(x_i - x_j)$ are identical in f_I and since the number of factors in f_I and f_P is the same, $f_P = \pm f_I$. For the particular permutation 2143, $f_P = f_I$ since precisely two terms $(x_2 - x_1)$ and $(x_4 - x_3)$ of f_P have their subscripts out of the original order in f_I.

Next, we note that, if a set of transpositions will reduce P to the natural order I, precisely the same set will transform f_P to f_I in the sense that, if integers i and j are to be interchanged in the permutations, x_i and x_j are interchanged in the polynomial. For example, 2143 may be reduced to 1234 by interchanging 1 and 2, then 3 and 4: 2143, 1243, 1234. If we interchange x_1 and x_2 in f_P, we have

$$(x_1 - x_2)(x_1 - x_4)(x_1 - x_3)(x_2 - x_4)(x_2 - x_3)(x_4 - x_3);$$

then interchanging x_3 and x_4 we obtain

$$(x_1 - x_2)(x_1 - x_3)(x_1 - x_4)(x_2 - x_3)(x_2 - x_4)(x_3 - x_4) = f_I.$$

Finally, we note what a transposition does to f_P. Suppose x_j and x_i are exchanged, what happens to the factor? There are several possibilities to examine in detail:

1. For those factors which had no x_i or x_j there is no change.
2. If there was a pair $(x_a - x_i)$ and $(x_a - x_j)$, there now is the pair $(x_a - x_j)$ and $(x_a - x_i)$; again no change in the polynomial.
3. Similarly if a pair $(x_i - x_b)$ and $(x_j - x_b)$ existed, no over-all change results.
4. If the pair was $(x_i - x_c)$, $(x_c - x_j)$, the new pair of terms reads $(x_j - x_c)$, $(x_c - x_i)$; two factors have changed sign.
5. Also for a pair of the type $(x_d - x_i)$, $(x_j - x_d)$, the result is two changes of sign.
6. The only factor involving x_i or x_j in which no pairing can be done is that which reads $(x_i - x_j)$ or $(x_j - x_i)$. The transposition changes the sign of this factor. The result can be expressed as follows: If P is transformed into Q by a transposition, $f_P = - f_Q$.

The proof is now essentially complete; for suppose the numbers p and q of the statement of the theorem were of different parity, p odd, say, and q even, then f_P, being reduced by p transpositions to f_I, is $- f_I$, while the same polynomial, being reduced to f_I by q transpositions, is $+ f_I$. Hence $f_P = + f_I = - f_I$, or $2f_I = 0$. But f_I is clearly not identically zero.

The proof just completed answers the questions raised in §2 for the evaluation of $\Delta(\mathbf{X}_1, \mathbf{X}_2, \cdots, \mathbf{X}_n)$. Recall that for $\mathbf{X}_i = [x_{i1}, x_{i2}, \cdots, x_{in}]$ for $i = 1, 2, \cdots, n$, $\Delta(\mathbf{X}_1, \mathbf{X}_2, \cdots, \mathbf{X}_n)$ may be expressed as the sum of $n!$ terms of the form

$$x_{1i_1}x_{2i_2} \cdots x_{ni_n} \Delta(\mathbf{E}_{i_1}, \mathbf{E}_{i_2}, \cdots, \mathbf{E}_{i_n}),$$

where $i_1, i_2, \cdots, i_n$ is a permutation of $1, 2, \cdots, n$.

The number r of transpositions used to bring the order of arguments $\mathbf{E}_{i_1}, \mathbf{E}_{i_2}, \cdots, \mathbf{E}_{i_n}$ to the order $\mathbf{E}_1, \mathbf{E}_2, \cdots, \mathbf{E}_n$ is always odd or always even. If P is the permutation $i_1, i_2, \cdots, i_n$ of $1, 2, \cdots, n$, denote by $S(P)$ the number of inversions in the permutation P. Then r and $S(P)$ are both odd or both even so that

$$\Delta(\mathbf{E}_{i_1}, \mathbf{E}_{i_2}, \cdots, \mathbf{E}_{i_n}) = (-1)^{S(P)} \Delta(\mathbf{E}_1, \mathbf{E}_2, \cdots, \mathbf{E}_n),$$

regardless of the particular transpositions used in rearranging $\mathbf{E}_{i_1}, \mathbf{E}_{i_2}, \cdots, \mathbf{E}_{i_n}$ to the order $\mathbf{E}_1, \mathbf{E}_2, \cdots, \mathbf{E}_n$. Since $\Delta(\mathbf{E}_1, \mathbf{E}_2, \cdots, \mathbf{E}_n) = 1$, the value of $\Delta(\mathbf{E}_{i_1}, \mathbf{E}_{i_2}, \cdots, \mathbf{E}_{i_n})$ is 1 if $i_1, i_2, \cdots, i_n$ results from an even number of transpositions and -1 otherwise. Thus finally,

$$\Delta(\mathbf{X}_1, \mathbf{X}_2, \cdots, \mathbf{X}_n) = \sum (-1)^{S(P)} x_{1i_1}x_{2i_2} \cdots x_{ni_n}, \tag{3.2}$$

where the sign $\sum$ indicates that a sum is to be taken of the $n!$ terms of the type indicated in (3.2) for all permutations P represented by $i_1, i_2, \cdots, i_n$ of the integers $1, 2, \cdots, n$.

At this point we may say that *if* Δ exists it is uniquely defined since the basic properties of Δ have led to the unique answer (3.2). There is still one more thing to be done. We have not proved that this evaluation does indeed produce a mapping with the basic properties (i), (ii), and (iii) prescribed for Δ. This proof is primarily a matter of simple verification and the chief difficulty is the somewhat cumbersome notation. We shall establish property (ii) and leave the others for the student.

Suppose $\mathbf{X}_j = \mathbf{X}_k$ for $j \neq k$ so that $x_{ji} = x_{ki}$ for $i = 1, 2, \cdots, n$. Consider any one of the expressions

$$x_{1i_1}x_{2i_2} \cdots x_{ju} \cdots x_{kv} \cdots x_{ni_n}. \tag{3.3}$$

The sign $(-1)^{S(P)}$ which is assigned to this expression to obtain one of the terms of (3.2) depends upon the parity of the permutation

$$P = i_1, i_2, \cdots, u, \cdots, v, \cdots, i_n$$

as a permutation of $1, 2, \cdots, n$. Whatever this parity may be, the permutation

$$P' = i_1, i_2, \cdots, v, \cdots, u, \cdots, i_n$$

has the opposite parity since P' arises from P by the interchange of u and v. But the parity of P' determines the sign attached to the expression

$$x_{1i_1}x_{2i_2} \cdots x_{jv} \cdots x_{ku} \cdots x_{ni_n} \tag{3.4}$$

to obtain a term of (3.2). As unsigned expressions, (3.3) and (3.4) are equal since $x_{jv} = x_{kv}$, $x_{ju} = x_{ku}$, and the remaining elements are identical. However, as terms in the evaluation of $\Delta(\mathbf{X}_1, \cdots, \mathbf{X}_n)$ by (3.2) they have opposite signs. Thus, for any term in the sum there is a term which is its negative. Hence the sum is zero and $\Delta(\mathbf{X}_1, \cdots, \mathbf{X}_n) = 0$ if $\mathbf{X}_j = \mathbf{X}_k$ with $j \neq k$.

EXERCISES

1. Find the number of inversions in the following permutations. Find an economical way of rearranging each permutation to the natural order. Compare the number of transpositions required by the economical and the inversion method.

(a) 213564	(e) 618975423
(b) 1327465	(f) 956742318
(c) 42137865	(g) 87654321
(d) 4132	(h) 31768425

2. Write f_P for the following permutations, determining whether $f_P = f_I$ or $f_P = -f_I$; also compute the number of inversions in P.

(a) 4132	(c) 4123
(b) 3142	(d) 25413

3. Show that precisely one half of the $n!$ permutations of order n are the result of an even number of transpositions.

4. For a determinant of order 6, what are the signs of the following expressions occurring in the evaluation of Δ?

(a) $x_{15}x_{21}x_{32}x_{43}x_{56}x_{64}$
(b) $x_{31}x_{12}x_{63}x_{24}x_{55}x_{46}$
(c) $x_{12}x_{21}x_{34}x_{43}x_{56}x_{65}$

How many terms in all would there be for a determinant of order 6?

5. Find $\Delta(\mathbf{X}_1, \mathbf{X}_2, \mathbf{X}_3, \mathbf{X}_4)$ if

(a) $\mathbf{X}_1 = [0, 1, 0, 0]$, $\mathbf{X}_2 = [0, 0, 1, 0]$,
$\mathbf{X}_3 = [0, 0, 0, 1]$, $\mathbf{X}_4 = [2, 0, 0, 0]$.

(b) $\mathbf{X}_1 = [0, 1, 0, -1]$, $\mathbf{X}_2 = [1, 0, 1, 0]$,
$\mathbf{X}_3 = [0, -1, 0, 1]$, $\mathbf{X}_4 = [1, 0, -1, 0]$.

6. Prove properties (i) and (iii) for $\Delta(\mathbf{X}_1, \mathbf{X}_2, \cdots, \mathbf{X}_n)$ from the evaluation (3.2) and thus complete the proof of the existence of Δ.

7. Let n vectors be given by

$$\mathbf{X}_i = a_{i1}\mathbf{Y}_1 + \cdots + a_{in}\mathbf{Y}_n \qquad (i = 1, 2, \cdots, n).$$

Show that

$$\Delta(\mathbf{X}_1, \mathbf{X}_2, \cdots, \mathbf{X}_n) = \sum (-1)^{S(P)} a_{1i_1}a_{2i_2} \cdots a_{ni_n} \Delta(\mathbf{Y}_1, \mathbf{Y}_2, \cdots, \mathbf{Y}_n),$$

where again the sum $\sum$ is taken over all permutations P of $1, 2, \cdots, n$ and $S(P)$ is the number of inversions in the permutation P.

Hint. Note that the $\mathbf{E}_i$ played no essential role in the derivation of (3.2) until the very last step, when we set $\Delta(\mathbf{E}_1, \mathbf{E}_2, \cdots, \mathbf{E}_n) = 1$.

8. Using the notation of Exercise 7 and letting $\mathbf{A}_i = [a_{i1}, a_{i2}, \cdots, a_{in}]$ for $i = 1, 2, \cdots, n$, show that

$$\Delta(\mathbf{X}_1, \mathbf{X}_2, \cdots, \mathbf{X}_n) = \Delta(\mathbf{A}_1, \mathbf{A}_2, \cdots, \mathbf{A}_n) \cdot \Delta(\mathbf{Y}_1, \mathbf{Y}_2, \cdots, \mathbf{Y}_n).$$

9. Occasionally there is need for a function called the *permanent* whose definition is the same as (3.2) except that $(-1)^{S(P)}$ does not occur. Which of rules (i)–(v) for a determinant does the permanent satisfy?

4. Classical Notation and Elementary Properties of Determinants

The nth-order determinant Δ was originally defined as a function on ordered sets of n vectors $\{\mathbf{X}_1, \mathbf{X}_2, \cdots, \mathbf{X}_n\}$ of $V_n(R)$. However, because of the theoretically valid method of evaluation

$$\Delta(\mathbf{X}_1, \mathbf{X}_2, \cdots, \mathbf{X}_n) = \sum (-1)^{S(P)} x_{1i_1}x_{2i_2} \cdots x_{ni_n}, \tag{4.1}$$

Δ can be thought of as a function of the individual components of the vectors $\mathbf{X}_i$. We will recognize this fact by adopting an alternate notation for $\Delta(\mathbf{X}_1, \mathbf{X}_2, \cdots, \mathbf{X}_n)$ in the next paragraph.

An older concept of a determinant is that of a value assigned to the n by n array of numbers

$$X = \begin{bmatrix} x_{11} & x_{12} & \cdots & x_{1n} \\ x_{21} & x_{22} & \cdots & x_{2n} \\ \cdot & \cdot & & \cdot \\ \cdot & \cdot & & \cdot \\ \cdot & \cdot & & \cdot \\ x_{n1} & x_{n2} & \cdots & x_{nn} \end{bmatrix} \tag{4.2}$$

by the formula (and with the notation)

$$\det X = \begin{vmatrix} x_{11} & x_{12} & \cdots & x_{1n} \\ x_{21} & x_{22} & \cdots & x_{2n} \\ \cdot & \cdot & & \cdot \\ \cdot & \cdot & & \cdot \\ \cdot & \cdot & & \cdot \\ x_{n1} & x_{n2} & \cdots & x_{nn} \end{vmatrix} = \sum (-1)^{S(P)} x_{1i_1} x_{2i_2} \cdots x_{ni_n}. \tag{4.3}$$

The square array of numbers X of (4.2) is called an $n \times n$ (read "n by n") *matrix*, or a *square matrix of order n*. If the numbers in the ith horizontal row of the matrix X are considered as the components of the vector $\mathbf{X}_i = [x_{i1}, x_{i2}, \cdots, x_{in}]$ for $i = 1, 2, \cdots, n$, a comparison of equations (4.1) and (4.3) reveals that

$$\Delta(\mathbf{X}_1, \mathbf{X}_2, \cdots, \mathbf{X}_n) = \begin{vmatrix} x_{11} & x_{12} & \cdots & x_{1n} \\ x_{21} & x_{22} & \cdots & x_{2n} \\ \cdot & \cdot & & \cdot \\ \cdot & \cdot & & \cdot \\ \cdot & \cdot & & \cdot \\ x_{n1} & x_{n2} & \cdots & x_{nn} \end{vmatrix}. \tag{4.4}$$

The right-hand side of equation (4.4) is commonly called an nth-order determinant although from our definitions it would more properly be described as the *value* of an nth-order determinant. This right-hand side is the classical notation for the value $\Delta(\mathbf{X}_1, \mathbf{X}_2, \cdots, \mathbf{X}_n)$ when Δ is considered as a function of the components of the vectors $\mathbf{X}_i$.

We shall frequently adopt the classical notation for determinants in the remaining sections of this chapter as a means of familiarizing the student with the form he is likely to encounter in most applications. However, we emphasize that this is merely another notation for $\Delta(\mathbf{X}_1, \mathbf{X}_2, \cdots, \mathbf{X}_n)$ or $\det X$.

Example 1. The various notations for determinants can be illustrated for the 2×2 matrix $A = \begin{bmatrix} a_{11} & a_{12} \\ a_{21} & a_{22} \end{bmatrix}$. Thus, there are three different notations for the numerical value, $a_{11}a_{22} - a_{12}a_{21}$:

$$\det A = \Delta([a_{11}, a_{12}], [a_{21}, a_{22}]) = \begin{vmatrix} a_{11} & a_{12} \\ a_{21} & a_{22} \end{vmatrix}.$$

The more symmetrical display of the components of the vectors $\mathbf{X}_i$ of $\Delta(\mathbf{X}_1, \mathbf{X}_2, \cdots, \mathbf{X}_n)$ in the notation

$$\det X = \begin{vmatrix} x_{11} & x_{12} & \cdots & x_{1n} \\ x_{21} & x_{22} & \cdots & x_{2n} \\ \vdots & \vdots & & \vdots \\ x_{n1} & x_{n2} & \cdots & x_{nn} \end{vmatrix}$$

immediately raises the question: If we consider the numbers of the ith vertical column of the matrix X as the components of the vector $\mathbf{X}_i' = [x_{1i}, x_{2i}, \cdots, x_{ni}]$ for $i = 1, 2, \cdots, n$, what is the value of $\Delta(\mathbf{X}_1', \mathbf{X}_2', \cdots, \mathbf{X}_n')$? This question can be phrased more conveniently if we define the *transpose* of the $n \times n$ matrix X of (4.2) as the $n \times n$ matrix

$$X^{\mathsf{T}} = \begin{bmatrix} x_{11} & x_{21} & \cdots & x_{n1} \\ x_{12} & x_{22} & \cdots & x_{n2} \\ \vdots & \vdots & & \vdots \\ x_{1n} & x_{2n} & \cdots & x_{nn} \end{bmatrix},$$

whose rows are the columns of X. Our question now becomes: What is the value of $\det X^{\mathsf{T}}$?

THEOREM 4.1. *If X is an $n \times n$ matrix, $\det X = \det X^{\mathsf{T}}$; or, in the classical notation,*

$$(4.5) \qquad \begin{vmatrix} x_{11} & x_{12} & \cdots & x_{1n} \\ x_{21} & x_{22} & \cdots & x_{2n} \\ \vdots & \vdots & & \vdots \\ x_{n1} & x_{n2} & \cdots & x_{nn} \end{vmatrix} = \begin{vmatrix} x_{11} & x_{21} & \cdots & x_{n1} \\ x_{12} & x_{22} & \cdots & x_{n2} \\ \vdots & \vdots & & \vdots \\ x_{1n} & x_{2n} & \cdots & x_{nn} \end{vmatrix}.$$

Proof. The value of the left determinant of (4.5) is obtained from the formula

$$(4.6) \qquad \sum (-1)^{S(P)} x_{1i_1} x_{2i_2} \cdots x_{ni_n},$$

where the sum is extended over the $n!$ permutations $P = i_1, i_2, \cdots, i_n$ of the integers $1, 2, \cdots, n$. On the other hand, the value of the right determinant of (4.5), because of the interchange of the roles of rows and columns in the matrix X^{T}, is given by

$$\sum (-1)^{S(P)} x_{i_1 1} x_{i_2 2} \cdots x_{i_n n}, \tag{4.7}$$

where the sum is extended over the same $n!$ permutations $P = i_1, i_2, \cdots, i_n$.

Apart from signs, the same terms occur in both (4.6) and (4.7) because each term involves an element x_{ij} from each row and each column. Specifically, let us consider a typical term

$$(-1)^{S(P)} x_{i_1 1} x_{i_2 2} \cdots x_{i_n n} \tag{4.8}$$

of (4.7), where P is the permutation $i_1, i_2, \cdots, i_n$ of $1, 2, \cdots, n$. Now if we rearrange the individual elements of (4.8) until the first subscripts are in ascending order, we get (ignoring the sign)

$$x_{1j_1} x_{2j_2} \cdots x_{nj_n},$$

which occurs in the term

$$(-1)^{S(P')} x_{1j_1} x_{2j_2} \cdots x_{nj_n} \tag{4.9}$$

of (4.6), where P' is the permutation $j_1, j_2, \cdots, j_n$ of $1, 2, \cdots, n$. In order to complete our proof, we must show $(-1)^{S(P)} = (-1)^{S(P')}$.

Let us interrupt the proof to illustrate our reasoning thus far for fourth-order determinants.

Example 2. For the fourth-order determinants

$$\begin{vmatrix} x_{11} & x_{12} & x_{13} & x_{14} \\ x_{21} & x_{22} & x_{23} & x_{24} \\ x_{31} & x_{32} & x_{33} & x_{34} \\ x_{41} & x_{42} & x_{43} & x_{44} \end{vmatrix} \quad \text{and} \quad \begin{vmatrix} x_{11} & x_{21} & x_{31} & x_{41} \\ x_{12} & x_{22} & x_{32} & x_{42} \\ x_{13} & x_{23} & x_{33} & x_{43} \\ x_{14} & x_{24} & x_{34} & x_{44} \end{vmatrix},$$

we have the following unsigned expression occurring in the evaluation of the right determinant:

$$x_{21}x_{42}x_{13}x_{34} \quad \text{(second subscripts in ascending order);}$$

rearranging, this becomes an unsigned expression

$$x_{13}x_{21}x_{34}x_{42} \quad \text{(first subscripts in ascending order)}$$

of the left determinant.

Note that the permutations P and P' of this illustration are 2413 and 3142 respectively. Each has three inversions so that the signs of both these expressions will be minus.

Returning to the general case, we see that our problem is to prove that $S(P)$ and $S(P')$ are both even or both odd. But the permutation P' of the second subscripts is created in the process of reducing the permutation P of the first subscripts to the natural order $1, 2, \cdots, n$. Each inversion corrected in the permutation P creates precisely one for P' since the second subscripts began in natural order and those not accompanying the integer being worked with remain in natural order. As an illustration, in Example 2 we begin with $x_{21}x_{42}x_{13}x_{34}$ and we then successively correct the inversions of 4 in the first subscripts to obtain: $x_{21}x_{13}x_{42}x_{34}$; $x_{21}x_{13}x_{34}x_{42}$. Note that the three leading second subscripts 1, 3, 4 are still in natural order although the second subscripts as a whole have two inversions. Finally we have $x_{13}x_{21}x_{34}x_{42}$.

We see in this way that the number of inversions in P is precisely the same as the number in P'. This is what was needed to prove that $S(P)$ and $S(P')$ are both even or both odd, and the theorem is proved.

We can now state a general principle: *If X is an $n \times n$ matrix, the roles of rows and columns of X may be interchanged in any general prescription or result concerning the evaluation of det X.*

The relation $\Delta(\mathbf{X}_1, \mathbf{X}_2, \cdots, \mathbf{0}, \cdots, \mathbf{X}_n) = 0$ given in Problem 2 of §1 will provide a simple illustration of this principle. We have asked the student to show that

$$\Delta(\mathbf{X}_1, \mathbf{X}_2, \cdots, \mathbf{0}, \cdots, \mathbf{X}_n) = \begin{vmatrix} x_{11} & x_{12} & \cdots & x_{1n} \\ x_{21} & x_{22} & \cdots & x_{2n} \\ \vdots & \vdots & & \vdots \\ 0 & 0 & \cdots & 0 \\ \vdots & \vdots & & \vdots \\ x_{n1} & x_{n2} & \cdots & x_{nn} \end{vmatrix} = 0.$$

Thus, we have the following property for determinants:

If every number of one row of an $n \times n$ matrix X is zero, det $X = 0$.

The principle det X = det X^{T} immediately yields:

If every number of one column of an $n \times n$ matrix X is zero, det $X = 0$.

We shall list other properties of determinants that play a role in a practical evaluation of $\Delta(\mathbf{X}_1, \mathbf{X}_2, \cdots, \mathbf{X}_n)$ if $n > 3$. The classical notation for determinants will be illustrated by giving the row (column) statement for an $n \times n$ matrix X and its consequences for det X. Although explicit proofs will be omitted, we shall give references to the row statements as interpretations of properties of the function Δ. The column statements are obtained from the general principle, $\det X = \det X^T$.

P1. If an $n \times n$ matrix B differs from an $n \times n$ matrix A only in that two rows (columns) of A have been interchanged, then $\det B = -\det A$. Classically,

$$\begin{vmatrix} a_{11} & a_{12} & \cdots & a_{1n} \\ \vdots & \vdots & & \vdots \\ a_{i1} & a_{i2} & \cdots & a_{in} \\ \vdots & \vdots & & \vdots \\ a_{j1} & a_{j2} & \cdots & a_{jn} \\ \vdots & \vdots & & \vdots \\ a_{n1} & a_{n2} & \cdots & a_{nn} \end{vmatrix} = - \begin{vmatrix} a_{11} & a_{12} & \cdots & a_{1n} \\ \vdots & \vdots & & \vdots \\ a_{j1} & a_{j2} & \cdots & a_{jn} \\ \vdots & \vdots & & \vdots \\ a_{i1} & a_{i2} & \cdots & a_{in} \\ \vdots & \vdots & & \vdots \\ a_{n1} & a_{n2} & \cdots & a_{nn} \end{vmatrix}.$$

This is an immediate consequence of property (iv) for Δ,

$$\Delta(\mathbf{A}_1, \cdots, \mathbf{A}_i, \cdots, \mathbf{A}_j, \cdots, \mathbf{A}_n) = -\Delta(\mathbf{A}_1, \cdots, \mathbf{A}_j, \cdots, \mathbf{A}_i, \cdots, \mathbf{A}_n).$$

P2. If an $n \times n$ matrix B differs from an $n \times n$ matrix A only in that all elements of one row (column) of A are multiplied by the same number a, then $\det B = a \det A$. Again classically,

$$\begin{vmatrix} a_{11} & a_{12} & \cdots & a_{1n} \\ \vdots & \vdots & & \vdots \\ aa_{i1} & aa_{i2} & \cdots & aa_{in} \\ \vdots & \vdots & & \vdots \\ a_{n1} & a_{n2} & \cdots & a_{nn} \end{vmatrix} = a \begin{vmatrix} a_{11} & a_{12} & \cdots & a_{1n} \\ \vdots & \vdots & & \vdots \\ a_{i1} & a_{i2} & \cdots & a_{in} \\ \vdots & \vdots & & \vdots \\ a_{n1} & a_{n2} & \cdots & a_{nn} \end{vmatrix},$$

where we have indicated the change to be in the ith row of A.

This property for determinants is a consequence of choosing $b = 0$ in property (i) for Δ.

P3. If two rows (columns) of an $n \times n$ matrix are proportional; that is, considering the ith row of A as a vector $\mathbf{A}_i$, $\mathbf{A}_i = t\mathbf{A}_j$ for $i \neq j$ (or considering the ith column of A as a vector $\mathbf{A}_i'$, $\mathbf{A}_i' = t\mathbf{A}_j'$ for $i \neq j$), then $\det A = 0$.

This is an immediate consequence of property (v) for Δ as the vectors are linearly dependent. Why?

P4. If an $n \times n$ matrix B differs from an $n \times n$ matrix A only in that a multiple of one row of A has been added to another row of A (a multiple of one column of A has been added to another column of A), then $\det B = \det A$.

Classically,

$$\begin{vmatrix} a_{11} & a_{12} & \cdots & a_{1n} \\ \vdots & \vdots & & \vdots \\ a_{i1} & a_{i2} & \cdots & a_{in} \\ \vdots & \vdots & & \vdots \\ a_{j1} & a_{j2} & \cdots & a_{jn} \\ \vdots & \vdots & & \vdots \\ a_{n1} & a_{n2} & \cdots & a_{nn} \end{vmatrix} = \begin{vmatrix} a_{11} & a_{12} & \cdots & a_{1n} \\ \vdots & \vdots & & \vdots \\ a_{i1} & a_{i2} & \cdots & a_{in} \\ \vdots & \vdots & & \vdots \\ a_{j1} + ca_{i1} & a_{j2} + ca_{i2} & \cdots & a_{jn} + ca_{in} \\ \vdots & \vdots & & \vdots \\ a_{n1} & a_{n2} & \cdots & a_{nn} \end{vmatrix}.$$

This property follows from property (i) for Δ with $a = c$, $b = 1$.

EXERCISES

1. Determine the value of det A and det A^{T} for the following matrices A by means of (4.3) and verify Theorem 4.1 for these special cases:

(a) $A = \begin{bmatrix} 1 & 2 \\ -1 & 1 \end{bmatrix}$ (b) $A = \begin{bmatrix} 3 & 1 \\ 2 & 0 \end{bmatrix}$

(c) $A = \begin{bmatrix} 1 & 2 & -1 \\ 3 & 1 & 0 \\ 0 & 2 & 4 \end{bmatrix}$ (d) $A = \begin{bmatrix} 2 & 1 & -1 \\ 3 & 1 & 4 \\ 1 & 0 & 2 \end{bmatrix}$

2. Determine the property of determinants that implies each of the following results:

(a) $\begin{vmatrix} 1 & 2 \\ 2 & 1 \end{vmatrix} = - \begin{vmatrix} 2 & 1 \\ 1 & 2 \end{vmatrix}$ (b) $\begin{vmatrix} 1 & 2 & 3 \\ 1 & 0 & 1 \\ 2 & 4 & 6 \end{vmatrix} = 0$

(c) $\begin{vmatrix} 4 & 1 & -1 \\ 2 & 1 & 3 \\ 1 & 2 & 1 \end{vmatrix} = \begin{vmatrix} 4 & 2 & 1 \\ 1 & 1 & 2 \\ -1 & 3 & 1 \end{vmatrix}$ (d) $\begin{vmatrix} 1 & 2 & 1 \\ -1 & 1 & 0 \\ 2 & 1 & 3 \end{vmatrix} = \begin{vmatrix} 1 & 2 & 1 \\ 0 & 3 & 1 \\ 2 & 1 & 3 \end{vmatrix}$

(e) $\begin{vmatrix} 1 & 3 & 2 \\ 2 & 4 & 4 \\ 1 & 5 & 2 \end{vmatrix} = 0$

3. If A is a $n \times n$ matrix of odd order such that $a_{ij} = -a_{ji}$, show that det $A = 0$.

4. By repeated application of property P4, show that the following determinants vanish:

(a) $\begin{vmatrix} 1 & 2 & 5 \\ 2 & 3 & -1 \\ 1 & 3 & 16 \end{vmatrix}$ (b) $\begin{vmatrix} a+d & 3a & b+2a & b+d \\ 2b & b+d & c-b & c-d \\ a+c & c-2d & d & a+3d \\ b-d & c-d & a+c & a+b \end{vmatrix}$

5. Minors, Cofactors, and the Evaluation of Determinants

We shall now consider an idea which stems from the classical notation for det X and is of both practical and theoretical importance in determining the value of $\Delta(\mathbf{X}_1, \mathbf{X}_2, \cdots, \mathbf{X}_n)$. Let us consider an $n \times n$ matrix

$$X = \begin{bmatrix} x_{11} & x_{12} & \cdots & x_{1n} \\ x_{21} & x_{22} & \cdots & x_{2n} \\ \cdot & \cdot & & \cdot \\ \cdot & \cdot & & \cdot \\ \cdot & \cdot & & \cdot \\ x_{n1} & x_{n2} & \cdots & x_{nn} \end{bmatrix}.$$

If k rows and k columns are deleted from X, the smaller submatrix remaining will be denoted by $X(i_1, i_2, \cdots, i_k; j_1, j_2, \cdots, j_k)$, where the integers $i_1, i_2, \cdots, i_k$ indicate the rows deleted and the integers $j_1, j_2, \cdots, j_k$ indicate the columns deleted. Of particular interest will be the submatrices $X(i; j)$ obtained by deleting the row and column of X occupied by the element x_{ij}. We will call det $X(i; j)$ the *minor of the element* x_{ij} in X. The *cofactor of* x_{ij}, denoted by C_{ij}, is defined by the equation

$$C_{ij} = (-1)^{i+j} \det X(i; j). \tag{5.1}$$

Example 1. If $X = \begin{bmatrix} 0 & -3 & 2 & 1 \\ 2 & 2 & -2 & 1 \\ 3 & 1 & -1 & 2 \\ 1 & 3 & 1 & -2 \end{bmatrix}$,

the minor of the element in the first row, first column is

$$\det X(1; 1) = \begin{vmatrix} 2 & -2 & 1 \\ 1 & -1 & 2 \\ 3 & 1 & -2 \end{vmatrix},$$

and the cofactor of the same element is

$$C_{11} = (-1)^{1+1} \begin{vmatrix} 2 & -2 & 1 \\ 1 & -1 & 2 \\ 3 & 1 & -2 \end{vmatrix}.$$

Similarly, the minor of the element in the second row, third column is

$$\det X(2; 3) = \begin{vmatrix} 0 & -3 & 1 \\ 3 & 1 & 2 \\ 1 & 3 & -2 \end{vmatrix} = -16,$$

and the cofactor of the same element is

$$C_{23} = (-1)^{2+3} \begin{vmatrix} 0 & -3 & 1 \\ 3 & 1 & 2 \\ 1 & 3 & -2 \end{vmatrix} = 16.$$

The concepts of minors and cofactors of order $(n - k)$ in X can be defined for the submatrices $X(i_1, i_2, \cdots, i_k; j_1, j_2, \cdots, j_k)$. However, we will confine our attention to the $(n - 1)$-order cofactors of elements x_{ij} of X and will illustrate their use in the following theorem. The method of evaluating $\Delta(\mathbf{X}_1, \mathbf{X}_2, \cdots, \mathbf{X}_n)$ furnished in this theorem is commonly called *the expansion of a determinant by means of minors.*

THEOREM 5.1.

$$\Delta(\mathbf{X}_1, \mathbf{X}_2, \cdots, \mathbf{X}_n) = \begin{vmatrix} x_{11} & x_{12} & \cdots & x_{1n} \\ x_{21} & x_{22} & \cdots & x_{2n} \\ \cdot & \cdot & & \cdot \\ \cdot & \cdot & & \cdot \\ \cdot & \cdot & & \cdot \\ x_{n1} & x_{n2} & \cdots & x_{nn} \end{vmatrix} = x_{i1}C_{i1} + x_{i2}C_{i2} + \cdots + x_{in}C_{in},$$

where i may have any value $1, 2, \cdots, n$.

Proof. We shall consider first the case in which $i = 1$ in the statement of the theorem; in which case, we are *expanding* det X *by means of minors of the first row.*

Let $\mathbf{X}_1 = [x_{11}, x_{12}, \cdots, x_{1n}] = x_{11}\mathbf{E}_1 + x_{12}\mathbf{E}_2 + \cdots + x_{1n}\mathbf{E}_n$, where the set of vectors $\{\mathbf{E}_i\}$ is the natural basis of $V_n(R)$. Then

$$\begin{aligned} &\Delta(x_{11}\mathbf{E}_1 + x_{12}\mathbf{E}_2 + \cdots + x_{1n}\mathbf{E}_n, \mathbf{X}_2, \cdots, \mathbf{X}_n) \\ &\qquad = x_{11}\,\Delta(\mathbf{E}_1, \mathbf{X}_2, \cdots, \mathbf{X}_n) + \cdots + x_{1n}\,\Delta(\mathbf{E}_n, \mathbf{X}_2, \cdots, \mathbf{X}_n), \end{aligned} \tag{5.2}$$

by repeated application of the defining property (i) for the function Δ. It should be clear from the right-hand side of (5.2) that our proof will be complete once we have shown

$$\Delta(\mathbf{E}_j, \mathbf{X}_2, \cdots, \mathbf{X}_n) = C_{1j} \qquad \text{for } j = 1, 2, \cdots, n.$$

Let us show that $\Delta(\mathbf{E}_1, \mathbf{X}_2, \cdots, \mathbf{X}_n) = C_{11}$. In

$$\Delta(\mathbf{E}_1, \mathbf{X}_2, \cdots, \mathbf{X}_n) = \sum (-1)^{S(P)}\, x_{1i_1}x_{2i_2} \cdots x_{ni_n}, \tag{5.3}$$

$x_{1k} = 0$ if $k \neq 1$ as these components of $\mathbf{E}_1$ are zero. Hence, the only terms in the evaluation (5.3) that are not trivially zero are those of the form

$$(-1)^{S(P)}\, x_{11}x_{2i_2}x_{3i_3} \cdots x_{ni_n}.$$

Since P leaves 1 fixed, the number of inversions in P is the same as the number of inversions in the permutation $P^* = i_2, i_3, \cdots, i_n$ of the integers $2, 3, \cdots, n$. Therefore, since $x_{11} = 1$ for $\mathbf{E}_1$,

$$\Delta(\mathbf{E}_1, \mathbf{X}_2, \cdots, \mathbf{X}_n) = \sum (-1)^{S(P^*)}\, x_{2i_2}x_{3i_3} \cdots x_{ni_n}, \tag{5.4}$$

where the summation extends over all permutations P^* of the integers 2, 3, $\cdots$, n. But the sum in (5.4) is precisely the evaluation of

$$\begin{vmatrix} x_{22} & x_{23} & \cdots & x_{2n} \\ x_{32} & x_{33} & \cdots & x_{3n} \\ \vdots & \vdots & & \vdots \\ x_{n2} & x_{n3} & \cdots & x_{nn} \end{vmatrix} = (-1)^{1+1} \det X(1;\ 1) = C_{11}.$$

Next we extend this result to show that $\Delta(\mathbf{E}_j, \mathbf{X}_2, \cdots, \mathbf{X}_n) = C_{1j}$. Here we have

$$\Delta(\mathbf{E}_j, \mathbf{X}_2, \cdots, \mathbf{X}_n) = \begin{vmatrix} 0 & \cdots & 1 & \cdots & 0 \\ x_{21} & \cdots & x_{2j} & \cdots & x_{2n} \\ x_{31} & \cdots & x_{3j} & \cdots & x_{3n} \\ \vdots & & \vdots & & \vdots \\ x_{n1} & \cdots & x_{nj} & \cdots & x_{nn} \end{vmatrix}.$$

We exchange the jth column with the $(j-1)$st, then the new $(j-1)$st with the $(j-2)$d, and continue until the original jth column is in the first column and the order of the remaining columns is not disturbed. There have been $(j-1)$ interchanges of columns, and we apply property P1 of the preceding section to obtain

(5.5)

$$\Delta(\mathbf{E}_j, \mathbf{X}_2, \cdots, \mathbf{X}_n) = (-1)^{j-1} \begin{vmatrix} 1 & 0 & \cdots & 0 & 0 & \cdots & 0 \\ x_{2j} & x_{21} & \cdots & x_{2,\,j-1} & x_{2,\,j+1} & \cdots & x_{2n} \\ x_{3j} & x_{31} & \cdots & x_{3,\,j-1} & x_{3,\,j+1} & \cdots & x_{3n} \\ \vdots & \vdots & & \vdots & \vdots & & \vdots \\ x_{nj} & x_{n1} & \cdots & x_{n,\,j-1} & x_{n,\,j+1} & \cdots & x_{nn} \end{vmatrix}.$$

Note that the $(n-1) \times (n-1)$ array of numbers in the lower right-hand corner of (5.5) is $X(1;\ j)$. An application of the results for

$$\Delta(\mathbf{E}_1, \mathbf{X}_2, \cdots, \mathbf{X}_n)$$

of the first case considered gives

$$\Delta(\mathbf{E}_j, \mathbf{X}_2, \cdots, \mathbf{X}_n) = (-1)^{j-1}(-1)^{1+1} \det X(1;\ j) = C_{1j}.$$

Our proof of the theorem for $i = 1$ is now complete.

The proof of the theorem for an arbitrary i, that is, the expansion of det X by means of minors of the ith row

$$\Delta(\mathbf{X}_1, \cdots, \mathbf{X}_n) = x_{i1}C_{i1} + x_{i2}C_{i2} + \cdots + x_{in}C_{in},$$

now follows simply. We move the ith vector $\mathbf{X}_i$ to the first position by $i - 1$ interchanges without affecting the relative order of the remaining vectors. Thus,

$$\Delta(\mathbf{X}_1, \cdots, \mathbf{X}_i, \cdots, \mathbf{X}_n) = (-1)^{i-1}\,\Delta(\mathbf{X}_i, \mathbf{X}_1, \cdots, \mathbf{X}_{i-1}, \mathbf{X}_{i+1}, \cdots, \mathbf{X}_n),$$

and applying the theorem for $i = 1$,

$$\begin{aligned}\Delta(\mathbf{X}_1, \cdots, \mathbf{X}_n) &= (-1)^{i-1}\sum_{k=1}^{n}(-1)^{1+k}\, x_{ik} \det X(i; k)\\ &= \sum_{k=1}^{n}(-1)^{i+k}\, x_{ik} \det X(i; k)\\ &= x_{i1}C_{i1} + x_{i2}C_{i2} + \cdots + x_{in}C_{in}.\end{aligned}$$

Example 2. We have the following row expansion by minors for

$$\begin{aligned}\begin{vmatrix} 1 & 2 & -1 \\ 0 & 1 & 3 \\ 1 & 2 & 4 \end{vmatrix} &= 1\begin{vmatrix} 1 & 3 \\ 2 & 4 \end{vmatrix} - 2\begin{vmatrix} 0 & 3 \\ 1 & 4 \end{vmatrix} - 1\begin{vmatrix} 0 & 1 \\ 1 & 2 \end{vmatrix}\\ &= 1(-2) - 2(-3) - 1(-1) = 5,\end{aligned}$$

or

$$\begin{aligned}&= 0\begin{vmatrix} 2 & -1 \\ 2 & 4 \end{vmatrix} + 1\begin{vmatrix} 1 & -1 \\ 1 & 4 \end{vmatrix} - 3\begin{vmatrix} 1 & 2 \\ 1 & 2 \end{vmatrix}\\ &= 0(10) + 1(5) - 3(0) = 5,\end{aligned}$$

or

$$\begin{aligned}&= 1\begin{vmatrix} 2 & -1 \\ 1 & 3 \end{vmatrix} - 2\begin{vmatrix} 1 & -1 \\ 0 & 3 \end{vmatrix} + 4\begin{vmatrix} 1 & 2 \\ 0 & 1 \end{vmatrix}\\ &= 1(7) - 2(3) + 4(1) = 5.\end{aligned}$$

Theorem 5.1 provides a method of evaluation for $\Delta(\mathbf{X}_1, \cdots, \mathbf{X}_n)$ by reducing the order of the determinant (while increasing the number of necessary evaluations). It should be pointed out that the property det X = det X^{T} provides an immediate proof for the expansion of det X by means of minors of a column of X,

$$\det X = x_{1i}C_{1i} + x_{2i}C_{2i} + \cdots + x_{ni}C_{ni}$$

for each value of $i = 1, 2, \cdots, n$.

The properties of determinants given in the preceding section, together with Theorem 5.1, furnish a more practical method of evaluating $\Delta(\mathbf{X}_1, \mathbf{X}_2, \cdots, \mathbf{X}_n)$. The process is analogous to the process of elimination used to solve linear equations in Chapters 2 and 3. We shall illustrate with an example.

Example 3. Let us evaluate the determinant

$$\det D = \begin{vmatrix} 0 & -3 & 2 & 1 \\ 2 & 2 & -2 & 1 \\ 3 & 1 & -1 & 2 \\ 1 & 3 & 1 & -2 \end{vmatrix}.$$

Now, interchanging the first and last columns of D, we obtain by property P1 of §4 (for columns)

$$\det D = -\det D_1 = -\begin{vmatrix} 1 & -3 & 2 & 0 \\ 1 & 2 & -2 & 2 \\ 2 & 1 & -1 & 3 \\ -2 & 3 & 1 & 1 \end{vmatrix}.$$

We next add (-1) times the first row of D_1 to the second row (both rows being considered as vectors of $V_4(R)$), (-2) times the first row to the third, and $(+2)$ times the first row to the fourth to obtain

$$\det D = -\det D_2 = -\begin{vmatrix} 1 & -3 & 2 & 0 \\ 0 & 5 & -4 & 2 \\ 0 & 7 & -5 & 3 \\ 0 & -3 & 5 & 1 \end{vmatrix}.$$

Now, adding $-\frac{7}{5}$ times the second row of D_2 to the third, and $\frac{3}{5}$ times the second row to the fourth, we have

$$\det D = -\det D_3 = -\begin{vmatrix} 1 & -3 & 2 & 0 \\ 0 & 5 & -4 & 2 \\ 0 & 0 & \frac{3}{5} & \frac{1}{5} \\ 0 & 0 & \frac{13}{5} & \frac{11}{5} \end{vmatrix}.$$

Finally, multiplying the third row of D_3 by $-\frac{13}{3}$ and adding to the fourth row, we obtain

$$\det D = -\det D_4 = -\begin{vmatrix} 1 & -3 & 2 & 0 \\ 0 & 5 & -4 & 2 \\ 0 & 0 & \frac{3}{5} & \frac{1}{5} \\ 0 & 0 & 0 & \frac{4}{3} \end{vmatrix}.$$

We now expand the last determinant by minors of the first column to obtain

$$\det D = -1 \cdot \begin{vmatrix} 5 & -4 & 2 \\ 0 & \frac{3}{5} & \frac{1}{5} \\ 0 & 0 & \frac{4}{3} \end{vmatrix}.$$

Repeating the expansion, we obtain in turn

$$\det D = -(1)(5)\begin{vmatrix} \frac{3}{5} & \frac{1}{5} \\ 0 & \frac{4}{3} \end{vmatrix} = -(1)(5)(\tfrac{3}{5})(\tfrac{4}{3}) = -4.$$

Note that the value of det D_4 is merely the product of the elements whose position subscripts in D_4 are jj for $j = 1, 2, 3, 4$.

The previous example illustrates the following theorem, whose proof we leave for the student:

THEOREM 5.2. *If X is an $n \times n$ matrix whose elements x_{ij} have the property $x_{ij} = 0$ for $i > j$, then* $\det X = x_{11}x_{22}x_{33} \cdots x_{nn}$.

A judicious combination of row modifications or column modifications and expansion by minors often facilitates the evaluation of det X.

EXERCISES

1. Let A be the 3×3 matrix $\begin{bmatrix} 1 & 2 & 3 \\ 4 & 5 & 6 \\ 7 & 8 & 9 \end{bmatrix}$. For the matrix A determine the following:

(a) The minors of the elements 5; 6; 7.
(b) The cofactors of the elements 5; 6; 7.

2. Evaluate the following determinants by the most economical procedure possible:

$$\text{(a)} \begin{vmatrix} 1 & 3 & 1 \\ 2 & 1 & -1 \\ 1 & 0 & 1 \end{vmatrix} \quad \text{(b)} \begin{vmatrix} 1 & -1 & 1 & -1 \\ 2 & 0 & 1 & 1 \\ 1 & -1 & 0 & 0 \\ 1 & 1 & 1 & 1 \end{vmatrix} \quad \text{(c)} \begin{vmatrix} 1 & 2 & 3 & -1 & 2 \\ 0 & 1 & 2 & 4 & 1 \\ 1 & 0 & -1 & 3 & -2 \\ 2 & 0 & 1 & 0 & 1 \\ 1 & 1 & -1 & 2 & 2 \end{vmatrix}$$

3. What is the value of these determinants?

$$\text{(a)} \begin{vmatrix} a_{11} & 0 & & \cdots & 0 \\ a_{21} & a_{22} & 0 & \cdots & 0 \\ \vdots & \vdots & & & \vdots \\ & & & & 0 \\ a_{n1} & a_{n2} & & \cdots & a_{nn} \end{vmatrix} \qquad \text{(b)} \begin{vmatrix} 0 & \cdots & & 0 & a_{1n} \\ 0 & \cdots & 0 & a_{2,n-1} & a_{2n} \\ \vdots & & & \vdots & \vdots \\ 0 & & & . & \\ a_{n1} & \cdots & & a_{n,n-1} & a_{nn} \end{vmatrix}$$

4. Show that

$$-\begin{vmatrix} 1 & x_1 & x_1^2 \\ 1 & x_2 & x_2^2 \\ 1 & x_3 & x_3^2 \end{vmatrix} = (x_1 - x_2)(x_1 - x_3)(x_2 - x_3) = f_I(x_1, x_2, x_3),$$

where $f_I(x_1, x_2, x_3)$ is the function introduced in the proof of Theorem 3.1.

5. Generalize Exercise 4 to obtain an expression for $f_I(x_1, x_2, \cdots, x_n)$ as a determinant.

6. Let $\mathbf{X}_0 = [1, 2, 3]$, $\mathbf{X}_1 = [-1, 0, -1]$, $\mathbf{X}_2 = [4, 1, 5]$, and $\mathbf{X}_3 = [2, 0, -1]$. Show that

$$\Delta(\mathbf{X}_1 - \mathbf{X}_0, \mathbf{X}_2 - \mathbf{X}_0, \mathbf{X}_3 - \mathbf{X}_0) = -\begin{vmatrix} 1 & 2 & 3 & 1 \\ -1 & 0 & -1 & 1 \\ 4 & 1 & 5 & 1 \\ 2 & 0 & -1 & 1 \end{vmatrix}.$$

7. Let $\{\mathbf{X}_i = [x_{i1}, x_{i2}, \cdots, x_{in}]\}$ for $i = 0, 1, \cdots, n$ be $n + 1$ vectors from $V_n(R)$. Show that

$$\Delta(\mathbf{X}_1 - \mathbf{X}_0, \mathbf{X}_2 - \mathbf{X}_0, \cdots, \mathbf{X}_n - \mathbf{X}_0) = (-1)^n \begin{vmatrix} x_{01} & x_{02} & \cdots & x_{0n} & 1 \\ x_{11} & x_{12} & \cdots & x_{1n} & 1 \\ \vdots & \vdots & & \vdots & \vdots \\ x_{n1} & x_{n2} & \cdots & x_{nn} & 1 \end{vmatrix}.$$

8. Let the cofactors of x_{ij} in the $n \times n$ matrix X be denoted by C_{ij}. Show that $C_{ij} = \Delta(\mathbf{X}_1, \mathbf{X}_2, \cdots, \mathbf{X}_{i-1}, \mathbf{E}_j, \mathbf{X}_{i+1}, \cdots, \mathbf{X}_n)$, where the vectors $\mathbf{X}_i$ are the rows of the matrix X.

9. Using the notation of Exercise 8, show that

$$x_{j1}C_{i1} + x_{j2}C_{i2} + \cdots + x_{jn}C_{in} = 0 \qquad \text{for } j \neq i.$$

Hint: Write $x_{jk}C_{ik} = x_{jk}\,\Delta(\mathbf{X}_1, \mathbf{X}_2, \cdots, \mathbf{X}_{i-1}, \mathbf{E}_k, \mathbf{X}_{i+1}, \cdots, \mathbf{X}_n)$ and sum using the linearity properties of Δ. Note now that two arguments of Δ are identical.

6. Applications of Determinants

We now turn to some of the applications of determinants that were indicated in the introduction to this chapter.

Dependence of vectors. We saw in property (v) of §1 that if the vectors $\mathbf{A}_1, \mathbf{A}_2, \cdots, \mathbf{A}_n$ were linearly dependent, then $\Delta(\mathbf{A}_1, \mathbf{A}_2, \cdots, \mathbf{A}_n) = 0$. Now we prove the converse.

THEOREM 6.1. Let $\mathbf{A}_1 = [a_{11}, a_{12}, \cdots, a_{1n}], \cdots, \mathbf{A}_n = [a_{n1}, a_{n2}, \cdots, a_{nn}]$ *be n vectors of* $V_n(R)$. *If* $\Delta(\mathbf{A}_1, \mathbf{A}_2, \cdots, \mathbf{A}_n) = 0$, *the vectors* $\mathbf{A}_1, \mathbf{A}_2, \cdots, \mathbf{A}_n$ *are linearly dependent.*

Proof. We seek real numbers $c_1, c_2, \cdots, c_n$ such that

$$c_1\mathbf{A}_1 + c_2\mathbf{A}_2 + \cdots + c_n\mathbf{A}_n = \mathbf{0}$$

and not all the c_i are zero. This is equivalent, as we have seen in Chapter 3, §3, to finding a nonzero solution to the system of equations

$$
(6.1)\qquad
\begin{aligned}
a_{11}c_1 + a_{21}c_2 + \cdots + a_{n1}c_n &= 0 \\
a_{12}c_1 + a_{22}c_2 + \cdots + a_{n2}c_n &= 0 \\
\cdots\cdots\cdots\cdots & \\
a_{1n}c_1 + a_{2n}c_2 + \cdots + a_{nn}c_n &= 0.
\end{aligned}
$$

Let the largest minor of the $n \times n$ matrix

$$
A = \begin{bmatrix} a_{11} & a_{12} & \cdots & a_{1n} \\ a_{21} & a_{22} & \cdots & a_{2n} \\ \vdots & \vdots & & \vdots \\ a_{n1} & a_{n2} & \cdots & a_{nn} \end{bmatrix}
$$

which is not zero be of order k. (If all elements of the matrix A are zero, there is no problem since all the $\mathbf{A}_i$ are zero.) First let us assume that such a nonzero minor occurs in rows 2 through $k + 1$ and columns 1 through k. Then all determinants of the form

$$
(6.2)\qquad
\begin{vmatrix} a_{11} & a_{12} & \cdots & a_{1k} & a_{1i} \\ a_{21} & a_{22} & \cdots & a_{2k} & a_{2i} \\ \vdots & \vdots & & \vdots & \vdots \\ a_{k+1,\,1} & a_{k+1,\,2} & \cdots & a_{k+1,\,k} & a_{k+1,\,i} \end{vmatrix}
$$

for $i = 1, 2, \cdots, n$ will have the value zero, either because two columns are the same ($i = 1, 2, \cdots, k$) or because they are minors of order $k + 1$ of A ($i = k + 1, \cdots, n$).

If these determinants of (6.2) are expanded by means of minors of the last column, we have:

$$
a_{1i}c_1 + a_{2i}c_2 + \cdots + a_{k+1,\,i}c_{k+1} = 0,
$$

where we have denoted the cofactor of a_{ji} by c_j. Note that $c_1 \neq 0$. Then:

$$
a_{1i}c_1 + a_{2i}c_2 + \cdots + a_{k+1,\,i}c_{k+1} + a_{k+2,\,i}\cdot 0 + \cdots + a_{ni}\cdot 0 = 0
$$

for each $i = 1, 2, \cdots, n$. This gives a solution of the original equations (6.1) in which $c_{k+2}, \cdots, c_n = 0$ but $c_1 \neq 0$.

If the minor of order k which was used above is zero, it is necessary to take a minor of A which is not zero and adjoin the corresponding elements of a (fixed) other row and of all columns to get similar minors of order $k + 1$ as in (6.2). The essential feature is the same in any case: a solution is obtained to the original equations (6.1) with at least one nonzero c_i. The student may be interested in trying the general proof either by devising a notation to handle an arbitrary minor or by rearranging terms to move the nonzero minor into a desirable position.

Property (v) of § 1 and Theorem 6.1 now yield the following result:

Vectors $\mathbf{A}_1 = [a_{11}, a_{12}, \cdots, a_{1n}], \cdots, \mathbf{A}_n = [a_{n1}, a_{n2}, \cdots, a_{nn}]$ *are linearly dependent if and only if*

$$\Delta(\mathbf{A}_1, \mathbf{A}_2, \cdots, \mathbf{A}_n) = \begin{vmatrix} a_{11} & a_{12} & \cdots & a_{1n} \\ a_{21} & a_{22} & \cdots & a_{2n} \\ \cdot & \cdot & & \cdot \\ \cdot & \cdot & & \cdot \\ \cdot & \cdot & & \cdot \\ a_{n1} & a_{n2} & \cdots & a_{nn} \end{vmatrix} = 0.$$

Example 1. To determine whether the vectors $[1, 0, 2, -1]$, $[3, 1, 1, -2]$, $[-2, 1, -1, 3]$, and $[2, 2, 2, 0]$ are linearly dependent, we compute

$$\begin{vmatrix} 1 & 0 & 2 & -1 \\ 3 & 1 & 1 & -2 \\ -2 & 1 & -1 & 3 \\ 2 & 2 & 2 & 0 \end{vmatrix} = \begin{vmatrix} 1 & 0 & 2 & -1 \\ 0 & 1 & -5 & 1 \\ 0 & 1 & 3 & 1 \\ 0 & 2 & -2 & 2 \end{vmatrix} = \begin{vmatrix} 1 & 0 & 2 & -1 \\ 0 & 1 & -5 & 1 \\ 0 & 0 & 8 & 0 \\ 0 & 0 & 8 & 0 \end{vmatrix} = 0.$$

Thus, the vectors are known to be dependent although an explicit linear relation between them has not been obtained. A linear relation may be obtained by following the proof of Theorem 6.1 in this special case with the nonzero minor $\begin{vmatrix} 3 & 1 & 1 \\ -2 & 1 & -1 \\ 2 & 2 & 2 \end{vmatrix}$.

The content (volume) of a parallelotope. First, let us recall the definition of an n-dimensional parallelotope in Euclidean n-dimensional space (Chapter 4, § 3). Let $P_0, P_1, \cdots, P_n$ be $n + 1$ points of E_n such that the vectors $\mathbf{X}_i = \mathbf{P}_i - \mathbf{P}_0$ for $i = 1, 2, \cdots, n$ are linearly independent. The n-dimensional parallelotope π whose edges through P_0 are P_0P_i consists of the points $R(r_1, r_2, \cdots, r_n)$ of E_n for which

$$\mathbf{R} = \mathbf{P}_0 + t_1(\mathbf{P}_1 - \mathbf{P}_0) + \cdots + t_n(\mathbf{P}_n - \mathbf{P}_0), \tag{6.3}$$

where $0 \leq t_i \leq 1$ for $i = 1, 2, \cdots, n$.

We define the content of π to be

$$C(P_0, P_1, \cdots, P_n) = |\,\Delta(\mathbf{X}_1, \mathbf{X}_2, \cdots, \mathbf{X}_n)\,|. \tag{6.4}$$

This definition agrees with our observations concerning determinants for E_2 and E_3 in §§ 1 and 2. Moreover, this choice of a definition of content is not surprising when it is pointed out that the defining properties (i), (ii), and (iii) for determinants were motivated by intuitive ideas concerning the content of parallelotopes. Certainly the content of π should not depend upon its position in E_n but only on the vectors $\mathbf{X}_i = \mathbf{P}_i - \mathbf{P}_0$ associated with its sides. Hence, content should reflect a mapping from ordered sets of n vectors of $V_n(R)$ to the real numbers.

Specifically, as to property (iii) for determinants, it seems reasonable to select a fixed parallelotope of E_n as a basis for comparison of content and assign to this fixed parallelotope the unit content. What could be a better selection than the parallelotope whose sides are associated with the natural basis vectors $\mathbf{E}_i$ of $V_n(R)$? The sides are mutually perpendicular and each side is of unit length. Thus, the content of the "n-dimensional unit cube" is taken as a unit of content for E_n; that is

$$\Delta(\mathbf{E}_1, \mathbf{E}_2, \cdots, \mathbf{E}_n) = 1.$$

The other defining properties for determinants have a similar intuitive basis related to the content of parallelotopes and we shall leave it to the student to find the connection.

It is an interesting and not trivial exercise to show that the definition of content given in (6.4) agrees with the intuitive concept of content that we discussed in Chapter 4. Again, we shall leave the proof to the student.

Simultaneous linear equations. The application of determinants to the solution of simultaneous linear equations is demonstrated in this theorem:

THEOREM 6.2 (CRAMER'S RULE). *If the system of equations:*

$$\begin{aligned} a_{11}x_1 + a_{12}x_2 + \cdots + a_{1n}x_n &= b_1 \\ a_{21}x_1 + a_{22}x_2 + \cdots + a_{2n}x_n &= b_2 \\ \cdots\cdots\cdots\cdots&\cdots \\ a_{n1}x_1 + a_{n2}x_2 + \cdots + a_{nn}x_n &= b_n \end{aligned} \tag{6.5}$$

has a unique solution, the determinant of the matrix A whose elements are a_{ij}, that is,

$$\det A = \begin{vmatrix} a_{11} & a_{12} & \cdots & a_{1n} \\ a_{21} & a_{22} & \cdots & a_{2n} \\ \vdots & \vdots & & \vdots \\ a_{n1} & a_{n2} & \cdots & a_{nn} \end{vmatrix},$$

is not zero, and the solution may be expressed in the form

$$x_i = \frac{\Delta_i}{\Delta},$$

where Δ is the determinant just given and Δ_i is obtained by substituting the vector $[b_1, b_2, \cdots, b_n]$ for $[a_{1i}, a_{2i}, \cdots, a_{ni}]$, considering the determinant as a function of the columns of A. Conversely, if $\Delta \neq 0$, the system has a unique solution of the form mentioned.

Proof of Theorem 6.2. If $\Delta = 0$, $\det A^{\mathsf{T}} = 0$; and from Theorem 6.1 we know that the vectors $\mathbf{A}_1 = [a_{11}, a_{21}, \cdots, a_{n1}]$, $\mathbf{A}_2 = [a_{12}, a_{22}, \cdots, a_{n2}]$, $\cdots$, $\mathbf{A}_n = [a_{1n}, a_{2n}, \cdots, a_{nn}]$ are linearly dependent so that there exist real numbers $c_1, c_2, \cdots, c_n$ not all zero such that

$$c_1\mathbf{A}_1 + c_2\mathbf{A}_2 + \cdots + c_n\mathbf{A}_n = \mathbf{0}.$$

Now if $x_1, x_2, \cdots, x_n$ satisfy the equations (6.5), that is, if

$$x_1\mathbf{A}_1 + x_2\mathbf{A}_2 + \cdots + x_n\mathbf{A}_n = \mathbf{B},$$

where $\mathbf{B} = [b_1, b_2, \cdots, b_n]$, then so do $x_1 + c_1, x_2 + c_2, \cdots, x_n + c_n$ since

$$\begin{aligned}(x_1 + c_1)\mathbf{A}_1 &+ (x_2 + c_2)\mathbf{A}_2 + \cdots + (x_n + c_n)\mathbf{A}_n \\ &= (x_1\mathbf{A}_1 + x_2\mathbf{A}_2 + \cdots + x_n\mathbf{A}_n) + c_1\mathbf{A}_1 + c_2\mathbf{A}_2 + \cdots + c_n\mathbf{A}_n \\ &= \mathbf{B} + \mathbf{0} = \mathbf{B}.\end{aligned}$$

Thus, if there is one solution, there are others, and the solution is not unique.

Next suppose $\Delta \neq 0$. Now $\mathbf{A}_1, \mathbf{A}_2, \cdots, \mathbf{A}_n$ are independent. Then these vectors form a basis for $V_n(R)$. Since $\mathbf{B}$ is a vector of $V_n(R)$ it may be written in one and only one way as a linear combination of $\mathbf{A}_1, \mathbf{A}_2, \cdots, \mathbf{A}_n$. This means that there is precisely one set of values which satisfies the equations. It remains to show that these values are given by $x_i = \dfrac{\Delta_i}{\Delta}\cdot$

We must show that

$$\frac{\Delta_1}{\Delta}\mathbf{A}_1 + \frac{\Delta_2}{\Delta}\mathbf{A}_2 + \cdots + \frac{\Delta_n}{\Delta}\mathbf{A}_n = \mathbf{B}$$

or

$$\Delta_1\mathbf{A}_1 + \Delta_2\mathbf{A}_2 + \cdots + \Delta_n\mathbf{A}_n - \Delta\mathbf{B} = \mathbf{0}.$$

This vector equation is equivalent to a set of scalar equations of which a typical member is:

$$a_{i1}\Delta_1 + a_{i2}\Delta_2 + \cdots + a_{in}\Delta_n - b_i\Delta = 0.$$

To see that this equation is valid let us introduce a matrix D of $n + 1$ rows and consider

$$\det D = \begin{vmatrix} a_{i1} & a_{i2} & \cdots & a_{in} & b_i \\ a_{11} & a_{12} & \cdots & a_{1n} & b_1 \\ a_{21} & a_{22} & \cdots & a_{2n} & b_2 \\ \cdot & \cdot & & \cdot & \cdot \\ \cdot & \cdot & & \cdot & \cdot \\ \cdot & \cdot & & \cdot & \cdot \\ a_{n1} & a_{n2} & \cdots & a_{nn} & b_n \end{vmatrix}.$$

Now det $D = 0$ because the first row is equal to a later row of D. Hence, if we expand D in cofactors of the first row we have:

$$a_{i1}\begin{vmatrix} a_{12} & \cdots & a_{1n} & b_1 \\ a_{22} & \cdots & a_{2n} & b_2 \\ \vdots & & \vdots & \vdots \\ a_{n2} & \cdots & a_{nn} & b_n \end{vmatrix} + a_{i2}(-1)^1 \begin{vmatrix} a_{11} & a_{13} & \cdots & a_{1n} & b_1 \\ a_{21} & a_{23} & \cdots & a_{2n} & b_2 \\ \vdots & \vdots & & \vdots & \vdots \\ a_{n1} & a_{n3} & \cdots & a_{nn} & b_n \end{vmatrix} + \cdots$$

$$+ a_{in}(-1)^{n-1}\begin{vmatrix} a_{11} & a_{12} & \cdots & a_{1,n-1} & b_1 \\ a_{21} & a_{22} & \cdots & a_{2,n-1} & b_2 \\ \vdots & \vdots & & \vdots & \vdots \\ a_{n1} & a_{n2} & \cdots & a_{n,n-1} & b_n \end{vmatrix}$$

$$+ b_i(-1)^n \begin{vmatrix} a_{11} & a_{12} & \cdots & a_{1n} \\ a_{21} & a_{22} & \cdots & a_{2n} \\ \vdots & \vdots & & \vdots \\ a_{n1} & a_{n2} & \cdots & a_{nn} \end{vmatrix} = 0.$$

Next, in the first minor above, move the column of b's to the first position without disturbing the order of the remaining $n - 1$ columns. This takes $n - 1$ interchanges and the result is Δ_1. In the second minor, move the b column to the second place; this takes $n - 2$ interchanges to give Δ_2. Continue in this way up to the last two minors, which remain as they are. In the original equation, the power of -1 associated with the coefficient a_{ik} is $k - 1$; the number of interchanges given above is $n - k$. Thus the total is $k - 1 + n - k = n - 1$. Then:

$$a_{i1}(-1)^{n-1}\Delta_1 + a_{i2}(-1)^{n-1}\Delta_2 + \cdots + a_{in}(-1)^{n-1}\Delta_n + b_i(-1)^n\Delta = 0,$$

or

$$a_{i1}\Delta_1 + a_{i2}\Delta_2 + \cdots + a_{in}\Delta_n - b_i\Delta = 0,$$

which is the desired equation.

It must be understood that Cramer's rule is not being offered as a *practical* method of solving equations. We have already offered such a method. It is essentially as much work to evaluate two determinants as to solve the whole system of equations by the procedure of Chapter 3. The use of the rule is primarily theoretical. It furnishes a definite formula for the results which was not provided before. Also, in certain cases, Δ may be of an especially simple form and only one or two of the x_i may be required. In these cases, Cramer's rule may be resorted to directly.

EXERCISES

1. Determine whether or not the following sets of vectors are linearly dependent by evaluating a determinant:

(a) $[1, 2, -1]$, $[2, -1, 3]$, $[1, 7, -6]$.

(b) $[1, 2, -1, 3]$, $[2, -4, 1, 0]$, $[0, 1, 2, -1]$, $[3, -1, 2, 2]$.

(c) $[x, x^2, 1]$, $[-1, x, x]$, $[0, 2x^2, x^2 + 1]$.

2. The vectors $[1, -1, 0, 0]$ and $[1, -4, -3, 1]$ are contained in $L\{[2, 1, 3, -1], [1, 2, 3, -1]\}$. Show how linear expressions for $[1, -1, 0, 0]$ and $[1, -4, -3, 1]$ in terms of $[2, 1, 3, -1]$ and $[1, 2, 3, -1]$ may be obtained by finding a nonzero minor of order 2 in the determinant

$$\begin{vmatrix} 1 & -1 & 0 & 0 \\ 2 & 1 & 3 & -1 \\ 1 & 2 & 3 & -1 \\ 1 & -4 & -3 & 1 \end{vmatrix}$$

and following the proof of Theorem 6.1 in this special case.

3. Prove: A set of k vectors of $V_n(R)$ is a set of linearly independent vectors if and only if one of the kth-order determinants obtained by taking k corresponding components from each vector is not zero.

4. Find the content of the parallelotope of E_4 defined by the points $P_0(1, 2, -1, 3)$, $P_1(1, 2, 4, 6)$, $P_2(0, 0, 1, 0)$, $P_3(1, 2, -1, 4)$, and $P_4(1, 3, 2, 3)$.

5. Show that the coordinates (r_1, r_2) of any point on the line joining points $X(x_1, x_2)$ and $Y(y_1, y_2)$ of E_2 satisfy the equation

$$\begin{vmatrix} r_1 & r_2 & 1 \\ x_1 & x_2 & 1 \\ y_1 & y_2 & 1 \end{vmatrix} = 0.$$

6. In the notation of Exercise 5, what does the determinant

$$\begin{vmatrix} r_1 & r_2 & 1 \\ x_1 & x_2 & 1 \\ y_1 & y_2 & 1 \end{vmatrix}$$

represent if (r_1, r_2) does not lie on the line joining X and Y?

Hint: Check the definition of area of a parallelogram.

7. Show that the coordinates (r_1, r_2, r_3) of any point in the plane containing the noncollinear points $X(x_1, x_2, x_3)$, $Y(y_1, y_2, y_3)$, $Z(z_1, z_2, z_3)$ of E_3 satisfy the equation

$$\begin{vmatrix} r_1 & r_2 & r_3 & 1 \\ x_1 & x_2 & x_3 & 1 \\ y_1 & y_2 & y_3 & 1 \\ z_1 & z_2 & z_3 & 1 \end{vmatrix} = 0.$$

8. In the notation of Exercise 7, what does the determinant

$$\begin{vmatrix} r_1 & r_2 & r_3 & 1 \\ x_1 & x_2 & x_3 & 1 \\ y_1 & y_2 & y_3 & 1 \\ z_1 & z_2 & z_3 & 1 \end{vmatrix}$$

represent if (r_1, r_2, r_3) does not lie in the plane containing the points X, Y, and Z?

9. Generalize Exercises 5, 6, 7, and 8 to obtain the equation of a hyperplane in E_n and give the analogous interpretation of Δ if $(r_1, r_2, \cdots, r_n)$ does not lie in the hyperplane. (See Exercise 7, § 5.)

10. Solve the following systems of equations by Cramer's rule for the designated unknowns *only* or show that no unique solution exists.

(a)
$$\begin{aligned} x + 3y - z &= 4 \\ 2x - y + z &= 1 \\ 3x + y + 2z &= 5 \end{aligned} \qquad \text{for } y.$$

(b)
$$\begin{aligned} x - 2y + z - t &= 0 \\ y + t &= 1 \\ x - z &= 1 \\ x + y &= 1 \end{aligned} \qquad \text{for } z.$$

(c)
$$\begin{aligned} x - y + z &= 3 \\ x + 2y + 2z &= 1 \\ x + 5y + 3z &= -1 \end{aligned} \qquad \text{for } x.$$

(d)
$$\begin{aligned} x + y &= 1 \\ x - z &= 1 \\ x + t &= 1 \\ x - w &= 1 \\ x + y + z + t + w &= 1 \end{aligned} \qquad \text{for all unknowns.}$$

11. Show that a solution of the equations

$$\begin{aligned} a_{11}x_1 + a_{12}x_2 + a_{13}x_3 &= 0 \\ a_{21}x_1 + a_{22}x_2 + a_{23}x_3 &= 0 \end{aligned}$$

is given by

$$x_1 = \begin{vmatrix} a_{12} & a_{13} \\ a_{22} & a_{23} \end{vmatrix}, \qquad x_2 = \begin{vmatrix} a_{13} & a_{11} \\ a_{23} & a_{21} \end{vmatrix}, \qquad x_3 = \begin{vmatrix} a_{11} & a_{12} \\ a_{21} & a_{22} \end{vmatrix}.$$

Note that the vector $[x_1, x_2, x_3]$ is orthogonal to the vectors $[a_{11}, a_{12}, a_{13}]$ and $[a_{21}, a_{22}, a_{23}]$.

CHAPTER 6

Linear Transformations and Matrices

We shall now study certain types of mappings from one vector space to another or to the same vector space. These mappings are called linear transformations because of linear conditions contained in their definition. Although they are special mappings, they are of importance both in practical applications and in theory. Matrices are introduced to represent linear transformations, and the algebra of matrices is studied both from the viewpoint of the transformations and for its own sake since it contains many features not found in elementary algebra.

1. Linear Transformations

The concept of an isomorphism between an n-dimensional real vector space V and $V_n(R)$ was mentioned briefly in §4 of Chapter 3. We wish to investigate mappings between vector spaces which generalize this concept. Before doing so, it will be well to review and illustrate the definition of an isomorphism.

As in Chapter 3, we indicate the relation between a vector $\mathbf{X}$ of V and its image $[x_1, x_2, \cdots, x_n]$ of $V_n(R)$ under a mapping T by

$$\mathbf{X} \xrightarrow{\mathrm{T}} [x_1, x_2, \cdots, x_n]. \tag{1.1}$$

Let T be a one-to-one mapping of an n-dimensional vector space V onto $V_n(R)$ such that, for any two vectors $\mathbf{X}$ and $\mathbf{Y}$ of V and any real number r:

(i) If $\quad \mathbf{X} \xrightarrow{\mathrm{T}} [x_1, x_2, \cdots, x_n], \quad \mathbf{Y} \xrightarrow{\mathrm{T}} [y_1, y_2, \cdots, y_n],$

then $\quad \mathbf{X} + \mathbf{Y} \xrightarrow{\mathrm{T}} [x_1, x_2, \cdots, x_n] + [y_1, y_2, \cdots, y_n].$

(ii) If $\mathbf{X} \xrightarrow{\mathrm{T}} [x_1, x_2, \cdots, x_n]$, then $r\mathbf{X} \xrightarrow{\mathrm{T}} r[x_1, x_2, \cdots, x_n]$.

Then T is called an *isomorphism* of V onto $V_n(R)$.

Example 1. A simple geometric illustration of a class of isomorphisms of $V_2(R)$ onto itself may be obtained by considering the rotations of the plane. Specifically, let a vector $[x_1, x_2]$ of $V_2(R)$ be associated with the directed line segment from the origin O to the point $X(x_1, x_2)$ in a Cartesian coordinate system for the plane. A rotation through an angle θ about the origin will take the point $X(x_1, x_2)$ to the point $X^*(x_1^*, x_2^*)$ and the segment OX to the segment OX^* (see Figure 1.1).

The corresponding mapping of $V_2(R)$ onto $V_2(R)$ may be denoted by T_θ and defined by assigning to $[x_1, x_2]$ the image $[x_1^*, x_2^*]$. This mapping is one-to-one since each segment OX is rotated into precisely one segment OX^* and, in turn, for any segment OY^* there is precisely one segment OY which is taken to it by the rotation.

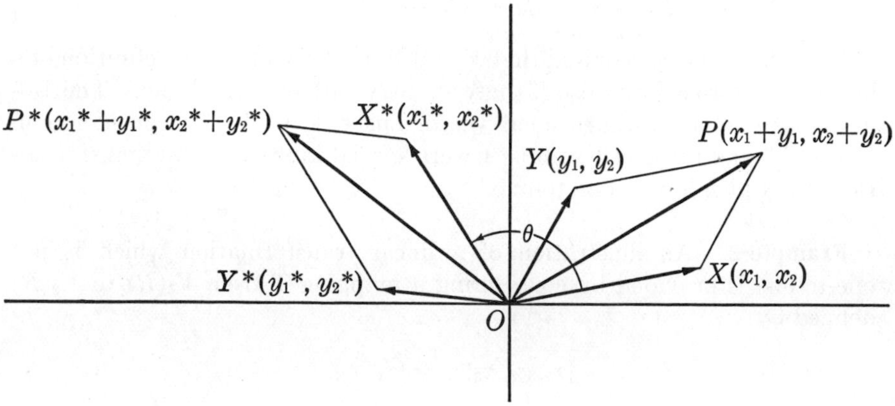

Figure 1.1

It remains to show that if

$$[x_1, x_2] \xrightarrow{\mathrm{T}_\theta} [x_1^*, x_2^*], \quad [y_1, y_2] \xrightarrow{\mathrm{T}_\theta} [y_1^*, y_2^*],$$

then

$$[x_1, x_2] + [y_1, y_2] \xrightarrow{\mathrm{T}_\theta} [x_1^*, x_2^*] + [y_1^*, y_2^*] \quad \text{and} \quad r[x_1, x_2] \xrightarrow{\mathrm{T}_\theta} r[x_1^*, x_2^*].$$

Figure 1.1 illustrates the first part; the segment OP associated with $[x_1, x_2] + [y_1, y_2]$ is the diagonal of the parallelogram $OXPY$. Under the rotation this parallelogram is rotated to $OX^*P^*Y^*$ and OP to OP^*. Since OP^* is the diagonal of $OX^*P^*Y^*$, the coordinates of P^* are $(x_1^* + y_1^*, x_2^* + y_2^*)$. That is,

$$[x_1, x_2] + [y_1, y_2] \xrightarrow{\mathrm{T}_\theta} [x_1^* + y_1^*, x_2^* + y_2^*] = [x_1^*, x_2^*] + [y_1^*, y_2^*].$$

The relation $r[x_1, x_2] \xrightarrow{\mathrm{T}_\theta} r[x_1^*, x_2^*]$ may be seen in an analogous manner.

We now introduce a new concept by simultaneously removing two of the restrictions imposed in the definition of an isomorphism from V to $V_n(R)$:

1. We replace $V_n(R)$ by an arbitrary real vector space W.
2. The mapping T is now required only to be single-valued into W, not necessarily one-to-one.

DEFINITION 1.1. *A single-valued mapping* T *from a real vector space* V *to a real vector space* W *is called a* LINEAR TRANSFORMATION *from* V *to* W *if, for all vectors* **X**, **Y** *of* V *and all real numbers* r, T *satisfies the following properties:*

$$(1.2)\quad \begin{cases} \text{(i) } \textit{If}\quad \mathbf{X} \xrightarrow{T} \mathbf{X}^*,\quad \mathbf{Y} \xrightarrow{T} \mathbf{Y}^*,\quad \textit{then}\quad \mathbf{X}+\mathbf{Y} \xrightarrow{T} \mathbf{X}^*+\mathbf{Y}^*. \\ \text{(ii) } \textit{If}\quad \mathbf{X} \xrightarrow{T} \mathbf{X}^*,\quad \textit{then}\quad r\mathbf{X} \xrightarrow{T} r\mathbf{X}^*. \end{cases}$$

Note that it is *not* required that V and W be distinct in the definition of a linear transformation; also T may or may not be one-to-one. The isomorphisms of an n-dimensional vector space V to $V_n(R)$ considered in Chapter 3 and those of Example 1 were special kinds of linear transformations for which T was one-to-one.

Example 2. An illustration of a linear transformation which is not one-to-one is provided by considering a mapping T from $V_3(R)$ to $V_2(R)$ defined by

$$[x_1, x_2, x_3] \xrightarrow{T} [x_1, x_2].$$

We must verify that T is a linear transformation; or

$$[x_1, x_2, x_3] + [y_1, y_2, y_3] \xrightarrow{T} [x_1, x_2] + [y_1, y_2]; \quad r[x_1, x_2, x_3] \xrightarrow{T} r[x_1, x_2].$$

First,

$$\begin{aligned} [x_1, x_2, x_3] + [y_1, y_2, y_3] &= [x_1 + y_1, x_2 + y_2, x_3 + y_3] \\ &\xrightarrow{T} [x_1 + y_1, x_2 + y_2] = [x_1, x_2] + [y_1, y_2]. \end{aligned}$$

Similarly, $r[x_1, x_2, x_3] = [rx_1, rx_2, rx_3] \xrightarrow{T} [rx_1, rx_2] = r[x_1, x_2]$. Hence T is a linear transformation from $V_3(R)$ to $V_2(R)$.

This transformation may be illustrated geometrically by considering a linear coordinate system in space and associating the vector $[x_1, x_2, x_3]$ with the directed line segment from O to $X(x_1, x_2, x_3)$. We may associate the segment from O to $(x_1, x_2, 0)$ in the x_1, x_2 coordinate plane with the vector $[x_1, x_2]$. Then the transformation may be visualized as a projection of OX parallel to the x_3-axis.

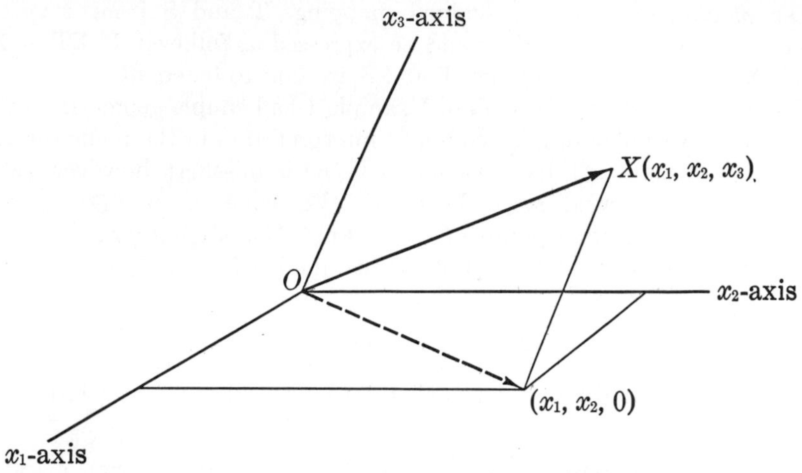

Figure 1.2

The same geometric illustration could, of course, be used for a linear transformation T* from $V_3(R)$ to $V_3(R)$ given by

$$[x_1, x_2, x_3] \xrightarrow{T^*} [x_1, x_2, 0].$$

Note that T and T* are not identical mappings since they have different spaces as image sets. In particular, T maps $V_3(R)$ onto $V_2(R)$ while T* maps $V_3(R)$ into $V_3(R)$.

A more convenient notation for linear transformations or, more generally, for single-valued mappings from a vector space V to a vector space W is obtained by writing $\mathbf{X}\mathrm{T} = \mathbf{X}^*$ in place of $\mathbf{X} \xrightarrow{T} \mathbf{X}^*$. We could also return to the notation of Chapter 1 and write $\mathrm{T}(\mathbf{X}) = \mathbf{X}^*$, but we will choose the order $\mathbf{X}\mathrm{T}$ instead. The abandonment of parentheses is merely a matter of convenience. The position of T at the right of $\mathbf{X}$ is more or less an arbitrary choice. Most (by no means all) algebraists write linear transformations this way. When we come to represent linear transformations by matrices this choice will permit us to retain our notation for vectors of $V_n(R)$. On the other hand, it will cause a slight complication when we consider linear equations. Good arguments exist for writing T on either side of the vector; our best advice is to be able to use either notation.

In the new notation which we are adopting, the requirements of (1.2) for a linear transformation can be written:

$$(1.3) \qquad \begin{cases} \text{(i)} \ (\mathbf{X} + \mathbf{Y})\mathrm{T} = \mathbf{X}\mathrm{T} + \mathbf{Y}\mathrm{T}; \\ \text{(ii)} \ (r\mathbf{X})\mathrm{T} = r(\mathbf{X}\mathrm{T}). \end{cases}$$

The *equality* of two single-valued mappings T and S from a vector space V to a vector space W would be expressed as follows: If $\mathbf{XT} = \mathbf{XS}$ for all $\mathbf{X} \in V$, then the mappings T and S are said to be equal.

The linear transformations T_θ of Example 1 had simple geometric interpretations. A similar simple geometric interpretation in the plane for any linear transformation T from $V_2(R)$ to $V_2(R)$ is missing; however, there are interesting observations to be made. For example, if $X(x_1, x_2)$ and $Y(y_1, y_2)$ are two distinct points of E_2, we know (§2 of Chapter 2) that the equations for the points $R(r_1, r_2)$ of the line joining X and Y may be given in the vector form

$$\mathbf{R} = (1 - t)\mathbf{X} + t\mathbf{Y}.$$

Now, applying a linear transformation T to both sides of this relation, we obtain

$$\mathbf{RT} = \{(1 - t)\mathbf{X} + t\mathbf{Y}\}\mathrm{T} = \{(1 - t)\mathbf{X}\}\mathrm{T} + \{t\mathbf{Y}\}\mathrm{T} = (1 - t)(\mathbf{XT}) + t(\mathbf{YT}),$$

by the use of properties (1.3).

If $\mathbf{XT} \neq \mathbf{YT}$, $\mathbf{RT} = (1 - t)(\mathbf{XT}) + t(\mathbf{YT})$ can be regarded as the equation of a line: $\mathbf{R}^* = (1 - t)\mathbf{X}^* + t\mathbf{Y}^*$, where $\mathbf{R}^* = \mathbf{RT}$, $\mathbf{X}^* = \mathbf{XT}$, and $\mathbf{Y}^* = \mathbf{YT}$. On the other hand, if $\mathbf{XT} = \mathbf{YT}$, then $\mathbf{RT} = \mathbf{XT}$ for all points R on the line joining X and Y.

Thus, we see that a linear transformation T maps lines into lines or lines into points. The only time that T maps lines into points occurs when $\mathbf{XT} = \mathbf{YT}$ for distinct vectors $\mathbf{X}$ and $\mathbf{Y}$. This means, of course, that the mapping is *not* one-to-one.

In the case where $\mathbf{XT} \neq \mathbf{YT}$, note that properties of segments of a line are preserved under a linear transformation T. If, for example, a particular choice of $\mathbf{R}$ corresponds to the midpoint of the segment XY ($t = \frac{1}{2}$), the corresponding value of $\mathbf{R}^*$ yields the midpoint of X^*Y^* since the values of the coefficients in $\mathbf{R}^* = (1 - t)\mathbf{X}^* + t\mathbf{Y}^*$ are not affected.

The student should realize that the interpretation given above for $V_2(R)$ extends readily to lines of E_n and E_m for a linear transformation T of $V_n(R)$ to $V_m(R)$.

We conclude this section with two more examples of linear transformations with simple geometric interpretations.

Example 3. Let T be defined by:

$$[x_1, x_2, \cdots, x_n]\mathrm{T} = [ax_1, ax_2, \cdots, ax_n].$$

The student may easily verify that T is a linear transformation from $V_n(R)$ to $V_n(R)$. If $n = 2$, we may make our usual association of vectors and directed segments from the origin. The segment OX is transformed by T to the segment OX^*, where the coordinates of X are (x_1, x_2) and those of X^* are (ax_1, ax_2). Such a linear transformation is called a *dilation* if

$a > 1$ and a *contraction* if $0 < a < 1$. The reason for these names is clear from Figure 1.3.

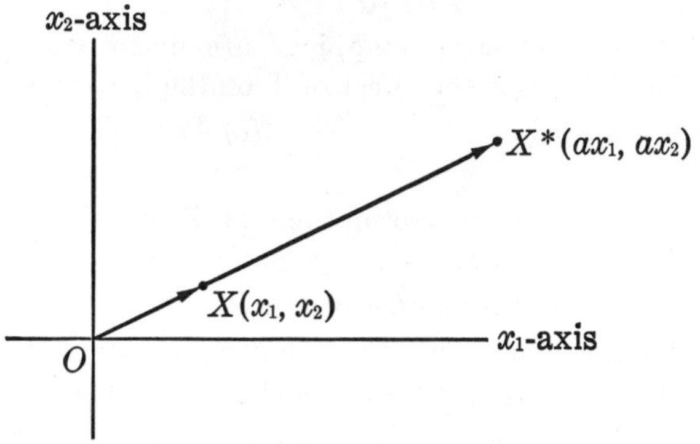

Figure 1.3

Example 4. Let T be a mapping from $V_2(R)$ to $V_2(R)$ such that $[x_1, x_2]\mathrm{T} = [x_1 + ax_2, x_2]$. Again the student can easily check that T is a linear transformation.

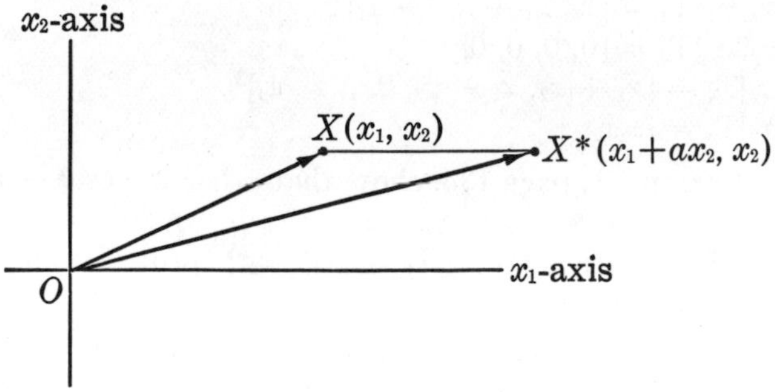

Figure 1.4

In the geometric interpretation, a point $X(x_1, x_2)$ is shifted a distance proportional to its x_2-coordinate in a direction parallel to the x_1-axis. Points on the x_2-axis move to (ax_2, x_2); that is, in a Cartesian coordinate system, we would say that these points go to the line through the origin with slope $1/a$. Such a linear transformation is called a *shear*.

Of course not all linear transformations have easily visualized geometric representations even when they involve only $V_2(R)$ or $V_3(R)$. The student may try to depict the consequence of

$$[x_1, x_2, x_3]\mathrm{T} = [x_3 - 2x_2, 4x_1, x_1 + 2x_2 - x_3]$$

for example; it is easy to see that T is a linear transformation.

EXERCISES

1. Show that the mapping given in the last paragraph of the section is a linear transformation from $V_3(R)$ to $V_3(R)$.

2. Prove that the following mappings are linear transformations of $V_2(R)$ to itself and describe the effect of T on the line segments OX:

(a) $[x_1, x_2]\mathrm{T} = [x_2, x_1]$

(b) $[x_1, x_2]\mathrm{T} = [x_1 - x_2, x_2 - x_1]$

(c) $[x_1, x_2]\mathrm{T} = [2x_1, x_2]$

3. Which of the linear transformations of Exercise 2 are one-to-one? What are the image sets of any that are not one-to-one?

4. In a plane, consider the line L given by $\mathbf{R} = (1 - t)[1, 1] + t[-1, 2]$.

(a) Sketch the line assuming a Cartesian coordinate system.

(b) Sketch the lines into which each of the transformations of Exercise 2 takes L.

5. If the linear transformation of Exercise 2(b) is applied to the vectors $\mathbf{R} = (1 - t)[2, 1] + t[3, 2]$, what happens to the line represented by this equation?

6. Determine which of the following mappings are linear transformations:

(a) $[x_1, x_2]\mathrm{T}_1 = [x_1 + 1, x_2]$

(b) $[x_1, x_2, x_3]\mathrm{T}_2 = [x_3, x_1 + x_2, -x_2]$

(c) $[x_1, x_2, x_3]\mathrm{T}_3 = [0, 0, 0, 0]$

(d) $[x_1, x_2]\mathrm{T}_4 = [x_1 + x_2, x_1 - x_2, 2x_1, x_2, x_1]$

(e) $[x_1, x_2]\mathrm{T}_5 = [x_1x_2, x_2]$.

7. (a) In Example 1, page 135, show that $x_1^* = x_1 \cos\theta - x_2 \sin\theta$ and $x_2^* = x_1 \sin\theta + x_2 \cos\theta$.

(b) Using the notation $[x_1, x_2]\mathrm{T}_\theta = [x_1^*, x_2^*]$, prove algebraically that T_θ is a linear transformation.

8. In E_3, consider a mapping which takes an arbitrary point X to a point X^*, where XX^* is a line segment parallel to the x_3-axis and having a point on the x_1, x_2 coordinate plane as its midpoint. Describe this mapping in vector language as a mapping from $V_3(R)$ to $V_3(R)$ by the customary associations and determine whether the mapping is a linear transformation.

9. Let V be a vector space with the direct sum decomposition $V = S \oplus W$. Let T be a mapping that takes any vector $\mathbf{X}$ of V into its projection on S (see Problem 5, §5, Chapter 3). Prove that T is a linear transformation from V to S. The linear transformation T is called the *projection* of V on S along W.

2. Elementary Properties of Linear Transformations

The fundamental properties of a linear transformation T from a vector space V to a vector space W,

$$(\mathbf{X} + \mathbf{Y})\mathrm{T} = \mathbf{X}\mathrm{T} + \mathbf{Y}\mathrm{T}, \quad (a\mathbf{X})\mathrm{T} = a(\mathbf{X}\mathrm{T}), \tag{2.1}$$

have several simple implications. For example, if we set $a = 0$ in the second expression we obtain $(0\mathbf{X})\mathrm{T} = 0(\mathbf{X}\mathrm{T})$, or $\mathbf{0}\mathrm{T} = \mathbf{0}$. Of course the $\mathbf{0}$ vector on the left side of $\mathbf{0}\mathrm{T} = \mathbf{0}$ is the $\mathbf{0}$ vector of V, and the $\mathbf{0}$ vector on the right is the $\mathbf{0}$ vector of W. We will not bother to distinguish between these $\mathbf{0}$ vectors in writing, for the context of a discussion will usually make it clear which vector space we are talking about.

The two relations of (2.1) may be combined in a single requirement,

$$(a\mathbf{X} + b\mathbf{Y})\mathrm{T} = a(\mathbf{X}\mathrm{T}) + b(\mathbf{Y}\mathrm{T}), \tag{2.2}$$

for all real numbers a, b and all vectors $\mathbf{X}$, $\mathbf{Y}$ of V. Merely take $a = b = 1$ for the first relation of (2.1) and $b = 0$ for the second.

The relation (2.2) has the following generalization, whose inductive proof we leave as an exercise for the student: Let $\mathbf{X}_1, \mathbf{X}_2, \cdots, \mathbf{X}_k$ be arbitrary vectors of V and $c_1, c_2, \cdots, c_k$ be arbitrary real numbers. Then,

$$(c_1\mathbf{X}_1 + c_2\mathbf{X}_2 + \cdots + c_k\mathbf{X}_k)\mathrm{T} = c_1(\mathbf{X}_1\mathrm{T}) + c_2(\mathbf{X}_2\mathrm{T}) + \cdots + c_k(\mathbf{X}_k\mathrm{T}). \tag{2.3}$$

We now provide a description of linear transformations that will be convenient for our purposes. In the examples of § 1, we defined linear transformations by indicating the effect on the components of vectors in V. A somewhat more general method is to specify the images of a basis for V.

THEOREM 2.1. *A linear transformation* T *from a vector space* V *to a vector space* W *is completely determined by the images of a set of basis vectors of* V. *Given any basis* $\{\mathbf{X}_1, \mathbf{X}_2, \cdots, \mathbf{X}_n\}$ *of* V *and any (ordered) set of vectors* $\{\mathbf{Y}_1, \mathbf{Y}_2, \cdots, \mathbf{Y}_n\}$ *of* W *(where equalities among the* $\mathbf{Y}_i$ *are not excluded), there is one and only one linear transformation* T *such that* $\mathbf{X}_i\mathrm{T} = \mathbf{Y}_i$, *for* $i = 1, 2, \cdots, n$.

Proof. First we will show that such a transformation T exists. Let $\mathbf{Z}_1$ be any vector of V; since $\{\mathbf{X}_1, \mathbf{X}_2, \cdots, \mathbf{X}_n\}$ is a basis for V, we may find constants $a_1, a_2, \cdots, a_n$ such that $\mathbf{Z}_1 = a_1\mathbf{X}_1 + \cdots + a_n\mathbf{X}_n$. Define $\mathbf{Z}_1\mathrm{T} = a_1\mathbf{Y}_1 + a_2\mathbf{Y}_2 + \cdots + a_n\mathbf{Y}_n$. Then if $\mathbf{Z}_2 = b_1\mathbf{X}_1 + \cdots + b_n\mathbf{X}_n$ is any other vector of V:

$$\begin{aligned}(\mathbf{Z}_1 + \mathbf{Z}_2)\mathrm{T} &= (a_1\mathbf{X}_1 + \cdots + a_n\mathbf{X}_n + b_1\mathbf{X}_1 + \cdots + b_n\mathbf{X}_n)\mathrm{T} \\ &= \{(a_1 + b_1)\mathbf{X}_1 + \cdots + (a_n + b_n)\mathbf{X}_n\}\mathrm{T} \\ &= (a_1 + b_1)\mathbf{Y}_1 + \cdots + (a_n + b_n)\mathbf{Y}_n \\ &= a_1\mathbf{Y}_1 + \cdots + a_n\mathbf{Y}_n + b_1\mathbf{Y}_1 + \cdots + b_n\mathbf{Y}_n \\ &= \mathbf{Z}_1\mathrm{T} + \mathbf{Z}_2\mathrm{T}.\end{aligned}$$

$$\begin{aligned}(a\mathbf{Z}_1)\mathrm{T} = (aa_1\mathbf{X}_1 + \cdots + aa_n\mathbf{X}_n)\mathrm{T} &= aa_1\mathbf{Y}_1 + \cdots + aa_n\mathbf{Y}_n \\ &= a(a_1\mathbf{Y}_1 + \cdots + a_n\mathbf{Y}_n) \\ &= a(\mathbf{Z}_1\mathrm{T}).\end{aligned}$$

Hence T is linear. It remains to show that T is unique.

We recall that the definition of equality for mappings from one vector space to another implies that two linear transformations S and T from V to W are equal if $\mathbf{X}\mathrm{S} = \mathbf{X}\mathrm{T}$ for all $\mathbf{X}$ of V. Now suppose that S is a linear transformation with the property that $\mathbf{X}_i\mathrm{S} = \mathbf{Y}_i$; then

$$\begin{aligned} \mathbf{Z}_1\mathrm{S} &= (a_1\mathbf{X}_1 + \cdots + a_n\mathbf{X}_n)\mathrm{S} = a_1(\mathbf{X}_1\mathrm{S}) + \cdots + a_n(\mathbf{X}_n\mathrm{S}) \\ &= a_1\mathbf{Y}_1 + \cdots + a_n\mathbf{Y}_n = \mathbf{Z}_1\mathrm{T} \end{aligned}$$

for any vector $\mathbf{Z}_1$ of V. Hence $\mathrm{S} = \mathrm{T}$.

Note the complete freedom for the set of image vectors $\{\mathbf{Y}_1, \cdots, \mathbf{Y}_n\}$. It need not be a basis of W (in fact it may not have the right number of vectors); it need not generate W; indeed all the $\mathbf{Y}_i$ might be $\mathbf{0}$!

In the normal situation we have present a basis $\{\mathbf{X}_1, \cdots, \mathbf{X}_n\}$ of V and a basis $\{\mathbf{X}_1', \cdots, \mathbf{X}_m'\}$ of W. (The particular case $V = W$, $n = m$, $\mathbf{X}_i' = \mathbf{X}_i$ should be kept in mind.) Then the $\mathbf{Y}_i$ of the previous theorem are themselves expressed in terms of $\mathbf{X}_1', \cdots, \mathbf{X}_m'$, and the linear transformations from V to W are represented by a system of equations:

$$\begin{aligned} \mathbf{X}_1\mathrm{T} &= \mathbf{Y}_1 = a_{11}\mathbf{X}_1' + a_{12}\mathbf{X}_2' + \cdots + a_{1m}\mathbf{X}_m' \\ \mathbf{X}_2\mathrm{T} &= \mathbf{Y}_2 = a_{21}\mathbf{X}_1' + a_{22}\mathbf{X}_2' + \cdots + a_{2m}\mathbf{X}_m' \\ &\cdots\cdots\cdots\cdots\cdots\cdots \\ \mathbf{X}_n\mathrm{T} &= \mathbf{Y}_n = a_{n1}\mathbf{X}_1' + a_{n2}\mathbf{X}_2' + \cdots + a_{nm}\mathbf{X}_m'. \end{aligned} \tag{2.4}$$

We will say that equations (2.4) represent the linear transformation T relative to the bases $\{\mathbf{X}_i\}$ and $\{\mathbf{X}_i'\}$, where, for brevity, we imply that $\{\mathbf{X}_i\}$ means the basis $\{\mathbf{X}_1, \mathbf{X}_2, \cdots, \mathbf{X}_n\}$ of V with a similar implication for $\{\mathbf{X}_i'\}$. The abbreviation $\{\mathbf{X}_i\}$ for a basis $\{\mathbf{X}_1, \mathbf{X}_2, \cdots, \mathbf{X}_k\}$ of a vector space will be used often throughout the remainder of this text, and the number of vectors involved will be clear from the context.

The number of vectors in a basis for V need not be the same as that for W unless V and W have the same dimension. If $V = W$, we would normally use the same basis vectors for both spaces; that is, $\mathbf{X}_i' = \mathbf{X}_i$ in (2.4). In this case, the mapping T will be from V to V and for brevity we will say that T is a linear transformation *on* V.

There are two important subspaces, one of V and one of W, that play an important role in the theory of linear transformations.

DEFINITION 2.1. *If* T *is a linear transformation from V to W, the set of all image vectors in W, that is, all vectors of the form* $\mathbf{X}\mathrm{T}$, *where* $\mathbf{X} \in V$, *is called the* RANGE, *or* RANK SPACE, *of* T. *The set of all vectors* $\mathbf{Z}$ *of V such that* $\mathbf{Z}\mathrm{T} = \mathbf{0}$ *is called the* NULL SPACE *of* T.

Several remarks are in order. If $\mathbf{X}_1, \mathbf{X}_2, \cdots, \mathbf{X}_n$ is any basis of V, an arbitrary vector $\mathbf{X}$ of V may be written $\mathbf{X} = a_1\mathbf{X}_1 + a_2\mathbf{X}_2 + \cdots + a_n\mathbf{X}_n$

and $\mathbf{X}T = a_1(\mathbf{X}_1T) + a_2(\mathbf{X}_2T) + \cdots + a_n(\mathbf{X}_nT)$. Hence the range of T, denoted by $(V)T$, is contained in $L\{\mathbf{X}_1T, \mathbf{X}_2T, \cdots, \mathbf{X}_nT\}$. Conversely, any vector of $L\{\mathbf{X}_1T, \mathbf{X}_2T, \cdots, \mathbf{X}_nT\}$ is contained in $(V)T$ so that $(V)T = L\{\mathbf{X}_1T, \mathbf{X}_2T, \cdots, \mathbf{X}_nT\}$. Thus we see that the range of T is a subspace (maybe all) of W.

The term "space" in "null space" is justified by the facts that if $\mathbf{Z}_1T = \mathbf{0}$, $\mathbf{Z}_2T = \mathbf{0}$, then $(\mathbf{Z}_1 + \mathbf{Z}_2)T = \mathbf{0}$ and $(a\mathbf{Z}_1)T = \mathbf{0}$. Therefore the null space of T is a subspace (maybe all) of V. The linear transformation T is said to *annihilate a vector* $\mathbf{Z} \in V$ if $\mathbf{Z}$ is in the null space of V. We say that T *annihilates a subspace* V^* of V if V^* is contained in the null space of T. Thus T annihilates its null space.

Pictorially, we can illustrate the previous definitions by a diagram.

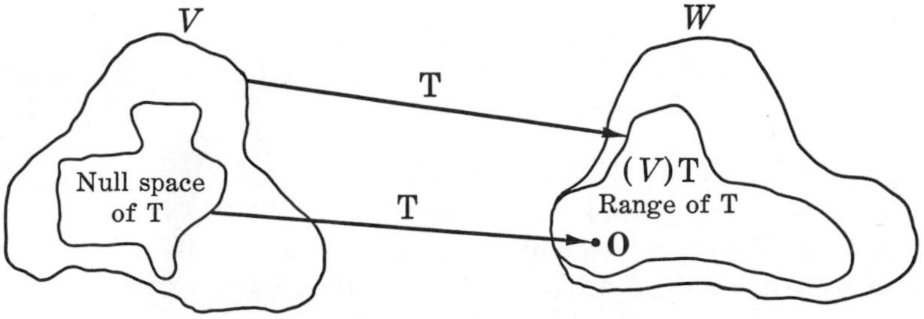

Figure 2.1

We have indicated that the null space of T consists of all vectors mapping upon $\mathbf{0}$ of W. The range of T, $(V)T$, is the subspace of W that V is mapped *onto* (it may be all of W; our diagram is not intended to exclude this possibility).

Example 1. We illustrate the concept of range and null space for the linear transformation T from $V_3(R)$ to $V_4(R)$ given by

$$\begin{aligned}[1, 0, 0]T &= [0, 1, 0, 2]\\ [0, 1, 0]T &= [0, 1, 1, 0]\\ [0, 0, 1]T &= [0, 1, -1, 4].\end{aligned}$$

The range of T is

$$W^* = L\{[0, 1, 0, 2], \quad [0, 1, 1, 0], \quad [0, 1, -1, 4]\}.$$

Clearly $W^* \neq V_4(R)$, and we may determine the dimension of W^* by noting that the first two generators are linearly independent and

$$[0, 1, -1, 4] = 2[0, 1, 0, 2] - [0, 1, 1, 0].$$

Hence the dimension of W^* is 2.

In order to determine the null space for T, we note that, for any vector $[x_1, x_2, x_3]$ of V,

$$\begin{aligned}[x_1, x_2, x_3]\mathrm{T} &= (x_1[1, 0, 0] + x_2[0, 1, 0] + x_3[0, 0, 1])\mathrm{T} \\ &= x_1([1, 0, 0]\mathrm{T}) + x_2([0, 1, 0]\mathrm{T}) + x_3([0, 0, 1]\mathrm{T}) \\ &= x_1[0, 1, 0, 2] + x_2[0, 1, 1, 0] + x_3[0, 1, -1, 4] \\ &= [0, x_1 + x_2 + x_3, x_2 - x_3, 2x_1 + 4x_3].\end{aligned}$$

If $[x_1, x_2, x_3] \in V$ is in the null space for T, $[x_1, x_2, x_3]\mathrm{T} = \mathbf{0}$; therefore from our expression for $[x_1, x_2, x_3]\mathrm{T}$ we must have

$$\begin{aligned} x_1 + x_2 + x_3 &= 0 \\ x_2 - x_3 &= 0 \\ 2x_1 + 4x_3 &= 0. \end{aligned}$$

These equations have the solution vectors $[-2a, a, a]$, where a is an arbitrary real number. Hence the null space for T is $L\{[-2, 1, 1]\}$. This subspace of $V_3(R)$ has dimension 1.

In Example 1 we see that the dimension of $V_3(R)$ is the sum of the dimensions of the range and the null space of T. The example illustrates the following theorem, which may, in the proper setting, be considered as a statement of the results in Chapter 3, §3, on the dimension of the solution space of a system of linear equations. This relation will be considered in more detail in Chapter 7, §4.

THEOREM 2.2. *The dimension of the vector space V is equal to the sum of the dimensions of the range and the null space of any linear transformation* T *from V to any vector space W.*

Proof. Let $\mathbf{X}_1, \cdots, \mathbf{X}_n$ be a basis for V and let $\mathbf{X}_i\mathrm{T} = \mathbf{Y}_i$ for $i = 1, 2, \cdots, n$. The range of T is $L\{\mathbf{Y}_1, \mathbf{Y}_2, \cdots, \mathbf{Y}_n\}$; let the dimension of this range be r. If necessary, renumber the $\mathbf{X}_i$ and the corresponding $\mathbf{Y}_i$ so that $\mathbf{Y}_1, \cdots, \mathbf{Y}_r$ form a basis for the range. Then, for $i = 1, \cdots, n - r$,

$$\mathbf{Y}_{r+i} = \sum_{j=1}^{r} a_{ij}\mathbf{Y}_j;$$

that is,

$$\mathbf{X}_{r+i}\mathrm{T} = \sum_{j=1}^{r} a_{ij}\mathbf{X}_j\mathrm{T}.$$

Now, if

$$\mathbf{Z}_i = \mathbf{X}_{r+i} - \sum_{j=1}^{r} a_{ij}\mathbf{X}_j,$$

then $\mathbf{Z}_i\mathrm{T} = \mathbf{0}$, for $i = 1, 2, \cdots, n - r$. We maintain that $\mathbf{Z}_1, \cdots, \mathbf{Z}_{n-r}$ form a basis for the null space of T.

First, the $\mathbf{Z}_i$ are independent. If

$$c_1\mathbf{Z}_1 + \cdots + c_{n-r}\mathbf{Z}_{n-r} = \mathbf{0},$$

then

$$c_1\mathbf{X}_{r+1} + c_2\mathbf{X}_{r+2} + \cdots + c_{n-r}\mathbf{X}_n + \sum_{j=1}^{r} d_j\mathbf{X}_j = \mathbf{0},$$

where the d_j are combinations of the a_{ij} and the c's. *All* these coefficients must be zero. Hence $c_1 = c_2 = \cdots = c_{n-r} = 0$. Second, if $\mathbf{Z}\mathrm{T} = \mathbf{0}$, and $\mathbf{Z} = b_1\mathbf{X}_1 + \cdots + b_n\mathbf{X}_n$, let us consider the vector

$$(\mathbf{Z} - b_{r+1}\mathbf{Z}_1 - b_{r+2}\mathbf{Z}_2 - \cdots - b_n\mathbf{Z}_{n-r}) = \mathbf{Z}'.$$

Certainly $\mathbf{Z}'\mathrm{T} = \mathbf{0}$, but $\mathbf{Z}'$ is a linear combination of $\mathbf{X}_1, \cdots, \mathbf{X}_r$ since terms in higher indices of $\mathbf{X}$ have been removed. (The student may wish to write out $\mathbf{Z}'$ and verify this statement.) Say $\mathbf{Z}' = s_1\mathbf{X}_1 + \cdots + s_r\mathbf{X}_r$; then $\mathbf{Z}'\mathrm{T} = \mathbf{0} = s_1\mathbf{Y}_1 + \cdots + s_r\mathbf{Y}_r$. But $\mathbf{Y}_1, \cdots, \mathbf{Y}_r$ are independent so that $s_1 = \cdots = s_r = 0$ and $\mathbf{Z}' = \mathbf{0}$. Therefore $\mathbf{Z} = b_{r+1}\mathbf{Z}_1 + \cdots + b_n\mathbf{Z}_{n-r}$.

Originally, we defined linear transformations as generalizations of certain one-to-one mappings. Let us now determine conditions under which a linear transformation T will, in fact, be a one-to-one mapping. Although the theory may be stated when $W \neq V$, the important applications occur when $W = V$. We impose this restriction in the following theorem:

THEOREM 2.3. *A linear transformation* T *on a vector space* V *is a one-to-one mapping of* V *if and only if either of the following conditions holds:*

(i) *The null space of* T *is the* $\mathbf{0}$ *vector.*

(ii) *The range of* T *is* V.

Proof. Let us consider condition (i). For the "if" part, we must show that $\mathbf{X}\mathrm{T} = \mathbf{Y}\mathrm{T}$ implies $\mathbf{X} = \mathbf{Y}$. From $\mathbf{X}\mathrm{T} = \mathbf{Y}\mathrm{T}$ it follows that $(\mathbf{X} - \mathbf{Y})\mathrm{T} = \mathbf{0}$, and if the null space of T consists of the $\mathbf{0}$ vector alone $\mathbf{X} - \mathbf{Y} = \mathbf{0}$, or $\mathbf{X} = \mathbf{Y}$. As to the "only if" part, we assume that T is a one-to-one mapping. Now if the null space of T is not the $\mathbf{0}$ vector, there is some vector $\mathbf{Z} \neq \mathbf{0}$ such that $\mathbf{Z}\mathrm{T} = \mathbf{0}$. Thus both $\mathbf{Z}\mathrm{T} = \mathbf{0}$ and $\mathbf{0}\mathrm{T} = \mathbf{0}$, and we have the contradiction that T is not a one-to-one mapping. Therefore the null space of T must consist of the $\mathbf{0}$ vector alone.

For condition (ii) we use the results of Theorem 2.2 to obtain

$$\dim V = \dim\,(\text{null space of T}) + \dim\,(\text{range of T}).$$

Using this result, first assume range of T $= V$, then

$$\dim\,(\text{range of T}) = \dim V$$

and therefore dim (null space of T) $= 0$. Hence the null space of T is the $\mathbf{0}$ vector and it follows from condition (i) that T is one-to-one. We leave to the student the proof of the "only if" part of (ii).

EXERCISES

1. Prove formula (2.3).

2. A proof has been given that (2.2) implies (2.1), but it was not proved that (2.1) implies (2.2). Prove this implication and conclude that (2.2) can be used as the defining relation for linear transformations.

3. If a linear transformation T from $V_3(R)$ to $V_2(R)$ is given by

$$\begin{aligned}[1, 0, 0]\mathrm{T} &= [2, 1]\\ [0, 1, 0]\mathrm{T} &= [0, 1]\\ [0, 0, 1]\mathrm{T} &= [1, 1],\end{aligned}$$

find the image of an arbitrary vector $[x_1, x_2, x_3]$ of $V_3(R)$. What is the null space of T? the range of T?

4. Define T from $V_3(R)$ to $V_3(R)$ by

$$\begin{aligned}\mathbf{E}_1\mathrm{T} &= \mathbf{E}_1 + \mathbf{E}_2 - \mathbf{E}_3\\ \mathbf{E}_2\mathrm{T} &= \mathbf{E}_1 - \mathbf{E}_2 + \mathbf{E}_3\\ \mathbf{E}_3\mathrm{T} &= \mathbf{E}_1 - 3\mathbf{E}_2 + 3\mathbf{E}_3.\end{aligned}$$

Find the range and null space of T.

5. Let $\mathbf{X}_1 = [1, 1, -1]$, $\mathbf{X}_2 = [1, 0, 1]$, $\mathbf{X}_3 = [2, 1, -1]$ form a basis for $V_3(R)$, and let $\mathbf{X}_1' = [1, 0, 1, 0]$, $\mathbf{X}_2' = [0, 1, 1, 0]$, $\mathbf{X}_3' = [1, 0, 0, 1]$, $\mathbf{X}_4' = [1, 1, 1, 0]$ form a basis for $V_4(R)$; define T from $V_3(R)$ to $V_4(R)$ by

$$\begin{aligned}\mathbf{X}_1\mathrm{T} &= \mathbf{X}_1' - \mathbf{X}_4'\\ \mathbf{X}_2\mathrm{T} &= \mathbf{X}_1' + \mathbf{X}_2' + \mathbf{X}_3'\\ \mathbf{X}_3\mathrm{T} &= \mathbf{X}_1' + 2\mathbf{X}_2' + 2\mathbf{X}_3' + \mathbf{X}_4'.\end{aligned}$$

Find bases for the range and null space of T.

6. In Exercise 5, re-express T in terms of the $\mathbf{E}_i$ basis vectors for both $V_3(R)$ and $V_4(R)$.

7. Show that the linear transformation T of $V_3(R)$ given by

$$\begin{aligned}\mathbf{E}_1\mathrm{T} &= \mathbf{E}_1 + \mathbf{E}_2\\ \mathbf{E}_2\mathrm{T} &= \mathbf{E}_2 + \mathbf{E}_3\\ \mathbf{E}_3\mathrm{T} &= \mathbf{E}_1 + \mathbf{E}_2 + \mathbf{E}_3\end{aligned}$$

is a one-to-one mapping of $V_3(R)$ onto $V_3(R)$.

8. In Exercise 7, re-express T in terms of the basis vectors $\mathbf{X}_1 = [1, 2, 0]$, $\mathbf{X}_2 = [1, 0, -1]$, $\mathbf{X}_3 = [0, 1, -1]$; that is, obtain the relations

$$\mathbf{X}_i\mathrm{T} = a_{i1}\mathbf{X}_1 + a_{i2}\mathbf{X}_2 + a_{i3}\mathbf{X}_3$$

for $i = 1, 2, 3$.

9. Prove the "only if" part of condition (ii) of Theorem 2.3.

10. Assume that we have a direct sum decomposition of the vector space $V = S \oplus W$ and that T is the projection of V on S along W. What is the null space of T? What is the range of T? Give a geometric description of the range and null space if V is $V_3(R)$. (See Exercise 9 of § 1.)

11. Find linear transformations T_1 and T_2 on $V_2(R)$ such that:

(a) $V_2(R)$ = null space of $T_1 \oplus$ range of T_1, both spaces on the right being one-dimensional.

(b) Null space of T_2 = range of T_2, with both spaces one-dimensional.

12. Let V be a vector space with basis $\{\mathbf{X}_1, \mathbf{X}_2, \cdots, \mathbf{X}_n\}$. Define a linear transformation from V to $V_n(R)$ by

$$\mathbf{X}_i\mathrm{T} = \mathbf{E}_i \qquad (i = 1, 2, \cdots, n).$$

Show that T is one-to-one. Discuss the relation between T and the isomorphism presented in § 4 of Chapter 3.

3. Algebraic Operations on Linear Transformations

We have indicated in the problems of Chapter 1 (Exercises 9 and 10 of § 3) the concept of the successive application of two single-valued mappings. In our present notation, if T_1 is a single-valued mapping from the set V to the set W_1 and T_2 is a single-valued mapping from the set W_1 to the set W_2,

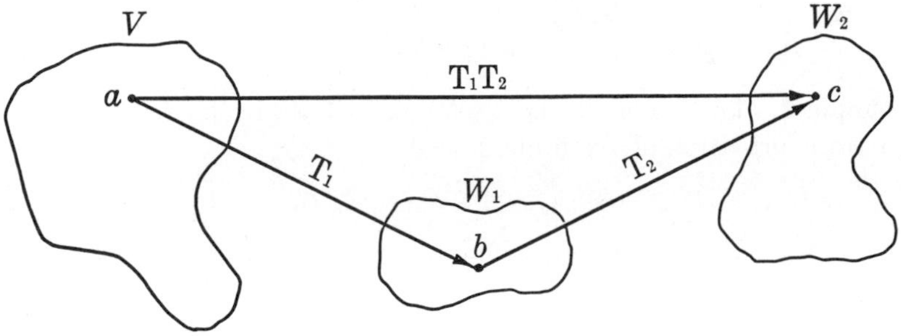

Figure 3.1

then the result of performing first T_1, then T_2, assigns to each element a of V a unique element c of W_2. This assignment provides a single-valued mapping from V to W_2. We shall denote the result of two successive mappings (performing first T_1, then T_2) by T_1T_2. The mapping T_1T_2 is defined to be the *product* of T_1 and T_2. Note that it is not necessary for T_1 to be an "onto" mapping in order that T_1T_2 be defined.

Here we shall be primarily concerned with the case in which V, W_1, and W_2 are all real vector spaces and T_1 and T_2 are linear transformations. In this case, the product mapping T_1T_2 is defined by the relation

$$\mathbf{X}(T_1T_2) = (\mathbf{X}T_1)T_2, \tag{3.1}$$

for all $\mathbf{X}$ of V.

In the functional notation of Chapter 1 for mappings, (3.1) would have the form $(T_1T_2)(\mathbf{X}) = T_2(T_1(\mathbf{X}))$. Our notation for linear transformations makes it unnecessary to print T_1 and T_2 in reverse order on the right-hand side of the equation.

Example 1. We return to the mappings T_θ considered in Example 1 of §1 to see a particularly simple illustration of the product of two linear transformations. Here all the spaces V, W_1, W_2 are identified with $V_2(R)$.

Consider T_{θ_1} and T_{θ_2}; what is $T_{\theta_1}T_{\theta_2}$? Clearly, $T_{\theta_1}T_{\theta_2} = T_{\theta_1+\theta_2}$.

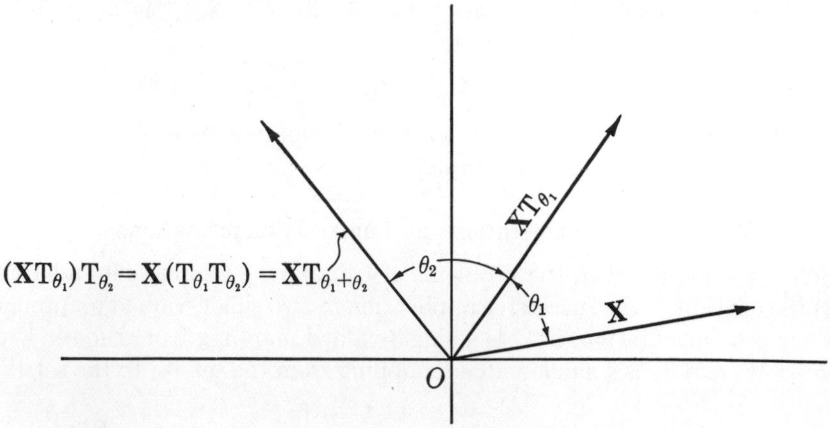

Figure 3.2

Example 2. Let V and W_1 be $V_3(R)$ and let W_2 be $V_2(R)$. If T^* is the linear transformation of Example 2 of §1:

$$[x_1, x_2, x_3]T^* = [x_1, x_2, 0].$$

Define T_2 by
$$[x_1, x_2, x_3]T_2 = [x_1, x_2].$$

Then T^*T_2 is the transformation T of that example:

$$[x_1, x_2, x_3](T^*T_2) = ([x_1, x_2, x_3]T^*)T_2 = [x_1, x_2, 0]T_2 = [x_1, x_2] = [x_1, x_2, x_3]T.$$

Note that if T_a is the linear transformation,

$$[x_1, x_2, x_3]T_a = [x_1, x_2, ax_3],$$

$T_aT_2 = T^*T_2$ although $T_a \neq T^*$ if $a \neq 0$.

In the examples, the product of two linear transformations is again a linear transformation. This is no coincidence.

THEOREM 3.1. *If V, W_1, W_2 are vector spaces and T_1 is a linear transformation from V to W_1, and T_2 a linear transformation from W_1 to W_2, then T_1T_2 is a linear transformation from V to W_2.*

Proof. We must verify the two conditions of (1.3) for the mapping T_1T_2. Thus,

$$\begin{aligned}(\mathbf{X} + \mathbf{Y})(T_1T_2) &= \{(\mathbf{X} + \mathbf{Y})T_1\}T_2 = (\mathbf{X}T_1 + \mathbf{Y}T_1)T_2 \\ &= (\mathbf{X}T_1)T_2 + (\mathbf{Y}T_1)T_2 = \mathbf{X}(T_1T_2) + \mathbf{Y}(T_1T_2); \\ (a\mathbf{X})(T_1T_2) &= \{(a\mathbf{X})T_1\}T_2 = \{a(\mathbf{X}T_1)\}T_2 = a\{(\mathbf{X}T_1)T_2\} = a\{\mathbf{X}(T_1T_2)\}.\end{aligned}$$

The student should go through the proof and supply the reasons for each step from properties whose use is permitted by the hypothesis.

In Example 1, for the linear transformations T_{θ_1} and T_{θ_2}, $T_{\theta_1}T_{\theta_2} = T_{\theta_2}T_{\theta_1} = T_{\theta_1+\theta_2}$. However, the commutativity of these products is due to the special character of the transformations. The commutative law for the product of linear transformations fails in general. Indeed there is no reason why T_2T_1 should be defined when T_1T_2 is. Even when $W_2 = V$, so that both T_1T_2 and T_2T_1 are defined, T_1T_2 is a linear transformation from V to V and T_2T_1 is a linear transformation from W_1 to W_1. Moreover, the

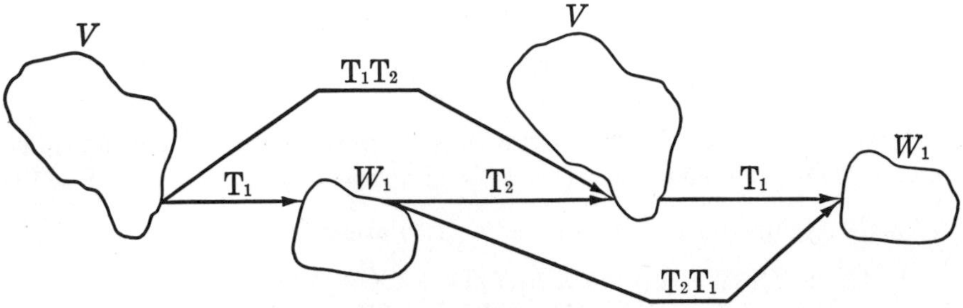

Figure 3.3

following example will show that even when $W_1 = V$, so that both T_1T_2 and T_2T_1 are linear transformations on V, the products T_1T_2 and T_2T_1 may not be equal.

Example 3. Let V, W_1, W_2 be $V_2(R)$. Let T_1 and T_2 be defined by

$$[x_1, x_2]T_1 = [x_2, 2x_1] \quad \text{and} \quad [x_1, x_2]T_2 = [x_1 + x_2, x_2].$$

It is easily verified that T_1 and T_2 are linear transformations. Then

$$\begin{aligned} [x_1, x_2](T_1T_2) &= ([x_1, x_2]T_1)T_2 = [x_2, 2x_1]T_2 = [x_2 + 2x_1, 2x_1], \\ [x_1, x_2](T_2T_1) &= ([x_1, x_2]T_2)T_1 = [x_1 + x_2, x_2]T_1 = [x_2, 2x_1 + 2x_2], \end{aligned}$$

so that, in particular, $[1, 0](T_1T_2) = [2, 2]$ and $[1, 0](T_2T_1) = [0, 2]$. Hence the transformations T_1T_2 and T_2T_1 are not equal.

THEOREM 3.2. *If* T_1, T_2, T_3 *are single-valued mappings respectively from* V *to* W_1, W_1 *to* W_2, *and* W_2 *to* W_3,

$$(T_1T_2)T_3 = T_1(T_2T_3).$$

Proof. The proof is simply an exercise in the use of the definition of the product. It expresses formally the fact that both expressions stand for the transformation obtained by first performing T_1, then T_2, then T_3. Thus,

$$\begin{aligned} \mathbf{X}\{(T_1T_2)T_3\} &= \{\mathbf{X}(T_1T_2)\}T_3 = \{(\mathbf{X}T_1)T_2\}T_3 \\ &= (\mathbf{X}T_1)(T_2T_3) = \mathbf{X}\{T_1(T_2T_3)\}. \end{aligned}$$

We now turn to another algebraic combination of mappings of vector spaces which makes specific use of properties of vector spaces and is not applicable to sets in general.

If T_1 and T_2 are single-valued mappings of the vector space V to the vector space W, then the *sum* of T_1 and T_2 (written $T_1 + T_2$) is a single-valued mapping from V to W defined, for all $\mathbf{X}$ of V, by:

$$\mathbf{X}(T_1 + T_2) = \mathbf{X}T_1 + \mathbf{X}T_2. \tag{3.2}$$

Example 4. Let T_1 and T_2 be as in Example 3. Then,

$$\begin{aligned}[x_1, x_2](T_1 + T_2) = [x_1, x_2]T_1 + [x_1, x_2]T_2 &= [x_2, 2x_1] + [x_1 + x_2, x_2] \\ &= [x_1 + 2x_2, 2x_1 + x_2].\end{aligned}$$

It is easily verified that $(T_1 + T_2)$ is a linear transformation.

THEOREM 3.3. *If T_1 and T_2 are linear transformations from the vector space V to the vector space W, $T_1 + T_2$ is a linear transformation from V to W.*

Proof. Again the two conditions of (1.3) are to be verified:

$$\begin{aligned}(\mathbf{X} + \mathbf{Y})(T_1 + T_2) &= (\mathbf{X} + \mathbf{Y})T_1 + (\mathbf{X} + \mathbf{Y})T_2 \\ &= \mathbf{X}T_1 + \mathbf{Y}T_1 + \mathbf{X}T_2 + \mathbf{Y}T_2 \\ &= \mathbf{X}T_1 + \mathbf{X}T_2 + \mathbf{Y}T_1 + \mathbf{Y}T_2 \\ &= \mathbf{X}(T_1 + T_2) + \mathbf{Y}(T_1 + T_2); \\ (a\mathbf{X})(T_1 + T_2) &= (a\mathbf{X})T_1 + (a\mathbf{X})T_2 = a(\mathbf{X}T_1) + a(\mathbf{X}T_2) \\ &= a\{\mathbf{X}T_1 + \mathbf{X}T_2\} = a\{\mathbf{X}(T_1 + T_2)\}.\end{aligned}$$

The student should verify each step and note in particular where the commutative law for the addition of vectors is applied in the first condition.

In many ways the concept of the sum of two linear transformations is less geometrically direct than the idea of a product. For example the sum

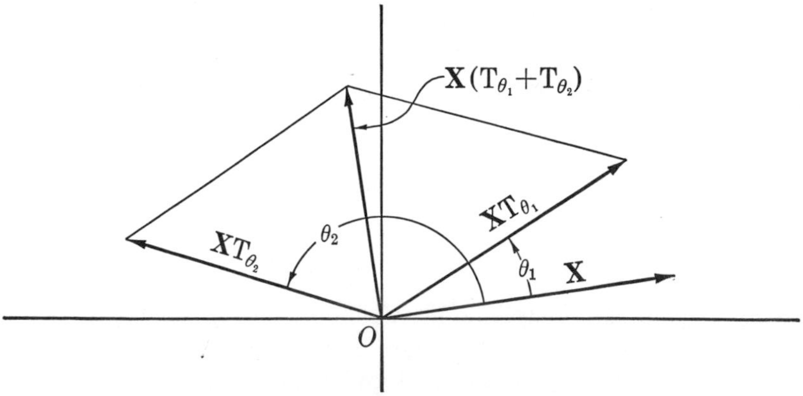

Figure 3.4

$T_{\theta_1} + T_{\theta_2}$ of rotations of Example 1, § 1, is, in general, not identifiable with a rotation at all. The sum of two linear transformations is used primarily as an algebraic convenience to assemble transformations from algebraically simpler ones or perform intermediate manipulations on the way to a definite result (see Exercise 4).

Contrary to the situation for the product of two linear transformations, the sum of two linear transformations is *always* commutative; that is, $T_1 + T_2 = T_2 + T_1$. This property is easily verified. It is stated in the following theorem together with other algebraic properties of linear transformations that are immediate consequences of the definitions of the sum and the product of linear transformations. Their proofs are left for the student.

THEOREM 3.4. *Let V_1, V, W_1, W_2 be real vector spaces;* T_1, T_2, T_3 *linear transformations from V to W_1;* T_4 *a linear transformation from V_1 to V;* T_5 *a linear transformation from W_1 to W_2. Then*

(i) $T_1 + T_2 = T_2 + T_1$; (*Commutative law*)

(ii) $(T_1 + T_2) + T_3 = T_1 + (T_2 + T_3)$; (*Associative law*)

(iii) $T_4(T_1 + T_2) = T_4T_1 + T_4T_2$

(iv) $(T_1 + T_2)T_5 = T_1T_5 + T_2T_5$. (*Distributive laws*)

We have already noted that there is a linear transformation of the vector space V to the vector space W which maps every vector of V to the $\mathbf{0}$ vector of W. Denote this linear transformation by 0; if T is any other single-valued mapping of V to W (not necessarily a linear transformation), it is obvious that

$$\mathbf{X}(T + 0) = \mathbf{X}(0 + T) = \mathbf{X}T$$

for all $\mathbf{X}$ of V. Hence $T + 0 = 0 + T = T$.

For transformations from the vector space V to V there is another special linear transformation which we denote by I (the identity transformation); it is defined by the relation $\mathbf{X}I = \mathbf{X}$ for all $\mathbf{X}$ of V. Now, if T is any single-valued mapping from V to V (not necessarily a linear transformation),

$$\mathbf{X}(IT) = (\mathbf{X}I)T = \mathbf{X}T, \quad \mathbf{X}(TI) = (\mathbf{X}T)I = \mathbf{X}T$$

for all $\mathbf{X}$ of V. Hence $IT = TI = T$.

Let us now consider the set of all linear transformations on the vector space V; that is, mappings from V to V. We have a set of transformations for which an operation of addition (sum) and an operation of multiplication (product) will always be defined. If we turn to the list of laws in Chapter 1 which defined a field, we see by the results of this section (and Exercise 8 below) that A1, A2, A3, A4, A5, M1, M2, M3, and D are all satisfied. Moreover, by Example 3 of this section, M5 is not satisfied (at least not for $V_2(R)$, and similar examples may be exhibited for all vector spaces of dimension greater than 1). As we have seen in §2, many linear transformations are not one-to-one so that they cannot be reversed or inverted in order to satisfy M4.

An algebraic system consisting of a set of objects having operations of multiplication and addition defined such that laws A1, A2, A3, A4, A5, M1, M2, and D of §2, Chapter 1, are valid is called a *ring* (for example, the even integers). If M3 also holds, the system is called a *ring with identity* (for example, the integers). The remarks of the preceding paragraph lead to the following theorem:

THEOREM 3.5. *The linear transformations on a vector space V form a ring with identity with respect to the sum and product of mappings as defined in* (3.1) *and* (3.2).

EXERCISES

1. Let linear transformations T_1, T_2, T_3 from $V_2(R)$ to $V_2(R)$ and $V_2(R)$ to $V_3(R)$ be defined as follows:

$$[x_1, x_2]T_1 = [x_1 - x_2, x_2];$$
$$[x_1, x_2]T_2 = [x_1 - x_2, x_2, x_1];$$
$$[x_1, x_2]T_3 = [x_2, x_1 - x_2, x_1 + x_2].$$

(a) Find: (i) $[1, 0](T_2 + T_3)$; (ii) $[0, 1](T_2 + T_3)$; (iii) $[1, -1](T_1T_2)$; (iv) $[1, -1](T_1T_3)$; (v) $[1, -1]\{T_1(T_2 + T_3)\}$; (vi) $[0, 1]T_1^3$.

(b) $[x_1, x_2](T_1T_2) = ?$

(c) $[x_1, x_2](T_1T_3) = ?$

(d) $[x_1, x_2](T_2 + T_3) = ?$

(e) $[x_1, x_2]\{T_1(T_2 + T_3)\} = ?$

2. Let linear transformations T_1, T_2, T_3 from $V_3(R)$ to $V_4(R)$ and $V_3(R)$ to $V_3(R)$ be defined in the manner of equations (2.4) as follows: Let

$$\mathbf{X}_1 = [1, 0, 1], \quad \mathbf{X}_2 = [1, -1, 1], \quad \mathbf{X}_3 = [0, 1, 1];$$
$$\mathbf{X}_1' = [1, 0, 0, 1], \quad \mathbf{X}_2' = [1, -1, 0, 0], \quad \mathbf{X}_3' = [0, 1, 1, 0], \quad \mathbf{X}_4' = [1, 0, 3, 0],$$

and define T_1, T_2, T_3 by

$$\begin{aligned} \mathbf{X}_1T_1 &= \mathbf{X}_1' + \mathbf{X}_3' \\ \mathbf{X}_2T_1 &= \mathbf{X}_1' - \mathbf{X}_2' \\ \mathbf{X}_3T_1 &= \mathbf{X}_2' + \mathbf{X}_4' \end{aligned} \qquad \begin{aligned} \mathbf{X}_1T_2 &= \mathbf{X}_1' - \mathbf{X}_2' + 2\mathbf{X}_3' \\ \mathbf{X}_2T_2 &= \mathbf{X}_1' - \mathbf{X}_3' + \mathbf{X}_4' \\ \mathbf{X}_3T_2 &= \mathbf{X}_2' + \mathbf{X}_3' \end{aligned}$$

$$\begin{aligned} \mathbf{X}_1T_3 &= \mathbf{X}_1 + \mathbf{X}_2 \\ \mathbf{X}_2T_3 &= \mathbf{X}_2 + \mathbf{X}_3 \\ \mathbf{X}_3T_3 &= \mathbf{X}_1 + \mathbf{X}_3 \end{aligned}$$

(a) Find T_3T_1 in terms of the bases $\{\mathbf{X}_i\}$ and $\{\mathbf{X}_i'\}$.

(b) Find $T_1 + T_2$ in terms of the bases $\{\mathbf{X}_i\}$ and $\{\mathbf{X}_i'\}$.

(c) Re-express T_1, T_2, T_3 in terms of the $\{\mathbf{E}_i\}$ bases for $V_3(R)$ and $V_4(R)$.

(d) Find T_3T_1 in terms of the $\{\mathbf{E}_i\}$ bases.
(e) Find $T_1 + T_2$ in terms of the $\{\mathbf{E}_i\}$ bases.
(f) Find $T_3(T_1 + T_2)$ in terms of the $\{\mathbf{E}_i\}$ bases.

3. For what values of θ_1, θ_2, and θ_3 is $T_{\theta_1} + T_{\theta_2} = T_{\theta_3}$ in Example 1 of § 1?

4. Write T_1 of Exercise 2 as the sum of four linear transformations T_{11}, T_{12}, T_{13}, T_{14} such that T_{1i} is a linear transformation from $V_3(R)$ to $V_4(R)$, whose range is $L\{\mathbf{X}_i'\}$, for $i = 1, 2, 3, 4$.

5. Prove Theorem 3.4.

6. If, in Theorem 3.4, the words "linear transformation(s)" are replaced by "single-valued mapping(s)" each time they occur, which parts of the conclusion remain valid?

7. Prove, for linear transformations T_1 and T_2 for which the product T_1T_2 is defined, that the null space of T_1T_2 contains the null space of T_1 and that the range of T_1T_2 is contained in the range of T_2.

8. Implicit in the discussion at the end of the section is the definition of the *negative* of a linear transformation T (or single-valued mapping) from a vector space V to a vector space W. Give an explicit definition of this negative and verify that if the negative of T is written $-$ T,

$$T + (-T) = 0.$$

Show that $-$ T is a linear transformation if T is.

9. If we have a direct sum decomposition of a vector space

$$V = W_1 \oplus W_2$$

and if T_1 is the projection of V on W_1 along W_2, and T_2 the projection of V on W_2 along W_1, describe the following linear transformations: $T_1 + T_2$, T_1T_2, T_2T_1, T_1^2, T_2^2. (See Exercise 9, § 1.)

10. If T is a linear transformation from a vector space V to a vector space W, define (aT) for any real number a by $\mathbf{X}(aT) = a(\mathbf{X}T)$ for all $\mathbf{X}$ of V.

(a) Show that (aT) is a linear transformation from V to W.

(b) Show that the set of all linear transformations from a vector space V to a vector space W relative to the sum of linear transformations and the scalar multiplication (aT) forms a *vector space*.

(c) Let $\{\mathbf{X}_1, \cdots, \mathbf{X}_n\}$ and $\{\mathbf{X}_1', \cdots, \mathbf{X}_m'\}$ be bases for V and W. For $i = 1, 2, \cdots, n$ and $j = 1, 2, \cdots, m$, define linear transformations T_{ij} by $\mathbf{X}_iT_{ij} = \mathbf{X}_j'$ and $\mathbf{X}_kT_{ij} = \mathbf{0}$ for $k \neq i$. Show that these form a basis for the vector space in (b).

11. Prove for a linear transformation T on a vector space V that $V = \{\text{null space of T}\} \oplus \{\text{range of T}\}$ if and only if $\{\text{null space of } T^2\}$ $=$ $\{\text{null space of T}\}$.

4. Linear Transformations and Matrices

In general, the discussion so far of linear transformations has been applicable to any vector spaces V and W. Now, as a matter of convenience, we shall deal specifically with linear transformations from $V = V_n(R)$ to $W = V_m(R)$. Furthermore we wish to consider in some detail the consequences of using as bases for both spaces the natural basis vectors $\mathbf{E}_i$. This choice will simplify considerably the description of a linear transformation. In order to distinguish between the natural bases of $V_n(R)$ and $V_m(R)$, we will write $\mathbf{E}_i$ for the n-dimensional vectors and $\mathbf{E}_i'$ for the m-dimensional vectors. This means that in equations (2.4), $\mathbf{X}_i = \mathbf{E}_i$, $\mathbf{X}_i' = \mathbf{E}_i'$. Then, rewriting these equations, we may represent (or define) a linear transformation T from $V_n(R)$ to $V_m(R)$ by the equations

$$\begin{aligned}
\mathbf{E}_1\mathrm{T} &= a_{11}\mathbf{E}_1' + a_{12}\mathbf{E}_2' + \cdots + a_{1m}\mathbf{E}_m' = [a_{11}, a_{12}, \cdots, a_{1m}]\\
\mathbf{E}_2\mathrm{T} &= a_{21}\mathbf{E}_1' + a_{22}\mathbf{E}_2' + \cdots + a_{2m}\mathbf{E}_m' = [a_{21}, a_{22}, \cdots, a_{2m}]\\
&\cdots\cdots\cdots\cdots\cdots\cdots\\
\mathbf{E}_n\mathrm{T} &= a_{n1}\mathbf{E}_1' + a_{n2}\mathbf{E}_2' + \cdots + a_{nm}\mathbf{E}_m' = [a_{n1}, a_{n2}, \cdots, a_{nm}];
\end{aligned} \tag{4.1}$$

or briefly,

$$\mathbf{E}_i\mathrm{T} = [a_{i1}, a_{i2}, \cdots, a_{im}], \qquad \text{for } i = 1, 2, \cdots, n.$$

In view of the right-hand side of equations (4.1), it is reasonable to associate with T the rectangular array of nm real numbers

$$A = \begin{bmatrix} a_{11} & a_{12} & \cdots & a_{1m}\\ a_{21} & a_{22} & \cdots & a_{2m}\\ \vdots & \vdots & & \vdots\\ a_{n1} & a_{n2} & \cdots & a_{nm}\end{bmatrix}. \tag{4.2}$$

We are, then, led to a generalization of the concept of matrix mentioned in §4 of Chapter 5: A rectangular array of nm real numbers in n horizontal rows and m vertical columns, as in (4.2), is called an $n \times m$ real *matrix*.

The individual numbers a_{ij} are called the *elements* of a matrix.

A few comments with respect to notation are in order. Matrices will be denoted by italic capital letters when no more explicit designation is needed. These letters are rather overworked, being already used for points of E_n and vector spaces. However, the context and the particular letters selected will help to distinguish the usages.

When attention is to be called to the elements of a matrix, a double subscript notation will be used. The first subscript designates the horizontal row, the second the vertical column occupied by the element. The matrix will be designated by $[a_{ij}]$, where the subscripts have no meaning other than to denote a typical element of the matrix. An $n \times m$ matrix, when designated by $[a_{ij}]$, would be written in expanded form as the matrix A of (4.2).

It is evident that a $1 \times n$ matrix cannot be distinguished in this notation from an element of $V_n(R)$. This ambiguity is intentional.

DEFINITION 4.1. EQUALITY OF MATRICES. *The equality of matrices is defined for matrices of the same order. Two* $n \times m$ *matrices* $[a_{ij}]$ *and* $[b_{ij}]$ *are equal,* $[a_{ij}] = [b_{ij}]$, *if and only if* $a_{ij} = b_{ij}$ *for all* i *and* j. *Thus the corresponding elements of equal matrices are equal.*

We shall indicate the association of the linear transformation T and the matrix $[a_{ij}]$ determined by equations (4.1) by

$$\mathrm{T} \longrightarrow [a_{ij}]. \tag{4.3}$$

The association $\mathrm{T} \longrightarrow [a_{ij}]$ depends upon the fact that the bases $\{\mathbf{E}_i\}$ and $\{\mathbf{E}_i'\}$ were used in representing T, and we shall say that $[a_{ij}]$ is the matrix of T relative to the bases $\{\mathbf{E}_i\}$ and $\{\mathbf{E}_i'\}$. The ith row of $[a_{ij}]$, considered as a vector of $V_m(R)$, is the image of $\mathbf{E}_i$ under T.

If $[b_{ij}]$ is any $n \times m$ matrix, the linear transformation T from $V_n(R)$ to $V_m(R)$ defined by

$$\mathbf{E}_i\mathrm{T} = [b_{i1}, b_{i2}, \cdots, b_{im}] \qquad \text{for } i = 1, 2, \cdots, n$$

will be associated with the matrix $[b_{ij}]$.

Thus, since we have chosen equations (4.1) to represent linear transformations, the association $\mathrm{T} \longrightarrow [a_{ij}]$ establishes a single-valued mapping from the set of all linear transformations from $V_n(R)$ to $V_m(R)$ onto the set of all $n \times m$ matrices. Moreover, we can show that this mapping is one-to-one. Consider the effect of $\mathrm{T} \longrightarrow [a_{ij}]$ on an arbitrary vector $\mathbf{X} = [x_1, x_2, \cdots, x_n]$ of $V_n(R)$:

$$\begin{aligned} \mathbf{X}\mathrm{T} &= (x_1\mathbf{E}_1 + x_2\mathbf{E}_2 + \cdots + x_n\mathbf{E}_n)\mathrm{T} = x_1(\mathbf{E}_1\mathrm{T}) + \cdots + x_n(\mathbf{E}_n\mathrm{T}) \\ &= x_1[a_{11}, a_{12}, \cdots, a_{1m}] + \cdots + x_n[a_{n1}, a_{n2}, \cdots, a_{nm}] \\ &= [x_1a_{11} + x_2a_{21} + \cdots + x_na_{n1}, \cdots, x_1a_{1m} + x_2a_{2m} + \cdots + x_na_{nm}]. \end{aligned} \tag{4.4}$$

Now if $\mathrm{T}_1 \longrightarrow [a_{ij}]$, $\mathrm{T}_2 \longrightarrow [a_{ij}]$, it is clear from (4.4) that $\mathbf{X}\mathrm{T}_1 = \mathbf{X}\mathrm{T}_2$ for all $\mathbf{X}$ of $V_n(R)$ so that $\mathrm{T}_1 = \mathrm{T}_2$ and the mapping $\mathrm{T} \longrightarrow [a_{ij}]$ is one-to-one.

Example 1. The rotations of the plane were given in Exercise 7 of §1 by

$$[x_1, x_2]\mathrm{T}_\theta = [x_1 \cos\theta - x_2 \sin\theta, x_1 \sin\theta + x_2 \cos\theta].$$

We obtain the 2×2 matrix associated with T_θ relative to the $\{\mathbf{E}_i\}$ basis by noting

$$\begin{aligned} [1, 0]\mathrm{T}_\theta &= [\cos\theta, \sin\theta] \\ [0, 1]\mathrm{T}_\theta &= [-\sin\theta, \cos\theta]. \end{aligned}$$

Thus,

$$\mathrm{T}_\theta \longrightarrow \begin{bmatrix} \cos\theta & \sin\theta \\ -\sin\theta & \cos\theta \end{bmatrix}.$$

Example 2. If a linear transformation T of $V_2(R)$ is given by $T \longrightarrow \begin{bmatrix} 2 & 1 \\ -1 & 1 \end{bmatrix}$ relative to the $\{\mathbf{E}_i\}$ basis, we may determine the image of an arbitrary vector $\mathbf{X} = [x_1, x_2]$ of $V_2(R)$ by (4.4). Thus,

$$[x_1, x_2]T = [2x_1 - x_2, x_1 + x_2].$$

We now wish to consider the matrices associated with the sum and product of linear transformations. We let T_1 and T_2 be linear transformations from $V_n(R)$ to $V_m(R)$ given by

$$\begin{aligned} \mathbf{E}_i T_1 &= [a_{i1}, a_{i2}, \cdots, a_{im}] \qquad \text{for } i = 1, 2, \cdots, n \\ \mathbf{E}_i T_2 &= [b_{i1}, b_{i2}, \cdots, b_{im}] \qquad \text{for } i = 1, 2, \cdots, n. \end{aligned}$$

Thus T_1 and T_2 are associated with the $n \times m$ matrices $[a_{ij}]$ and $[b_{ij}]$ relative to the $\{\mathbf{E}_i\}$ bases of $V_n(R)$ and $V_m(R)$.

We let T_3 be a linear transformation from $V_m(R)$ to $V_p(R)$ given by

$$\mathbf{E}_i T_3 = [c_{i1}, c_{i2}, \cdots, c_{ip}] \qquad \text{for } i = 1, 2, \cdots, m,$$

so that T_3 is associated with the $m \times p$ matrix $[c_{ij}]$ relative to the $\{\mathbf{E}_i\}$ bases of $V_m(R)$ and $V_p(R)$.

The question naturally arises: "What are the matrices associated with the transformations $T_1 + T_2$, T_1T_3?" Let us begin with a simple example.

Example 3. Let T_1 and T_2 be defined by

$$\begin{aligned} [1, 0, 0]T_1 &= [1, -1, 2] \qquad & [1, 0, 0]T_2 &= [-1, 1, -2] \\ [0, 1, 0]T_1 &= [0, 1, -1] \qquad & [0, 1, 0]T_2 &= [1, 0, 1] \\ [0, 0, 1]T_1 &= [1, 2, 0] \qquad & [0, 0, 1]T_2 &= [0, 1, 1]. \end{aligned}$$

Then,

$$\begin{aligned} [1, 0, 0](T_1 + T_2) &= [1, 0, 0]T_1 + [1, 0, 0]T_2 = [1, -1, 2] + [-1, 1, -2] \\ &= [0, 0, 0] \\ [0, 1, 0](T_1 + T_2) &= [0, 1, 0]T_1 + [0, 1, 0]T_2 = [0, 1, -1] + [1, 0, 1] \\ &= [1, 1, 0] \\ [0, 0, 1](T_1 + T_2) &= [0, 0, 1]T_1 + [0, 0, 1]T_2 = [1, 2, 0] + [0, 1, 1] \\ &= [1, 3, 1]. \end{aligned}$$

Thus,

$$T_1 + T_2 \longrightarrow \begin{bmatrix} 0 & 0 & 0 \\ 1 & 1 & 0 \\ 1 & 3 & 1 \end{bmatrix} = \begin{bmatrix} 1 + (-1) & (-1) + 1 & 2 + (-2) \\ 0 + \quad 1 & 1 + 0 & (-1) + \quad 1 \\ 1 + \quad 0 & 2 + 1 & 0 + \quad 1 \end{bmatrix}.$$

To find the elements of the matrix associated with $T_1 + T_2$ we have merely added the corresponding elements of the matrices associated with T_1 and T_2.

Now, let T_3 be defined by

$$\begin{aligned}[1, 0, 0]T_3 &= [1, -1],\\ [0, 1, 0]T_3 &= [0, \quad 1],\\ [0, 0, 1]T_3 &= [2, \quad 3].\end{aligned}$$

Then,

$$\begin{aligned}[1, 0, 0](T_1T_3) &= ([1, 0, 0]T_1)T_3 = (1[1, 0, 0] - 1[0, 1, 0] + 2[0, 0, 1])T_3\\ &= 1([1, 0, 0]T_3) - 1([0, 1, 0]T_3) + 2([0, 0, 1]T_3)\\ &= 1[1, -1] - 1[0, 1] + 2[2, 3]\\ &= [1 \cdot 1 - 1 \cdot 0 + 2 \cdot 2,\ 1(-1) - 1 \cdot 1 + 2 \cdot 3] = [5, 4].\end{aligned}$$

Similarly,

$$\begin{aligned}[0, 1, 0](T_1T_3) &= (0[1, 0, 0] + 1[0, 1, 0] - 1[0, 0, 1])T_3\\ &= 0[1, -1] + 1[0, 1] - 1[2, 3]\\ &= [0 \cdot 1 + 1 \cdot 0 - 1 \cdot 2,\ 0(-1) + 1 \cdot 1 - 1 \cdot 3] = [-2, -2],\end{aligned}$$

and

$$\begin{aligned}[0, 0, 1](T_1T_3) &= (1[1, 0, 0] + 2[0, 1, 0] + 0[0, 0, 1])T_3\\ &= 1[1, -1] + 2[0, 1] + 0[2, 3]\\ &= [1 \cdot 1 + 2 \cdot 0 + 0 \cdot 2,\ 1(-1) + 2 \cdot 1 + 0 \cdot 3] = [1, 1].\end{aligned}$$

Hence, $T_1T_3 \longrightarrow \begin{bmatrix} 5 & 4 \\ -2 & -2 \\ 1 & 1 \end{bmatrix}$, and the manner in which the matrix associated with T_1T_3 is obtained from T_1 and T_3 may not be as apparent as in the sum $T_1 + T_2$.

Returning to the general problem, we have

$$\begin{aligned}\mathbf{E}_i(T_1 + T_2) = \mathbf{E}_iT_1 + \mathbf{E}_iT_2 &= [a_{i1}, a_{i2}, \cdots, a_{im}] + [b_{i1}, b_{i2}, \cdots, b_{im}]\\ &= [a_{i1} + b_{i1}, a_{i2} + b_{i2}, \cdots, a_{im} + b_{im}]\end{aligned}$$

for $i = 1, 2, \cdots, n$. Thus,

$$T_1 + T_2 \longrightarrow [a_{ij} + b_{ij}]. \tag{4.5}$$

The problem of representing T_1T_3 is harder, as we might expect from the example:

$$\begin{aligned}\mathbf{E}_i(T_1T_3) &= (\mathbf{E}_iT_1)T_3 = (a_{i1}\mathbf{E}_1' + a_{i2}\mathbf{E}_2' + \cdots + a_{im}\mathbf{E}_m')T_3\\ &= a_{i1}(\mathbf{E}_1'T_3) + a_{i2}(\mathbf{E}_2'T_3) + \cdots + a_{im}(\mathbf{E}_m'T_3)\\ &= a_{i1}[c_{11}, c_{12}, \cdots, c_{1p}] + a_{i2}[c_{21}, c_{22}, \cdots, c_{2p}]\\ &\qquad + \cdots + a_{im}[c_{m1}, c_{m2}, \cdots, c_{mp}]\\ &= [a_{i1}c_{11} + a_{i2}c_{21} + \cdots + a_{im}c_{m1},\ a_{i1}c_{12} + a_{i2}c_{22} + \cdots + a_{im}c_{m2},\\ &\qquad \cdots,\ a_{i1}c_{1p} + a_{i2}c_{2p} + \cdots + a_{im}c_{mp}].\end{aligned}$$

This can be succinctly expressed by the statement: the jth component of the transformation of the basis vector $\mathbf{E}_i$ is $\sum_{k=1}^{m} a_{ik}c_{kj}$; or

$$\mathbf{E}_i(\mathrm{T}_1\mathrm{T}_3) = \left[\sum_{k=1}^{m} a_{ik}c_{k1}, \sum_{k=1}^{m} a_{ik}c_{k2}, \cdots, \sum_{k=1}^{m} a_{ik}c_{kp}\right]$$

for $i = 1, 2, \cdots, n$. Thus,

$$\mathrm{T}_1\mathrm{T}_3 \longrightarrow \left[\sum_{k=1}^{m} a_{ik}c_{kj}\right]. \tag{4.6}$$

EXERCISES

1. What is the form of the matrix associated with the linear transformation $[x_1, x_2, \cdots, x_n]\mathrm{T} = [ax_1, ax_2, \cdots, ax_n]$?

2. If we denote the linear transformation in Exercise 1 by T_a, what is the matrix associated with $\mathrm{T}_a\mathrm{T}_b$?

3. What is the form of the matrix associated with the linear transformation $[x_1, x_2]\mathrm{T} = [x_1 + ax_2, x_2]$?

4. What is the image of an arbitrary vector of appropriate dimension under the linear transformation associated with the following matrices?

(a) $\begin{bmatrix} a & 0 \\ 0 & 1 \end{bmatrix}$ (b) $\begin{bmatrix} 1 & 0 & 0 \\ 0 & 0 & 1 \\ 0 & 1 & 0 \end{bmatrix}$ (c) $\begin{bmatrix} a & 1 & 0 \\ 0 & 1 & 1 \end{bmatrix}$

5. Write the matrices associated with the following transformations:

(a) T_1 is from $V_2(R)$ to $V_2(R)$.
$\mathbf{E}_1\mathrm{T}_1 = [1, 2]$, $\mathbf{E}_2\mathrm{T}_1 = [1, -1]$.

(b) T_2 is from $V_2(R)$ to $V_3(R)$.
$[1, 0]\mathrm{T}_2 = [1, -1, 1]$, $[0, 1]\mathrm{T}_2 = [0, 0, 1]$.

6. Write $\mathrm{T}_1\mathrm{T}_2$ of Exercise 5 as a transformation from $V_2(R)$ to $V_3(R)$ and find the matrix associated with $\mathrm{T}_1\mathrm{T}_2$.

7. Write the matrices associated with the following transformations:

(a) T_1 is from $V_3(R)$ to $V_3(R)$.
$[1, 0, 0]\mathrm{T}_1 = [1, 2, 0]$,
$[0, 1, 0]\mathrm{T}_1 = [1, 0, 2]$,
$[0, 0, 1]\mathrm{T}_1 = [-1, 1, 1]$.

(b) T_2 is from $V_3(R)$ to $V_3(R)$.
$[1, 0, 0]\mathrm{T}_2 = [0, 0, 1]$,
$[0, 1, 0]\mathrm{T}_2 = [-1, 0, 1]$,
$[0, 0, 1]\mathrm{T}_2 = [0, 0, 0]$.

8. Write $\mathrm{T}_1 + \mathrm{T}_2$ and $\mathrm{T}_1\mathrm{T}_2$ of Exercise 7 as transformations on $V_3(R)$ and determine the matrices associated with $\mathrm{T}_1 + \mathrm{T}_2$, $\mathrm{T}_1\mathrm{T}_2$, and $\mathrm{T}_2\mathrm{T}_1$.

5. Algebraic Operations on Matrices

If we are to use matrices as an aid in expressing operations with linear transformations, it seems reasonable that we should define algebraic operations for matrices. Moreover, the expressions (4.5) and (4.6) for the matrices associated with the sum and product of two linear transformations suggest the following useful definitions:

DEFINITION 5.1. ADDITION OF MATRICES. *If* $[a_{ij}]$ *and* $[b_{ij}]$ *are two* $n \times m$ *matrices, their sum is defined to be the* $n \times m$ *matrix* $[c_{ij}]$ *where* $c_{ij} = a_{ij} + b_{ij}$. *Thus,*

$$[a_{ij}] + [b_{ij}] = [a_{ij} + b_{ij}],$$

and matrices of the same order are added by adding corresponding elements. We do not define addition for matrices that are not of the same order.

DEFINITION 5.2. SCALAR MULTIPLICATION OF MATRICES. *The product of a real number* a *and the matrix* $[a_{ij}]$ *is the matrix* $[b_{ij}]$ *where* $b_{ij} = aa_{ij}$. *Thus,*

$$a[a_{ij}] = [aa_{ij}],$$

and the product of a matrix by a real number a *multiplies each element of the matrix by* a.

Example 1. $$\begin{bmatrix} 1 & -1 & 2 \\ 0 & 1 & -1 \\ 1 & 2 & 0 \end{bmatrix} + \begin{bmatrix} -1 & 1 & -2 \\ 1 & 0 & 1 \\ 0 & 1 & 1 \end{bmatrix} = \begin{bmatrix} 0 & 0 & 0 \\ 1 & 1 & 0 \\ 1 & 3 & 1 \end{bmatrix};$$

$$3\begin{bmatrix} 1 & 4 & 0 \\ 1 & -1 & 2 \\ 0 & 1 & 0 \end{bmatrix} = \begin{bmatrix} 3 & 12 & 0 \\ 3 & -3 & 6 \\ 0 & 3 & 0 \end{bmatrix}.$$

The student will note that the matrices used in the example for addition are the matrices associated with T_1 and T_2 of Example 3, §4. The sum, on the other hand, is the matrix associated with the linear transformation $T_1 + T_2$.

Using the preceding definitions for addition and scalar multiplication and, for the *zero matrix*, a matrix all of whose elements are zero, one can easily see that the set of all $n \times m$ matrices forms a vector space of dimension nm. The student should carry out the details and compare the result with Exercise 10 of §3.

DEFINITION 5.3. MULTIPLICATION OF MATRICES. *The product of the* $n \times m$ *matrix* $[a_{ij}]$ *and the* $m \times p$ *matrix* $[b_{ij}]$ *is the* $n \times p$ *matrix* $[c_{ij}]$, *where* $c_{ij} = \sum_{k=1}^{m} a_{ik}b_{kj}$. *Since this product is dependent on the order, we write* $[a_{ij}][b_{ij}] = [c_{ij}]$. *Then* $[b_{ij}][a_{ij}]$ *is not defined unless* $p = n$. *In this special case* $[b_{ij}][a_{ij}] = [d_{ij}]$ *where* $d_{ij} = \sum_{k=1}^{n} b_{ik}a_{kj}$.

Example 2.

$$\begin{bmatrix} 1 & -1 & 2 \\ 0 & 1 & -1 \\ 1 & 2 & 0 \end{bmatrix}\begin{bmatrix} 1 & -1 \\ 0 & 1 \\ 2 & 3 \end{bmatrix}$$

$$= \begin{bmatrix} 1\cdot 1 + (-1)\cdot 0 + 2\cdot 2 & 1\cdot(-1) + (-1)\cdot 1 + 2\cdot 3 \\ 0\cdot 1 + \quad 1\cdot 0 - 1\cdot 2 & 0\cdot(-1) + \quad 1\cdot 1 - 1\cdot 3 \\ 1\cdot 1 + \quad 2\cdot 0 + 0\cdot 2 & 1\cdot(-1) + \quad 2\cdot 1 + 0\cdot 3 \end{bmatrix}$$

$$= \begin{bmatrix} 5 & 4 \\ -2 & -2 \\ 1 & 1 \end{bmatrix}.$$

The student will note here that the first two matrices are the matrices associated with the linear transformations T_1 and T_3 of Example 3, §4. Their product is the matrix associated with (T_1T_3). The product

$$\begin{bmatrix} 1 & -1 \\ 0 & 1 \\ 2 & 3 \end{bmatrix}\begin{bmatrix} 1 & -1 & 2 \\ 0 & 1 & -1 \\ 1 & 2 & 0 \end{bmatrix}$$

is not defined. This is not surprising, as the linear transformation T_3T_1 is not defined.

Example 3. Let

$$A = \begin{bmatrix} 1 & 1 & 1 & -1 \\ 0 & 1 & 1 & 2 \\ 2 & 1 & 0 & 1 \end{bmatrix}, \qquad C = \begin{bmatrix} 1 & -1 & 3 \\ 2 & 3 & 5 \\ 4 & 1 & 2 \\ -3 & 2 & 1 \end{bmatrix}.$$

AC and CA are both defined and

$$AC = \begin{bmatrix} 10 & 1 & 9 \\ 0 & 8 & 9 \\ 1 & 3 & 12 \end{bmatrix}, \qquad CA = \begin{bmatrix} 7 & 3 & 0 & 0 \\ 12 & 10 & 5 & 4 \\ 8 & 7 & 5 & 0 \\ -1 & 0 & -1 & 8 \end{bmatrix}.$$

Multiplication of matrices will become reasonably easy with practice and utilization of the rule "across the row of the first, down the column of the second." That is, to obtain the element in the ith row and jth column of the product, take the ith row of the first matrix, multiply its elements by the corresponding elements of the jth column of the second, and add these products together. This is illustrated in detail in Example 2. Another way of stating the same thing is to say that this element of the product is the scalar product of the ith row of the first and the jth column of the second, both regarded as vectors of $V_m(R)$.

The concept of matrix multiplication can be used efficiently in determining the image of the vector $\mathbf{X} = [x_1, x_2, \cdots, x_n]$ under a linear transformation T from $V_n(R)$ to $V_m(R)$. Let $T \longrightarrow [a_{ij}]$ relative to the $\{\mathbf{E}_i\}$ bases and consider the matrix product

$$XA = [x_1, x_2, \cdots, x_n]\begin{bmatrix} a_{11} & a_{12} & \cdots & a_{1m} \\ a_{21} & a_{22} & \cdots & a_{2m} \\ \vdots & \vdots & & \vdots \\ a_{n1} & a_{n2} & \cdots & a_{nm} \end{bmatrix},$$

or $\quad XA = [x_1a_{11} + x_2a_{21} + \cdots + x_na_{n1}, \cdots, x_1a_{1m} + x_2a_{2m} + \cdots + x_na_{nm}].$

The result is a $1 \times m$ matrix whose elements are identical with the components of **XT** of (4.4). To the vector relation $\mathbf{XT} = \mathbf{Y}$ corresponds a matrix relation of the components of **X** and **Y**

(5.1) $$[x_1, x_2, \cdots, x_n]A = [y_1, y_2, \cdots, y_m].$$

It is unnecessary to distinguish longer between the vector **X** and the $1 \times n$ matrix X; **X** will serve for both.

The representations (4.5) and (4.6) for the sum and product of two linear transformations can be combined with the definitions for the sum and product of matrices to yield the following theorem:

THEOREM 5.1. *Let* T_1 *and* T_2 *be linear transformations from* $V_n(R)$ *to* $V_m(R)$ *and* T_3 *be a linear transformation from* $V_m(R)$ *to* $V_p(R)$. *If* T_1, T_2, *and* T_3 *are associated with matrices (relative to the* $\{\mathbf{E}_i\}$ *basis) by* $T_1 \longrightarrow [a_{ij}]$, $T_2 \longrightarrow [b_{ij}]$, $T_3 \longrightarrow [c_{ij}]$, *then*

$$T_1 + T_2 \longrightarrow [a_{ij}] + [b_{ij}].$$
$$T_1T_3 \longrightarrow [a_{ij}][c_{ij}].$$

The results of this theorem are not surprising; the operations of addition and multiplication for matrices were motivated by the representation of linear transformations.

THEOREM 5.2. *The multiplication of matrices is associative when it is defined; that is,* $A(BC) = (AB)C$.

Preliminary remark: A proof of this theorem can be given directly in terms of Definition 5.3. It would involve considerable manipulation of summation signs and subscripts, but it is straightforward, just not neat. In the language of mathematicians, "It lacks elegance." Not only is the proof to be given neater, it will use the associations of Theorem 5.1 and illustrate another form of an isomorphism similar to that for vector spaces.

Proof. Suppose that matrices A, B, C are compatible in the sense that $(AB)C$ exists. To fix our ideas, say that A is $n \times m$, B is $m \times r$, and C is $r \times p$. Then $A(BC)$ also exists, and both are $n \times p$.

Now, with A we associate a linear transformation T_1 from $V_n(R)$ to $V_m(R)$; that is, $T_1 \longrightarrow A$; with B we associate a linear transformation $T_2 \longrightarrow B$ from $V_m(R)$ to $V_r(R)$; and with C we associate a linear transformation $T_3 \longrightarrow C$ from $V_r(R)$ to $V_p(R)$. By Theorem 5.1,

$$(T_1T_2)T_3 \longrightarrow (AB)C,$$
$$T_1(T_2T_3) \longrightarrow A(BC).$$

But $(T_1T_2)T_3 = T_1(T_2T_3)$ by Theorem 3.2. Then, because the mapping from linear transformations of $V_n(R)$ to $V_p(R)$ onto $n \times p$ matrices is one-to-one, it follows that $(AB)C = A(BC)$.

Let us look for a moment at the idea that proved so effective in the last proof. First, it should be pointed out that, although we have indicated a close association between linear transformations and matrices, the set of all matrices (with an addition and multiplication where possible) forms an algebraic system in its own right. We have two algebraic systems of elements: linear transformations and matrices. For convenience, let us take $m = n$ so that the linear transformations are from $V_n(R)$ to $V_n(R)$ and the matrices are square. In this case we have both a sum and a product defined for each system. Now, relative to the $\{\mathbf{E}_i\}$ basis, we have a one-to-one mapping

$$T \longrightarrow [a_{ij}]$$

between the two sets. Then, from Theorem 5.1, we have the property that if

$$T_1 \longrightarrow [a_{ij}], \quad T_2 \longrightarrow [b_{ij}],$$

then

$$T_1 + T_2 \longrightarrow [a_{ij}] + [b_{ij}];$$
$$T_1T_2 \longrightarrow [a_{ij}][b_{ij}].$$

The mapping between linear transformations and matrices makes the sum and product of two linear transformations correspond to the sum and product of their associated matrices. Any property of linear transformations that involves only the operations of addition and multiplication will be reflected by means of the association $T \longrightarrow [a_{ij}]$ as a similar property of addition and multiplication of matrices. We would say that *algebraically* (with respect to addition and multiplication) the two sets are indistinguishable, or *isomorphic;* any algebraic theorem proved about one system is at once true in the other. From Theorem 3.5 we have immediately the following result:

THEOREM 5.3. *The set of all $n \times n$ matrices forms a ring with identity with respect to the addition and multiplication of matrices as defined in Definitions* 5.1 *and* 5.3.

The identity matrix for the ring of $n \times n$ matrices is associated with the identity linear transformation. Since $\mathbf{X}\mathrm{I} = \mathbf{X}$ or $\mathbf{E}_i\mathrm{I} = \mathbf{E}_i$, the $n \times n$ identity matrix is

$$I = \begin{bmatrix} 1 & 0 & \cdots & 0 \\ 0 & 1 & \cdots & 0 \\ \vdots & \vdots & & \vdots \\ 0 & 0 & \cdots & 1 \end{bmatrix}$$

with the only nonzero elements being 1's down the main diagonal.

It is easy to see directly that neither law M4 nor law M5 for fields holds in general for $n \times n$ matrices. For example, $\begin{bmatrix} 1 & 1 \\ 1 & 1 \end{bmatrix}$ has no multiplicative inverse. If there were a matrix A such that

$$A\begin{bmatrix} 1 & 1 \\ 1 & 1 \end{bmatrix} = \begin{bmatrix} 1 & 0 \\ 0 & 1 \end{bmatrix} \quad \text{(the } 2 \times 2 \text{ identity matrix),}$$

then

$$\begin{bmatrix} 1 & 1 \\ -1 & -1 \end{bmatrix} = \left(A\begin{bmatrix} 1 & 1 \\ 1 & 1 \end{bmatrix}\right)\begin{bmatrix} 1 & 1 \\ -1 & -1 \end{bmatrix} = A\left(\begin{bmatrix} 1 & 1 \\ 1 & 1 \end{bmatrix}\begin{bmatrix} 1 & 1 \\ -1 & -1 \end{bmatrix}\right)$$
$$= A\begin{bmatrix} 0 & 0 \\ 0 & 0 \end{bmatrix} = \begin{bmatrix} 0 & 0 \\ 0 & 0 \end{bmatrix};$$

an obvious contradiction.

Many matrices do have multiplicative inverses; for example,

$$\begin{bmatrix} 1 & 1 \\ 1 & 2 \end{bmatrix}\begin{bmatrix} 2 & -1 \\ -1 & 1 \end{bmatrix} = \begin{bmatrix} 2 & -1 \\ -1 & 1 \end{bmatrix}\begin{bmatrix} 1 & 1 \\ 1 & 2 \end{bmatrix} = \begin{bmatrix} 1 & 0 \\ 0 & 1 \end{bmatrix}.$$

Matrices that do have multiplicative inverses are called *nonsingular*. In the next section the properties of singularity and nonsingularity will be examined in more detail.

EXERCISES

1. Find the sum of the following matrices:

(a) $\begin{bmatrix} 1 & -1 \\ 2 & 0 \end{bmatrix} + \begin{bmatrix} -1 & 2 \\ 3 & 1 \end{bmatrix}$. (b) $\begin{bmatrix} 1 & 2 & -1 \\ 0 & 1 & 3 \end{bmatrix} + \begin{bmatrix} 1 & 3 & 5 \\ 2 & 4 & 6 \end{bmatrix}$.

2. Show that the matrices

$$3\begin{bmatrix} 1 & 0 & -2 \\ 1 & 0 & 1 \end{bmatrix} \quad \text{and} \quad \begin{bmatrix} 3 & 0 \\ 0 & 3 \end{bmatrix}\begin{bmatrix} 1 & 0 & -2 \\ 1 & 0 & 1 \end{bmatrix}$$

are equal.

3. Generalize Exercise 2 and express the matrix $a[a_{ij}]$ as the product of two matrices.

4. Find the products listed, if they exist, among

$$A = \begin{bmatrix} 1 & -1 \\ 2 & 3 \end{bmatrix}, \quad B = \begin{bmatrix} 1 & 1 & 1 \\ -1 & 2 & 4 \end{bmatrix},$$

$$C = \begin{bmatrix} 1 & 0 & 0 \\ 0 & 1 & 0 \\ 0 & 1 & 1 \end{bmatrix}, \quad D = \begin{bmatrix} 1 & 1 \\ -1 & 1 \\ 2 & 3 \end{bmatrix}.$$

(a) AD; (b) $(AB)C$; (c) $A(BC)$; (d) BD; (e) BDA; (f) ABD; (g) CB; (h) A^2.

5. Let linear transformations T and S on $V_3(R)$ be given by

$$\mathrm{T} \longrightarrow \begin{bmatrix} 1 & 2 & -1 \\ 1 & 0 & 1 \\ 0 & 2 & 1 \end{bmatrix}, \quad \mathrm{S} \longrightarrow \begin{bmatrix} 1 & -1 & 1 \\ 1 & 2 & 0 \\ 1 & 1 & 1 \end{bmatrix}.$$

Find:

(a) The image of $[1, -1, 0]$ under T.
(b) The image of $[0, 2, -2]$ under S.
(c) The matrix associated with the linear transformation TS.
(d) The matrix associated with T + S.
(e) The image of $[1, -1, 0]$ under TS. Compare your answer with (b).

6. Given the matrices

$$A = \begin{bmatrix} 1 & -1 \\ 2 & 1 \end{bmatrix}, \quad B = \begin{bmatrix} 1 & 2 \\ 1 & 1 \end{bmatrix},$$

show that $AB \neq BA$.

7. Find all the 2×2 matrices that commute with the matrix

$$\begin{bmatrix} \cos\theta & \sin\theta \\ -\sin\theta & \cos\theta \end{bmatrix}$$

and determine the linear transformations of $V_2(R)$ that commute with rotations. (See Example 1, §4.)

8. Let $a + bi$ be an element of the ring (also field) of complex numbers; i.e., $(a + bi) + (c + di) = (a + c) + (b + d)i$; $(a + bi)(c + di) = (ac - bd) + (ad + bc)i$. Show that the one-to-one correspondence

$$a + bi \longrightarrow \begin{bmatrix} a & b \\ -b & a \end{bmatrix}$$

makes the sum and product of complex numbers correspond to the sum and product of matrices of the form

$$\begin{bmatrix} a & b \\ -b & a \end{bmatrix}.$$

Thus, an isomorphism is established between the complex numbers and a set of 2×2 matrices.

9. Prove Theorem 5.1 directly in terms of the definition of matrix multiplication.

10. In the matrix product of an $n \times m$ matrix $[a_{ij}]$ and an $m \times p$ matrix $[b_{ij}]$, show that the ith row of $[a_{ij}][b_{ij}]$ is a linear combination of the rows of $[b_{ij}]$. Show that the jth column of $[a_{ij}][b_{ij}]$ is a linear combination of the columns of $[a_{ij}]$.

6. Nonsingular Linear Transformations and Matrices

The subject of one-to-one linear transformations was discussed in §2 with reference to the range and null space of such transformations. We shall now consider these transformations in more detail and relate them to the nonsingular matrices introduced at the close of the last section. Throughout this section we shall deal only with single-valued mappings from a real vector space V to V and these will be called briefly *mappings on* V. (The student is invited to consider what generalizations can easily be made.)

Let us begin by placing an idea first introduced in an exercise (Exercise 10, §3, Chapter 1) in the context of vector spaces and of our present notation.

THEOREM 6.1. *Let* T_1 *be a mapping on* V. *We consider the existence and properties of a mapping* T_2 *on* V *such that* $T_1T_2 = T_2T_1 = I$ (*the identity mapping*):

(i) *If* T_1 *is one-to-one onto* V, *then a mapping* T_2 *exists.*
(ii) *If a mapping* T_2 *exists, then* T_1 *is one-to-one onto* V.
(iii) *If* T_2 *exists, then it is uniquely defined.*
(iv) *If* T_2 *exists, then it is one-to-one onto* V.

Proof. (i) If T_1 is one-to-one onto V, then, for any vector $\mathbf{X}$ of V, there is a unique vector $\mathbf{Y}$ of V such that $\mathbf{Y}T_1 = \mathbf{X}$. Define T_2 by $\mathbf{X}T_2 = \mathbf{Y}$. It is clear that T_2 is a mapping on V being uniquely defined for every vector of V. Now, if $\mathbf{Y}T_1 = \mathbf{X}$, we have: $(\mathbf{Y}T_1)T_2 = \mathbf{X}T_2 = \mathbf{Y}$ by the definition of T_2. Similarly $(\mathbf{X}T_2)T_1 = \mathbf{Y}T_1 = \mathbf{X}$. Thus both T_1T_2 and T_2T_1 map every vector of V onto itself; they are the identity mapping.

(ii) If T_1 is not one-to-one, then there are distinct vectors $\mathbf{X}$ and $\mathbf{Y}$ of V such that $\mathbf{X}T_1 = \mathbf{Y}T_1 = \mathbf{Z}$. Now if $T_1T_2 = I$, we must have $\mathbf{Z}T_2 = \mathbf{X}$, $\mathbf{Z}T_2 = \mathbf{Y}$, and T_2 would not be single-valued; hence we have a contradiction to our hypothesis.

If T_1 is not onto V, then there is a vector $\mathbf{X}$ which is not an image under T_1. However, $\mathbf{X}(T_2T_1) = \mathbf{X}$ or $(\mathbf{X}T_2)T_1 = \mathbf{X}$, and $\mathbf{X}$ is the image of $(\mathbf{X}T_2)$ under T_1; again a contradiction.

(iii) Suppose T_1 is one-to-one onto V and $T_1T_2 = T_1T_3 = I$. If $\mathbf{X}$ is any vector of V, let $\mathbf{X} = \mathbf{Y}T_1$; then $\mathbf{X}T_2 = (\mathbf{Y}T_1)T_2 = \mathbf{Y}$ and $\mathbf{X}T_3 = (\mathbf{Y}T_1)T_3 = \mathbf{Y}$. Hence $\mathbf{X}T_2 = \mathbf{X}T_3$ for all $\mathbf{X}$ of V so that $T_2 = T_3$.

(iv) The mapping T_2 has the same relation to T_1 as T_1 to T_2 so that the argument of (ii) applies equally well to T_2; thus T_2 is one-to-one onto V.

The mapping T_2 is called the *inverse* of T_1; conversely, T_1 is the inverse of T_2. We write $T_1^{-1} = T_2$ or $T_2^{-1} = T_1$ so that $T_1T_1^{-1} = T_1^{-1}T_1 = I$.

Our primary concern is with linear transformations. Here we may drop the separate requirements of "one-to-one" and "onto V," for condition (ii) of Theorem 2.3 essentially states that a linear transformation on V is one-to-one if and only if it is "onto" V.

THEOREM 6.2. *If T_1 is a linear transformation on V for which there is a mapping T_2 on V such that $T_1T_2 = I$, then $T_2T_1 = I$.*

Proof. If T_1 is one-to-one, then there is a mapping T_3 such that $T_3T_1 = I$. Then $T_3 = T_3(T_1T_2) = (T_3T_1)T_2 = T_2$. If T_1 is not one-to-one, the first argument of part (ii) in the proof of Theorem 6.1 shows that $T_1T_2 \neq I$.

The question now arises: "Is the inverse of a one-to-one linear transformation on V again a linear transformation?"

When we look at the examples of one-to-one linear transformations, T_θ (Example 1, §1), for $V_2(R)$, we see that the inverse of T_θ is simply $T_{2\pi-\theta}$ (or $T_{-\theta}$ if we interpret the minus sign as implying clockwise rotation). The example may be generalized.

THEOREM 6.3. *If T is a one-to-one linear transformation on V, T^{-1} is also a linear transformation.*

Proof. Given any two vectors $\mathbf{X}_1$ and $\mathbf{X}_2$ of V and any two real numbers a and b, we must show that

$$(a\mathbf{X}_1 + b\mathbf{X}_2)T^{-1} = a(\mathbf{X}_1T^{-1}) + b(\mathbf{X}_2T^{-1}).$$

Since T is one-to-one, there are unique vectors $\mathbf{Y}_1$ and $\mathbf{Y}_2$ of V such that $\mathbf{X}_1 = \mathbf{Y}_1T$, $\mathbf{X}_2 = \mathbf{Y}_2T$. Then,

$$\begin{aligned}(a\mathbf{X}_1 + b\mathbf{X}_2)T^{-1} &= \{a(\mathbf{Y}_1T) + b(\mathbf{Y}_2T)\}T^{-1} = \{(a\mathbf{Y}_1)T + (b\mathbf{Y}_2)T\}T^{-1}\\ &= \{(a\mathbf{Y}_1 + b\mathbf{Y}_2)T\}T^{-1} = (a\mathbf{Y}_1 + b\mathbf{Y}_2)(TT^{-1}) = a\mathbf{Y}_1 + b\mathbf{Y}_2\\ &= a(\mathbf{X}_1T^{-1}) + b(\mathbf{X}_2T^{-1}),\end{aligned}$$

since $\mathbf{Y}_1 = \mathbf{X}_1T^{-1}$ and $\mathbf{Y}_2 = \mathbf{X}_2T^{-1}$ from the definition of T^{-1}. The previous steps use the linearity of T and the assumption $TT^{-1} = I$.

DEFINITION 6.1. *A linear transformation on V which is one-to-one and thus possesses an inverse that is one-to-one is called a* NONSINGULAR *linear transformation.*

(The student should compare this definition with the definition of a nonsingular matrix in the preceding section.)

Example 1. Let T be a linear transformation of $V_3(R)$ defined by

$$[x_1, x_2, x_3]\mathrm{T} = [x_1 - x_2, x_2, x_3].$$

If T_1 is the linear transformation

$$[x_1, x_2, x_3]\mathrm{T}_1 = [x_1 + x_2, x_2, x_3],$$

we see that

$$[x_1, x_2, x_3](\mathrm{T} \cdot \mathrm{T}_1) = [x_1 - x_2, x_2, x_3]\mathrm{T}_1 = [x_1, x_2, x_3].$$

The transformation T_1 is the inverse T^{-1} of the transformation T. The student can easily show that $\mathrm{T}^{-1}\mathrm{T}$ (or $\mathrm{T}_1\mathrm{T}$) is I; moreover, we leave it to the student to show that T and T_1 are one-to-one mappings on $V_3(R)$.

We next prove two properties of nonsingular linear transformations which will be useful in the sequel. These properties are closely related to those deduced in Theorem 2.3, which the student should recall before proceeding.

THEOREM 6.4. *A linear transformation* T *on a vector space* V *is nonsingular if and only if the vectors* $\mathbf{X}_1\mathrm{T}, \mathbf{X}_2\mathrm{T}, \cdots, \mathbf{X}_r\mathrm{T}$ *are linearly independent whenever the vectors* $\mathbf{X}_1, \mathbf{X}_2, \cdots, \mathbf{X}_r$ *are linearly independent.*

Proof. Suppose that T is nonsingular and that, for some set of linearly independent vectors $\{\mathbf{X}_1, \mathbf{X}_2, \cdots, \mathbf{X}_r\}$,

$$a_1(\mathbf{X}_1\mathrm{T}) + a_2(\mathbf{X}_2\mathrm{T}) + \cdots + a_r(\mathbf{X}_r\mathrm{T}) = \mathbf{0}.$$

Then

$$(a_1\mathbf{X}_1 + a_2\mathbf{X}_2 + \cdots + a_r\mathbf{X}_r)\mathrm{T} = \mathbf{0}$$

and

$$(a_1\mathbf{X}_1 + a_2\mathbf{X}_2 + \cdots + a_r\mathbf{X}_r)\mathrm{T}\mathrm{T}^{-1} = \mathbf{0}\mathrm{T}^{-1} = \mathbf{0}.$$

Thus, $a_1\mathbf{X}_1 + a_2\mathbf{X}_2 + \cdots + a_r\mathbf{X}_r = \mathbf{0}$ and, necessarily, $a_1 = a_2 = \cdots = a_r = 0$ as the vectors $\mathbf{X}_1, \mathbf{X}_2, \cdots, \mathbf{X}_r$ are linearly independent. Hence, $\mathbf{X}_1\mathrm{T}, \mathbf{X}_2\mathrm{T}, \cdots, \mathbf{X}_r\mathrm{T}$ are linearly independent.

Now for the "if" part. Suppose that T maps any set of linearly independent vectors onto a set of linearly independent vectors. Any nonzero vector $\mathbf{Z}$ is linearly independent and therefore $\mathbf{Z}\mathrm{T} \neq \mathbf{0}$ if $\mathbf{Z} \neq \mathbf{0}$ since $\mathbf{0}$ is a linearly dependent vector. Hence, the null space of T is the $\mathbf{0}$ vector and it follows from Theorem 2.3 (i) that T is one-to-one and nonsingular.

COROLLARY. *A linear transformation* T *is nonsingular if and only if the set of images of a fixed basis of* V *is again a basis of* V.

The "only if" part of this corollary is an immediate consequence of Theorem 6.4. (Why?) On the other hand, the "if" part is an immediate consequence of Theorem 2.3 (ii); that is, the range of T is V and hence T is one-to-one and therefore nonsingular.

Example 2. Let T be the linear transformation on $V_3(R)$ given by

$$[x_1, x_2, x_3]\mathrm{T} = [x_1 + 2x_2 - x_3, x_1 + 2x_3, 2x_1 - x_2 + 3x_3].$$

The natural basis vectors $\mathbf{E}_1$, $\mathbf{E}_2$, $\mathbf{E}_3$ are mapped by T onto the vectors $[1, 1, 2]$, $[2, 0, -1]$, and $[-1, 2, 3]$ respectively. Since

$$\begin{vmatrix} 1 & 1 & 2 \\ 2 & 0 & -1 \\ -1 & 2 & 3 \end{vmatrix} = 5,$$

these vectors are linearly independent (Why?) and hence T is a nonsingular linear transformation.

We now desire to obtain a relation between nonsingular transformations and nonsingular matrices. We therefore replace the vector space V by the vector space $V_n(R)$.

THEOREM 6.5. *The matrix of a nonsingular linear transformation on $V_n(R)$, relative to the natural basis $\{\mathbf{E}_i\}$, is nonsingular. Conversely, any nonsingular $n \times n$ matrix is the matrix, relative to the natural basis $\{\mathbf{E}_i\}$, of a nonsingular linear transformation on $V_n(R)$.*

Proof. Let T be a nonsingular linear transformation on V; let A and B be the matrices associated with T and T^{-1} relative to the natural basis $\{\mathbf{E}_i\}$. Then AB is associated with TT^{-1}; that is, AB is the matrix associated with the identity transformation. This matrix is clearly the $n \times n$ identity matrix so that $AB = I$. Similarly $BA = I$ and B is an inverse matrix of A.

Now, assume that A is an $n \times n$ matrix possessing an inverse A^{-1}. Let T_1 be the linear transformation associated with A, relative to the $\{\mathbf{E}_i\}$ basis, and let T_2 be similarly associated with A^{-1}. Then $\mathrm{T}_1\mathrm{T}_2$ is associated with the matrix $AA^{-1} = I$ (the $n \times n$ identity matrix); that is, $\mathrm{T}_1\mathrm{T}_2$ is the identity transformation. Hence, from Theorem 6.2, T_1 is a nonsingular linear transformation.

The following corollaries are immediate consequences of our previous results for nonsingular linear transformations. The student should provide the proofs.

COROLLARY 1. *If A and B are $n \times n$ matrices such that $AB = I$, then $BA = I$ and A and B are nonsingular matrices.*

COROLLARY 2. *If $AB = I$ and $AC = I$ where A, B, C are $n \times n$ matrices, $B = C$. Inverses of nonsingular matrices are unique.*

This section will conclude with an application of the Corollary of Theorem 6.4 to the recognition of nonsingular matrices.

THEOREM 6.6. *An $n \times n$ matrix A is nonsingular if and only if the following equivalent conditions apply:*

(i) *The rows of A regarded as vectors of $V_n(R)$ are linearly independent.*

(ii) *The determinant of A is not zero.*

(iii) *The columns of A (the rows of A^{T}) regarded as vectors of $V_n(R)$ are linearly independent.*

Proof. That the three conditions are equivalent has been proved in the chapter on determinants. Thus the theorem will be proved if we establish it for any one of them. The image of $\mathbf{E}_i$, under the linear transformation associated with A with respect to the $\{\mathbf{E}_i\}$ basis, is precisely the ith row of A regarded as a vector of $V_n(R)$. Hence, this transformation is nonsingular if and only if the rows of A are a basis of $V_n(R)$; that is, if and only if the rows are linearly independent. Further, A is nonsingular if and only if the transformation is nonsingular.

EXERCISES

1. Show that the mapping T on $V_3(R)$ defined by

$$[x_1, x_2, x_3]\mathrm{T} = [x_1 - 2, x_2, x_3 + x_1]$$

is a one-to-one mapping on $V_3(R)$ which is not a linear transformation. What is $[x_1, x_2, x_3]\mathrm{T}^{-1}$?

2. Is the linear transformation T defined by

$$[x_1, x_2]\mathrm{T} = [x_1 - x_2, x_1 + x_2]$$

nonsingular? If so, find its inverse.

3. Is the linear transformation T defined by

$$[x_1, x_2, x_3]\mathrm{T} = [x_1 + x_2 + x_3, x_2 + x_3, x_3]$$

nonsingular? If so, find its inverse.

4. Prove the following: Let T be a linear transformation on a vector space V. If the vectors $\mathbf{X}_1\mathrm{T}, \cdots, \mathbf{X}_k\mathrm{T}$ are linearly independent, then the vectors $\mathbf{X}_1, \cdots, \mathbf{X}_k$ are linearly independent. (Note that there is no reference to the nonsingularity of T in this partial converse to Theorem 6.4.)

5. Write the matrix associated with T of Exercise 2 with respect to the $\{\mathbf{E}_i\}$ basis. Find an inverse of this matrix if there is one.

6. Write the matrix associated with T of Exercise 3 with respect to the $\{\mathbf{E}_i\}$ basis. Find an inverse of this matrix if there is one.

7. Let $A = \begin{bmatrix} 1 & 0 & 1 \\ 1 & 1 & 0 \end{bmatrix}$, $B = \begin{bmatrix} 1 & -1 \\ -1 & 2 \\ 0 & 1 \end{bmatrix}$.

(a) Show that $AB = I$, $BA \neq I$. Discuss this result with respect to Corollary 1 of Theorem 6.5.

(b) Let T_1 be the linear transformation from $V_2(R)$ to $V_3(R)$ whose matrix is A with respect to the $\{\mathbf{E}_i\}$ basis. Similarly, let T_2 be the linear transformation from $V_3(R)$ to $V_2(R)$ whose matrix is B. Is either of these transformations one-to-one? What is the significance of the equation $T_1T_2 = I$?

8. Which of the following matrices are nonsingular?

$$\begin{bmatrix} 1 & -1 & 2 \\ 1 & 1 & 3 \\ 2 & 1 & 1 \end{bmatrix}, \quad \begin{bmatrix} 1 & -1 & 2 \\ 1 & 1 & 4 \\ 1 & 3 & 6 \end{bmatrix}, \quad \begin{bmatrix} 1 & 0 & 1 \\ -1 & 0 & 1 \\ 0 & 1 & 0 \end{bmatrix}$$

9. If A and B are nonsingular $n \times n$ matrices, show that AB is nonsingular with inverse $B^{-1}A^{-1}$.

10. How may Exercise 9 be applied to show that the product of two nonsingular linear transformations is nonsingular?

11. Prove Corollary 1 of Theorem 6.5.

12. Prove Corollary 2 of Theorem 6.5.

*13. Discuss whether the separate requirements of "one-to-one" and "onto" were necessary in the hypothesis of Theorem 6.1. Can you find a single-valued mapping of a set into itself which is one-to-one but not onto; onto but not one-to-one? If so, investigate the question of inverses for these mappings.

7. Nonsingular Matrices and Changes of Bases in Vector Spaces

In this section we shall discuss $n \times n$ nonsingular matrices directly without recourse to associated linear transformations. The first item on our agenda is the question of finding the inverse of a nonsingular matrix. Possibly the student has already discovered from the exercises of the previous section a construction for the inverse of a nonsingular matrix. We shall give a formula which is perhaps of more theoretical than practical value except for $n = 2$ or 3. Let us look first at an example.

Example 1. Let

$$A = \begin{bmatrix} 1 & 2 & -1 \\ 0 & 1 & 3 \\ 2 & 3 & -3 \end{bmatrix};$$

then $\det A = 2$ and A is nonsingular. Let us construct A^{-1} in a straightforward manner. We are looking for a matrix $B = [b_{ij}]$ such that

$$\begin{bmatrix} 1 & 2 & -1 \\ 0 & 1 & 3 \\ 2 & 3 & -3 \end{bmatrix} \begin{bmatrix} b_{11} & b_{12} & b_{13} \\ b_{21} & b_{22} & b_{23} \\ b_{31} & b_{32} & b_{33} \end{bmatrix} = \begin{bmatrix} 1 & 0 & 0 \\ 0 & 1 & 0 \\ 0 & 0 & 1 \end{bmatrix}, \qquad \text{or}$$

$$\begin{bmatrix} 1\cdot b_{11}+2\cdot b_{21}-1\cdot b_{31} & 1\cdot b_{12}+2\cdot b_{22}-1\cdot b_{32} & 1\cdot b_{13}+2\cdot b_{23}-1\cdot b_{33} \\ 0\cdot b_{11}+1\cdot b_{21}+3\cdot b_{31} & 0\cdot b_{12}+1\cdot b_{22}+3\cdot b_{32} & 0\cdot b_{13}+1\cdot b_{23}+3\cdot b_{33} \\ 2\cdot b_{11}+3\cdot b_{21}-3\cdot b_{31} & 2\cdot b_{12}+3\cdot b_{22}-3\cdot b_{32} & 2\cdot b_{13}+3\cdot b_{23}-3\cdot b_{33} \end{bmatrix} = \begin{bmatrix} 1 & 0 & 0 \\ 0 & 1 & 0 \\ 0 & 0 & 1 \end{bmatrix}.$$

When corresponding columns are equated, there are three systems of equations, each with three unknowns.

The unique solutions give $B = \frac{1}{2}\begin{bmatrix} -12 & 3 & 7 \\ 6 & -1 & -3 \\ -2 & 1 & 1 \end{bmatrix}$. Note that the determinant of all three systems of equations is $\det A = 2$.

THEOREM 7.1. *If $A = [a_{ij}]$ is a nonsingular $n \times n$ matrix; if C_{ij} is the cofactor of a_{ij} (in $\det A$); and if $d_{ij} = C_{ji}/\det A$, then $A^{-1} = D = [d_{ij}]$.*

Proof. We merely apply Theorem 5.1, Chapter 5, and Exercise 9 of §5, Chapter 5, to the matrix product

$$[a_{ij}][d_{ij}] = \left[\sum_{k=1}^{n} a_{ik}d_{kj}\right] = \left[\sum_{k=1}^{n} \frac{a_{ik}C_{jk}}{\det A}\right].$$

The element $\sum_{k=1}^{n} \frac{a_{ik}C_{jk}}{\det A} = 0$ or 1 according as $i \neq j$ or $i = j$. Thus $AD = I$ and $D = A^{-1}$.

Example 2. Consider the matrix A of Example 1,

$$A = \begin{bmatrix} 1 & 2 & -1 \\ 0 & 1 & 3 \\ 2 & 3 & -3 \end{bmatrix}.$$

We have remarked that $\det A = 2$; now note that $C_{11} = -12$, $C_{12} = 6$, $C_{13} = -2$, $C_{21} = 3$, $C_{22} = -1$, $C_{23} = 1$, $C_{31} = 7$, $C_{32} = -3$, $C_{33} = 1$. Thus,

$$D = \begin{bmatrix} -\frac{12}{2} & \frac{3}{2} & \frac{7}{2} \\ \frac{6}{2} & -\frac{1}{2} & -\frac{3}{2} \\ -\frac{2}{2} & \frac{1}{2} & \frac{1}{2} \end{bmatrix},$$

and this is identical with the final result of Example 1.

Another way to find inverses of nonsingular matrices which is more practical if $n > 3$ will be given in the next chapter.

We turn now to an application of nonsingular matrices which is not directly connected with the use of matrices to represent linear transformations relative to the $\{\mathbf{E}_i\}$ basis. The concept to be discussed is the idea of the *matrix of a change of basis* of a vector space V. Suppose $\{\mathbf{X}_1, \mathbf{X}_2, \cdots, \mathbf{X}_n\}$ is one basis of V and $\{\mathbf{Y}_1, \mathbf{Y}_2, \cdots, \mathbf{Y}_n\}$ is another. Now, by the definition of basis, we may express the $\mathbf{Y}_i$ as linear combinations of the $\mathbf{X}_i$ and vice versa:

$$
\begin{aligned}
\mathbf{Y}_1 &= a_{11}\mathbf{X}_1 + a_{12}\mathbf{X}_2 + \cdots + a_{1n}\mathbf{X}_n \\
\mathbf{Y}_2 &= a_{21}\mathbf{X}_1 + a_{22}\mathbf{X}_2 + \cdots + a_{2n}\mathbf{X}_n \\
&\cdots\cdots\cdots\cdots\cdots \\
\mathbf{Y}_n &= a_{n1}\mathbf{X}_1 + a_{n2}\mathbf{X}_2 + \cdots + a_{nn}\mathbf{X}_n
\end{aligned}
\tag{7.1}
$$

and

$$
\begin{aligned}
\mathbf{X}_1 &= b_{11}\mathbf{Y}_1 + b_{12}\mathbf{Y}_2 + \cdots + b_{1n}\mathbf{Y}_n \\
\mathbf{X}_2 &= b_{21}\mathbf{Y}_1 + b_{22}\mathbf{Y}_2 + \cdots + b_{2n}\mathbf{Y}_n \\
&\cdots\cdots\cdots\cdots\cdots \\
\mathbf{X}_n &= b_{n1}\mathbf{Y}_1 + b_{n2}\mathbf{Y}_2 + \cdots + b_{nn}Y_n.
\end{aligned}
\tag{7.2}
$$

We let $A = [a_{ij}]$ be the $n \times n$ matrix consisting of the coefficients a_{ij} in equations (7.1) and say that A is *the matrix of the change of basis from* $\{\mathbf{X}_i\}$ *to* $\{\mathbf{Y}_i\}$. Similarly, $\mathbf{B} = [b_{ij}]$ is the matrix of the change of basis from $\{\mathbf{Y}_i\}$ to $\{\mathbf{X}_i\}$ given by equations (7.2).

We claim that A and B are nonsingular matrices and that $AB = I$. To see this more easily, we introduce a new notational device; we rewrite equations (7.1) and (7.2) as

$$
\begin{bmatrix} \mathbf{Y}_1 \\ \mathbf{Y}_2 \\ \cdot \\ \cdot \\ \cdot \\ \mathbf{Y}_n \end{bmatrix} = A \begin{bmatrix} \mathbf{X}_1 \\ \mathbf{X}_2 \\ \cdot \\ \cdot \\ \cdot \\ \mathbf{X}_n \end{bmatrix}
\tag{7.1$'$}
$$

and similarly

$$
\begin{bmatrix} \mathbf{X}_1 \\ \mathbf{X}_2 \\ \cdot \\ \cdot \\ \cdot \\ \mathbf{X}_n \end{bmatrix} = B \begin{bmatrix} \mathbf{Y}_1 \\ \mathbf{Y}_2 \\ \cdot \\ \cdot \\ \cdot \\ \mathbf{Y}_n \end{bmatrix}.
\tag{7.2$'$}
$$

Note that the $n \times 1$ arrays of vectors are not, in themselves, matrices since the elements are vectors, not real numbers. We may accept equations (7.1)$'$ and (7.2)$'$ in either of two ways:

1. They may be considered just a formal notation reminding us to use the familiar matrix multiplication to obtain the relations:

$$\mathbf{Y}_i = a_{i1}\mathbf{X}_1 + a_{i2}\mathbf{X}_2 + \cdots + a_{in}\mathbf{X}_n$$

and
$$\mathbf{X}_i = b_{i1}\mathbf{Y}_1 + b_{i2}\mathbf{Y}_2 + \cdots + b_{in}\mathbf{Y}_n \qquad \text{for } i = 1, 2, \cdots, n.$$

2. When the vector space V is $V_n(R)$, the columns may be thought of as abbreviations of matrices; in this case, the ith row of $\begin{bmatrix} \mathbf{X}_1 \\ \mathbf{X}_2 \\ \cdot \\ \cdot \\ \cdot \\ \mathbf{X}_n \end{bmatrix}$ is the ordered n-tuple of components of the vector $\mathbf{X}_i$.

In any case, we obtain:

$$\begin{bmatrix} \mathbf{Y}_1 \\ \mathbf{Y}_2 \\ \cdot \\ \cdot \\ \cdot \\ \mathbf{Y}_n \end{bmatrix} = A \begin{bmatrix} \mathbf{X}_1 \\ \mathbf{X}_2 \\ \cdot \\ \cdot \\ \cdot \\ \mathbf{X}_n \end{bmatrix} = A \left\{ B \begin{bmatrix} \mathbf{Y}_1 \\ \mathbf{Y}_2 \\ \cdot \\ \cdot \\ \cdot \\ \mathbf{Y}_n \end{bmatrix} \right\} = AB \begin{bmatrix} \mathbf{Y}_1 \\ \mathbf{Y}_2 \\ \cdot \\ \cdot \\ \cdot \\ \mathbf{Y}_n \end{bmatrix}.$$

The precise justifications of the individual steps depend on which of the cases above is chosen, but the result is defensible in either case. The matrix AB expresses the $\mathbf{Y}_i$ in terms of the $\mathbf{Y}_i$. However, since the set $\{\mathbf{Y}_i\}$ is a basis, its elements are linearly independent and there is only *one* way in which the $\mathbf{Y}_i$ can be written as linear combinations of the $\{\mathbf{Y}_i\}$; that is,

$$\begin{aligned} \mathbf{Y}_1 &= 1\mathbf{Y}_1 + 0\mathbf{Y}_2 + \cdots + 0\mathbf{Y}_n \\ \mathbf{Y}_2 &= 0\mathbf{Y}_1 + 1\mathbf{Y}_2 + \cdots + 0\mathbf{Y}_n \\ &\cdots\cdots\cdots\cdots \\ \mathbf{Y}_n &= 0\mathbf{Y}_1 + 0\mathbf{Y}_2 + \cdots + 1\mathbf{Y}_n, \end{aligned}$$

or
$$\begin{bmatrix} \mathbf{Y}_1 \\ \mathbf{Y}_2 \\ \cdot \\ \cdot \\ \cdot \\ \mathbf{Y}_n \end{bmatrix} = I \begin{bmatrix} \mathbf{Y}_1 \\ \mathbf{Y}_2 \\ \cdot \\ \cdot \\ \cdot \\ \mathbf{Y}_n \end{bmatrix},$$

where I is the $n \times n$ identity matrix. Hence $AB = I$. We have proved:

THEOREM 7.2. *If A is the matrix of the change of basis of a vector space V from $\{\mathbf{X}_i\}$ to $\{\mathbf{Y}_i\}$, A is nonsingular and A^{-1} is the matrix of the change of basis from $\{\mathbf{Y}_i\}$ to $\{\mathbf{X}_i\}$.*

COROLLARY. *If* $\mathbf{Z} = c_1\mathbf{X}_1 + \cdots + c_n\mathbf{X}_n$, *then* $\mathbf{Z} = d_1\mathbf{Y}_1 + \cdots + d_n\mathbf{Y}_n$ *where the vector* $[d_1, d_2, \cdots, d_n]$ *is defined by*

$$[d_1, d_2, \cdots, d_n] = [c_1, c_2, \cdots, c_n]A^{-1}.$$

Proof. $$\mathbf{Z} = [c_1, c_2, \cdots, c_n]\begin{bmatrix}\mathbf{X}_1\\ \cdot\\ \cdot\\ \cdot\\ \mathbf{X}_n\end{bmatrix} = [c_1, c_2, \cdots, c_n]A^{-1}\begin{bmatrix}\mathbf{Y}_1\\ \cdot\\ \cdot\\ \cdot\\ \mathbf{Y}_n\end{bmatrix}$$

$$= [d_1, d_2, \cdots, d_n]\begin{bmatrix}\mathbf{Y}_1\\ \cdot\\ \cdot\\ \cdot\\ \mathbf{Y}_n\end{bmatrix}.$$

Example 3. Let $\mathbf{X}_1 = [1, 1, -1]$, $\mathbf{X}_2 = [1, -1, 0]$, $\mathbf{X}_3 = [0, 1, 2]$ be the members of a basis for $V_3(R)$. Let

$$\begin{aligned}\mathbf{Y}_1 &= [\ \ 1, 2, \ \ 1] = \mathbf{X}_1 + 0\mathbf{X}_2 + \mathbf{X}_3\\ \mathbf{Y}_2 &= [\ \ 2, 0, -1] = \mathbf{X}_1 + \mathbf{X}_2 + 0\mathbf{X}_3\\ \mathbf{Y}_3 &= [-2, 3, \ \ 2] = 0\mathbf{X}_1 - 2\mathbf{X}_2 + \mathbf{X}_3\end{aligned}$$

be the elements of a second basis. Using the second interpretation of (7.1)′, we have

$$\begin{bmatrix}1 & 2 & 1\\ 2 & 0 & -1\\ -2 & 3 & 2\end{bmatrix} = \begin{bmatrix}1 & 0 & 1\\ 1 & 1 & 0\\ 0 & -2 & 1\end{bmatrix}\begin{bmatrix}1 & 1 & -1\\ 1 & -1 & 0\\ 0 & 1 & 2\end{bmatrix},$$

which may be readily verified. Now

$$\begin{bmatrix}1 & 0 & 1\\ 1 & 1 & 0\\ 0 & -2 & 1\end{bmatrix}^{-1} = \begin{bmatrix}-1 & 2 & 1\\ 1 & -1 & -1\\ 2 & -2 & -1\end{bmatrix};$$

hence

$$\begin{bmatrix}1 & 1 & -1\\ 1 & -1 & 0\\ 0 & 1 & 2\end{bmatrix} = \begin{bmatrix}-1 & 2 & 1\\ 1 & -1 & -1\\ 2 & -2 & -1\end{bmatrix}\begin{bmatrix}1 & 2 & 1\\ 2 & 0 & -1\\ -2 & 3 & 2\end{bmatrix},$$

which may be interpreted as

$$\begin{aligned}\mathbf{X}_1 &= -\mathbf{Y}_1 + 2\mathbf{Y}_2 + \mathbf{Y}_3\\ \mathbf{X}_2 &= \mathbf{Y}_1 - \mathbf{Y}_2 - \mathbf{Y}_3\\ \mathbf{X}_3 &= 2\mathbf{Y}_1 - 2\mathbf{Y}_2 - \mathbf{Y}_3.\end{aligned}$$

Again the student may check the validity of these equations. Now let $\mathbf{Z} = [3, 2, 5] = \mathbf{X}_1 + 2\mathbf{X}_2 + 3\mathbf{X}_3$; then

$$\mathbf{Z} = [1, 2, 3]\begin{bmatrix} -1 & 2 & 1 \\ 1 & -1 & -1 \\ 2 & -2 & -1 \end{bmatrix}\begin{bmatrix} \mathbf{Y}_1 \\ \mathbf{Y}_2 \\ \mathbf{Y}_3 \end{bmatrix} = [7, -6, -4]\begin{bmatrix} \mathbf{Y}_1 \\ \mathbf{Y}_2 \\ \mathbf{Y}_3 \end{bmatrix}.$$

This is also easily checked. Note that the coefficients of $\mathbf{X}_1, \cdots, \mathbf{X}_n$ are changed to the coefficients of $\mathbf{Y}_1, \cdots, \mathbf{Y}_n$ by the *inverse* of the matrix which represents the change of basis from $\{\mathbf{X}_i\}$ to $\{\mathbf{Y}_i\}$.

EXERCISES

1. Find, by the method of Theorem 7.1, the inverse of the matrix

$$\begin{bmatrix} 1 & 3 & 0 & 0 \\ 2 & 5 & 0 & 0 \\ 0 & 0 & 2 & 1 \\ 0 & 0 & 1 & 1 \end{bmatrix}.$$

Why is the method reasonably practical here in spite of the size of the matrix?

2. Find the inverses of the following matrices:

$$\text{(a)} \begin{bmatrix} 2 & 1 \\ -1 & 3 \end{bmatrix} \qquad \text{(b)} \begin{bmatrix} -1 & 1 & 2 \\ 1 & 0 & 3 \\ 0 & 1 & 1 \end{bmatrix} \qquad \text{(c)} \begin{bmatrix} 2 & 1 & -1 \\ 0 & 1 & 0 \\ 1 & 3 & -1 \end{bmatrix}$$

3. Prove that A^{T} is nonsingular if and only if A is nonsingular, and that $(A^{-1})^{\mathsf{T}} = (A^{\mathsf{T}})^{-1}$.

4. Let $\mathbf{X}_1 = [1, -1, 1]$, $\mathbf{X}_2 = [1, 0, 1]$, $\mathbf{X}_3 = [0, 1, 1]$,
and $\mathbf{Y}_1 = [2, -1, 2]$, $\mathbf{Y}_2 = [1, 1, 2]$, $\mathbf{Y}_3 = [1, 0, 2]$.

(a) Find the matrices of the change of basis from $\{\mathbf{X}_i\}$ to $\{\mathbf{Y}_i\}$ and $\{\mathbf{Y}_i\}$ to $\{\mathbf{X}_i\}$. Verify Theorem 7.2 for this example.

(b) If $\mathbf{Z} = \mathbf{X}_1 + 2\mathbf{X}_2 - \mathbf{X}_3$, find $\mathbf{Z}$ as a linear combination of the $\mathbf{Y}_i$ using matrix multiplication (Corollary of Theorem 7.2).

(c) If a subspace W of $V_3(R)$ is defined by $\mathbf{Z} = c_1\mathbf{X}_1 + c_2\mathbf{X}_2 + c_3\mathbf{X}_3 \in W$ if and only if $c_1 + c_2 + c_3 = 0$, find an equivalent condition on c_1', c_2', c_3' if $\mathbf{Z} = c_1'\mathbf{Y}_1 + c_2'\mathbf{Y}_2 + c_3'\mathbf{Y}_3$.

5. Let V, a subspace of $V_4(R)$, have the basis $\mathbf{X}_1 = [1, -1, 0, 1]$, $\mathbf{X}_2 = [1, -1, 2, 0]$, $\mathbf{X}_3 = [0, 1, 1, 1]$.

(a) Let A be the 3×3 matrix of Example 1. Find the vectors $\{\mathbf{Y}_i\}$ given by (7.1)$'$ and show that they are also a basis for V.

Hint: Write the $\{\mathbf{X}_i\}$ in terms of the $\{\mathbf{Y}_i\}$.

(b) Under the hypothesis of part (a), let $\mathbf{Z} = [3, -2, 3, 3]$. Show that $\mathbf{Z} \in V$ and write $\mathbf{Z}$ in terms of the $\{\mathbf{X}_i\}$ and $\{\mathbf{Y}_i\}$ bases.

6. Prove the following converse of Theorem 7.2: If A is an arbitrary $n \times n$ nonsingular matrix, $\{\mathbf{X}_i\}$ a basis of the n-dimensional vector space V, and

$$\begin{bmatrix} \mathbf{Y}_1 \\ \cdot \\ \cdot \\ \cdot \\ \mathbf{Y}_n \end{bmatrix} = A \begin{bmatrix} \mathbf{X}_1 \\ \cdot \\ \cdot \\ \cdot \\ \mathbf{X}_n \end{bmatrix},$$

then $\{\mathbf{Y}_i\}$ is a basis of V.

7. If $A = [a_{ij}]$ is an $n \times n$ matrix and C_{ij} is the cofactor of the element a_{ij} in A, the matrix $[C_{ij}]^{\mathsf{T}}$ is called the *adjoint* matrix of A. Show that $A[C_{ij}]^{\mathsf{T}} = (\det A) \cdot I$, where I is the $n \times n$ identity matrix.

8. Is it possible to interpret Theorem 7.2 in terms of linear transformations? Discuss the difference, if any, between a system of equations such as (7.1) representing a change of basis and a system of equations such as (2.4) with the qualifications that $V = W$, $\mathbf{X}_i = \mathbf{X}_i'$.

9. The results of this section can provide a mapping from the set of ordered pairs of bases of $V_n(R)$ to the set of nonsingular $n \times n$ matrices where the image of the pair of bases $(\{\mathbf{X}_i\}, \{\mathbf{Y}_i\})$ is the matrix of the change of bases from $\{\mathbf{X}_i\}$ to $\{\mathbf{Y}_i\}$. Show that this is an onto mapping but not a one-to-one mapping. Specifically, for $V_3(R)$, illustrate how the same matrix can be used for more than one change of basis.

8. Matrices of Linear Transformations with Respect to Arbitrary Bases

The student has undoubtedly noted the constant qualification "relative to the $\{\mathbf{E}_i\}$ basis" when matrices associated with linear transformations of $V_n(R)$ to $V_m(R)$ have been discussed. Perhaps he has felt that this qualification was superfluous since no other association of matrices and linear transformations has been made. In this section we will remove the restriction to $\{\mathbf{E}_i\}$ bases and, at the same time, permit our discussion to include more general vector spaces V and W. The restriction to the $\{\mathbf{E}_i\}$ bases resulted in a simplification of the discussion of the relations between matrices and linear transformations of $V_n(R)$ until an adequate notation and machinery could be developed to handle the general case. We now have these prerequisites and proceed to the general case.

We have seen that, if $\mathbf{X}_1, \mathbf{X}_2, \cdots, \mathbf{X}_n$ constitute a basis for a vector space V and if $\mathbf{X}_1', \mathbf{X}_2', \cdots, \mathbf{X}_m'$ form a basis for a vector space W, a linear transformation T from V to W is completely defined by the system of equations (2.4) which, for convenience, we repeat here (deleting the reference to $\mathbf{Y}_i$ since we shall use these letters for a different purpose shortly).

$$\begin{aligned} \mathbf{X}_1\mathrm{T} &= a_{11}\mathbf{X}_1' + a_{12}\mathbf{X}_2' + \cdots + a_{1m}\mathbf{X}_m' \\ \mathbf{X}_2\mathrm{T} &= a_{21}\mathbf{X}_1' + a_{22}\mathbf{X}_2' + \cdots + a_{2m}\mathbf{X}_m' \\ &\cdots\cdots\cdots\cdots \\ \mathbf{X}_n\mathrm{T} &= a_{n1}\mathbf{X}_1' + a_{n2}\mathbf{X}_2' + \cdots + a_{nm}\mathbf{X}_m'. \end{aligned} \tag{8.1}$$

In the notation of the preceding section this system may be written

$$\begin{bmatrix} \mathbf{X}_1\mathrm{T} \\ \mathbf{X}_2\mathrm{T} \\ \cdot \\ \cdot \\ \cdot \\ \mathbf{X}_n\mathrm{T} \end{bmatrix} = A \begin{bmatrix} \mathbf{X}_1' \\ \mathbf{X}_2' \\ \cdot \\ \cdot \\ \cdot \\ \mathbf{X}_m' \end{bmatrix}, \tag{8.1$'$}$$

where A is the $n \times m$ matrix $[a_{ij}]$. We say that *the $n \times m$ matrix A is the matrix of the linear transformation* T *with respect to the basis* $\{\mathbf{X}_i\}$ *of V and the basis* $\{\mathbf{X}_i'\}$ *of W.*

Note that in this language a basis is regarded as an ordered set of vectors since, if two vectors $\mathbf{X}_i$ and $\mathbf{X}_j$ are interchanged (or if $\mathbf{X}_i'$ and $\mathbf{X}_j'$ are exchanged), the matrix changes.

Again, it is a simple matter to show that if the bases $\{\mathbf{X}_i\}$ of V and $\{\mathbf{X}_i'\}$ of W are fixed, then there is a one-to-one correspondence between the linear transformations T from V to W and the $n \times m$ matrices representing T relative to the chosen bases. We leave the details of the proof to the student.

Now suppose that $\mathbf{Z} = c_1\mathbf{X}_1 + c_2\mathbf{X}_2 + \cdots + c_n\mathbf{X}_n$ is any vector of V, what is $\mathbf{Z}\mathrm{T}$? Clearly,

$$\begin{aligned} \mathbf{Z}\mathrm{T} &= c_1(\mathbf{X}_1\mathrm{T}) + c_2(\mathbf{X}_2\mathrm{T}) + \cdots + c_n(\mathbf{X}_n\mathrm{T}) \\ &= [c_1, c_2, \cdots, c_n] \begin{bmatrix} \mathbf{X}_1\mathrm{T} \\ \mathbf{X}_2\mathrm{T} \\ \cdot \\ \cdot \\ \cdot \\ \mathbf{X}_n\mathrm{T} \end{bmatrix} = [c_1, c_2, \cdots, c_n]A \begin{bmatrix} \mathbf{X}_1' \\ \mathbf{X}_2' \\ \cdot \\ \cdot \\ \cdot \\ \mathbf{X}_m' \end{bmatrix}. \end{aligned}$$

THEOREM 8.1. *If $\mathbf{Z} = c_1\mathbf{X}_1 + c_2\mathbf{X}_2 + \cdots + c_n\mathbf{X}_n$ is any vector of V, and* T *is a linear transformation from V to W defined by* (8.1) *or* (8.1)$'$, *and if $\mathbf{Z}\mathrm{T} = c_1'\mathbf{X}_1' + c_2'\mathbf{X}_2' + \cdots + c_m'\mathbf{X}_m'$, then*

$$[c_1', c_2', \cdots, c_m'] = [c_1, c_2, \cdots, c_n]A.$$

Example 1. Define a transformation T from $V = L\{[1, -1, 0], [0, 1, 1]\}$ to $W = L\{[1, 0, 1, 0], [1, 1, 0, 0], [1, -1, 0, 1]\}$ by:

$$\begin{aligned}[1, -1, 0]\mathrm{T} &= 1[1, 0, 1, 0] + 0[1, 1, 0, 0] + 2[1, -1, 0, 1]\\ [0, 1, 1]\mathrm{T} &= 3[1, 0, 1, 0] - 1[1, 1, 0, 0] + 1[1, -1, 0, 1].\end{aligned}$$

The matrix associated with T relative to the bases $\{[1, -1, 0], [0, 1, 1]\}$ of V and $\{[1, 0, 1, 0], [1, 1, 0, 0], [1, -1, 0, 1]\}$ of W is

$$A = \begin{bmatrix} 1 & 0 & 2 \\ 3 & -1 & 1 \end{bmatrix}.$$

If $\mathbf{Z} = [2, -1, 1] = 2[1, -1, 0] + [0, 1, 1]$, we may find $\mathbf{Z}\mathrm{T}$ either by computing

$$[2, 1]\begin{bmatrix} 1 & 0 & 2 \\ 3 & -1 & 1 \end{bmatrix} = [5, -1, 5]$$

as the vector of coefficients of the basis for W or by writing in full,

$$\begin{aligned}\mathbf{Z}\mathrm{T} &= 2[1, -1, 0]\mathrm{T} + [0, 1, 1]\mathrm{T}\\ &= 2\{1[1, 0, 1, 0] + 0[1, 1, 0, 0] + 2[1, -1, 0, 1]\}\\ &\quad + 1\{3[1, 0, 1, 0] - 1[1, 1, 0, 0] + 1[1, -1, 0, 1]\}\\ &= 5[1, 0, 1, 0] - 1[1, 1, 0, 0] + 5[1, -1, 0, 1].\end{aligned}$$

Example 1 provides an illustration of part of the answer to another question which may have occurred to the student: "Why bother with matrices of T for other than the $\{\mathbf{E}_i\}$ bases? The natural bases are easier to work with, and is not one basis as good as another?" We see that we may deal with vector spaces V and W which are defined by certain conditions and which are subspaces of other spaces. Quite possibly V and W do not have any of the $\mathbf{E}_i$ vectors of the larger spaces at all. This is the case in Example 1. The student may convince himself that the bases given for V and W are about as simple, by any criterion, as could be selected. Even when $V = V_n(R)$ and $W = V_m(R)$, there may be specific reasons for referring transformations to bases different from the $\{\mathbf{E}_i\}$ bases.

The full justification for the generalizations of the present section depends on the applicability of the matrix language to the new situation. Theorem 8.1 is a straightforward generalization of equation (5.1); what about the basic equivalences of transformation addition and matrix addition, transformation multiplication and matrix multiplication, given by Theorem 5.1?

THEOREM 8.2. *Let* T_1 *and* T_2 *be linear transformations from* V *to* W *and* T_3 *be a linear transformation from* W *to* U. *If* T_1 *and* T_2 *have the matrices* A *and* B *with respect to a basis* $\{\mathbf{X}_i\}$ *of* V *and a basis* $\{\mathbf{X}_i'\}$ *of* W, *and if* T_3 *has the matrix* C *with respect to the basis* $\{\mathbf{X}_i'\}$ *of* W *and a basis* $\{\mathbf{X}_1'', \mathbf{X}_2'', \cdots, \mathbf{X}_p''\}$ *of* U, *then* $\mathrm{T}_1 + \mathrm{T}_2$ *has the matrix* $A + B$ *with respect to* $\{\mathbf{X}_i\}$ *and* $\{\mathbf{X}_i'\}$, *and* $\mathrm{T}_1\mathrm{T}_3$ *has the matrix* AC *with respect to* $\{\mathbf{X}_i\}$ *and* $\{\mathbf{X}_i''\}$.

Proof. We carry out an analysis in the matrix shorthand:

$$\begin{bmatrix} \mathbf{X}_1(\mathrm{T}_1 + \mathrm{T}_2) \\ \mathbf{X}_2(\mathrm{T}_1 + \mathrm{T}_2) \\ \cdot \\ \cdot \\ \cdot \\ \mathbf{X}_n(\mathrm{T}_1 + \mathrm{T}_2) \end{bmatrix} = \begin{bmatrix} \mathbf{X}_1\mathrm{T}_1 \\ \mathbf{X}_2\mathrm{T}_1 \\ \cdot \\ \cdot \\ \cdot \\ \mathbf{X}_n\mathrm{T}_1 \end{bmatrix} + \begin{bmatrix} \mathbf{X}_1\mathrm{T}_2 \\ \mathbf{X}_2\mathrm{T}_2 \\ \cdot \\ \cdot \\ \cdot \\ \mathbf{X}_n\mathrm{T}_2 \end{bmatrix} = A \begin{bmatrix} \mathbf{X}_1' \\ \mathbf{X}_2' \\ \cdot \\ \cdot \\ \cdot \\ \mathbf{X}_m' \end{bmatrix} + B \begin{bmatrix} \mathbf{X}_1' \\ \mathbf{X}_2' \\ \cdot \\ \cdot \\ \cdot \\ \mathbf{X}_m' \end{bmatrix}$$

$$= (A + B) \begin{bmatrix} \mathbf{X}_1' \\ \mathbf{X}_2' \\ \cdot \\ \cdot \\ \cdot \\ \mathbf{X}_m' \end{bmatrix}.$$

Since
$$\begin{bmatrix} \mathbf{X}_1\mathrm{T}_1 \\ \mathbf{X}_2\mathrm{T}_1 \\ \cdot \\ \cdot \\ \cdot \\ \mathbf{X}_n\mathrm{T}_1 \end{bmatrix} = A \begin{bmatrix} \mathbf{X}_1' \\ \mathbf{X}_2' \\ \cdot \\ \cdot \\ \cdot \\ \mathbf{X}_m' \end{bmatrix}, \quad \begin{bmatrix} \mathbf{X}_1\mathrm{T}_1\mathrm{T}_3 \\ \mathbf{X}_2\mathrm{T}_1\mathrm{T}_3 \\ \cdot \\ \cdot \\ \cdot \\ \mathbf{X}_n\mathrm{T}_1\mathrm{T}_3 \end{bmatrix} = A \begin{bmatrix} \mathbf{X}_1'\mathrm{T}_3 \\ \mathbf{X}_2'\mathrm{T}_3 \\ \cdot \\ \cdot \\ \cdot \\ \mathbf{X}_m'\mathrm{T}_3 \end{bmatrix} = AC \begin{bmatrix} \mathbf{X}_1'' \\ \mathbf{X}_2'' \\ \cdot \\ \cdot \\ \cdot \\ \mathbf{X}_p'' \end{bmatrix}.$$

It must be emphasized that these are merely indications of the proof and are not complete. In particular, what lies behind the two apparent uses of a distributive law in the first part, and what permits us to stick on T_3's where we want to in the other? We will answer the latter and leave the former to the student. The first equation which the shorthand of the second part presents is, in more detail:

$$\mathbf{X}_1\mathrm{T}_1 = a_{11}\mathbf{X}_1' + a_{12}\mathbf{X}_2' + \cdots + a_{1m}\mathbf{X}_m'.$$

Then

$$\mathbf{X}_1\mathrm{T}_1\mathrm{T}_3 = a_{11}\mathbf{X}_1'\mathrm{T}_3 + a_{12}\mathbf{X}_2'\mathrm{T}_3 + \cdots + a_{1m}\mathbf{X}_m'\mathrm{T}_3$$

because of the linearity of T_3. Similar relations hold for each row, and the second matrix relation of the second part expresses this fact.

Now, although we have achieved generality, we have lost simplicity. We had one matrix for each transformation, one isomorphism between linear transformations from $V_n(R)$ to $V_m(R)$ and $n \times m$ matrices. Now we have many matrices for each transformation, many isomorphisms from the set of linear transformations from V to W to the set of $n \times m$ matrices. As soon as we change the basis of V or of W, a new matrix is introduced for a particular transformation. Is there any relation between these matrices? Yes; the relation is a fairly simple one.

THEOREM 8.3. *Let* T *be a linear transformation from V to W such that* T *has the matrix A relative to the bases $\{\mathbf{X}_i\}$ and $\{\mathbf{X}_i'\}$ and the matrix B relative to the bases $\{\mathbf{Y}_i\}$ and $\{\mathbf{Y}_i'\}$. Further, let P be the matrix of the change of basis from $\{\mathbf{X}_i\}$ to $\{\mathbf{Y}_i\}$ and Q the matrix of the change of basis from $\{\mathbf{X}_i'\}$ to $\{\mathbf{Y}_i'\}$. Then $B = PAQ^{-1}$.*

Before proceeding with the proof, let us illustrate the ideas of the theorem by the following diagram:

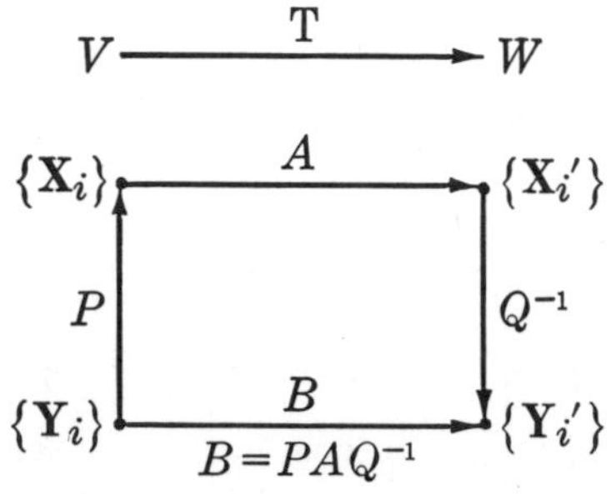

Figure 8.1

We think of expressing T, relative to the bases $\{\mathbf{Y}_i\}$ and $\{\mathbf{Y}_i'\}$, in two ways: Directly, by means of the matrix B expressing the $\mathbf{Y}_i\mathrm{T}$ in terms of the $\mathbf{Y}_i'$ (as indicated by the lower horizontal arrow); or by first expressing $\mathbf{Y}_i$ in terms of the $\mathbf{X}_i$ (as is done by the matrix P of the change of basis from $\{\mathbf{X}_i\}$ to $\{\mathbf{Y}_i\}$), then expressing $\mathbf{X}_i\mathrm{T}$ in terms of $\mathbf{X}_i'$ by means of the matrix A, and finally coming back to the $\mathbf{Y}_i'$ (as can be done by the matrix Q^{-1} of the change of basis from $\{\mathbf{Y}_i'\}$ to $\{\mathbf{X}_i'\}$).

The proof essentially follows the description above, and we use the matrix shorthand to express our hypotheses:

$$\begin{bmatrix} \mathbf{X}_1\mathrm{T} \\ \mathbf{X}_2\mathrm{T} \\ \cdot \\ \cdot \\ \cdot \\ \mathbf{X}_n\mathrm{T} \end{bmatrix} = A \begin{bmatrix} \mathbf{X}_1' \\ \mathbf{X}_2' \\ \cdot \\ \cdot \\ \cdot \\ \mathbf{X}_m' \end{bmatrix}, \quad \begin{bmatrix} \mathbf{Y}_1\mathrm{T} \\ \mathbf{Y}_2\mathrm{T} \\ \cdot \\ \cdot \\ \cdot \\ \mathbf{Y}_n\mathrm{T} \end{bmatrix} = B \begin{bmatrix} \mathbf{Y}_1' \\ \mathbf{Y}_2' \\ \cdot \\ \cdot \\ \cdot \\ \mathbf{Y}_m' \end{bmatrix}, \quad \begin{bmatrix} \mathbf{Y}_1 \\ \mathbf{Y}_2 \\ \cdot \\ \cdot \\ \cdot \\ \mathbf{Y}_n \end{bmatrix} = P \begin{bmatrix} \mathbf{X}_1 \\ \mathbf{X}_2 \\ \cdot \\ \cdot \\ \cdot \\ \mathbf{X}_n \end{bmatrix},$$

$$\begin{bmatrix} \mathbf{Y}_1' \\ \mathbf{Y}_2' \\ \cdot \\ \cdot \\ \cdot \\ \mathbf{Y}_m' \end{bmatrix} = Q \begin{bmatrix} \mathbf{X}_1' \\ \mathbf{X}_2' \\ \cdot \\ \cdot \\ \cdot \\ \mathbf{X}_m' \end{bmatrix} \quad \text{or} \quad \begin{bmatrix} \mathbf{X}_1' \\ \mathbf{X}_2' \\ \cdot \\ \cdot \\ \cdot \\ \mathbf{X}_m' \end{bmatrix} = Q^{-1} \begin{bmatrix} \mathbf{Y}_1' \\ \mathbf{Y}_2' \\ \cdot \\ \cdot \\ \cdot \\ \mathbf{Y}_m' \end{bmatrix}.$$

Then,

$$\begin{bmatrix} Y_1 \\ Y_2 \\ \cdot \\ \cdot \\ \cdot \\ Y_n \end{bmatrix} = P \begin{bmatrix} X_1 \\ X_2 \\ \cdot \\ \cdot \\ \cdot \\ X_n \end{bmatrix} \quad \text{or} \quad \begin{bmatrix} Y_1T \\ Y_2T \\ \cdot \\ \cdot \\ \cdot \\ Y_nT \end{bmatrix} = P \begin{bmatrix} X_1T \\ X_2T \\ \cdot \\ \cdot \\ \cdot \\ X_nT \end{bmatrix} = PA \begin{bmatrix} X_1' \\ X_2' \\ \cdot \\ \cdot \\ \cdot \\ X_m' \end{bmatrix} = PAQ^{-1} \begin{bmatrix} Y_1' \\ Y_2' \\ \cdot \\ \cdot \\ \cdot \\ Y_m' \end{bmatrix}.$$

Comparing this last result with the hypothesis we see that the matrix corresponding to T relative to the bases $\{Y_i\}$ and $\{Y_i'\}$ is both B and PAQ^{-1}. But our correspondence is one-to-one for fixed bases so that $B = PAQ^{-1}$.

Example 2. For the spaces V and W of Example 1, define new bases $\{[1, 0, 1], [1, 1, 2]\}$ and $\{[0, 1, 1, -1], [2, 0, 0, 1], [1, 0, -1, 1]\}$. Now,

$$\begin{aligned} [1, 0, 1] &= [1, -1, 0] + [0, 1, 1] \\ [1, 1, 2] &= [1, -1, 0] + 2[0, 1, 1] \end{aligned}$$

so that the matrix P of the change of basis for V is

$$P = \begin{bmatrix} 1 & 1 \\ 1 & 2 \end{bmatrix}.$$

Similarly, for the bases of W,

$$\begin{aligned} [0, 1, 1, -1] &= [1, 0, 1, 0] - [1, -1, 0, 1] \\ [2, 0, 0, 1] &= [1, 1, 0, 0] + [1, -1, 0, 1] \\ [1, 0, -1, 1] &= -[1, 0, 1, 0] + [1, 1, 0, 0] + [1, -1, 0, 1], \end{aligned}$$

and the matrix Q of the change of basis is

$$Q = \begin{bmatrix} 1 & 0 & -1 \\ 0 & 1 & 1 \\ -1 & 1 & 1 \end{bmatrix} \quad \text{with} \quad Q^{-1} = \begin{bmatrix} 0 & 1 & -1 \\ 1 & 0 & 1 \\ -1 & 1 & -1 \end{bmatrix}.$$

Then,

$$B = \begin{bmatrix} 1 & 1 \\ 1 & 2 \end{bmatrix} \begin{bmatrix} 1 & 0 & 2 \\ 3 & -1 & 1 \end{bmatrix} \begin{bmatrix} 0 & 1 & -1 \\ 1 & 0 & 1 \\ -1 & 1 & -1 \end{bmatrix} = \begin{bmatrix} -4 & 7 & -8 \\ -6 & 11 & -13 \end{bmatrix}$$

is the matrix of T of Example 1 relative to these new bases.

The student should verify from the original definition that

$$\begin{aligned} [1, 0, 1]T &= -4[0, 1, 1, -1] + 7[2, 0, 0, 1] - 8[1, 0, -1, 1] \\ [1, 1, 2]T &= -6[0, 1, 1, -1] + 11[2, 0, 0, 1] - 13[1, 0, -1, 1]. \end{aligned}$$

Using the same vector **Z** of Example 1, we note

$$\mathbf{Z} = 3[1, 0, 1] - [1, 1, 2];$$

and, applying Theorem 8.1, we have

$$[3, -1]\begin{bmatrix} -4 & 7 & -8 \\ -6 & 11 & -13 \end{bmatrix} = [-6, 10, -11];$$

or

$$\mathbf{Z}\mathrm{T} = -6[0, 1, 1, -1] + 10[2, 0, 0, 1] - 11[1, 0, -1, 1] = [9, -6, 5, 5],$$

which may be checked with the final equation of Example 1.

The results of Theorem 8.3 may have a slightly different form when we are discussing a linear transformation of a vector space V to V. In this case (as mentioned in §2), we normally take the basis $\{\mathbf{X}_i'\}$ to be the basis $\{\mathbf{X}_i\}$. Similarly, we would take the basis $\{\mathbf{Y}_i'\}$ to be the basis $\{\mathbf{Y}_i\}$, and our diagram would be:

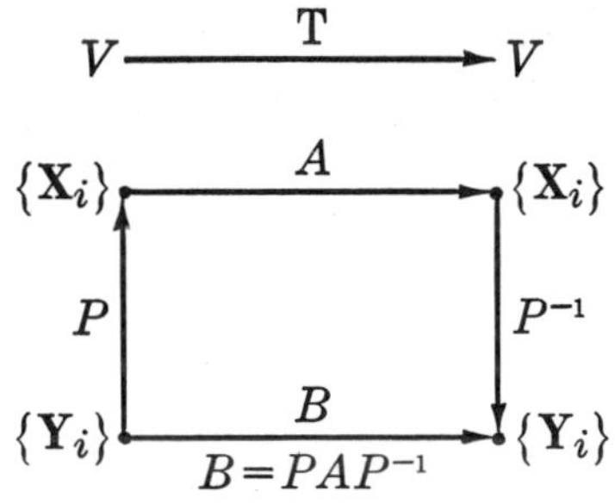

Figure 8.2

Of course, in this case, if we did not select the basis $\{\mathbf{X}_i'\}$ to be the basis $\{\mathbf{X}_i\}$, the general result of Theorem 8.3 would still apply. Consequently, the diagram above represents the following corollary:

COROLLARY. *If* T *is a linear transformation on a vector space V, A the matrix of* T *relative to the* $\{\mathbf{X}_i\}$ *basis, B the matrix of* T *relative to the* $\{\mathbf{Y}_i\}$ *basis, P the matrix of the change of basis from* $\{\mathbf{X}_i\}$ *to* $\{\mathbf{Y}_i\}$, *then* $B = PAP^{-1}$

EXERCISES

In the first four problems assume the following data:

$V = V_2(R)$; $\mathbf{X}_1 = [1, 1]$, $\mathbf{X}_2 = [3, 2]$; $\mathbf{Y}_1 = [-1, 0]$, $\mathbf{Y}_2 = [2, 1]$.
$W = V_3(R)$; $\mathbf{X}_1' = [2, 2, 3]$, $\mathbf{X}_2' = [2, -4, 1]$, $\mathbf{X}_3' = [1, 4, -2]$;
$\mathbf{Y}_1' = [1, 1, 0]$, $\mathbf{Y}_2' = [-1, 2, 1]$, $\mathbf{Y}_3' = [2, -1, 2]$.

Let a linear transformation T from V to W have the matrix $\begin{bmatrix} 1 & 2 & -3 \\ 2 & 1 & 1 \end{bmatrix}$ relative to the bases $\{\mathbf{X}_i\}$ and $\{\mathbf{X}_i'\}$.

1. Find the matrix P of the change of basis from $\{\mathbf{X}_i\}$ to $\{\mathbf{Y}_i\}$. Similarly find the matrix Q of the change of basis from $\{\mathbf{X}_i'\}$ to $\{\mathbf{Y}_i'\}$.

2. Find P^{-1} and Q^{-1} for the matrices of Exercise 1. Write the corresponding equations for the vectors $\{\mathbf{X}_i\}$ in terms of the $\{\mathbf{Y}_i\}$ and the $\{\mathbf{X}_i'\}$ in terms of the $\{\mathbf{Y}_i'\}$.

3. Find the matrix of T relative to the bases $\{\mathbf{Y}_i\}$ and $\{\mathbf{Y}_i'\}$.

4. If $\mathbf{Z} = [2, -3]$, find $\mathbf{Z}$ as a linear combination of $\mathbf{X}_1, \mathbf{X}_2$; of $\mathbf{Y}_1, \mathbf{Y}_2$. Use this result to find $\mathbf{Z}$T in terms of the $\{\mathbf{X}_i'\}$ basis; in terms of the $\{\mathbf{Y}_i'\}$ basis. Verify that the resulting vector is the same in both cases.

5. Let $V = L\{[1, 0, 1], [1, -2, 1]\}$, $W = I\{[1, 0, 1, -1], [0, 1, -1, 0]\}$. Let T be a linear transformation from V to W whose matrix relative to the given bases of V and W is

$$\begin{bmatrix} 1 & 2 \\ -1 & 3 \end{bmatrix}.$$

Find the matrix of T relative to the bases $\{[2, -2, 2], [0, 2, 0]\}$ of V and $\{[2, 1, 1, -2], [-1, 2, -3, 1]\}$ of W.

6. Let T be a linear transformation on $V_3(R)$ whose matrix relative to the natural basis $\{\mathbf{E}_i\}$ is

$$\begin{bmatrix} 1 & 0 & -1 \\ 0 & 2 & 1 \\ 1 & 0 & -1 \end{bmatrix}.$$

Find the matrix of T relative to the basis $\{[1, 1, -1], [1, 2, 0], [1, 0, 1]\}$ of $V_3(R)$.

7. The text states that the matrix of a linear transformation changes when two vectors of the $\{\mathbf{X}_i\}$ basis are permuted or when two vectors of the $\{\mathbf{X}_i'\}$ basis are interchanged. Precisely what are these changes when $\mathbf{X}_i$ and $\mathbf{X}_j$ are interchanged? when $\mathbf{X}_i'$ and $\mathbf{X}_j'$ are interchanged? Write the corresponding matrices P and Q and obtain Q^{-1}.

8. Let $\mathbf{X}$ be a nonzero vector of a vector space V and assume that T is a linear transformation on V such that the vectors $\mathbf{X}$, $\mathbf{X}$T, $\mathbf{X}\mathrm{T}^2, \cdots, \mathbf{X}\mathrm{T}^{k-1}$ are a basis for V and $\mathrm{T}^k = \mathrm{I}$. What is the matrix of T relative to the basis $\{\mathbf{X}, \mathbf{X}\mathrm{T}, \cdots, \mathbf{X}\mathrm{T}^{k-1}\}$ of V?

9. Similarity of Matrices and Equivalence Relations

In the preceding section we saw that if two matrices A and B represent the same linear transformation on a vector space V with respect to two bases $\{\mathbf{X}_i\}$ and $\{\mathbf{Y}_i\}$, then there is a nonsingular matrix P such that $B = PAP^{-1}$. In particular, P was the matrix of the change of basis from

$\{\mathbf{X}_i\}$ to $\{\mathbf{Y}_i\}$ by which the vectors $\mathbf{Y}_i$ were expressed in terms of the $\mathbf{X}_i$. Conversely, it is easy to see that if, for two $n \times n$ matrices A, B, there exists a nonsingular matrix P such that $B = PAP^{-1}$, then there is a linear transformation T of $V_n(R)$ such that A is the matrix of T with respect to the natural basis $\{\mathbf{E}_i\}$ while B is the matrix of T with respect to the basis $\{\mathbf{Y}_i\}$, where

$$\begin{bmatrix} \mathbf{Y}_1 \\ \cdot \\ \cdot \\ \cdot \\ \mathbf{Y}_n \end{bmatrix} = P \begin{bmatrix} \mathbf{E}_1 \\ \cdot \\ \cdot \\ \cdot \\ \mathbf{E}_n \end{bmatrix}.$$

We merely define $\mathbf{X}$T to be equal to $\mathbf{X}A$ for all $\mathbf{X} = [x_1, x_2, \cdots, x_n] \in V_n(R)$. Graphically,

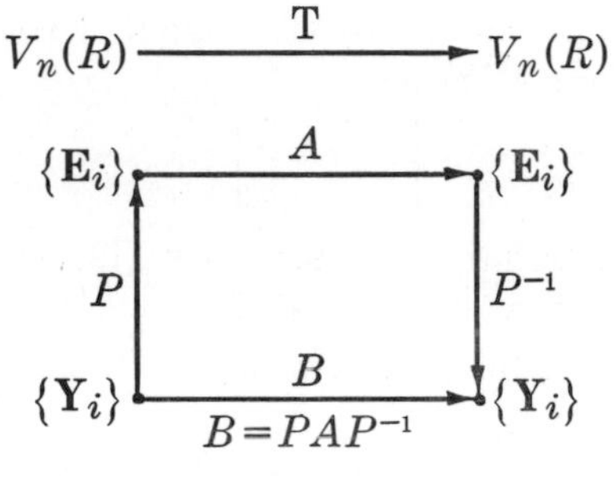

Figure 9.1

When two square matrices A and B are so related that they may represent the same linear transformation on a vector space V, they are said to be similar. Formally, and using only matrix language, we make the following definition:

DEFINITION 9.1. *An $n \times n$ matrix A is said to be* SIMILAR *to an $n \times n$ matrix B if there exists a nonsingular matrix R such that $B = RAR^{-1}$.*

If A is similar to B, then B is similar to A. That is, if $B = RAR^{-1}$, $BR = RA$, $R^{-1}BR = A$, and, if we write $R_1 = R^{-1}$, we have $R_1BR_1^{-1} = A$. Our informal definition of similarity of two matrices would lead one to expect this result.

The similarity of matrices is an example of a concept that is of great importance in mathematics: the notion of *equivalence*, or *equivalence relation*. In general, there are given a set S and a relation which may exist between elements of S which we denote by $\sim$ for the present. Three requirements are placed on the relation $\sim$:

(i) $x \sim x$ for all x in S (Reflexivity).
(ii) If $x \sim y$, then $y \sim x$ (Symmetry).
(iii) If $x \sim y$ and $y \sim z$, then $x \sim z$ (Transitivity).

If conditions (i), (ii), and (iii) are fulfilled, then the relation denoted by $\sim$ is called an *equivalence relation*. Two elements x and y of S are said to be *equivalent* if $x \sim y$.

Some equivalence relations the student has already met are:

For numbers: equality, equality of absolute value;

For triangles: congruence, similarity;

For vectors: equality, equality of length, the property of one being a nonzero scalar multiple of the other.

The student should check these examples to see that all three properties of an equivalence relation are satisfied. It is easy to see (Exercise 1) that similarity of matrices is an equivalence relation on the set of $n \times n$ matrices.

The student has probably noticed that in the examples given, the first requirement was always trivially evident. Its existence is logically necessary to ensure that an equivalence relation has the features we desire (see Exercise 6) but it is true that in most practical cases its validity is essentially automatic (see Exercise 7).

The primary use of equivalence relations on a set S is to separate the set S into convenient subsets. Let us put into one subset all the elements of S which are equivalent to a particular element a; indeed, let us repeat this process with each element of S so that we get a collection of subsets. These subsets will be called *equivalence classes*. In a vague sense, all the elements of an equivalence class have something in common. For example, under similarity of triangles, all the triangles in an equivalence class would have the same angles.

THEOREM 9.1. *If equivalence classes of a set S are formed with respect to an equivalence relation denoted by $\sim$, then*

(i) *Every element of S is in an equivalence class.*

(ii) *If two equivalence classes of S have an element in common, then they are identical.*

Proof. The first assertion is trivial from the construction of equivalence classes; since $x \sim x$, x is in the class of elements equivalent to x. (This is one use of the reflexivity property of the relation $\sim$ and illustrates its necessity if we want every element of S in an equivalence class.)

To prove the second statement, let a be an element common to the equivalence classes B and C. Let B be the class of elements equivalent to b, and C the class of elements equivalent to c. If x is an arbitrary element of B, we will show $x \in C$. Now, by assumption, $x \sim b$ and $a \sim b$; hence $x \sim a$. But also $a \sim c$, since a is common to B and C. Therefore from $x \sim a$ and $a \sim c$, we conclude $x \sim c$ or $x \in C$.

Similarly it is true that any element of C is an element of B. Hence, $B = C$.

To phrase the results of Theorem 9.1 in slightly different words, an equivalence relation on S provides a division of S into disjoint subsets. If we wish to call special attention to the fact that a particular equivalence class contains an element a, we may denote it by $E(a)$. The second part of the proof above established the fact that if $a \in E(b)$ and $a \in E(c)$, then

$$E(b) = E(a) = E(c).$$

In this notation, the equivalence classes are referred to as E-sets and we say that two E-sets are either equal or disjoint.

We may picture the situation by letting a set S be represented as a point set in the plane and dividing S into disjoint subsets representing the distinct equivalence classes; thus:

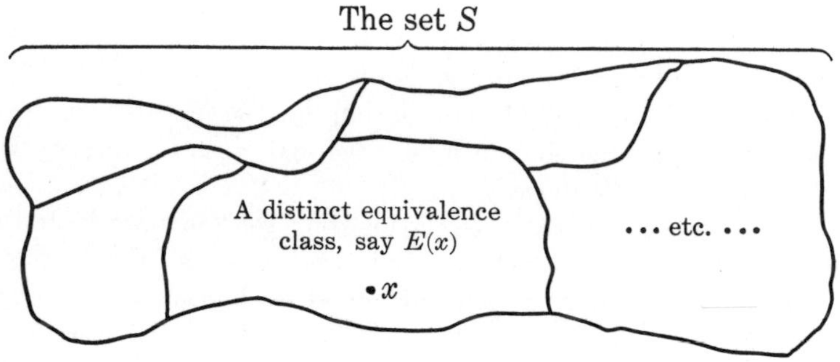

Figure 9.2

The diagram suggests the simplest way in which an equivalence relation may be defined on a set S. We merely take a subdivision of S into disjoint subsets and then define two elements of S to be equivalent if they are contained in the same subset. The student can easily verify that properties (i), (ii), and (iii) of an equivalence relation are satisfied for this definition. Thus, an equivalence relation provides a subdivision of a set S into disjoint subsets, and conversely a subdivision of a set S into disjoint subsets provides an equivalence relation on S.

Example 1. Let S be the set of integers. Define $a \sim b$ to mean "a and b have the same parity." Thus, $5 \sim 7$, $-3 \sim -1$, $2 \sim 18$, but $6 \not\sim 3$ (6 is not in relation with 3). Clearly $\sim$ is an equivalence relation. $E(1)$ consists of all the odd integers while $E(0)$ consists of all the even integers.

We may conclude that the set of $n \times n$ matrices is divided into E-sets of similar matrices under the equivalence relation of similarity of matrices. A study of these E-sets of similar matrices will constitute a considerable portion of the last two chapters of this book. However, before we are completely prepared for this topic we will have occasion to deal with other equivalence relations in the course of the next two chapters. These examples will aid in clarifying the uses and the importance of this concept.

EXERCISES

1. Establish that similarity of matrices is an equivalence relation: (a) from the informal definition of similarity; (b) from Definition 9.1. (Here Exercise 9, § 6, will be useful.)

2. Precisely where are properties (i) and (iii) of equivalence relations used in the proof of Theorem 9.1?

3. Discuss the following relations on the given sets from the standpoint of satisfying properties (i), (ii), and (iii).

(a) Real numbers: $a > b$.
(b) Real numbers: $a \leq b$.
(c) People: a is a brother of b.
(d) Male people: a is a brother of b.
(e) Integers: $a - b$ is divisible by 3.
(f) Real numbers: $\cos a = \cos b$.
(g) Real numbers: $a \neq b$.

4. To decide whether B is similar to A, we must seek a matrix P such that $BP = PA$. Show that this equality leads to a system of homogeneous equations.

5. Is $\begin{bmatrix} 1 & 2 \\ 3 & 4 \end{bmatrix}$ similar to $\begin{bmatrix} 5 & 6 \\ 7 & 8 \end{bmatrix}$?

6. Consider the following relation between integers: a and b are both even. Show that this relation is symmetric and transitive but not reflexive.

7. In the light of Exercise 6, what is wrong with the following "proof" that reflexivity is a consequence of symmetry and transitivity? If $x \sim y$ then $y \sim x$, but then, from $x \sim y$ and $y \sim x$, we get $x \sim x$ by property (iii).

*8. The student may have objected that the concept of *relation* was left undefined. Consider whether the following definition will meet intuitive standards: A relation on a set S is a set of ordered pairs of elements of S. Rephrase the definition of an equivalence relation as a particular type of subset R of the set of ordered pairs of elements of S.

CHAPTER 7

Sets of Linear Transformations and Matrices

In this chapter we shall consider some important sets of linear transformations and matrices. These will be applied to obtain additional information about vector spaces and their linear transformations. At the end of the chapter we shall utilize some of these special sets to introduce and study the important mathematical concept of a group.

1. Some Special Types of Square Matrices and Related Linear Transformations

We wish to study specific classes of square matrices which are of common occurrence or of specific use in applications. One such class, the *nonsingular matrices*, has already been utilized extensively in the preceding chapter. We have seen that these matrices are associated with the one-to-one linear transformations and that they may be recognized by the fact that they have nonzero determinants.

We shall begin now with some classes whose elements are more easily recognized and which also have the property that they form a *sub-ring* (with identity) of the ring of all $n \times n$ matrices. That is, the sum, difference, and product of two matrices in the set under consideration will again be in the set. It is easy to see that if these three conditions are satisfied (or if only the last two of them are verified), the set is a ring.

First we consider the *scalar* matrices. These are matrices $[a_{ij}]$ such that $a_{ij} = 0$ if $i \neq j$, and $a_{ii} = a$. That is, the off-diagonal elements are zero and the diagonal elements are all equal.

If we set up a correspondence between the real numbers and the scalar matrices such that

$$(1.1) \qquad a \longrightarrow \begin{bmatrix} a & 0 & \cdots & 0 \\ 0 & a & \cdots & 0 \\ \cdot & \cdot & \cdot & \cdot \\ \cdot & \cdot & \cdot & \cdot \\ \cdot & \cdot & \cdot & \cdot \\ 0 & 0 & \cdots & a \end{bmatrix},$$

it is simple to check that

$$a + b \longrightarrow \begin{bmatrix} a+b & 0 & \cdots & 0 \\ 0 & a+b & \cdots & 0 \\ \vdots & \vdots & \ddots & \vdots \\ 0 & 0 & \cdots & a+b \end{bmatrix} = \begin{bmatrix} a & 0 & \cdots & 0 \\ 0 & a & \cdots & 0 \\ \vdots & \vdots & \ddots & \vdots \\ 0 & 0 & \cdots & a \end{bmatrix} + \begin{bmatrix} b & 0 & \cdots & 0 \\ 0 & b & \cdots & 0 \\ \vdots & \vdots & \ddots & \vdots \\ 0 & 0 & \cdots & b \end{bmatrix}$$

and

$$ab \longrightarrow \begin{bmatrix} ab & 0 & \cdots & 0 \\ 0 & ab & \cdots & 0 \\ \vdots & \vdots & \ddots & \vdots \\ 0 & 0 & \cdots & ab \end{bmatrix} = \begin{bmatrix} a & 0 & \cdots & 0 \\ 0 & a & \cdots & 0 \\ \vdots & \vdots & \ddots & \vdots \\ 0 & 0 & \cdots & a \end{bmatrix} \begin{bmatrix} b & 0 & \cdots & 0 \\ 0 & b & \cdots & 0 \\ \vdots & \vdots & \ddots & \vdots \\ 0 & 0 & \cdots & b \end{bmatrix}.$$

The correspondence given in (1.1) is clearly one-to-one, and we conclude that the ring of scalar matrices is *isomorphic* to the ring (field) of real numbers (see § 5, Chapter 6).

If **X** is any vector of $V_n(R)$, $\mathbf{X} = [x_1, x_2, \cdots, x_n]$,

$$\mathbf{X} \begin{bmatrix} a & 0 & \cdots & 0 \\ 0 & a & \cdots & 0 \\ \vdots & \vdots & \ddots & \vdots \\ 0 & 0 & \cdots & a \end{bmatrix} = a\mathbf{X}.$$

The effect of a scalar matrix is a scalar multiplication of the vector. Such a matrix represents a linear transformation T that, in geometric language, is simply a dilation or contraction (§ 1, Chapter 6). It should be clear that *any* matrix representing T is a scalar matrix.

Let us now generalize scalar matrices a bit. We keep the off-diagonal elements 0 but let the diagonal elements be arbitrary. Such a matrix is a *diagonal* matrix. For convenience we write:

$$(1.2) \qquad \begin{bmatrix} a_{11} & 0 & \cdots & 0 \\ 0 & a_{22} & \cdots & 0 \\ \vdots & \vdots & \ddots & \vdots \\ 0 & 0 & \cdots & a_{nn} \end{bmatrix} = \text{Diagonal } [a_{11}, a_{22}, \cdots, a_{nn}].$$

The diagonal we have been using is called the *principal diagonal.*

It is easy to see that the sum, difference, and product of two diagonal matrices are again diagonal, while, if the other diagonal is used, the product is not, in general, in the set. Geometrically, the effect of such a matrix on a natural basis vector is an expansion or contraction while it acts on general vectors to produce the corresponding expansion or contraction in each component. Thus,

$$[x_1, x_2, \cdots, x_n]\{\text{Diagonal } [a_{11}, a_{22}, \cdots, a_{nn}]\} = [a_{11}x_1, a_{22}x_2, \cdots, a_{nn}x_n].$$

We extend our generalization still more to consider (lower) *triangular* matrices. Here the elements above the principal diagonal are zero; $a_{ij} = 0$ if $i < j$, but no other restriction is made. Obviously the sum and difference of two triangular matrices are again triangular. That the product has a similar property requires some proof. If we multiply

$$\begin{bmatrix} a_{11} & 0 & \cdots & 0 \\ a_{21} & a_{22} & \cdots & 0 \\ \vdots & \vdots & \ddots & \vdots \\ a_{n1} & a_{n2} & \cdots & a_{nn} \end{bmatrix} \begin{bmatrix} b_{11} & 0 & \cdots & 0 \\ b_{21} & b_{22} & \cdots & 0 \\ \vdots & \vdots & \ddots & \vdots \\ b_{n1} & b_{n2} & \cdots & b_{nn} \end{bmatrix} = [c_{ij}],$$

the general element c_{ij} is $\sum_{k=1}^{n} a_{ik}b_{kj}$. For those elements c_{ij} for which $i < j$ the individual summands are zero for $k < j$ (since $b_{kj} = 0$) and for $k \geq j$ (since then $k > i$ and $a_{ik} = 0$). Hence all summands are zero and $c_{ij} = 0$ if $i < j$.

The geometric effect of a transformation represented by such a matrix is more difficult to describe than in the preceding cases. The first basis vector is merely multiplied by the scalar a_{11}. The image of the second is a linear combination of the first and the second, and, in general, if $\mathbf{X}_i$ is the ith vector of the basis under consideration, the image of $\mathbf{X}_i$ is a linear combination of $\mathbf{X}_1, \mathbf{X}_2, \cdots, \mathbf{X}_i$.

The transpose of a matrix will enter into the next class of matrices we wish to discuss. Let us recall the definition of the transpose of an $n \times n$ matrix given in Chapter 5: The matrix

$$A^{\mathsf{T}} = [a_{ij}'],$$

where $a_{ij}' = a_{ji}$, is the transpose of the matrix $A = [a_{ij}]$. Note that we may readily extend this definition to non-square matrices and that the transpose of an $n \times m$ matrix is an $m \times n$ matrix whose rows are the columns of the original matrix.

The following theorem is valid for rectangular matrices:

THEOREM 1.1. *If A and B are matrices for which the product AB exists, then* $(AB)^{\mathsf{T}} = B^{\mathsf{T}}A^{\mathsf{T}}$.

Proof. If A is $m \times n$ and B is $n \times p$, then AB is $m \times p$, $(AB)^{\mathsf{T}}$ is $p \times m$, and it is immediate that these dimensions are correct for the product of the $p \times n$ matrix B^{T} with the $n \times m$ matrix A^{T}.

For the individual elements, let $A = [a_{ij}]$, $B = [b_{ij}]$; then $AB = [c_{ij}]$, where $c_{ij} = \sum_{k=1}^{n} a_{ik}b_{kj}$. But $(AB)^{\mathsf{T}} = [c_{ij}']$, where $c_{ij}' = c_{ji} = \sum_{k=1}^{n} a_{jk}b_{ki}$ $= \sum_{k=1}^{n} b_{ki}a_{jk}$. Now, the element b_{ik}' of B^{T} is b_{ki}, and similarly a_{kj}' of A^{T} is a_{jk}. Thus, $c_{ij}' = \sum_{k=1}^{n} b_{ik}'a_{kj}'$; this is precisely the expression for the element in the ith row and jth column of $B^{\mathsf{T}}A^{\mathsf{T}}$, so that the theorem is proved.

Now we return to square matrices and consider matrices such as

$$A = \begin{bmatrix} 1 & -1 & 2 \\ -1 & 3 & 4 \\ 2 & 4 & -2 \end{bmatrix},$$

having the property that $A^{\mathsf{T}} = A$ or $a_{ij} = a_{ji}$. These are *symmetric* matrices. Clearly the sum and difference of symmetric matrices are symmetric. However, if A and B are symmetric matrices,

$$(AB)^{\mathsf{T}} = B^{\mathsf{T}}A^{\mathsf{T}} = BA,$$

which is not, in general, equal to AB so that AB need not be symmetric. Therefore the class of symmetric matrices is *not* a sub-ring.

Of the sets of matrices considered so far, the diagonal and symmetric matrices will play the greatest role in future chapters. No simple geometric interpretation of linear transformations having symmetric matrices can be given. The importance of this set lies in other directions than the representation of linear transformations (see Chapter 8).

Several other special sets are considered in the exercises and more will be introduced with their applications in later sections of this chapter.

EXERCISES

1. Show that the nonsingular $n \times n$ matrices do not form a sub-ring of the ring of all $n \times n$ matrices.

2. Define *upper* triangular matrices $[a_{ij}]$ by the condition $a_{ij} = 0$ if $i > j$. Show that such matrices form a sub-ring.

3. Define *strictly* lower triangular matrices by the condition $a_{ij} = 0$ if $i \leq j$. Show that the matrices form a sub-ring without an identity. Do the similar problem for strictly upper triangular matrices.

4. If A is a strictly lower triangular $n \times n$ matrix, show that $A^n = 0$.

5. Define a *permutation* matrix as a square matrix with precisely one nonzero element in each row and each column and such that each nonzero element is 1.

(a) Prove that the product of two permutation matrices is a permutation matrix.

(b) Show that, if $\mathbf{X}$ is a vector of $V_n(R)$ and P is an $n \times n$ permutation matrix, then $\mathbf{X}P$ is a vector whose components are a permutation of the components of $\mathbf{X}$.

(c) Show that the permutation discussed in part (b) is odd or even according as det P is -1 or $+1$ respectively.

6. If the condition that each nonzero element be 1 is removed from the definition in Exercise 5, the result is a definition of *monomial* matrices.

(a) Generalize part (a) of Exercise 5 to monomial matrices.

(b) Describe the effect of monomial matrices on vectors $\mathbf{X}$ of $V_n(R)$.

7. Prove that $A^{\mathsf{T}}A$ is symmetric for any matrix A.

8. Prove that any square matrix is the sum of a symmetric and a *skew-symmetric* matrix where the latter is defined by either of the relations $a_{ij} = -a_{ji}$ or $A^{\mathsf{T}} = -A$.

9. Prove that the product of two symmetric matrices A and B is a symmetric matrix if and only if $AB = BA$.

10. Prove that, for any fixed $n \times n$ matrix A, the set of all matrices which commute with A (that is, all matrices B such that $AB = BA$) forms a sub-ring with identity.

2. Elementary Matrices. Inverses

In this section we shall study three special types of matrices which are grouped under the name of elementary matrices. These will be studied not in terms of their geometrical properties as representatives of transformations (which are, in fact, simple enough) but for what they do to other matrices when combined with them by matrix multiplication.

An *elementary matrix of the first kind* is a special type of $n \times n$ diagonal matrix; all the diagonal elements are 1 except for the element in the ith row, which is a real number a, $a \neq 0$. We denote this matrix by

$$D_i(a) = \text{Diagonal } [1, 1, \cdots, \underset{\substack{\uparrow \\ i\text{TH POSITION}}}{a}, 1, \cdots, 1].$$

Note that $D_i(a)$ is nonsingular and that $D_i(a)^{-1} = D_i(a^{-1})$, a matrix of the same type.

If A is an arbitrary $n \times n$ matrix, the matrix $D_i(a)A$ is identical with A except that its ith row, considered as a vector of $V_n(R)$, is a times the ith row of A. All other rows are unchanged. In $AD_i(a)$, it is the ith column which is multiplied by a.

An *elementary matrix of the second kind* is a special type of permutation matrix (Exercise 5, § 1). It is an $n \times n$ matrix such that every element on the principal diagonal is 1 except for the ith and jth rows. In these the diagonal element is 0, but the element in the ith row and jth column is 1 and that in the jth row and ith column is also 1. All other off-diagonal elements are 0. We denote this matrix by

$$P_{ij} = \begin{array}{c} \\ \\ \\ i \\ \\ j \\ \\ \\ \end{array} \overset{\begin{array}{cccccc} & & i & j & & \end{array}}{\begin{bmatrix} 1 & & & & & \\ & \ddots & & & & \\ & & 0 & \cdots & 1 & \\ & & \vdots & & \vdots & \\ & & 1 & \cdots & 0 & \\ & & & & & \ddots \\ & & & & & & 1 \end{bmatrix}},$$

where the i, j above and beside the matrix indicate the corresponding columns and rows. Note that P_{ij} is nonsingular and that $P_{ij}^{-1} = P_{ij} = P_{ij}^{\mathsf{T}}$.

The matrix $P_{ij}A$ differs from A in that the ith and jth rows are exchanged. The matrix AP_{ij} has the ith and jth columns of A interchanged.

An *elementary matrix of the third kind* is a type not previously considered. All elements on the principal diagonal are 1. The only nonzero element off the principal diagonal is an a in the ith row, jth column. We denote this matrix by

$$S_{ij}(a) = \begin{array}{c} \\ \\ \\ \\ \\ i \\ \\ \\ \end{array} \overset{\begin{array}{ccc} & j & \end{array}}{\begin{bmatrix} 1 & & & & & \\ & \ddots & & & & \\ & & 1 & & & \\ & & & \ddots & & \\ & & a & & 1 & \\ & & & & & \ddots \\ & & & & & & 1 \end{bmatrix}}.$$

$S_{ij}(a)$ is nonsingular, and $S_{ij}(a)^{-1} = S_{ij}(-a)$, a matrix of the same type. The matrix $S_{ij}(a)A$ differs from A in having a times the jth row of A added to the ith row; $AS_{ij}(a)$ has a times the ith column of A added to the jth column.

We are going to use these elementary matrices to give a method of finding the inverse of a numerical matrix. The idea is fairly simple; we give a prescription whereby, after successive multiplications on the left (right) by elementary matrices, the original nonsingular matrix A is reduced to the identity matrix. That is, if E_i stands for an elementary matrix without regard to classification, we begin with the matrix A, then compute:

$$E_1A = A_1, \quad E_2E_1A = A_2, \quad \cdots, \quad E_kE_{k-1}\cdots E_2E_1A = I.$$

Now if we multiply the equation

$$E_kE_{k-1}\cdots E_2E_1A = I \tag{2.1}$$

on the right by A^{-1}, we have

$$E_kE_{k-1}\cdots E_2E_1I = A^{-1}. \tag{2.2}$$

One interpretation of (2.1) and (2.2) is the following: If a succession of multiplications on the left by elementary matrices reduces the matrix A to I, the *same* left multiplications will change I to A^{-1}. Note particularly that we really do not have to write down the E_i; it is what they *do*, not what they *are*, that counts.

Example 1. We illustrate the preceding discussion by computing the inverse of a 3×3 matrix. The process is analogous to the process of elimination used for simultaneous linear equations. We begin with

$$A = \begin{bmatrix} 1 & 2 & -1 \\ 2 & 3 & 0 \\ 1 & -1 & 4 \end{bmatrix}; \quad B = I = \begin{bmatrix} 1 & 0 & 0 \\ 0 & 1 & 0 \\ 0 & 0 & 1 \end{bmatrix}.$$

Now, whatever we do to A (multiplying on the left by E_i), we must do the same thing to B. We obtain successively:

$$A_1 = \begin{bmatrix} 1 & 2 & -1 \\ 0 & -1 & 2 \\ 1 & -1 & 4 \end{bmatrix}, \quad B_1 = \begin{bmatrix} 1 & 0 & 0 \\ -2 & 1 & 0 \\ 0 & 0 & 1 \end{bmatrix}$$

$$A_2 = \begin{bmatrix} 1 & 2 & -1 \\ 0 & -1 & 2 \\ 0 & -3 & 5 \end{bmatrix}, \quad B_2 = \begin{bmatrix} 1 & 0 & 0 \\ -2 & 1 & 0 \\ -1 & 0 & 1 \end{bmatrix}$$

$$A_3 = \begin{bmatrix} 1 & 2 & -1 \\ 0 & 1 & -2 \\ 0 & -3 & 5 \end{bmatrix}, \quad B_3 = \begin{bmatrix} 1 & 0 & 0 \\ 2 & -1 & 0 \\ -1 & 0 & 1 \end{bmatrix}$$

$$A_4 = \begin{bmatrix} 1 & 2 & -1 \\ 0 & 1 & -2 \\ 0 & 0 & -1 \end{bmatrix}, \quad B_4 = \begin{bmatrix} 1 & 0 & 0 \\ 2 & -1 & 0 \\ 5 & -3 & 1 \end{bmatrix}$$

$$A_5 = \begin{bmatrix} 1 & 2 & -1 \\ 0 & 1 & -2 \\ 0 & 0 & 1 \end{bmatrix}, \quad B_5 = \begin{bmatrix} 1 & 0 & 0 \\ 2 & -1 & 0 \\ -5 & 3 & -1 \end{bmatrix}$$

$$A_6 = \begin{bmatrix} 1 & 2 & -1 \\ 0 & 1 & 0 \\ 0 & 0 & 1 \end{bmatrix}, \quad B_6 = \begin{bmatrix} 1 & 0 & 0 \\ -8 & 5 & -2 \\ -5 & 3 & -1 \end{bmatrix}$$

$$A_7 = \begin{bmatrix} 1 & 2 & 0 \\ 0 & 1 & 0 \\ 0 & 0 & 1 \end{bmatrix}, \qquad B_7 = \begin{bmatrix} -4 & 3 & -1 \\ -8 & 5 & -2 \\ -5 & 3 & -1 \end{bmatrix}$$

$$A_8 = \begin{bmatrix} 1 & 0 & 0 \\ 0 & 1 & 0 \\ 0 & 0 & 1 \end{bmatrix}, \qquad B_8 = \begin{bmatrix} 12 & -7 & 3 \\ -8 & 5 & -2 \\ -5 & 3 & -1 \end{bmatrix} = A^{-1}.$$

The procedure used in Example 1 is simple and quite general: For an arbitrary nonsingular matrix A, interchange rows, if necessary, to get a nonzero element a in the first row, first column (1–1 position). Some element in the first column *must* be nonzero since A is assumed to be nonsingular. Multiply the first row by $1/a$ so that the element in the 1–1 position is now 1. Bring all other elements of the first column to zero by adding the proper multiple of the first row to each successive row (A_3 in our example).

Now interchange rows after the first to secure a nonzero element in the 2–2 position and repeat the process, using the second row to reduce all elements of the second column below the 2–2 position to zero. A nonzero element in the second column required for this step must exist since otherwise the determinant of the original matrix would be zero. (Why?)

Continue until all the elements below the principal diagonal are zero and all the diagonal elements are 1 (A_5 in our example).

Now use the last row to eliminate the elements of the last column above the last row and the next-to-the-last row for the next-to-the-last column, and so on, until all the elements above the diagonal are zero.

Each step is to be repeated on the matrix which was originally the identity matrix I.

Note in our example that the elementary matrices were not actually written down. However, they were:

$$E_1 = \begin{bmatrix} 1 & 0 & 0 \\ -2 & 1 & 0 \\ 0 & 0 & 1 \end{bmatrix}, \quad E_2 = \begin{bmatrix} 1 & 0 & 0 \\ 0 & 1 & 0 \\ -1 & 0 & 1 \end{bmatrix}, \quad E_3 = \begin{bmatrix} 1 & 0 & 0 \\ 0 & -1 & 0 \\ 0 & 0 & 1 \end{bmatrix},$$

$$E_4 = \begin{bmatrix} 1 & 0 & 0 \\ 0 & 1 & 0 \\ 0 & 3 & 1 \end{bmatrix}, \quad E_5 = \begin{bmatrix} 1 & 0 & 0 \\ 0 & 1 & 0 \\ 0 & 0 & -1 \end{bmatrix}, \quad E_6 = \begin{bmatrix} 1 & 0 & 0 \\ 0 & 1 & 2 \\ 0 & 0 & 1 \end{bmatrix},$$

$$E_7 = \begin{bmatrix} 1 & 0 & 1 \\ 0 & 1 & 0 \\ 0 & 0 & 1 \end{bmatrix}, \quad E_8 = \begin{bmatrix} 1 & -2 & 0 \\ 0 & 1 & 0 \\ 0 & 0 & 1 \end{bmatrix}.$$

In practice, a number of the steps can be condensed into a single operation. Also, what has been done by left multiplications (manipulation of the rows) could be done by right multiplications (manipulation of the columns). Do difficulties arise if we mix the two procedures?

The method illustrated and outlined above is perhaps the simplest scheme for finding the inverse of matrices larger than 3×3. For 3×3 (or smaller) matrices, some people prefer to use the method given in Chapter 6, others the present system. For larger numerical matrices, this method is subject to difficulties created by accumulation of errors generated in exact division and multiplicative round-off. Readers are referred to texts in numerical matrix computation for other methods adapted to large-scale computation.

We leave the rigorous inductive proof of (2.1) to the student. However, if in equation (2.1) we multiply both sides successively on the left by $E_k^{-1}, E_{k-1}^{-1}, \cdots, E_1^{-1}$, we have:

$$\begin{aligned} E_{k-1} \cdots E_2E_1A &= E_k^{-1} \\ E_{k-2} \cdots E_2E_1A &= E_{k-1}^{-1}E_k^{-1} \\ &\cdots\cdots\cdots \\ E_1A &= E_2^{-1}E_3^{-1} \cdots E_{k-1}^{-1}E_k^{-1}, \end{aligned}$$

and finally

$$A = E_1^{-1}E_2^{-1} \cdots E_k^{-1}. \tag{2.3}$$

All the inverses in (2.3) are again elementary matrices, and we have the following theorem:

THEOREM 2.1. *A nonsingular matrix A can be written as the product of elementary matrices.*

We use this theorem to give a new proof of the following theorem essentially contained in Exercise 8, §3, Chapter 5:

THEOREM 2.2. *If A and B are $n \times n$ matrices, then*

$$\det\,(AB) = \det A \cdot \det B.$$

Proof. (1) If A is a singular matrix, it represents the singular linear transformation $\mathbf{X}T = \mathbf{X}A$ of $V_n(R)$ relative to $\{\mathbf{E}_i\}$. There is then a vector $\mathbf{X} \neq \mathbf{0}$ of $V_n(R)$ such that $\mathbf{X}A = \mathbf{0}$ (Theorem 2.3, Chapter 6). Hence $\mathbf{X}(AB) = \mathbf{0}$, so AB is singular. Thus, if $\det A = 0$, then $\det\,(AB) = 0$, and the theorem is proved in this case.

(2) If A is an elementary transformation of the first kind, $\det A = a$; AB has one row of B multiplied by a, so $\det\,(AB) = a \det B$. Thus $\det\,(AB) = \det A \cdot \det B$. If A is an elementary matrix of the second kind, $\det A = -1$, $\det\,(AB) = -\det B$ since two rows of B are interchanged to form AB. Hence $\det\,(AB) = -\det B = \det A \cdot \det B$. Again, if A is an elementary matrix of the third kind, $\det A = 1$, $\det\,(AB) = \det B$, as the determinant is not changed by the addition of a multiple of one row to the other, and $\det\,(AB) = \det A \cdot \det B$. Thus the theorem is true if A is an elementary matrix.

(3) Suppose the theorem proved when A is the product of $n-1$ elementary matrices. We proceed to the inductive proof for $A = E_n E_{n-1} \cdots E_1$. Let $E_{n-1} \cdots E_1 = A_1$, $A_1 B = B_1$. Then

$$\det (AB) = \det (E_n E_{n-1} \cdots E_1 B) = \det (E_n B_1) = \det E_n \det B_1$$

by part (2) of the proof. Further, $\det E_n \det B_1 = \det E_n \det (A_1 B) = \det E_n \det A_1 \det B$ by the inductive assumption. But $\det (E_n A_1) = \det E_n \cdot \det A_1$ by part (2) again, so that

$$\det (AB) = \det E_n \det A_1 \det B = \det (E_n A_1) \det B = \det A \cdot \det B.$$

EXERCISES

1. The following pairs of matrices satisfy matrix equations of the type $EA = B$ or $AE = B$ where E is an elementary matrix. Find E and the equation.

(a) $$A = \begin{bmatrix} 1 & 2 & 3 \\ 1 & -1 & 4 \\ 1 & 1 & 2 \end{bmatrix}, \qquad B = \begin{bmatrix} 1 & 5 & 3 \\ 1 & 3 & 4 \\ 1 & 3 & 2 \end{bmatrix}$$

(b) $$A = \begin{bmatrix} 1 & 2 \\ -3 & 5 \\ 4 & 1 \end{bmatrix}, \qquad B = \begin{bmatrix} 1 & 2 \\ 4 & 1 \\ -3 & 5 \end{bmatrix}$$

(c) $$A = \begin{bmatrix} 1 & -1 & 4 \\ 3 & 2 & 1 \end{bmatrix}, \qquad B = \begin{bmatrix} 2 & -1 & 4 \\ 6 & 2 & 1 \end{bmatrix}$$

2. Write each of the following matrices as the product of elementary matrices:

$$\text{(a)} \begin{bmatrix} 1 & -1 & 2 \\ 3 & 1 & 4 \\ 4 & 0 & 1 \end{bmatrix} \qquad \text{(b)} \begin{bmatrix} 1 & -1 & -2 \\ 2 & 1 & 1 \\ 1 & 5 & -3 \end{bmatrix}$$

3. Find the inverses of the matrices in Exercise 2.

4. Prove that the inverse of a nonsingular (lower) triangular matrix is lower triangular.

5. Prove that a matrix is nonsingular if and only if it is the product of elementary matrices.

6. Find the inverses of the following matrices:

$$\text{(a)} \begin{bmatrix} 1 & -1 & 2 & 3 \\ 2 & 1 & -2 & 3 \\ 1 & -1 & 2 & 5 \\ 1 & -1 & 3 & 3 \end{bmatrix} \qquad \text{(b)} \begin{bmatrix} 2 & 0 & -1 & 1 \\ 1 & 1 & -2 & 0 \\ 0 & 3 & 1 & -2 \\ 0 & 6 & 4 & -1 \end{bmatrix}$$

7. Provide a rigorous proof that the method of finding an inverse of a matrix illustrated by Example 1 and discussed in this section is valid.

Hint: Use induction on the size of the matrix and observe that if E_i^* is an elementary $(n-1) \times (n-1)$ matrix, then $\begin{bmatrix} 1 & 0 & \cdots & 0 \\ 0 & & & \\ \vdots & & \left[\quad E_i^* \quad \right] & \\ 0 & & & \end{bmatrix}$ is an elementary $n \times n$ matrix.

8. Show how Exercise 8, §3, Chapter 5, may be used to give a proof of Theorem 2.2.

3. The Rank of a Matrix

The word "rank" appears in four different contexts in the theory of matrices and linear transformations. These are:

1. The maximum number of linearly independent rows of an $n \times m$ matrix A when they are viewed as vectors of $V_m(R)$: *row rank of* A.
2. The maximum number of linearly independent columns of an $n \times m$ matrix A when these columns (or their transposes) are viewed as vectors of $V_n(R)$: *column rank of* A.
3. The order of the largest nonzero determinant which is obtainable by the possible deletion of rows and columns from the matrix: *determinant rank of* A.
4. The dimension of the range, or rank space, of a linear transformation T as defined in §2 of Chapter 6: *the rank of* T.

This section will be devoted to proving that all these definitions lead to the same number when A is the matrix corresponding to the linear transformation T; to methods of computing the rank; and to an application to linear equations.

For nonsingular $n \times n$ matrices and the corresponding linear transformations, we are finished. The rank is n by any definition. At the other end of the scale, the rank of a zero matrix (of any order) or the corresponding zero linear transformation is zero.

Before proceeding, it will be convenient to express the entire problem in terms of matrices. To this end, we define the *range of an* $n \times m$ *matrix* $A = [a_{ij}]$ as the range of the linear transformation T from $V_n(R)$ to $V_m(R)$ defined by

$$\mathbf{X}\mathrm{T} = \mathbf{X}A,$$

for all $\mathbf{X}$ of $V_n(R)$.

It is then a simple matter to see that the *range of a matrix A is generated* *by the rows of A* when they are viewed as vectors of $V_m(R)$. Indeed, these vectors are the images of the natural basis vectors $\{\mathbf{E}_i\}$ of $V_n(R)$:

$$\mathbf{E}_i\mathrm{T} = [a_{i1}, a_{i2}, \cdots, a_{im}], \qquad \text{for } i = 1, 2, \cdots, n.$$

Since any vector of $V_n(R)$ may be represented as a linear combination of the $\{\mathbf{E}_i\}$, any image vector is a linear combination of $\{\mathbf{E}_i\mathrm{T}\}$ or the rows of the matrix A. Thus we have proved:

THEOREM 3.1. *The row rank of a matrix A is equal to the dimension of the range of A.*

The problem of actually determining the row rank of a matrix is our old problem of determining how many independent vectors there are in a given set of vectors. We now offer, in terms of matrices, a method of solution of this problem which is more direct than any mentioned before. It is, however, closely related to the technique used in the last section to invert a nonsingular matrix. Specifically, *multiplication of a matrix A on the left by an elementary matrix does not change the row rank of A.* This is obvious when a row of A is multiplied by a nonzero scalar or when two rows are interchanged. When a multiple of one row is added to another, the resulting rows are linear combinations of the original rows so that the ranks are not increased; but if we reverse the process (invert the elementary matrix), the new rows go back to the original, so the rank has not been decreased. Indeed, multiplication on the left by *any* nonsingular $n \times n$ matrix P does not change the row rank, as can be seen either by representing P as a product of elementary matrices or directly by essentially the same argument as was given for elementary matrices of the third kind.

Given A, an $n \times m$ matrix, we determine the row rank as follows:

1. If necessary, move a row having a nonzero element in as far left a position as possible to the first row. By scalar multiplication make this nonzero element 1.

2. By addition of appropriate multiples of this new first row, reduce to zero all elements in the same column with this first nonzero element.

3. Continue to perform operations 1 and 2 successively, each time confining attention to rows lying below the one used in the preceding step.

When the process terminates, the final matrix will consist of rows such that each row has a 1 (if any nonzero elements appear in the row at all) as its first nonzero element and this 1 appears to the right of the initial 1 in any preceding row. Such a matrix is said to be in (row) *echelon form.*

Example 1. We illustrate the process on the following matrix:

$$\begin{bmatrix} 0 & 1 & 3 & -2 & -1 & 2 \\ 0 & 2 & 6 & -4 & -2 & 4 \\ 0 & 1 & 3 & -2 & 1 & 4 \\ 0 & 2 & 6 & 1 & -1 & 0 \end{bmatrix}.$$

Nothing can be done about the first column. The leading nonzero element of the first row is already 1 so we pass at once to step 2:

$$\begin{bmatrix} 0 & 1 & 3 & -2 & -1 & 2 \\ 0 & 0 & 0 & 0 & 0 & 0 \\ 0 & 0 & 0 & 0 & 2 & 2 \\ 0 & 0 & 0 & 5 & 1 & -4 \end{bmatrix}.$$

Now we return to step 1, restricting our attention to rows below the first:

$$\begin{bmatrix} 0 & 1 & 3 & -2 & -1 & 2 \\ 0 & 0 & 0 & 1 & \frac{1}{5} & -\frac{4}{5} \\ 0 & 0 & 0 & 0 & 2 & 2 \\ 0 & 0 & 0 & 0 & 0 & 0 \end{bmatrix}.$$

This time there are no nonzero elements below the new leading element (in the fourth column) so step 2 is vacuous and we return to step 1 for the last two rows:

$$\begin{bmatrix} 0 & 1 & 3 & -2 & -1 & 2 \\ 0 & 0 & 0 & 1 & \frac{1}{5} & -\frac{4}{5} \\ 0 & 0 & 0 & 0 & 1 & 1 \\ 0 & 0 & 0 & 0 & 0 & 0 \end{bmatrix}.$$

We leave to the student the proof of the following statement: *The row rank of a matrix in row echelon form is the number of nonzero rows.* In Example 1, the row rank of the echelon matrix and, hence, of the original matrix is 3.

Next we seek to establish the equality of the row rank and the determinant rank. This may be considered to be already accomplished if the student has solved Exercise 3, §6 of Chapter 5. In our present terms this exercise asserts the equality of these ranks. It is, perhaps, desirable to give a direct proof, and we do so in terms of the procedure just given for finding the row rank.

THEOREM 3.2. *The row rank of a matrix A is equal to the determinant rank of A.*

Proof. We are going to show that elementary row transformations (left multiplications by elementary matrices) do not change the determinant rank. Specifically, for each $k \times k$ submatrix of A with a nonzero determinant, there is a $k \times k$ submatrix with a nonzero determinant after any elementary row transformation.

Transformations corresponding to elementary matrices of the first kind merely multiply a row by a nonzero element. If they change the determinant of our $k \times k$ submatrix at all, it is merely by multiplying it by this nonzero element. We can stick to the same submatrix.

Transformations of the second kind exchange two rows. If both rows happen to belong to the $k \times k$ submatrix that we are considering, the sign of the determinant is changed; it is still nonzero. We retain the submatrix. If a new row is brought in and the old one removed, the determinant could be spoiled, but we simply choose a new $k \times k$ submatrix using the same columns, and the same rows except for the interloper; instead of this we use the row where the original row now resides.

Example 2. In the matrix

$$\begin{bmatrix} 0 & 1 & -1 & 2 \\ 1 & 1 & 2 & 3 \\ 1 & -1 & 1 & 4 \end{bmatrix},$$

the 2×2 matrix made by eliminating the first row and the first and fourth columns is $\begin{bmatrix} 1 & 2 \\ -1 & 1 \end{bmatrix}$, which has determinant 3. If the first and second rows are interchanged,

$$\begin{bmatrix} 1 & 1 & 2 & 3 \\ 0 & 1 & -1 & 2 \\ 1 & -1 & 1 & 4 \end{bmatrix},$$

the matrix in this position is now $\begin{bmatrix} 1 & -1 \\ -1 & 1 \end{bmatrix}$ and is singular; but the matrix obtained by eliminating the *second* row and the first and fourth columns is the original $\begin{bmatrix} 1 & 2 \\ -1 & 1 \end{bmatrix}$.

Similarly, for a transformation of the third kind, which adds a multiple of one row to another: if the two rows are both in our $k \times k$ submatrix, its determinant is unchanged. If a multiple of an outside row is imported, the determinant may become zero. We have seen that this change can be represented as the result of adding the determinants of two matrices differing only in one row. If the sum is zero and the original determinant was nonzero, the other summand must be its negative, hence nonzero. Then, in the transformed matrix we can use the same columns, and the same rows except the affected one, which will be replaced by the row whose multiple was added.

Example 3. In the matrix

$$\begin{bmatrix} 1 & 2 & 3 & -1 \\ 2 & 4 & -1 & -2 \\ 1 & 3 & 1 & -1 \end{bmatrix},$$

consider the matrix obtained by deleting row 1, columns 1 and 3: that is, $\begin{bmatrix} 4 & -2 \\ 3 & -1 \end{bmatrix}$; the determinant being 2.

If we subtract twice the first row from the second, we obtain the matrix

$$\begin{bmatrix} 1 & 2 & 3 & -1 \\ 0 & 0 & -7 & 0 \\ 1 & 3 & 1 & -1 \end{bmatrix},$$

and our 2×2 matrix is replaced by $\begin{bmatrix} 0 & 0 \\ 3 & -1 \end{bmatrix}$, whose determinant is 0. But if we consider that this has occurred because of the addition:

$$\begin{vmatrix} (-2)\cdot 2 & (-2)\cdot(-1) \\ 3 & -1 \end{vmatrix} + \begin{vmatrix} 4 & -2 \\ 3 & -1 \end{vmatrix} = \begin{vmatrix} -4 & 2 \\ 3 & -1 \end{vmatrix} + \begin{vmatrix} 4 & -2 \\ 3 & -1 \end{vmatrix}$$
$$= \begin{vmatrix} 0 & 0 \\ 3 & -1 \end{vmatrix}$$

and note that the matrix $\begin{bmatrix} 2 & -1 \\ 3 & -1 \end{bmatrix}$ involved in the first term above is still available by eliminating row 2, columns 1 and 3, we still are guaranteed a 2×2 matrix with the nonzero determinant.

We conclude that the determinant rank of a matrix is equal to the determinant rank of the echelon matrix to which it is reduced by elementary row transformations. But the determinant rank of an echelon matrix is the number of nonzero rows; certainly, it is not more than this, and we may obtain a nonzero determinant of maximum size by eliminating the rows of zeros and the columns which do not contain an initial 1 of some nonzero row. The result is an upper triangular matrix

$$\begin{bmatrix} 1 & b_{12} & \cdots & b_{1n} \\ 0 & 1 & \cdots & b_{2n} \\ \vdots & & \ddots & \vdots \\ 0 & \cdots & 0 & 1 \end{bmatrix}$$

which has determinant 1.

In Example 1, this matrix is obtained by eliminating the fourth row and the first, third, and sixth columns of the echelon form, leaving

$$\begin{bmatrix} 1 & -2 & -1 \\ 0 & 1 & \frac{1}{5} \\ 0 & 0 & 1 \end{bmatrix}.$$

Since we have already indicated that the row rank of the original matrix is equal to the number of nonzero rows of the echelon form, the proof of Theorem 3.2 is complete.

There remains the problem of obtaining the equality of the column rank of a matrix with the other ranks. Briefly, the column rank of A is the row rank of A^T. But all nonsingular $k \times k$ matrices appearing in A^T are transposes of nonsingular $k \times k$ matrices in A and conversely. Thus, the determinant rank of A^T is equal to the determinant rank of A. Hence the column rank of A is equal to the determinant rank of A.

As an alternate argument, it is clear that the discussion applied to elementary row transformations applies equally well to elementary column transformations and that a (column) echelon form can be obtained such that the number of nonzero columns is at once the column rank of A and the determinant rank of A. In either case we have the theorem:

THEOREM 3.3. *For any matrix A, the row rank, the column rank, the determinant rank, and the dimension of the range are all equal.*

EXERCISES

1. Reduce the following matrices to *row* echelon form and determine their rank:

$$\text{(a)} \begin{bmatrix} 1 & -1 & 0 & 1 \\ 1 & 1 & 2 & 3 \\ 1 & 2 & -1 & 1 \end{bmatrix} \qquad \text{(b)} \begin{bmatrix} 1 & -1 & 2 & 1 \\ 3 & 0 & 1 & 2 \\ 2 & 1 & -1 & 1 \end{bmatrix}$$

$$\text{(c)} \begin{bmatrix} 1 & 1 & 1 & -1 & 2 \\ 1 & -1 & 1 & 1 & 1 \\ 0 & 2 & 1 & -1 & 1 \end{bmatrix} \qquad \text{(d)} \begin{bmatrix} 2 & -1 & 4 & 5 \\ 3 & 2 & 1 & 4 \\ 5 & -1 & 1 & 3 \end{bmatrix}$$

2. Reduce the matrices in Exercise 1 to a *column* echelon form and verify your previous determination of their rank.

3. Find the rank of the following matrix as a function of h and k:

$$\begin{bmatrix} 1 & -1 & 2 & 3 \\ 2 & 1 & h & 1 \\ 0 & -3 & k & 5 \\ 3 & 3 & 4 & -1 \end{bmatrix}.$$

4. In each of the matrices of Exercise 1, find a nonzero determinant of maximal size.

5. Prove that the rank of AB is at least as small as the smaller of the rank of A and the rank of B.

6. Let A and B be $n \times n$ matrices, and prove that rank $(A + B) \leq$ rank A + rank B. Give examples of both equality and inequality.

7. Prove that the row rank of a matrix in row echelon form is the number of nonzero rows.

4. Applications of the Concept of Rank

We say that a matrix B is *equivalent* to a matrix A if there exist nonsingular matrices P and Q such that $PAQ = B$. The simple (but confusingly worded) proposition "Equivalence of matrices is an equivalence relation for the set of all $n \times m$ matrices" is left as an exercise.

It is natural to ask, "When are two $n \times m$ matrices A and B equivalent?" The answer is essentially contained in our discussion of rank in the preceding section. The alternate argument in the discussion preceding Theorem 3.3 shows that if Q is a nonsingular $m \times m$ matrix, the rank (we can now use the term without a modifier) of the $n \times m$ matrix AQ is the same as the rank of the $n \times m$ matrix A. This, together with the result that the rank of PA is equal to the rank of A for any nonsingular $n \times n$ matrix P, yields the following theorem:

THEOREM 4.1. *If P and Q are nonsingular matrices such that the product PAQ is defined, the ranks of the matrices PAQ and A are identical.*

So far, we have shown that equivalent matrices have the same rank. We now propose to demonstrate the converse.

What happens if, having brought a matrix A into a row echelon form by a matrix product PA, we continue and bring the result into a column echelon form by the matrix product $(PA)Q$? It is easy to see that a subsequent column echelon reduction of a row echelon form does not disturb the row echelon property.

Example 1. We begin with the row echelon form with which we concluded Example 1 of §3. Thus, we have

$$\begin{bmatrix} 0 & 1 & 3 & -2 & -1 & 2 \\ 0 & 0 & 0 & 1 & \frac{1}{5} & -\frac{4}{5} \\ 0 & 0 & 0 & 0 & 1 & 1 \\ 0 & 0 & 0 & 0 & 0 & 0 \end{bmatrix},$$

and we proceed to a column echelon form as follows:

$$\begin{bmatrix} 1 & 3 & -2 & -1 & 2 & 0 \\ 0 & 0 & 1 & \frac{1}{5} & -\frac{4}{5} & 0 \\ 0 & 0 & 0 & 1 & 1 & 0 \\ 0 & 0 & 0 & 0 & 0 & 0 \end{bmatrix}, \quad \begin{bmatrix} 1 & 0 & 0 & 0 & 0 & 0 \\ 0 & 0 & 1 & \frac{1}{5} & -\frac{4}{5} & 0 \\ 0 & 0 & 0 & 1 & 1 & 0 \\ 0 & 0 & 0 & 0 & 0 & 0 \end{bmatrix},$$

$$\begin{bmatrix} 1 & 0 & 0 & 0 & 0 & 0 \\ 0 & 1 & \frac{1}{5} & -\frac{4}{5} & 0 & 0 \\ 0 & 0 & 1 & 1 & 0 & 0 \\ 0 & 0 & 0 & 0 & 0 & 0 \end{bmatrix}, \quad \begin{bmatrix} 1 & 0 & 0 & 0 & 0 & 0 \\ 0 & 1 & 0 & 0 & 0 & 0 \\ 0 & 0 & 1 & 1 & 0 & 0 \\ 0 & 0 & 0 & 0 & 0 & 0 \end{bmatrix}, \quad \begin{bmatrix} 1 & 0 & 0 & 0 & 0 & 0 \\ 0 & 1 & 0 & 0 & 0 & 0 \\ 0 & 0 & 1 & 0 & 0 & 0 \\ 0 & 0 & 0 & 0 & 0 & 0 \end{bmatrix}.$$

In general, the requirement that a matrix of rank r be in both row and column echelon form will produce a matrix with r units on the "principal diagonal" in the first r rows (and columns) and zeros elsewhere. This matrix is clearly determined by the number of its rows and columns and its rank. This result may be expressed formally:

THEOREM 4.2. *Every $n \times m$ matrix of rank r is equivalent to precisely one matrix whose only nonzero elements are 1's occurring on the "principal diagonal" in the first r positions.*

COROLLARY. *Two $n \times m$ matrices are equivalent if and only if they have the same rank.*

We have seen (Chapter 6, §8) that if matrices A and B represent the same linear transformation with respect to two different choices of bases, then $B = PAQ^{-1}$ for appropriate nonsingular P and Q. Thus B is equivalent to A. Conversely, if B is equivalent to A, $B = PAQ = PA(Q^{-1})^{-1}$ so that B and A represent the same linear transformation for some choice of bases of the vector spaces $V_n(R)$ and $V_m(R)$. Thus, the rank of a linear transformation T may be described as the rank of any matrix representing T. In particular, one such matrix is the special one described in the last theorem. This special matrix representation is an example of a general procedure by which a particular matrix is chosen to represent a set of related matrices. The topic will be discussed in more detail in the next chapter.

Rank of a matrix and linear equations. Let us consider the system of linear equations

$$\begin{aligned} a_{11}x_1 + a_{12}x_2 + \cdots + a_{1n}x_n &= b_1 \\ a_{21}x_1 + a_{22}x_2 + \cdots + a_{2n}x_n &= b_2 \\ \cdots\cdots\cdots\cdots\cdots\cdots\cdots & \\ a_{m1}x_1 + a_{m2}x_2 + \cdots + a_{mn}x_n &= b_m; \end{aligned} \tag{4.1}$$

or

$$A\mathbf{X}^{\mathsf{T}} = \mathbf{B}^{\mathsf{T}}; \quad \mathbf{X}A^{\mathsf{T}} = \mathbf{B}, \tag{4.2}$$

where $\mathbf{X} = [x_1, x_2, \cdots, x_n]$, $\mathbf{B} = [b_1, b_2, \cdots, b_m]$, and $A = [a_{ij}]$ is the $m \times n$ matrix whose elements appear as the coefficients in (4.1). Further, define A_1, the *augmented matrix* of A, as the $m \times (n + 1)$ matrix obtained by adjoining the column $\mathbf{B}^{\mathsf{T}}$ to A.

THEOREM 4.3. *The system of linear equations* (4.1) *has solutions if and only if the rank of the augmented matrix A_1 is equal to the rank of the matrix A. If the ranks are equal to r, $n - r$ of the unknowns may be selected arbitrarily and the remaining r may be found uniquely in terms of them.*

Proof. The first statement is essentially a restatement of Theorem 3.2 of Chapter 3. If $\mathbf{B}$ is in the range of A^{T}, the ranks of A and A_1 will be equal, and conversely.

For the second part, select r linearly independent columns of A; by renumbering suppose they are the first r. Then every vector in the range of A^{T} can be written uniquely in terms of these vectors. Hence, assigning values at our pleasure to $x_{r+1}, \cdots, x_n$, we can find unique coefficients $x_1, x_2, \cdots, x_r$ such that

$$\begin{aligned} x_{r+1}[a_{1,\,r+1}, a_{2,\,r+1}, \cdots, a_{m,\,r+1}] + \cdots + x_n[a_{1n}, a_{2n}, \cdots, a_{mn}] - [b_1, b_2, \cdots, b_m] \\ = -\{x_1[a_{11}, a_{21}, \cdots, a_{m1}] + \cdots + x_r[a_{1r}, a_{2r}, \cdots, a_{mr}]\}, \end{aligned}$$

since the sum on the left is, by hypothesis, in the range of A^T. The vector equations are, on transposition and equating of components, simply equations (4.1), and the proof is complete. (The student should compare this statement and proof with Exercises 10–13 of §3, Chapter 3.)

If the vector **B** in the preceding proof is the zero vector, we see that for

$$\mathbf{X} = [x_1, x_2, \cdots, x_r, x_{r+1}, x_{r+2}, \cdots, x_n],$$

where the x_i are selected as in the proof,

$$\mathbf{X}A^\mathsf{T} = \mathbf{0}.$$

Thus, because of the complete freedom in the choice of $x_{r+1}, \cdots, x_n$, it should be clear that the set of all vectors **X**, such that $\mathbf{X}A^\mathsf{T} = \mathbf{0}$, forms a subspace of dimension $n - r$. The student will be asked to carry out this verification in Exercise 5, part (a).

As a simple consequence of this discussion we have an alternate proof of Theorem 2.2, Chapter 6, on the sum of the dimensions of the null space and range of a linear transformation T. We need merely to take any matrix representation of T and consider the system of equations arising from a determination of the null space of T.

EXERCISES

1. Test for equivalence the following matrices:

$$\begin{bmatrix} 1 & -1 & 2 & 3 & 1 \\ 1 & 1 & 1 & -1 & 2 \\ 1 & -2 & 1 & 3 & 1 \\ 1 & 0 & 0 & -1 & 2 \end{bmatrix}, \quad \begin{bmatrix} 2 & 1 & 3 & 4 & -1 \\ 1 & -3 & 1 & 2 & -1 \\ 3 & 4 & -1 & 2 & 1 \\ 0 & -6 & 5 & 4 & -3 \end{bmatrix}, \quad \begin{bmatrix} 1 & 2 & -1 & 3 & 4 \\ 1 & -1 & 2 & 1 & 0 \\ 2 & 1 & 1 & 4 & 4 \\ 1 & -4 & 5 & -1 & -4 \end{bmatrix}.$$

2. Solve the following system of linear equations if possible:

$$\begin{aligned} x - y + 2z + 3t + u &= 4 \\ x + y + z - t + 2u &= 4 \\ x - 2y + z + 3t + u &= 2 \\ x \qquad\qquad - t + 2u &= -2. \end{aligned}$$

3. To what does Theorem 4.3 reduce if the equations are homogeneous, i.e., if $b_i = 0, i = 1, 2, \cdots, m$? Prove that a set of homogeneous equations with more unknowns than equations always has a solution in which not all the x_i are zero. Give an example showing that this does not hold for non-homogeneous equations.

4. Prove directly, using matrix equations and without reference to rank, that matrix equivalence is an equivalence relation.

5. Fill in the details of the following proof that the row rank of an $m \times n$ matrix A is equal to the column rank. Note that the proof makes no use of determinants.

(a) Define the *null space* of A as the set of all vectors **X** of $V_m(R)$ such that $\mathbf{X}A = \mathbf{0}$. Let the row rank of A be r and the dimension of the null space, the *nullity* of A, be z. Show that $r + z = m$.

(b) Show that if Q is nonsingular, then A and AQ have the same null space. Hence, A and AQ have the same row rank.

(c) If P is nonsingular, A and PAQ have the same row rank. Hence the row rank of A is the number of 1's on the diagonal of R, the special matrix discussed in Theorem 4.2.

(d) Similarly A^{T} and $Q^{\mathsf{T}}A^{\mathsf{T}}P^{\mathsf{T}}$ have the same row rank, and this is still the number of 1's on the diagonal of R. Hence the row rank of A is the column rank of A.

6. Using the definition of nullity of Exercise 5, let A and B be matrices for which the product AB is defined and prove:

$$\text{nullity of } AB \leq \text{nullity of } A + \text{nullity of } B.$$

7. Show that if the $n \times n$ matrix A has rank r_1 and the $n \times n$ matrix B has rank r_2, then the rank of AB is $\geq r_1 + r_2 - n$.

5. Groups

In §1 we noted that, although sums and differences of symmetric matrices were again symmetric, products of such matrices were, in general, not in the set of symmetric matrices. On the other hand, if we consider nonsingular matrices or linear transformations, we note that products and inverses are again nonsingular but that sums are quite likely to be singular; for example, $A + (-A) = 0$. These examples indicate that we must often concentrate on just one operation defined over a given set of elements if we want the result to again be in the set. Thus our attention is directed toward algebraic systems having a "single composition" as well as to those systems having a "double composition," such as rings and fields. The most useful algebraic system of single composition is a *group*.

DEFINITION 5.1. *A* GROUP *is a set of elements G with a single operation (usually written either as multiplication, $\cdot$, or as addition, $+$) satisfying the following postulates:*

(i) *If $a \in G$, $b \in G$, then $a \cdot b \in G$.* (*Closure*)
(*In additive notation, $a + b \in G$.*)

(ii) *If $a \in G$, $b \in G$, $c \in G$, then $(a \cdot b) \cdot c = a \cdot (b \cdot c)$.* (*Associativity*)
(*In additive notation, $(a + b) + c = a + (b + c)$.*)

(iii) *There is an element $e \in G$ such that, for all elements $a \in G$,*

$$e \cdot a = a \cdot e = a. \qquad (Identity)$$

(*In additive notation, $a + e = e + a = a$.*)

(iv) *For every $a \in G$, there exists a (unique) element $a^{-1} \in G$ such that*

$$a \cdot a^{-1} = a^{-1} \cdot a = e. \qquad (Inverses)$$

(*In additive notation, $a + (-a) = (-a) + a = e$.*)

Note that the additive postulates are precisely the postulates A1, A2, A3, and A4 used in defining a field in §2 of Chapter 1. Moreover, when the operation of the group is indicated as multiplication, $\cdot$, the postulates satisfied by the elements of G could be written as M1, M2, M3, and M4.

If the commutative law (M5 or A5) should happen to hold for the elements of G, the group is called *commutative*, or *Abelian*.

It is easy to give numerous examples of groups.

1. The elements of any ring form an Abelian group under addition.

2. The nonzero elements of any field form an Abelian group under multiplication. (Why is a similar statement for all rings false?)

3. The number 1 by itself is a group under multiplication. The number 0 is a group under addition.

4. The numbers 1, -1 form a group of two elements under multiplication.

5. The complex numbers 1, -1, $+i$, $-i$ form a group of four elements under multiplication.

6. Define a multiplication on the eight symbols $\{\pm 1, \pm i, \pm j, \pm k\}$ with the rules $i^2 = j^2 = k^2 = -1$; $ij = -ji = k$, $jk = -kj = i$; $ki = -ik = j$ and by the usual rule of signs with 1 as the identity element. The result is a group of eight elements called the *quaternion group*.

7. Define "addition" of two elements, written 0 and 1, as follows: $0 + 0 = 1 + 1 = 0$, $0 + 1 = 1 + 0 = 1$. This set forms a group of two elements under the "addition."

8. Any vector space is an Abelian group under addition.

9. The symmetric $n \times n$ matrices form a group under addition.

10. The nonsingular $n \times n$ matrices form a group under multiplication as do the nonsingular linear transformations from $V_n(R)$ to $V_n(R)$.

These last two examples of groups are of particular importance in our present discussion. The transformation group is called the *full linear group* of $V_n(R)$. If we adopt a basis for $V_n(R)$ we at once have a one-to-one correspondence between the set of nonsingular transformations of $V_n(R)$ and the set of $n \times n$ nonsingular matrices, as was discussed in Chapter 6. If T_1 and T_2 are two linear transformations of $V_n(R)$ and A and B are the matrices which correspond to them respectively, we also know that to the transformation T_1T_2 there corresponds the matrix AB. This is an example of an isomorphism between groups.

DEFINITION 5.2. *Let G and G' be two groups (which, for convenience, are both written multiplicatively) and suppose there is a one-to-one mapping from G onto G' such that:*

$$\text{If } g_1 \longrightarrow g_1',\ g_2 \longrightarrow g_2', \quad \text{then} \quad g_1g_2 \longrightarrow g_1'g_2',$$

for all $g_1, g_2 \in G$. Briefly, the product of the images is the image of the products. In this case the groups G and G' are called ISOMORPHIC. *The mapping from G onto G' is called an* ISOMORPHISM.

Of course, there are many isomorphisms from the full linear group of $V_n(R)$ to the group of $n \times n$ nonsingular matrices. We get a new one whenever we choose a new basis for $V_n(R)$. There are several remarks which can be made about all these isomorphisms.

1. The image of the identity transformation is always the identity matrix. If I is the identity transformation and A its corresponding matrix, T any nonsingular linear transformation and B its matrix, we have: $\mathrm{T} = \mathrm{IT} \longrightarrow AB$ and $\mathrm{T} \longrightarrow B$. Hence $AB = B$ and, multiplying on the right by B^{-1}, we have $ABB^{-1} = BB^{-1}$, or $A = I$.

2. Similarly, the image of an inverse transformation is always the inverse of the image of the original. If $\mathrm{T} \longrightarrow A$ and $\mathrm{T}^{-1} \longrightarrow B$, then $\mathrm{TT}^{-1} = \mathrm{I} \longrightarrow AB$. Hence from Remark 1, $AB = I$. (There is no ambiguity in using "I" for both the identity transformation and the identity matrix.)

3. If in two different isomorphisms the transformation T has images A and B, we know that a nonsingular matrix P (the matrix corresponding to the change of basis) exists such that $B = PAP^{-1}$. Conversely, if we have an isomorphism such that the image of T is A, we get a new isomorphism using any nonsingular matrix P and letting the new image of T be PAP^{-1}. (If $P = aI$, the images are unchanged.)

A subset of a group G that is again a group with respect to the initial operation is called a *subgroup* of G. In order to determine whether a nonempty subset of a group G is indeed a subgroup it suffices to check closure and the fact that the inverse of an element of the subset is again in the subset. The associative law is valid since it holds for the entire group, and the presence of the identity in the subset is assured when we note that if A is in the subset, A^{-1} is also and so $AA^{-1} = I$ is present.

EXERCISES

1. Select the groups from the following systems:

(a) (Lower) triangular matrices under addition.

(b) (Lower) triangular matrices under multiplication.

(c) The set of nonsingular matrices which commute with a given matrix A under multiplication. (B is in the set if and only if $BA = AB$ and B is nonsingular.)

(d) The set of 2×2 matrices $\begin{bmatrix} a & b \\ -b & a \end{bmatrix}$, where a and b are real numbers, under multiplication.

(e) Those diagonal matrices in which none of the diagonal terms are zero, under multiplication.

(f) The set of all elementary matrices of the first kind under multiplication.

2. Wherever the answer is negative in Exercise 1, select a subset, by deleting as few elements as possible, which will be a group.

3. Show that the set of $n \times n$ permutation matrices is a group under multiplication. (See Exercise 5, §1.)

4. Show that the set of $n \times n$ monomial matrices is a group under multiplication. (See Exercise 6, §1.)

5. Determine all the subgroups of the *quaternion group* (sixth example of groups in this section).

6. Prove that in any isomorphism of a group G onto a group G', the identity of G must map onto the identity of G'.

7. An isomorphism of a group *onto* itself is called an *automorphism.* Show that the correspondence $A \longrightarrow PAP^{-1}$, where P is a fixed nonsingular $n \times n$ matrix and A is an arbitrary nonsingular matrix, expresses an automorphism of the group of nonsingular matrices.

8. Generalize Exercise 7 to show that, if x is a fixed element of a group G, the correspondence $g \longrightarrow xgx^{-1}$, for $g \in G$, is an automorphism of G. (Here we have written the group G multiplicatively.)

9. Prove that the set of all automorphisms of a group forms a group under the multiplication of mappings.

10. Prove that the group of all $n \times n$ permutation matrices is isomorphic to the group of all one-to-one mappings of the finite set of elements $a_1, a_2, \cdots, a_n$ onto itself.

6. Orthogonal Group of Linear Transformations

We wish to generalize the rotations T_θ of $V_2(R)$ discussed in §1 of Chapter 6.

DEFINITION 6.1. *A linear transformation* T *from* $V_n(R)$ *to* $V_n(R)$ *is called an* ORTHOGONAL TRANSFORMATION *if*

$$(\mathbf{X}\mathrm{T}, \mathbf{X}\mathrm{T}) = (\mathbf{X}, \mathbf{X})$$

for all $\mathbf{X}$ *of* $V_n(R)$*; that is, if* T *changes only the direction, not the length, of a vector of* $V_n(R)$.

The first thing to be pointed out is that the set of all orthogonal transformations of $V_n(R)$ is a subgroup of the full linear group of $V_n(R)$.

In order to prove the preceding statement, we may say at once that an orthogonal transformation is nonsingular. Certainly the null space of an orthogonal transformation T consists of the zero vector alone since any nonzero vector mapping onto zero would have its length changed. Hence T is nonsingular by Theorem 2.3 of Chapter 6, and the set of all orthogonal transformations is at least a subset of the full linear group.

Next, closure under multiplication is also evident. If neither T_1 nor T_2 changes lengths of vectors, then certainly T_1 followed by T_2 cannot change a length.

Finally, if T is an orthogonal transformation, so is T^{-1}. Suppose T^{-1} changed the length of **X**. Then the length of $(\mathbf{X}T^{-1})T$ is different from the length of **X**. But $(\mathbf{X}T^{-1})T = \mathbf{X}$ since $T^{-1}T = I$.

We shall call the subgroup of orthogonal transformations of the full linear group the *orthogonal group* of $V_n(R)$.

The angle θ between vectors $\mathbf{X}, \mathbf{Y} \in V_n(R)$ has been defined in §3 of Chapter 4 as

$$\theta = \text{arc cosine} \frac{(\mathbf{X}, \mathbf{Y})}{(\mathbf{X}, \mathbf{X})^{1/2}(\mathbf{Y}, \mathbf{Y})^{1/2}}. \tag{6.1}$$

An important property of orthogonal transformations is expressed in the following theorem:

THEOREM 6.1. *If* T *is an orthogonal transformation of* $V_n(R)$, *then, for all vectors* **X**, **Y** *of* $V_n(R)$, *the angle* θ *between* **X** *and* **Y** *is the angle between* **XT** *and* **YT**; *that is, an orthogonal transformation preserves angles between vectors.*

Proof. We first give an informal exposition. Let **X** and **Y** be represented by segments in E_n with a common initial point. Complete the triangle by a segment representing $\mathbf{X} - \mathbf{Y}$:

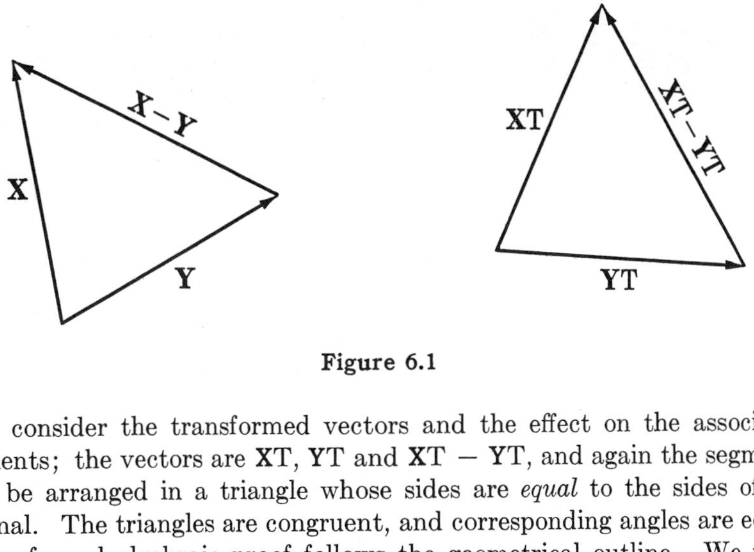

Figure 6.1

Now consider the transformed vectors and the effect on the associated segments; the vectors are **XT**, **YT** and $\mathbf{X}T - \mathbf{Y}T$, and again the segments may be arranged in a triangle whose sides are *equal* to the sides of the original. The triangles are congruent, and corresponding angles are equal.

The formal algebraic proof follows the geometrical outline. We must prove that

$$\frac{(\mathbf{X}, \mathbf{Y})}{(\mathbf{X}, \mathbf{X})^{1/2}(\mathbf{Y}, \mathbf{Y})^{1/2}} = \frac{(\mathbf{X}T, \mathbf{Y}T)}{(\mathbf{X}T, \mathbf{X}T)^{1/2}(\mathbf{Y}T, \mathbf{Y}T)^{1/2}}. \tag{6.2}$$

The denominators in (6.2) are equal by hypothesis. Therefore it suffices to prove that $(\mathbf{X}, \mathbf{Y}) = (\mathbf{X}\mathrm{T}, \mathbf{Y}\mathrm{T})$ for all vectors $\mathbf{X}, \mathbf{Y}$ of $V_n(R)$. Now consider the equality

$$(\mathbf{X} - \mathbf{Y}, \mathbf{X} - \mathbf{Y}) = ((\mathbf{X} - \mathbf{Y})\mathrm{T}, (\mathbf{X} - \mathbf{Y})\mathrm{T}) = (\mathbf{X}\mathrm{T} - \mathbf{Y}\mathrm{T}, \mathbf{X}\mathrm{T} - \mathbf{Y}\mathrm{T}).$$

We expand both sides to obtain

$$(\mathbf{X}, \mathbf{X}) - 2(\mathbf{X}, \mathbf{Y}) + (\mathbf{Y}, \mathbf{Y}) = (\mathbf{X}\mathrm{T}, \mathbf{X}\mathrm{T}) - 2(\mathbf{X}\mathrm{T}, \mathbf{Y}\mathrm{T}) + (\mathbf{Y}\mathrm{T}, \mathbf{Y}\mathrm{T});$$

or, since

$$(\mathbf{X}, \mathbf{X}) = (\mathbf{X}\mathrm{T}, \mathbf{X}\mathrm{T}) \quad \text{and} \quad (\mathbf{Y}, \mathbf{Y}) = (\mathbf{Y}\mathrm{T}, \mathbf{Y}\mathrm{T}),$$
$$-2(\mathbf{X}, \mathbf{Y}) = -2(\mathbf{X}\mathrm{T}, \mathbf{Y}\mathrm{T}).$$

The name assigned to orthogonal transformations reflects the property of preserving angles, specifically right angles. As such, it is somewhat ambiguous since other transformations of $V_n(R)$, dilations for example, preserve angles but do not preserve lengths.

What can we say about the matrices which represent orthogonal transformations? In this generality the answer would have to be "Not very much." However, if we ask about representing orthogonal transformations with respect to orthonormal bases of $V_n(R)$, we can give a characterization of an interesting set of matrices which are associated with orthogonal transformations.

THEOREM 6.2. *If* $\{\mathbf{X}_1, \mathbf{X}_2, \cdots, \mathbf{X}_n\}$ *is an orthonormal basis for* $V_n(R)$ *and* T *is an orthogonal transformation whose matrix with respect to* $\{\mathbf{X}_i\}$ *is* A, *then:*

(i) *The rows of* A, *as vectors of* $V_n(R)$, *have length* 1.

(ii) *The rows of* A, *as vectors of* $V_n(R)$, *are mutually orthogonal.*

(iii) $A^{-1} = A^{\mathsf{T}}$; *hence statements* (i) *and* (ii) *are valid when "columns" is substituted for "rows."*

(iv) *The determinant of* A *is* ± 1.

Proof. (i) If $A = [a_{ij}]$, the image of the basis vector $\mathbf{X}_i$ under T is

$$\mathbf{X}_i\mathrm{T} = a_{i1}\mathbf{X}_1 + a_{i2}\mathbf{X}_2 + \cdots + a_{in}\mathbf{X}_n.$$

Hence,
$$1 = (\mathbf{X}_i, \mathbf{X}_i) = (a_{i1}\mathbf{X}_1 + \cdots + a_{in}\mathbf{X}_n, a_{i1}\mathbf{X}_1 + \cdots + a_{in}\mathbf{X}_n)$$
$$= a_{i1}^2 + a_{i2}^2 + \cdots + a_{in}^2$$

since $(\mathbf{X}_i, \mathbf{X}_j) = 0$ if $i \neq j$ and 1 if $i = j$; but this implies

$$([a_{i1}, a_{i2}, \cdots, a_{in}], [a_{i1}, a_{i2}, \cdots, a_{in}]) = 1.$$

(ii) The image of $\mathbf{X}_i$ must be orthogonal to the image of $\mathbf{X}_j$ for $i \neq j$. Then,

$$0 = (a_{i1}\mathbf{X}_1 + \cdots + a_{in}\mathbf{X}_n, a_{j1}\mathbf{X}_1 + \cdots + a_{jn}\mathbf{X}_n)$$
$$= a_{i1}a_{j1} + a_{i2}a_{j2} + \cdots + a_{in}a_{jn}$$

as above. Consequently,

$$([a_{i1}, a_{i2}, \cdots, a_{in}], [a_{j1}, a_{j2}, \cdots, a_{jn}]) = 0, \quad \text{if } i \neq j.$$

(iii) This statement follows from the preceding two. When AA^{T} is computed, the element in the i, j position is, by the definition of matrix multiplication, the inner product of the ith row of A and the jth column of A^{T}; that is, the inner product of the ith and jth rows of A.

(iv) We know that

$$1 = \det I = \det AA^{\mathsf{T}} = \det A \cdot \det A^{\mathsf{T}} = (\det A)^2.$$

A converse of Theorem 6.2 is available.

THEOREM 6.3. *If A is an $n \times n$ matrix such that $A^{\mathsf{T}} = A^{-1}$ and $\{\mathbf{X}_i\}$ is an orthonormal basis of $V_n(R)$, then A is the matrix representation of an orthogonal transformation of $V_n(R)$ with respect to the basis $\{\mathbf{X}_i\}$.*

Proof. Let T be the linear transformation defined as follows: If $\mathbf{X} = b_1\mathbf{X}_1 + b_2\mathbf{X}_2 + \cdots + b_n\mathbf{X}_n \in V_n(R)$, define

$$\mathbf{X}\mathrm{T} = c_1\mathbf{X}_1 + c_2\mathbf{X}_2 + \cdots + c_n\mathbf{X}_n,$$

where $[c_1, c_2, \cdots, c_n] = [b_1, b_2, \cdots, b_n]A$.

Now $(\mathbf{X}\mathrm{T}, \mathbf{X}\mathrm{T}) = c_1^2 + c_2^2 + \cdots + c_n^2$ since the $\{\mathbf{X}_i\}$ are orthonormal. Thus,

$$\begin{aligned}(\mathbf{X}\mathrm{T}, \mathbf{X}\mathrm{T}) &= [c_1, c_2, \cdots, c_n][c_1, c_2, \cdots, c_n]^{\mathsf{T}} \\ &= [b_1, b_2, \cdots, b_n]AA^{\mathsf{T}}[b_1, b_2, \cdots, b_n]^{\mathsf{T}} \\ &= [b_1, b_2, \cdots, b_n][b_1, b_2, \cdots, b_n]^{\mathsf{T}} \\ &= b_1^2 + b_2^2 + \cdots + b_n^2 \\ &= (\mathbf{X}, \mathbf{X}),\end{aligned}$$

and consequently T is an orthogonal transformation.

DEFINITION 6.2. *A real matrix A such that $A^{-1} = A^{\mathsf{T}}$ is called an* ORTHOGONAL MATRIX.

It is easily verified that the set of orthogonal $n \times n$ matrices forms a group isomorphic to the group of orthogonal transformations and that such an isomorphism is obtained for each choice of an orthonormal basis of $V_n(R)$.

Analogous to the case of the full linear group, if T is an orthogonal transformation of $V_n(R)$ and $\{\mathbf{X}_i\}$ and $\{\mathbf{Y}_i\}$ are orthogonal bases of $V_n(R)$, then the matrices A and B representing T with respect to these bases are related by the equation

$$B = PAP^{-1},$$

where P is the nonsingular matrix representing the change of basis from

$\{\mathbf{X}_i\}$ to $\{\mathbf{Y}_i\}$. We leave it to the student in the exercises (Exercise 7) to show that P is also an orthogonal matrix.

Example 1. Let us consider rotations and reflections in E_2. If we rotate Cartesian axes counterclockwise through an angle θ, the new coordinates (x', y') of a point whose old coordinates were (x, y) are given by:

$$[x', y'] = [x, y]\begin{bmatrix} \cos\theta & \sin\theta \\ -\sin\theta & \cos\theta \end{bmatrix}. \quad \text{(See §1, Chapter 6.)}$$

It is easy to see that any 2×2 orthogonal matrix whose determinant is $+1$ can be put in the form of the matrix of the change of coordinates given above. If $\begin{bmatrix} a & b \\ c & d \end{bmatrix}$ is such a matrix, we know that $a^2 + b^2 = 1$, $c^2 + d^2 = 1$, $ac + bd = 0$, and $ad - bc = 1$. If the last two equations are multiplied respectively by c and d and added, we have $a = d$. Substituting this in $ac + bd = 0$, we get $b = -c$ unless $a = 0$. In that case, the other equations will still yield $b = -c = \pm 1$. In any case we may choose θ so that $a = \cos\theta$, $b = \sin\theta$, and the result follows.

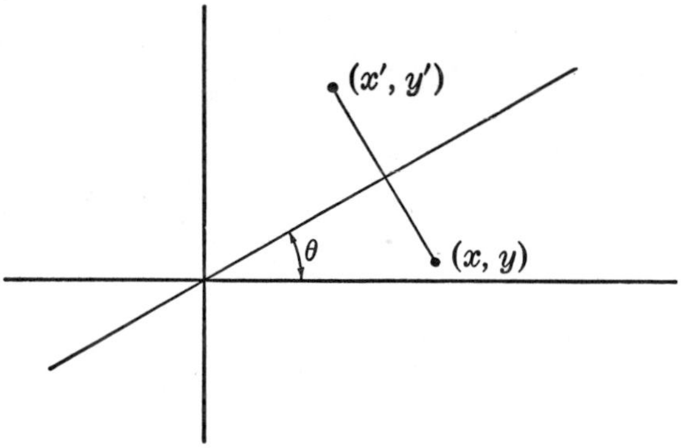

Figure 6.2

Again, if we reflect in a line making an angle θ with the x-axis (Figure 6.2), we obtain

$$[x', y'] = [x, y]\begin{bmatrix} \cos 2\theta & \sin 2\theta \\ \sin 2\theta & -\cos 2\theta \end{bmatrix}.$$

Any 2×2 orthogonal matrix with determinant -1 may be put in this form.

Geometrically, we can attach the following interpretation to orthogonal matrices and Cartesian coordinate systems in E_n: We think of an orthonormal basis $\{\mathbf{X}_i\}$ of $V_n(R)$ as the vectors corresponding to line segments from the origin $(0, 0, \cdots, 0)$ to the unit points X_i on n mutually perpendicular lines. A change of basis

$$\begin{bmatrix} \mathbf{Y}_1 \\ \cdot \\ \cdot \\ \cdot \\ \mathbf{Y}_n \end{bmatrix} = P \begin{bmatrix} \mathbf{X}_1 \\ \cdot \\ \cdot \\ \cdot \\ \mathbf{X}_n \end{bmatrix}$$

from one orthonormal basis $\{\mathbf{X}_i\}$ to $\{\mathbf{Y}_i\}$ corresponds to a change of coordinates

$$[x_1, x_2, \cdots, x_n] = [y_1, y_2, \cdots, y_n]P, \tag{6.3}$$

and P is an orthogonal matrix. Conversely, the change of coordinates given in (6.3) by an orthogonal matrix P may be interpreted as a change from the $\{\mathbf{E}_i\}$ basis to one in which the rows of P are the coordinates of the new unit points and consequently to a Cartesian coordinate system.

In E_n, we adopt a distinction between rotations of Cartesian coordinate systems and reflections analogous to Example 1. If $\det P = 1$ we say that (6.3) represents a *rotation*, and if $\det P = -1$ we say that (6.3) represents a *reflection*.

EXERCISES

1. Show that the transformation of $V_3(R)$ defined by

$$[x_1, x_2, x_3]\mathrm{T} = [x_1, x_2, x_3]\begin{bmatrix} \frac{2}{3} & \frac{2}{3} & \frac{1}{3} \\ -\frac{2}{3} & \frac{1}{3} & \frac{2}{3} \\ \frac{1}{3} & -\frac{2}{3} & \frac{2}{3} \end{bmatrix}$$

is an orthogonal transformation.

2. For the orthogonal transformation in Exercise 1, verify Theorem 6.1 for the vectors $[1, 2, -1]$ and $[1, 0, 3]$.

3. Determine the matrix of the orthogonal transformation of Exercise 1 relative to the orthonormal basis

$$\left\{\left[\frac{1}{\sqrt{2}}, \frac{1}{\sqrt{2}}, 0\right], \left[\frac{1}{\sqrt{2}}, -\frac{1}{\sqrt{2}}, 0\right], [0, 0, 1]\right\} \quad \text{of } V_3(R).$$

4. Show that all matrices which can represent an orthogonal transformation with respect to *any* basis of $V_n(R)$ have determinant ± 1. In fact, if the determinant of one matrix of T is $+1$, show that the determinant of all matrices of T is 1.

5. Show that the converse of Exercise 4 is not valid by proving that the matrix $\begin{bmatrix} 1 & 0 \\ 1 & 1 \end{bmatrix}$ cannot be the matrix of an orthogonal transformation for any basis of $V_2(R)$.

6. Derive the expression for the change of coordinates under reflection given in Example 1.

Hint: Rotate through $-\theta$, reflect in the x-axis, then rotate back through θ.

7. Prove that matrices expressing a change of orthonormal bases are orthogonal. Show conversely that if a transformation from an orthonormal basis is expressed by an orthogonal matrix, then the new basis is orthonormal.

Hint for the first part: If $\{\mathbf{X}_1, \mathbf{X}_2, \cdots, \mathbf{X}_n\}$ is an orthonormal basis of $V_n(R)$, the matrix whose ith row is $\mathbf{X}_i$ is an orthogonal matrix.

CHAPTER 8

Bilinear and Quadratic Forms

The inner product $(\mathbf{X}, \mathbf{Y})$, defined for two vectors $\mathbf{X}$ and $\mathbf{Y}$ of $V_n(R)$ in §6 of Chapter 3, was used to define the concepts of angle and length in n-dimensional Euclidean space. At that time, we indicated that there were other possible definitions for "inner product" and that these, in turn, could lead to possibly different concepts of angle and length from those used in our discussion of E_n. In this chapter, we wish to consider these possibilities and the relations between the general definition and the original one.

We shall also discuss the theory of quadratic forms. This theory will illustrate the way in which the concept of an equivalence relation may be used in the formulation and solution of mathematical problems.

1. Bilinear Mappings and Forms

Let us consider the set S of all ordered pairs of vectors of a real vector space V. A typical element of S is $\{\mathbf{X}, \mathbf{Y}\}$, where $\mathbf{X}$ and $\mathbf{Y}$ are in V and where curly brackets have been used to prevent confusion with the inner product $(\mathbf{X}, \mathbf{Y})$ if V is $V_n(R)$. (The set S is often denoted by $V \times V$ and called the *Cartesian product* of V with V.)

Next, let there be a single-valued mapping B from S to the real field R and denote the image or "value" of the ordered pair $\{\mathbf{X}, \mathbf{Y}\}$ under the mapping B by $\mathrm{B}(\mathbf{X}, \mathbf{Y})$. (Curly brackets are no longer necessary with the B to warn us.) We will assume that the mapping B has the following properties:

$$(1.1) \quad \begin{cases} \text{(i)} \ \mathrm{B}(a\mathbf{X}_1 + b\mathbf{X}_2, \mathbf{Y}_1) = a\mathrm{B}(\mathbf{X}_1, \mathbf{Y}_1) + b\mathrm{B}(\mathbf{X}_2, \mathbf{Y}_1) \\ \text{(ii)} \ \mathrm{B}(\mathbf{X}_1, a\mathbf{Y}_1 + b\mathbf{Y}_2) = a\mathrm{B}(\mathbf{X}_1, \mathbf{Y}_1) + b\mathrm{B}(\mathbf{X}_1, \mathbf{Y}_2) \end{cases}$$

for all vectors $\mathbf{X}_1, \mathbf{X}_2, \mathbf{Y}_1, \mathbf{Y}_2$ of V and all real numbers a and b. These properties are expressed by saying that B is a *bilinear mapping* (or *function*) *of* V.

Example 1. The mapping B defined by $\mathrm{B}(\mathbf{X}, \mathbf{Y}) = (\mathbf{X}, \mathbf{Y})$ (the scalar product) for all $\mathbf{X}, \mathbf{Y}$ of $V_n(R)$ has been shown in Chapter 3 to be a bilinear mapping of $V_n(R)$.

Example 2. The mapping B defined by $B(\mathbf{X}, \mathbf{Y}) = \Delta(\mathbf{X}, \mathbf{Y})$ (the determinant function of Chapter 5) is a bilinear mapping of $V_2(R)$.

The preceding examples will turn out to be highly suggestive in using the concept of bilinear mappings. We turn first to an idea suggested by the second; that is, the general formula for evaluating a determinant obtained by expanding Δ in terms of its values $\Delta(\mathbf{E}_{i_1}, \mathbf{E}_{i_2}, \cdots, \mathbf{E}_{i_n})$. We proceed with a generalization of that course here.

In order to obtain an expression for the value $B(\mathbf{X}, \mathbf{Y})$ of a bilinear mapping of a vector space V, we begin by letting $\{\mathbf{X}_i\}$ and $\{\mathbf{Y}_i\}$ be two bases for V and we do not insist that they be distinct. Again, as in Chapter 6, we use $\{\mathbf{X}_i\}$ as an abbreviation of the set of vectors $\{\mathbf{X}_1, \mathbf{X}_2, \cdots, \mathbf{X}_n\}$. Next, let the expressions for $\mathbf{X}$ and $\mathbf{Y}$ in terms of these bases be

$$\mathbf{X} = x_1\mathbf{X}_1 + x_2\mathbf{X}_2 + \cdots + x_n\mathbf{X}_n \quad \text{and} \quad \mathbf{Y} = y_1\mathbf{Y}_1 + y_2\mathbf{Y}_2 + \cdots + y_n\mathbf{Y}_n.$$

Then,

$$\begin{aligned} B(\mathbf{X}, \mathbf{Y}) &= B(x_1\mathbf{X}_1 + x_2\mathbf{X}_2 + \cdots + x_n\mathbf{X}_n, \mathbf{Y}) \\ &= x_1B(\mathbf{X}_1, \mathbf{Y}) + x_2B(\mathbf{X}_2, \mathbf{Y}) + \cdots + x_nB(\mathbf{X}_n, \mathbf{Y}), \end{aligned}$$

by repeated applications of the linearity property (1.1), (i). Now using (1.1), (ii), we obtain

$$\begin{aligned} B(\mathbf{X}_i, \mathbf{Y}) &= B(\mathbf{X}_i, y_1\mathbf{Y}_1 + y_2\mathbf{Y}_2 + \cdots + y_n\mathbf{Y}_n) \\ &= B(\mathbf{X}_i, \mathbf{Y}_1)y_1 + B(\mathbf{X}_i, \mathbf{Y}_2)y_2 + \cdots + B(\mathbf{X}_i, \mathbf{Y}_n)y_n \end{aligned}$$

for $i = 1, 2, \cdots, n$.

If we now let $B(\mathbf{X}_i, \mathbf{Y}_j) = a_{ij}$ for $i, j = 1, 2, \cdots, n$, the previous expansions can be combined to obtain

$$B(\mathbf{X}, \mathbf{Y}) = \sum_{i,j=1}^{n} x_iB(\mathbf{X}_i, \mathbf{Y}_j)y_j = \sum_{i,j=1}^{n} x_ia_{ij}y_j, \tag{1.2}$$

where $\sum_{i,j=1}^{n}$ denotes a summation extending over the n^2 terms $x_iB(\mathbf{X}_i, \mathbf{Y}_j)y_j$ or $x_ia_{ij}y_j$ for $i, j = 1, 2, \cdots, n$.

Example 3. Let a bilinear mapping B of $V_3(R)$ have an evaluation

$$B(\mathbf{X}, \mathbf{Y}) = x_1y_1 + 2x_1y_2 + 4x_1y_3 + x_2y_1 - x_2y_2 + 3x_2y_3 + 2x_3y_1 - x_3y_2 + x_3y_3$$

relative to bases $\{\mathbf{X}_i\}$ and $\{\mathbf{Y}_i\}$. We can express $B(\mathbf{X}, \mathbf{Y})$ as a matrix product

$$B(\mathbf{X}, \mathbf{Y}) = [x_1, x_2, x_3]\begin{bmatrix} 1 & 2 & 4 \\ 1 & -1 & 3 \\ 2 & -1 & 1 \end{bmatrix}\begin{bmatrix} y_1 \\ y_2 \\ y_3 \end{bmatrix}.$$

This example illustrates that the right-hand expression in (1.2) may be represented as a matrix product:

$$\text{(1.3)} \qquad \mathrm{B}(\mathbf{X}, \mathbf{Y}) = [x_1, x_2, \cdots, x_n]A[y_1, y_2, \cdots, y_n]^{\mathsf{T}},$$

where A is the $n \times n$ real matrix $[a_{ij}] = [\mathrm{B}(\mathbf{X}_i, \mathbf{Y}_j)]$. Thus, for any bilinear mapping B, the choice of a pair of bases $\{\mathbf{X}_i\}$ and $\{\mathbf{Y}_i\}$ of V leads to the definition of an $n \times n$ matrix A in terms of which a general formula for the evaluation of the mapping B may be phrased.

Conversely, given a pair of bases $\{\mathbf{X}_i\}$ and $\{\mathbf{Y}_i\}$ of V and any $n \times n$ real matrix A, we may define a mapping B of V by

$$\mathrm{B}(\mathbf{X}, \mathbf{Y}) = [x_1, x_2, \cdots, x_n]A[y_1, y_2, \cdots, y_n]^{\mathsf{T}},$$

where $\mathbf{X} = x_1\mathbf{X}_1 + x_2\mathbf{X}_2 + \cdots + x_n\mathbf{X}_n$ and $\mathbf{Y} = y_1\mathbf{Y}_1 + y_2\mathbf{Y}_2 + \cdots + y_n\mathbf{Y}_n$. The student may verify that the mapping B is bilinear; the requirements (i) and (ii) of (1.1) must be checked. We sum up the preceding discussion in the following theorem:

THEOREM 1.1. *Let* $\{\mathbf{X}_1, \mathbf{X}_2, \cdots, \mathbf{X}_n\}$ *and* $\{\mathbf{Y}_1, \mathbf{Y}_2, \cdots, \mathbf{Y}_n\}$ *be two bases of a vector space* V. *There is a one-to-one mapping between the set of all bilinear mappings* B *of* V *and the set of all* $n \times n$ *matrices* $A = [a_{ij}]$ *such that*

$$\mathrm{B}(\mathbf{X}, \mathbf{Y}) = [x_1, x_2, \cdots, x_n]A[y_1, y_2, \cdots, y_n]^{\mathsf{T}},$$

where $\mathbf{X} = x_1\mathbf{X}_1 + x_2\mathbf{X}_2 + \cdots + x_n\mathbf{X}_n$ *and* $\mathbf{Y} = y_1\mathbf{Y}_1 + y_2\mathbf{Y}_2 + \cdots + y_n\mathbf{Y}_n$.

The matrix $A = [\mathrm{B}(\mathbf{X}_i, \mathbf{Y}_j)]$ is called *the matrix of the bilinear mapping* B (relative to the bases $\{\mathbf{X}_i\}$ and $\{\mathbf{Y}_i\}$).

An expression of the type

$$[x_1, x_2, \cdots, x_n]A[y_1, y_2, \cdots, y_n]^{\mathsf{T}} = \sum_{i,j=1}^{n} x_i a_{ij} y_j$$

is called a *bilinear form*. For example,

$$[x_1, x_2]\begin{bmatrix} 1 & 2 \\ -1 & 3 \end{bmatrix}\begin{bmatrix} y_1 \\ y_2 \end{bmatrix} = x_1y_1 + 2x_1y_2 - x_2y_1 + 3x_2y_2$$

is a bilinear form. A bilinear form may be thought of as being similar to the general formula (4.1) of Chapter 5 for the expansion of a determinant; a bilinear form is a formula giving the value of a bilinear mapping when real numbers are substituted for the $\{x_i\}$ and $\{y_j\}$. Of course, a vector space V and bases $\{\mathbf{X}_i\}$ and $\{\mathbf{Y}_i\}$ must be in mind.

Example 4. If, in $V_n(R)$, the bases $\{\mathbf{X}_i\}$ and $\{\mathbf{Y}_i\}$ are selected as the natural basis $\{\mathbf{E}_i\}$, then the matrix of the bilinear mapping $\mathrm{B}(\mathbf{X}, \mathbf{Y}) = (\mathbf{X}, \mathbf{Y})$ is the $n \times n$ identity matrix I and

$$\mathrm{B}(\mathbf{X}, \mathbf{Y}) = [x_1, x_2, \cdots, x_n]I[y_1, y_2, \cdots, y_n]^{\mathsf{T}},$$

where $\mathbf{X} = [x_1, x_2, \cdots, x_n]$ and $\mathbf{Y} = [y_1, y_2, \cdots, y_n]$.

Example 5. If, in $V_2(R)$, we select the bases $\{\mathbf{X}_1, \mathbf{X}_2\} = \{\mathbf{Y}_1, \mathbf{Y}_2\} = \{\mathbf{E}_1, \mathbf{E}_2\}$, then the matrix of the bilinear mapping B of Example 2,

$$\mathrm{B}(\mathbf{X}, \mathbf{Y}) = \Delta(\mathbf{X}, \mathbf{Y}),$$

is $\begin{bmatrix} 0 & 1 \\ -1 & 0 \end{bmatrix}$. The bilinear form is $x_1y_2 - x_2y_1$, where $\mathbf{X} = [x_1, x_2]$ and $\mathbf{Y} = [y_1, y_2]$.

An especially simple expression of a bilinear mapping of $V_n(R)$ occurs when the bases $\{\mathbf{X}_i\}$ and $\{\mathbf{Y}_i\}$ are chosen as the natural basis $\{\mathbf{E}_i\}$ as in Examples 4 and 5. Here

$$\mathbf{X} = [x_1, x_2, \cdots, x_n] = x_1\mathbf{E}_1 + x_2\mathbf{E}_2 + \cdots + x_n\mathbf{E}_n,$$
$$\mathbf{Y} = [y_1, y_2, \cdots, y_n] = y_1\mathbf{E}_1 + y_2\mathbf{E}_2 + \cdots + y_n\mathbf{E}_n,$$

so that

$$(1.4) \qquad \begin{aligned} &\mathrm{B}(\mathbf{X}, \mathbf{Y}) = \mathbf{X}A\mathbf{Y}^{\mathsf{T}} = (\mathbf{X}A)\mathbf{Y}^{\mathsf{T}} = (\mathbf{X}A, \mathbf{Y}), \\ \text{or} \quad &\mathrm{B}(\mathbf{X}, \mathbf{Y}) = \mathbf{X}(A\mathbf{Y}^{\mathsf{T}}) = \mathbf{X}(\mathbf{Y}A^{\mathsf{T}})^{\mathsf{T}} = (\mathbf{X}, \mathbf{Y}A^{\mathsf{T}}). \end{aligned}$$

Thus, in this case, the procedure of evaluating a bilinear mapping B is reduced to applying a linear transformation to **X** (or **Y**) and then taking a scalar product. We see here that a bilinear mapping may be viewed as the result of a linear transformation and a particularly simple bilinear mapping. This procedure can be extended to the general case, but we will not undertake this extension here. At this time, we are primarily concerned with the matrix relations which have been developed.

The various concepts introduced in this section may be summarized in their mutual relationship:

The basic idea is that of a bilinear mapping; when a pair of bases is introduced, the mapping defines a matrix and a bilinear form.

Conversely, when a pair of bases is given, a matrix or a bilinear form defines a bilinear mapping. The form is simply a formula for evaluating the mapping in terms of the matrix; it forms a link between the mapping and the matrix:

$$\mathrm{B}(\mathbf{X}, \mathbf{Y}) = [x_1, x_2, \cdots, x_n]A[y_1, y_2, \cdots, y_n]^{\mathsf{T}}.$$

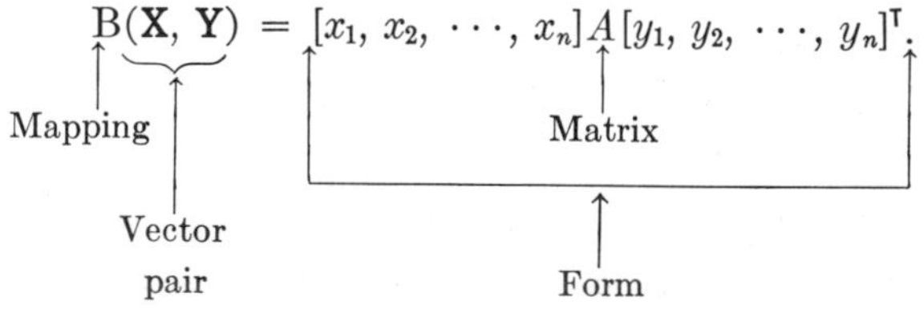

In general, we shall use $\mathrm{B}(\mathbf{X}, \mathbf{Y})$ to denote the general form or its value for particular values of **X** and **Y**. The context of the discussion will reveal whether the general or the particular usage is intended.

EXERCISES

1. Express the following bilinear forms as matrix products $\mathbf{X}A\mathbf{Y}^{\mathsf{T}}$:

(a) $2x_1y_1 + 3x_1y_2 - 4x_2y_1 + x_2y_2$ (b) $5x_1y_1 - x_2y_1 + 2x_2y_2$

(c) $x_1y_1 + x_1y_2 - x_1y_3 + 2x_2y_1 - x_2y_3$

2. Determine the matrix representing the inner product $(\mathbf{X}, \mathbf{Y})$ of $V_2(R)$ relative to the bases

$$\{\mathbf{X}_1 = [1, 2],\ \mathbf{X}_2 = [-1, 3]\} \quad \text{and} \quad \{\mathbf{Y}_1 = [1, -1],\ \mathbf{Y}_2 = [0, 1]\}.$$

3. A bilinear mapping B for $V_2(R)$ is defined by

$$\mathrm{B}(\mathbf{X}, \mathbf{Y}) = (\mathbf{X}A, \mathbf{Y}),$$

where $\mathbf{X} = [x_1, x_2]$, $\mathbf{Y} = [y_1, y_2]$, and $A = \begin{bmatrix} 1 & 3 \\ 1 & 2 \end{bmatrix}$.

(a) Find $\mathrm{B}([1, -1], [2, 3])$; $\mathrm{B}([1, 4], [2, 1])$.

(b) What is the matrix of B relative to the bases $\{\mathbf{X}_1^*, \mathbf{X}_2^*\}$ and $\{\mathbf{Y}_1^*, \mathbf{Y}_2^*\}$ if $\mathbf{X}_1^* = \mathbf{Y}_1^* = [1, -1]$, $\mathbf{X}_2^* = \mathbf{Y}_2^* = [2, 1]$?

(c) If P is the 2×2 nonsingular matrix taking the basis $\{\mathbf{E}_1, \mathbf{E}_2\}$ to $\{\mathbf{X}_1^*, \mathbf{X}_2^*\}$, show that PAP^{T} gives the matrix answer to part (b).

4. What are necessary and sufficient conditions on the elements b_{ij} in the bilinear form $\sum_{i,j=1}^{n} x_ib_{ij}y_j = \mathrm{B}(\mathbf{X}, \mathbf{Y})$ in order that $\mathrm{B}(\mathbf{X}, \mathbf{Y}) = \mathrm{B}(\mathbf{Y}, \mathbf{X})$ for all vectors $\mathbf{X}$ and $\mathbf{Y}$ of $V_n(R)$?

5. If B is a bilinear mapping, show that B*, defined by $\mathrm{B}^*(\mathbf{X}, \mathbf{Y}) = \mathrm{B}(\mathbf{X}, \mathbf{Y}) + \mathrm{B}(\mathbf{Y}, \mathbf{X})$, is also a bilinear mapping. Is $\mathrm{B}^*(\mathbf{X}, \mathbf{Y}) = \mathrm{B}^*(\mathbf{Y}, \mathbf{X})$ for all pairs $\{\mathbf{X}, \mathbf{Y}\}$?

6. Generalize the definition of a bilinear function to a mapping from ordered pairs of vectors $\{\mathbf{X}, \mathbf{Y}\}$, $\mathbf{X} \in V_1$ and $\mathbf{Y} \in V_2$, to the real field for two real vector spaces V_1 and V_2. Define the matrix of such a function and a corresponding bilinear form. What is the generalization of Theorem 1.1 in such a case? If $V_1 = V_n(R)$ and $V_2 = V_m(R)$, is there any statement which relates a general bilinear mapping to an inner product as in (1.4)?

2. Quadratic Forms

We shall defer a discussion of the applications of bilinear forms and consider at this time an important special case.

If we replace $[y_1, y_2, \cdots, y_n]^{\mathsf{T}}$ by $[x_1, x_2, \cdots, x_n]^{\mathsf{T}}$ in the bilinear form

$$\mathrm{B}(\mathbf{X}, \mathbf{Y}) = \sum_{i,j=1}^{n} x_ia_{ij}y_j = [x_1, x_2, \cdots, x_n]A[y_1, y_2, \cdots, y_n]^{\mathsf{T}},$$

where A is an $n \times n$ real matrix, we obtain a *real quadratic form*,

$$[x_1, x_2, \cdots, x_n]A[x_1, x_2, \cdots, x_n]^{\mathsf{T}} = \sum_{i,j=1}^{n} x_ia_{ij}x_j. \tag{2.1}$$

A quadratic form will be denoted by Q(**X**), where, again, we may use this notation either for the given form or for a real number obtained by assigning real values to $x_1, x_2, \cdots, x_n$.

When we wish to draw particular attention to the $\{x_i\}$ or to the number of them, we describe Q(**X**) as a *quadratic form in n variables*, $x_1, x_2, \cdots, x_n$.

A quadratic form may be obtained from any bilinear mapping B on a real vector space V by introducing a basis $\{\mathbf{X}_i\}$ of V, letting the basis $\{\mathbf{Y}_i\}$ be the same as the basis $\{\mathbf{X}_i\}$ in the discussion preceding (1.3), and writing

$$\text{(2.2)} \qquad \mathrm{Q}(\mathbf{X}) = \mathrm{B}(\mathbf{X}, \mathbf{X}) = \sum_{i,j=1}^{n} x_i a_{ij} x_j.$$

Moreover, any quadratic form may be obtained as such a reduction of a bilinear mapping; it is only necessary to construct the mapping B having the matrix $A = [a_{ij}]$ relative to a basis $\{\mathbf{X}_i\}$ and then specialize.

In the case $V = V_n(R)$, and where the basis $\{\mathbf{X}_i\}$ chosen to represent a bilinear mapping is the natural basis $\{\mathbf{E}_i\}$, we have

$$\text{(2.3)} \qquad \mathrm{Q}(\mathbf{X}) = \mathrm{B}(\mathbf{X}, \mathbf{X}) = \mathbf{X}A\mathbf{X}^{\mathsf{T}} = (\mathbf{X}A, \mathbf{X}),$$

where $\mathbf{X} = [x_1, x_2, \cdots, x_n]$ and A is the $n \times n$ real matrix $[a_{ij}]$.

Example 1. The bilinear form,

$$\mathrm{B}(\mathbf{X}, \mathbf{Y}) = [x_1, x_2]\begin{bmatrix} 1 & 5 \\ 2 & 1 \end{bmatrix}\begin{bmatrix} y_1 \\ y_2 \end{bmatrix} = x_1y_1 + x_2y_2 + 2x_1y_2 + 5x_2y_1,$$

gives rise to the quadratic form

$$\mathrm{Q}(\mathbf{X}) = x_1^2 + x_2^2 + 2x_1x_2 + 5x_2x_1.$$

We have, of course, the matrix expression

$$\mathrm{Q}(\mathbf{X}) = \mathrm{B}(\mathbf{X}, \mathbf{X}) = [x_1, x_2]\begin{bmatrix} 1 & 5 \\ 2 & 1 \end{bmatrix}\begin{bmatrix} x_1 \\ x_2 \end{bmatrix} = ([x_1 + 2x_2,\ 5x_1 + x_2],\ [x_1,\ x_2]).$$

Equally well, we could have combined the terms $2x_1x_2$ and $5x_2x_1$ in Q(**X**) and written

$$\mathrm{Q}(\mathbf{X}) = [x_1, x_2]\begin{bmatrix} 1 & 0 \\ 7 & 1 \end{bmatrix}\begin{bmatrix} x_1 \\ x_2 \end{bmatrix} = ([x_1 + 7x_2, x_2], [x_1, x_2]).$$

Or, yet again, we could have "averaged" the terms $2x_1x_2$ and $5x_2x_1$ and written

$$\mathrm{Q}(\mathbf{X}) = [x_1, x_2]\begin{bmatrix} 1 & \frac{7}{2} \\ \frac{7}{2} & 1 \end{bmatrix}\begin{bmatrix} x_1 \\ x_2 \end{bmatrix} = ([x_1 + \tfrac{7}{2}x_2, \tfrac{7}{2}x_1 + x_2], [x_1, x_2]).$$

In Example 1 we have an illustration of the general situation; many different bilinear forms give rise to the same quadratic form. However, the last matrix expression is typical. For $i \neq j$, the simple expedient of replacing $x_i a_{ij} x_j + x_j a_{ji} x_i$ by

$$x_i \left(\frac{a_{ij} + a_{ji}}{2}\right) x_j + x_j \left(\frac{a_{ij} + a_{ji}}{2}\right) x_i$$

allows us to assume without any loss of generality that the quadratic form,

$$\text{(2.4)} \qquad Q(\mathbf{X}) = \sum_{i,\, j=1}^{n} x_i a_{ij} x_j,$$

has the property that $a_{ij} = a_{ji}$ for $i \neq j$. Henceforth we shall always make this assumption. Then with each quadratic form we associate the symmetric matrix $A = [a_{ij}] = A^{\mathsf{T}}$. We then think of $Q(\mathbf{X})$ as being derived from a specialization of the *symmetric* bilinear form

$$B(\mathbf{X}, \mathbf{Y}) = \sum_{i,\, j=1}^{n} x_i a_{ij} y_j.$$

Before proceeding with our discussion of quadratic forms, we shall indicate a few places where quadratic forms arise in mathematics.

The student is familiar with the concept of an ellipse or a hyperbola (with center at the origin) as the locus of all points (x_1, x_2) of E_2 that satisfy an equation of the form

$$a_{11}x_1^2 + 2a_{12}x_1x_2 + a_{22}x_2^2 = 1.$$

The left member of the equation above is a quadratic form. The conics determined by equations of this form have analogues in space and E_n which may be represented by equations involving quadratic forms in 3 and n variables. Their classification will be a consequence of the general theory of quadratic forms.

We have alluded to the fact that there were alternative ways by which the distance between points of E_n could have been defined. In terms of quadratic forms, the distance from the point $(x_1, x_2, \cdots, x_n)$ to the point $(y_1, y_2, \cdots, y_n)$ could be defined as:

$$d^2(X, Y) = Q(\mathbf{Y} - \mathbf{X}) = ([y_1 - x_1, \cdots, y_n - x_n]A, [y_1 - x_1, \cdots, y_n - x_n]).$$

Of course, certain restrictions are imposed on the matrix A in this definition to satisfy our intuitive notions of distance. For example, what would: "$d(X, Y) > 0$ unless $Y = X$" imply? The answer will be a simple consequence of our general theory.

From slightly different points of view arise the applications of quadratic forms in the determination of the maxima and minima of functions of more than one variable and various expressions in mechanics, statistics, and physics.

We return to our general discussion of quadratic forms and illustrate with an example what we mean by a *linear change of variables* in a quadratic form.

Example 2. Select the third matrix expression for the quadratic form $Q(\mathbf{X}) = x_1{}^2 + x_2{}^2 + 2x_1x_2 + 5x_2x_1$ of Example 1. Thus,

$$Q(\mathbf{X}) = [x_1, x_2]\begin{bmatrix} 1 & \frac{7}{2} \\ \frac{7}{2} & 1 \end{bmatrix}\begin{bmatrix} x_1 \\ x_2 \end{bmatrix}.$$

If we replace the variables x_1 and x_2 by y_1 and $-\frac{7}{2}y_1 + y_2$ respectively, or in matrix form,

$$[x_1, x_2] = [y_1, y_2]\begin{bmatrix} 1 & -\frac{7}{2} \\ 0 & 1 \end{bmatrix},$$

the quadratic form

$$Q(\mathbf{X}) = [x_1, x_2]\begin{bmatrix} 1 & \frac{7}{2} \\ \frac{7}{2} & 1 \end{bmatrix}\begin{bmatrix} x_1 \\ x_2 \end{bmatrix}$$

will be replaced by the form

$$\begin{aligned} Q(\mathbf{Y}P) = Q^*(\mathbf{Y}) &= [y_1, y_2]\begin{bmatrix} 1 & -\frac{7}{2} \\ 0 & 1 \end{bmatrix}\begin{bmatrix} 1 & \frac{7}{2} \\ \frac{7}{2} & 1 \end{bmatrix}\begin{bmatrix} 1 & 0 \\ -\frac{7}{2} & 1 \end{bmatrix}\begin{bmatrix} y_1 \\ y_2 \end{bmatrix} \\ &= [y_1, y_2]\begin{bmatrix} -\frac{45}{4} & 0 \\ 0 & 1 \end{bmatrix}\begin{bmatrix} y_1 \\ y_2 \end{bmatrix}. \end{aligned}$$

DEFINITION 2.1. *Two real quadratic forms* $\sum_{i,j=1}^{n} x_i a_{ij} x_j$ *and* $\sum_{i,j=1}^{n} y_i b_{ij} y_j$ *are said to be equivalent over the real field R if there exists a linear change of variables* $[x_1, x_2, \cdots, x_n] = [y_1, y_2, \cdots, y_n]P$, *where* $P = [p_{ij}]$ *is a real nonsingular matrix, that transforms the first quadratic form into the second.*

We note that, by Definition 2.1, the quadratic forms $Q(\mathbf{X})$ and $Q^*(\mathbf{Y})$ in Example 2 are equivalent.

If we associate the symmetric matrix $A = A^{\mathsf{T}} = [a_{ij}]$ with the quadratic form $\sum_{i,j=1}^{n} x_i a_{ij} x_j$, the simple generalization of Example 2 indicates that a linear change of variables in effect changes the symmetric matrix associated with the resulting quadratic form. Thus, if in matrix form

$$(2.5) \qquad [x_1, x_2, \cdots, x_n] = [y_1, y_2, \cdots, y_n]P, \quad \text{or} \quad \mathbf{X} = \mathbf{Y}P,$$

where $P = [p_{ij}]$ is a nonsingular matrix (hence allowing us to solve for the variables y_i in terms of x_j), we see that the quadratic form

$$(2.6) \qquad Q(\mathbf{X}) = (\mathbf{X}A, \mathbf{X})$$

is replaced by the form

$$(2.7) \qquad \begin{aligned} Q(\mathbf{Y}P) = Q^*(\mathbf{Y}) &= (\mathbf{Y}PA, \mathbf{Y}P) = \mathbf{Y}PA(\mathbf{Y}P)^{\mathsf{T}} \\ &= \mathbf{Y}PAP^{\mathsf{T}}\mathbf{Y}^{\mathsf{T}} = (\mathbf{Y}PAP^{\mathsf{T}}, \mathbf{Y}). \end{aligned}$$

Conversely, let $[a_{ij}] = A$ and $[b_{ij}] = PAP^{\mathsf{T}}$, where P is a real nonsingular matrix, be two symmetric matrices associated with the quadratic forms $\sum_{i,j=1}^{n} x_i a_{ij} x_j$ and $\sum_{i,j=1}^{n} y_i b_{ij} y_j$. The change of variables

$$[x_1, x_2, \cdots, x_n] = [y_1, y_2, \cdots, y_n]P$$

changes the first quadratic form into the second.

Our discussion above yields:

THEOREM 2.1. *Two real quadratic forms are equivalent if and only if the symmetric matrices A and B associated with these forms are related by the equation $B = PAP^{\mathsf{T}}$, where P is a real nonsingular matrix.*

We can provide a slightly different interpretation of the equivalence of quadratic forms if we think of $\mathrm{Q}(\mathbf{X})$ as defining a mapping from $V_n(R)$ to R and as arising from a bilinear mapping B such that $\mathrm{Q}(\mathbf{X}) = \mathrm{B}(\mathbf{X}, \mathbf{X})$. However, we must assume in addition that $\mathrm{B}(\mathbf{X}, \mathbf{Y}) = \mathrm{B}(\mathbf{Y}, \mathbf{X})$ for all vectors $\mathbf{X}$ and $\mathbf{Y}$ of $V_n(R)$. Now, if $\{\mathbf{X}_i\}$ and $\{\mathbf{X}_i^*\}$ are two bases of $V_n(R)$, we let

$$\mathbf{X} = x_1\mathbf{X}_1 + x_2\mathbf{X}_2 + \cdots + x_n\mathbf{X}_n = x_1^*\mathbf{X}_1^* + x_2^*\mathbf{X}_2^* + \cdots + x_n^*\mathbf{X}_n^*. \tag{2.8}$$

We specialize in (1.2) to obtain

$$\begin{aligned} \mathrm{Q}(\mathbf{X}) &= \mathrm{B}(\mathbf{X}, \mathbf{X}) = \sum_{i,j=1}^{n} x_i \mathrm{B}(\mathbf{X}_i, \mathbf{X}_j) x_j, \\ \text{or} \quad \mathrm{Q}(\mathbf{X}) &= \mathrm{B}(\mathbf{X}, \mathbf{X}) = \sum_{i,j=1}^{n} x_i^* \mathrm{B}(\mathbf{X}_i^*, \mathbf{X}_j^*) x_j^*. \end{aligned} \tag{2.9}$$

The components of $\mathbf{X}$ in (2.8) are related by the matrix expression

$$[x_1, x_2, \cdots, x_n] = [x_1^*, x_2^*, \cdots, x_n^*]P,$$

where P is the nonsingular matrix representing the change of basis from $\{\mathbf{X}_1, \mathbf{X}_2, \cdots, \mathbf{X}_n\}$ to $\{\mathbf{X}_1^*, \mathbf{X}_2^*, \cdots, \mathbf{X}_n^*\}$ (Chapter 6, §7). Then,

$$\begin{aligned} \mathrm{Q}(\mathbf{X}) &= ([x_1, x_2, \cdots, x_n][\mathrm{B}(\mathbf{X}_i, \mathbf{X}_j)], [x_1, x_2, \cdots, x_n]) \\ &= ([x_1^*, x_2^*, \cdots, x_n^*]P[\mathrm{B}(\mathbf{X}_i, \mathbf{X}_j)], [x_1^*, x_2^*, \cdots, x_n^*]P) \\ &= ([x_1^*, x_2^*, \cdots, x_n^*]P[\mathrm{B}(\mathbf{X}_i, \mathbf{X}_j)]P^{\mathsf{T}}, [x_1^*, x_2^*, \cdots, x_n^*]). \end{aligned}$$

Since the expression for $\mathrm{B}(\mathbf{X}, \mathbf{X}) = \mathrm{Q}(\mathbf{X})$ with respect to a basis of $V_n(R)$ is unique, we must have

$$P[\mathrm{B}(\mathbf{X}_i, \mathbf{X}_j)]P^{\mathsf{T}} = [\mathrm{B}(\mathbf{X}_i^*, \mathbf{X}_j^*)].$$

Thus the quadratic forms $\sum x_i \mathrm{B}(\mathbf{X}_i, \mathbf{X}_j) x_j$ and $\sum x_i^* \mathrm{B}(\mathbf{X}_i^*, \mathbf{X}_j^*) x_j^*$ are equivalent.

From the preceding discussion we see that the equivalence of quadratic forms can be looked upon as representing the same mapping Q from

$V_n(R)$ to R with respect to two different bases. The similarity to the concept of linear transformations relative to different bases should be observed.

Regardless of which interpretation we might wish to attach to the concept of equivalence of quadratic forms, it is clear from Theorem 2.1 that it can be considered as a matrix problem.

The essential problem in most applications of quadratic forms is to determine the simplest form (in a vague sense) to which Q(**X**) can be reduced when certain transformations of variables are permitted. We shall turn to this question in the next section.

EXERCISES

1. What are the quadratic forms represented by the following matrix products?

(a) $[x_1, x_2]\begin{bmatrix} 1 & -3 \\ -3 & 4 \end{bmatrix}\begin{bmatrix} x_1 \\ x_2 \end{bmatrix}$

(b) $[x_1, x_2, x_3]\begin{bmatrix} 1 & -2 & 3 \\ -2 & 4 & 1 \\ 3 & 1 & 5 \end{bmatrix}\begin{bmatrix} x_1 \\ x_2 \\ x_3 \end{bmatrix}$

2. Express the following quadratic forms as matrix products:

(a) $2x_1^2 - 8x_1x_2 + 3x_2^2$

(b) $3x_1^2 - 2x_2^2 + 5x_3^2 + 6x_1x_2 - 4x_2x_3 + 8x_1x_3$

3. Let the quadratic form $x_1^2 + 4x_1x_2 + 3x_2^2$ be transformed by the change of variables

$$\begin{aligned} x_1 &= 3y_1 + 2y_2 \\ x_2 &= y_1 - y_2. \end{aligned}$$

(a) What is the transformed quadratic form Q*(**Y**)?

(b) Express the quadratic form of (a) as a matrix product PAP^{T}.

4. Replace the distance formula for E_2 by defining the distance from (x_1, x_2) to (y_1, y_2) to be

$$\{d(X, Y)\}^2 = [y_1 - x_1, y_2 - x_2]\begin{bmatrix} 1 & 2 \\ 2 & 5 \end{bmatrix}\begin{bmatrix} y_1 - x_1 \\ y_2 - x_2 \end{bmatrix}.$$

Show that $d(X, Y) > 0$ unless $X = Y$; $d(X, Y) = d(Y, X)$.

5. For the quadratic form

$$\mathrm{Q}([x_1, x_2]) = [x_1, x_2]\begin{bmatrix} a & b \\ b & c \end{bmatrix}\begin{bmatrix} x_1 \\ x_2 \end{bmatrix},$$

with $\begin{bmatrix} a & b \\ b & c \end{bmatrix} \neq 0$, show that there always exists a change of variables that yields a form Q*(**Y**) in which the coefficient of y_1y_2 is 0.

6. Show that the quadratic forms

$$Q([x_1, x_2]) = x_1^2 + x_2^2 + 8x_1x_2$$
$$Q^*([y_1, y_2]) = y_1^2 - 14y_2^2 + 2y_1y_2$$

are equivalent under the change of variables given by

$$[x_1, x_2] = [y_1, y_2]\begin{bmatrix} 1 & 0 \\ -3 & 1 \end{bmatrix}.$$

7. What is the expression of the quadratic form (relative to the $\{\mathbf{E}_i\}$ basis)

$$Q([x_1, x_2, x_3]) = x_1^2 + x_2^2 - 3x_3^2 + 4x_1x_2 + 2x_2x_3 + 6x_1x_3$$

relative to the basis $\mathbf{X}_1^* = [1, 2, -1]$, $\mathbf{X}_2^* = [1, 0, 2]$, $\mathbf{X}_3^* = [1, -1, 2]$?

8. Show that the matrix PAP^T of (2.7) is a symmetric matrix.

9. The set of all real numbers $Q(\mathbf{X})$ as $\mathbf{X}$ runs through all vectors of $V_n(R)$ is called the range of values of the quadratic form $Q(\mathbf{X})$. Prove that the range of values of two equivalent quadratic forms is the same.

10. Let B be a symmetric bilinear mapping of $V_n(R)$; that is, $B(\mathbf{X}, \mathbf{Y}) = B(\mathbf{Y}, \mathbf{X})$ for all vectors $\mathbf{X}$, $\mathbf{Y}$ of $V_n(R)$. If $Q(\mathbf{X}) = B(\mathbf{X}, \mathbf{X})$, show that

$$B(\mathbf{X}, \mathbf{Y}) = \tfrac{1}{2}\{Q(\mathbf{X} + \mathbf{Y}) - Q(\mathbf{X}) - Q(\mathbf{Y})\}.$$

3. Equivalence of Quadratic Forms; Congruence of Matrices

The investigation of the equivalence of two real quadratic forms has been reduced to the study of the matrix relation $B = PAP^\mathsf{T}$ for nonsingular matrices P and symmetric matrices A and B. For the moment we drop the requirement that A and B be symmetric and introduce the concept of *congruence of matrices*.

If two matrices A and B have the property that there exists a real nonsingular matrix P such that

$$B = PAP^\mathsf{T}, \tag{3.1}$$

then B is said to be congruent to A (over the real field R).

Congruence is an example of an equivalence relation defined for the set of all $n \times n$ matrices. (Why this limitation to square matrices?) Quite simply:

1. A is congruent to A since $A = IAI^\mathsf{T}$.

2. If B is congruent to A, then $B = PAP^\mathsf{T}$; hence, $A = P^{-1}B(P^\mathsf{T})^{-1} = P^{-1}B(P^{-1})^\mathsf{T}$, and A is congruent to B.

3. If B is congruent to A and C is congruent to B, then nonsingular matrices P and Q exist so that $B = PAP^\mathsf{T}$, $C = QBQ^\mathsf{T} = QPAP^\mathsf{T}Q^\mathsf{T} = (QP)A(QP)^\mathsf{T}$, and C is congruent to A since QP is nonsingular.

From this point, we return to the requirement that the matrices A and B be symmetric. Note that this restriction to the set S of all $n \times n$ symmetric matrices does not alter the character of congruence as an equivalence relation. Indeed, if B is congruent to A and A is symmetric, so is B; that is, $B = PAP^{\mathsf{T}}$, $B^{\mathsf{T}} = (P^{\mathsf{T}})^{\mathsf{T}}A^{\mathsf{T}}P^{\mathsf{T}} = PAP^{\mathsf{T}} = B$.

Let $E(A)$ consist of all matrices of S congruent to the matrix $A \in S$; that is, $E(A)$ consists of all matrices PAP^{T}, where P is an arbitrary nonsingular matrix. Corresponding to the general properties of any equivalence relation (Chapter 6, § 9), we observe the following properties of the subsets $E(A)$ in relation to S:

(i) Every symmetric matrix is in some E-subset.
(ii) Two matrices A and B are congruent if and only if $E(A) = E(B)$.
(iii) Either $E(A) = E(B)$ or $E(A) \cap E(B) = \emptyset$ (the empty set).

The relation of congruence for symmetric matrices (in view of the properties listed above) partitions the set S of all $n \times n$ symmetric matrices into nonintersecting subsets. Crudely, we may picture the situation as follows:

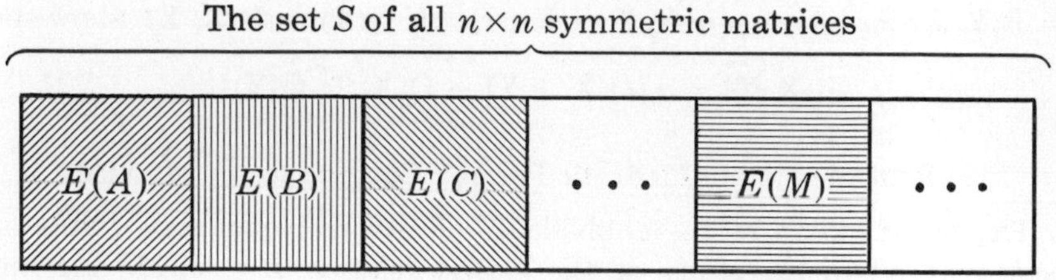

Figure 3.1

If we now select one matrix from each distinct subset $E(M)$ to represent that subset, every $n \times n$ symmetric matrix will be congruent to one and only one of our selected representatives. In terms of quadratic forms, we associate with each representative matrix the corresponding quadratic form in n variables, and then *every* quadratic form in n variables is equivalent to one and only one of these representative forms by a suitable change of variables.

The two general problems in the equivalence of quadratic forms in n variables can now be stated in terms of the subsets $E(M)$ and the choice of representatives:

1. Does there exist a simple, convenient choice of a representative matrix for each subset $E(M)$?

2. Do there exist some features (numbers, rank, order, etc.) of an arbitrary matrix A that will determine which subset contains A and consequently whether A is congruent to a particular representative?

Solution of Problem 1: We shall show first that each subset $E(M)$ contains diagonal matrices, and then our choice for a representative matrix of each subset $E(M)$ will be a particular diagonal matrix.

Our demonstration will use induction on the order n of the symmetric matrices involved. For $n = 1$, we have nothing to prove since any matrix $[a_{11}]$ in a subset $E(M)$ is a diagonal matrix. The inductive assumption is that every subset $E(M_1)$ of $(n-1) \times (n-1)$ symmetric matrices contains a diagonal matrix.

Now let $A = [a_{ij}]$ be an $n \times n$ symmetric matrix in a subset $E(M)$ and consider the associated quadratic form

$$\text{(3.2)} \qquad \mathrm{Q}(\mathbf{X}) = \sum_{i,j=1}^{n} x_i a_{ij} x_j.$$

We think of $\mathrm{Q}(\mathbf{X})$ as arising from a bilinear mapping B of $V_n(R)$, where

$$\text{(3.3)} \qquad \mathrm{B}(\mathbf{X}, \mathbf{Y}) = \sum_{i,j=1}^{n} x_i a_{ij} y_j = (\mathbf{X}A, \mathbf{Y})$$

is the expression for $\mathrm{B}(\mathbf{X}, \mathbf{Y})$ relative to the natural basis $\{\mathbf{E}_1, \mathbf{E}_2, \cdots, \mathbf{E}_n\}$ and $\mathbf{X} = x_1\mathbf{E}_1 + \cdots + x_n\mathbf{E}_n$, $\mathbf{Y} = y_1\mathbf{E}_1 + \cdots + y_n\mathbf{E}_n$.

For the bilinear mapping B of (3.3), we may assume that there is a vector $\mathbf{X}_1$ such that $\mathrm{B}(\mathbf{X}_1, \mathbf{X}_1) \neq 0$. Otherwise, from the relation

$$\mathrm{B}(\mathbf{X}, \mathbf{Y}) = \tfrac{1}{2}\{\mathrm{B}(\mathbf{X}+\mathbf{Y}, \mathbf{X}+\mathbf{Y}) - \mathrm{B}(\mathbf{X}, \mathbf{X}) - \mathrm{B}(\mathbf{Y}, \mathbf{Y})\}$$

(Exercise 10, §2), we would have $\mathrm{B}(\mathbf{X}, \mathbf{Y}) = 0$ for all vectors $\mathbf{X}$ and $\mathbf{Y}$ of $V_n(R)$, and consequently the matrix $[a_{ij}] = [0]$ would already be a diagonal matrix.

We select $\mathbf{X}_1$ as the first vector of a new basis for $V_n(R)$, with respect to which we shall evaluate $\mathrm{B}(\mathbf{X}, \mathbf{X})$. Our next step will be to select the remaining vectors of this new basis.

The set of all vectors $\mathbf{Z}$ of $V_n(R)$ such that $\mathrm{B}(\mathbf{X}_1, \mathbf{Z}) = 0$ forms a subspace V^* of $V_n(R)$. In particular, we see from (3.3) that V^* consists of all those vectors $\mathbf{Z} = [z_1, z_2, \cdots, z_n]$ for which $(\mathbf{X}_1 A, \mathbf{Z}) = 0$. The vector $\mathbf{X}_1 A \neq 0$. (Why?) Therefore, from our discussion of orthogonal subspaces (Chapter 3, §6) we conclude that V^* is of dimension $n - 1$. We select vectors $\mathbf{X}_2, \mathbf{X}_3, \cdots, \mathbf{X}_n$ of V^*, together with the vector $\mathbf{X}_1$, as a basis for $V_n(R)$. Note that $\mathrm{B}(\mathbf{X}_1, \mathbf{X}_i) = 0$ for $i \geq 2$.

Relative to the new basis $\{\mathbf{X}_1, \mathbf{X}_2, \cdots, \mathbf{X}_n\}$ of $V_n(R)$ and for the vector $\mathbf{X} = [x_1, x_2, \cdots, x_n] = x_1^*\mathbf{X}_1 + x_2^*\mathbf{X}_2 + \cdots + x_n^*\mathbf{X}_n$, we have

$$\mathrm{B}(\mathbf{X}, \mathbf{X}) = \sum_{i,j=1}^{n} x_i^* \mathrm{B}(\mathbf{X}_i, \mathbf{X}_j) x_j^*.$$

Since $B(\mathbf{X}_1, \mathbf{X}_i) = 0$ for $i \geq 2$, we conclude from our discussion following Theorem 2.1 that

$$(3.4) \qquad \begin{bmatrix} B(\mathbf{X}_1, \mathbf{X}_1) & 0 & \cdots & 0 \\ 0 & B(\mathbf{X}_2, \mathbf{X}_2) & \cdots & B(\mathbf{X}_2, \mathbf{X}_n) \\ \vdots & \vdots & & \vdots \\ 0 & B(\mathbf{X}_n, \mathbf{X}_2) & \cdots & B(\mathbf{X}_n, \mathbf{X}_n) \end{bmatrix} = P[a_{ij}]P^{\mathsf{T}},$$

where P is the nonsingular matrix representing the change of basis from $\{\mathbf{E}_i\}$ to $\{\mathbf{X}_i\}$.

Denote the $(n-1) \times (n-1)$ symmetric matrix of the lower right-hand corner of PAP^{T} in (3.4) by A_1. By induction, there is an $(n-1)\times(n-1)$ nonsingular matrix Q_1 such that $Q_1A_1Q_1^{\mathsf{T}} = \text{Diagonal } [d_2, d_3, \cdots, d_n]$. Therefore,

$$\begin{bmatrix} 1 & 0 & \cdots & 0 \\ 0 & & & \\ \vdots & & Q_1 & \\ 0 & & & \end{bmatrix} P[a_{ij}]P^{\mathsf{T}} \begin{bmatrix} 1 & 0 & \cdots & 0 \\ 0 & & & \\ \vdots & & Q_1^{\mathsf{T}} & \\ 0 & & & \end{bmatrix} = \begin{bmatrix} B(\mathbf{X}_1, \mathbf{X}_1) & 0 & & \cdots & 0 \\ 0 & d_2 & & & \\ \vdots & & d_3 & & \vdots \\ & & & \ddots & \\ 0 & \cdots & & & d_n \end{bmatrix}$$

is a diagonal matrix in the subset $E(M)$.

Example 1. Let $A = \begin{bmatrix} 0 & 4 & 3 \\ 4 & 2 & 1 \\ 3 & 1 & 0 \end{bmatrix}$, and define $B(\mathbf{X}, \mathbf{Y})$ as follows:

$$B(\mathbf{X}, \mathbf{Y}) = [x_1, x_2, x_3] \begin{bmatrix} 0 & 4 & 3 \\ 4 & 2 & 1 \\ 3 & 1 & 0 \end{bmatrix} \begin{bmatrix} y_1 \\ y_2 \\ y_3 \end{bmatrix}.$$

We note $B([0, 1, 0], [0, 1, 0]) = 2 \neq 0$. Hence, we choose as the first vector of our new basis $\mathbf{X}_1 = [0, 1, 0]$. Now, to find V^* we consider

$$[0, 1, 0] \begin{bmatrix} 0 & 4 & 3 \\ 4 & 2 & 1 \\ 3 & 1 & 0 \end{bmatrix} \begin{bmatrix} z_1 \\ z_2 \\ z_3 \end{bmatrix} = 4z_1 + 2z_2 + z_3 = 0.$$

A basis for V^* is clearly $\{[1, 0, -4], [1, -2, 0]\}$. We choose these vectors as $\mathbf{X}_2$ and $\mathbf{X}_3$.

The nonsingular matrix P giving the change of basis from the vectors $\{[1, 0, 0], [0, 1, 0], [0, 0, 1]\}$ to $\{[0, 1, 0], [1, 0, -4], [1, -2, 0]\}$ is

$$P = \begin{bmatrix} 0 & 1 & 0 \\ 1 & 0 & -4 \\ 1 & -2 & 0 \end{bmatrix}.$$

We compute PAP^{T}, or

$$\begin{bmatrix} 0 & 1 & 0 \\ 1 & 0 & -4 \\ 1 & -2 & 0 \end{bmatrix}\begin{bmatrix} 0 & 4 & 3 \\ 4 & 2 & 1 \\ 3 & 1 & 0 \end{bmatrix}\begin{bmatrix} 0 & 1 & 1 \\ 1 & 0 & -2 \\ 0 & -4 & 0 \end{bmatrix} = \begin{bmatrix} 2 & 0 & 0 \\ 0 & 0 & -12 \\ 0 & -12 & -8 \end{bmatrix},$$

and we are now ready for our induction step.

Since $\begin{bmatrix} 0 & 1 \\ 1 & -\frac{3}{2} \end{bmatrix}\begin{bmatrix} 0 & -12 \\ -12 & -8 \end{bmatrix}\begin{bmatrix} 0 & 1 \\ 1 & -\frac{3}{2} \end{bmatrix} = \begin{bmatrix} -8 & 0 \\ 0 & -27 \end{bmatrix}$, we see that

$$\begin{bmatrix} 1 & 0 & 0 \\ 0 & 0 & 1 \\ 0 & 1 & -\frac{3}{2} \end{bmatrix}\begin{bmatrix} 2 & 0 & 0 \\ 0 & 0 & -12 \\ 0 & -12 & -8 \end{bmatrix}\begin{bmatrix} 1 & 0 & 0 \\ 0 & 0 & 1 \\ 0 & 1 & -\frac{3}{2} \end{bmatrix} = \begin{bmatrix} 2 & 0 & 0 \\ 0 & -8 & 0 \\ 0 & 0 & -27 \end{bmatrix}$$

is a diagonal matrix in $E(A)$.

So far, we know that each subset $E(M)$ contains a diagonal matrix

$$D^* = \text{Diagonal } [d_1, d_2, \cdots, d_n].$$

By simply permuting rows and columns, we may collect the positive elements in the first rows, the negative ones next, and the zeros last. (This may be accomplished by the matrix product PD^*P^{T}, where P is a permutation matrix. Why?) Hence we may assume that $d_1, d_2, \cdots, d_p > 0$; $d_{p+1}, d_{p+2}, \cdots, d_r < 0$; and $d_{r+1} = \cdots = d_n = 0$. Now, taking

$$P = \text{Diagonal}\left[\frac{1}{\sqrt{d_1}}, \cdots, \frac{1}{\sqrt{d_p}}, \frac{1}{\sqrt{-d_{p+1}}}, \cdots, \frac{1}{\sqrt{-d_r}}, 1, 1, \cdots, 1\right],$$

we have

$$\begin{aligned} D &= PD^*P^{\mathsf{T}} \\ &= \text{Diagonal } [1, 1, \cdots, 1, -1, -1, \cdots, -1, 0, 0, \cdots, 0], \end{aligned} \tag{3.5}$$

where there are p $(+1)$'s and $(r-p)$ (-1)'s.

The answer to problem 1 is now complete. From each subset $E(M)$ we select a representative of the form

$$D = \text{Diagonal } [1, 1, \cdots, 1, -1, -1, \cdots, -1, 0, 0, \cdots, 0], \tag{3.6}$$

and every symmetric matrix A is congruent to such a diagonal matrix. In terms of quadratic forms, this yields the following result:

THEOREM 3.1. *Every quadratic form* $Q(\mathbf{X}) = \sum_{i,j=1}^{n} x_i a_{ij} x_j$ *is equivalent over the real field* R *to a form*

$$y_1^2 + y_2^2 + \cdots + y_p^2 - y_{p+1}^2 - \cdots - y_r^2$$

by means of the change of variables $[x_1, x_2, \cdots, x_n] = [y_1, y_2, \cdots, y_n]P$, *where* P *is a real nonsingular matrix.*

Solution of Problem 2 (Canonical Forms and Invariants): The representative matrix selected from a particular subset is called a *canonical form* for the members of $E(M)$. A set of such matrices which includes precisely one element from each set $E(M)$ is called a *set of canonical forms*. The question still remains whether the set of all matrices of the form D of (3.6) is a set of canonical forms. We know that there is at least one matrix D in each subset $E(M)$ and we shall show later that there is only one.

It is possible to have different sets of canonical forms for the same equivalence relation. For the congruence of symmetric matrices some people might find it more esthetic to put the zeros first or perhaps in the middle rather than last as we have in (3.6). All we can say is that a given set of representatives of the subsets $E(M)$ is a set of canonical forms for a particular equivalence relation. In our case the matrices D of (3.6) are canonical for the *congruence of symmetric matrices.*

A proof that there is precisely one matrix D in each subset $E(M)$ proceeds as follows:

First, we have noted that multiplication of a matrix A by a nonsingular matrix P on either left or right does not change the rank, so that all congruent matrices (members of $E(M)$) have the same rank. Hence, if two matrices D_1 and D_2 of the form of (3.6) were in one subset $E(M)$, both would have the same rank: the total number of positive and negative units.

It only remains to show that the number of plus signs is identical in both cases to see that $D_1 = D_2$. Suppose that

$$D_1 = \text{Diagonal}\ [\underbrace{1, 1, \cdots, 1,}_{p}\quad \underbrace{-1, -1, \cdots, -1,}_{r-p}\quad 0, 0, \cdots, 0]$$

$$D_2 = \text{Diagonal}\ [\underbrace{1, 1, \cdots, 1,}_{q}\quad \underbrace{-1, -1, \cdots, -1,}_{r-q}\quad 0, 0, \cdots, 0],$$

and that $p \neq q$, say $p > q$. If D_1 and D_2 are in the same subset $E(M)$, there is a nonsingular matrix P such that $D_1 = PD_2P^{\mathsf{T}}$. For any nonzero vector $\mathbf{X} = [x_1, x_2, \cdots, x_p, 0, 0, \cdots, 0]$ of $V_n(R)$, $\mathbf{X}D_1\mathbf{X}^{\mathsf{T}}$ will have the value

$$x_1{}^2 + x_2{}^2 + \cdots + x_p{}^2 > 0.$$

These vectors (with $\mathbf{0}$) form a subspace V_1 of dimension p; hence, the vectors $\mathbf{X}P$ form a subspace V_2 of the *same* dimension since P is nonsingular. For *every* nonzero vector $\mathbf{X}P$ of V_2, $(\mathbf{X}P)D_2(P^{\mathsf{T}}\mathbf{X}^{\mathsf{T}}) = \mathbf{X}D_1\mathbf{X}^{\mathsf{T}} > 0$. On the other hand, for any vector $\mathbf{Y}$ of the form $[0, 0, \cdots, 0, y_{q+1}, \cdots, y_n]$,

$$\mathbf{Y}D_2\mathbf{Y}^{\mathsf{T}} = -y_{q+1}{}^2 - y_{q+2}{}^2 - \cdots - y_r{}^2 \leq 0.$$

The vectors $\mathbf{Y}$ form a space V_3 of dimension $n - q$ which must have only the zero vector in common with V_2 because of the difference in signs in the last two inequalities. Then $\dim V_2 + \dim V_3 = p + n - q > n$. On the other hand, $\dim V_2 + \dim V_3 = \dim (V_2 + V_3) + \dim (V_2 \cap V_3)$ (see Theorem 5.2 of Chapter 3); moreover, $\dim (V_2 + V_3) \leq n$ since both V_2 and V_3 are subspaces of $V_n(R)$, and $\dim (V_2 \cap V_3) = 0$ because the intersection is the zero vector. Thus, $p + n - q \leq n + 0$, and a contradiction results. The same argument can be rephrased if $q > p$ to give the contradiction: $q + n - p > n$ and $q + n - p \leq n$. Hence $q = p$ and we have shown that there is precisely one diagonal matrix D of the form (3.6) in each subset $E(M)$.

The preceding method of proof suggests an interpretation for the number of positive 1's occurring in a canonical form D of (3.6). First, a definition:

DEFINITION 3.1. *A quadratic form* $Q(\mathbf{X}) = \sum_{i,j=1}^{n} x_i a_{ij} x_j$ *is said to be* POSITIVE DEFINITE *on a subspace* V *of* $V_n(R)$ *if* $Q(\mathbf{X}) > 0$ *for all nonzero vectors* $\mathbf{X}$ *of* V. *Similarly* $Q(\mathbf{X})$ *is said to be* NEGATIVE DEFINITE *on a subspace* V *of* $V_n(R)$ *if* $Q(\mathbf{X}) < 0$ *for all nonzero vectors* $\mathbf{X}$ *of* V.

If $Q_1(\mathbf{X})$ is the quadratic form whose associated matrix is D_1 of the preceding proof, then Q_1 is certainly positive definite on V_1. Moreover, if $D_1 = PBP^{\mathsf{T}}$ and V_2 consists of the vectors $\mathbf{X}P$ for $\mathbf{X} \in V_1$, where B is the symmetric matrix associated with the quadratic form $Q_2(\mathbf{X})$, then $Q_2(\mathbf{X})$ is positive definite on V_2 because $Q_2(\mathbf{X}P) = (\mathbf{X}PB, \mathbf{X}P) = (\mathbf{X}PBP^{\mathsf{T}}, \mathbf{X}) = (\mathbf{X}D_1, \mathbf{X}) > 0$ for $\mathbf{X} \neq 0$. Thus, for any quadratic form $Q(\mathbf{X})$ whose matrix is congruent to D_1 there is some subspace of dimension p on which $Q(\mathbf{X})$ is positive definite. On the other hand, a simple reversal of the preceding argument shows that there is no subspace of larger dimension with this property.

THEOREM 3.2. *Let t be the largest dimension of any subspace V on which the quadratic form $Q(\mathbf{X})$ is positive definite. If $Q(\mathbf{X})$ is equivalent to the canonical form*

$$y_1^2 + y_2^2 + \cdots + y_p^2 - y_{p+1}^2 - \cdots - y_r^2,$$

then $t = p$.

For historical reasons the number $(2p - r) = p + (p - r)$ is called the *signature* of a quadratic form or its associated symmetric matrix. The signature, rank, and order of a symmetric matrix A determine which subset $E(M)$ contains A. We say that these numbers constitute a *complete set of invariants* for symmetric matrices under congruence. Two symmetric matrices will be congruent if and only if they have the same rank, signature, and order. We now have the answer to problem 2 and we formalize our discussion in two theorems, with which we shall conclude this section.

THEOREM 3.3. *Every quadratic form* $Q(\mathbf{X}) = \sum_{i,j=1}^{n} x_i a_{ij} x_j$ *is equivalent over* R *to a* UNIQUE *form*

$$y_1^2 + y_2^2 + \cdots + y_p^2 - y_{p+1}^2 - \cdots - y_r^2,$$

where r *is the rank of the symmetric matrix* $A = [a_{ij}]$ *and* p *is the largest dimension of any subspace* V *on which* $Q(\mathbf{X})$ *is positive definite.*

THEOREM 3.4. *Two* $n \times n$ *symmetric matrices* A *and* B *are congruent if and only if they have the same rank and signature.*

EXERCISES

1. Show that the matrices

$$A = \begin{bmatrix} 1 & 2 & 3 \\ 2 & -2 & 1 \\ 3 & 1 & 0 \end{bmatrix} \quad \text{and} \quad B = \begin{bmatrix} 12 & 6 & 10 \\ 6 & 1 & 6 \\ 10 & 6 & 7 \end{bmatrix}$$

are congruent to each other.

2. Reduce the quadratic form

$$Q(\mathbf{X}) = x_2^2 + 3x_3^2 - 6x_1x_2 + 4x_2x_3 + 8x_1x_3$$

to canonical (diagonal) form.

3. Show that the quadratic form

$$Q^*(\mathbf{Y}) = 7y_2^2 + 11y_3^2 - 6y_1y_2 + 8y_1y_3 - 10y_2y_3$$

is equivalent to the quadratic form of Exercise 2.

4. How many subsets $E(M)$ are there for the set of all 3×3 symmetric matrices under the equivalence relation of congruence?

5. Prove that the number of nonequivalent real quadratic forms in n variables is

$$\frac{(n+1)(n+2)}{2}.$$

6. Provide a proof for Theorem 3.4.

7. Give a proof to show that the number of (-1)'s in the canonical form (3.6) of a quadratic form $Q(\mathbf{X})$ is equal to the largest dimension of any vector subspace of $V_n(R)$ on which $Q(\mathbf{X})$ is negative definite.

8. Prove that for any $\mathbf{X} \in V_n(R)$, $Q(\mathbf{X}) \geq 0$ if the rank of $Q(\mathbf{X})$ is equal to its signature.

9. Prove that a quadratic form $Q(\mathbf{X})$ is positive definite for all of $V_n(R)$ if and only if its canonical (diagonal) matrix is Diagonal $[1, 1, \cdots, 1]$.

10. Show that the quadratic forms

$$Q_1(\mathbf{X}) = [x_1, x_2, x_3]\begin{bmatrix} 6 & 1 & 1 \\ 1 & 10 & 3 \\ 1 & 3 & 1 \end{bmatrix}\begin{bmatrix} x_1 \\ x_2 \\ x_3 \end{bmatrix},$$

$$Q_2(\mathbf{X}) = [x_1, x_2, x_3]\begin{bmatrix} 1 & 2 & -1 \\ 2 & 5 & 0 \\ -1 & 0 & 6 \end{bmatrix}\begin{bmatrix} x_1 \\ x_2 \\ x_3 \end{bmatrix}$$

are positive definite for all of $V_n(R)$.

11. Show that a quadratic form $Q(\mathbf{X})$ associated with $A = [a_{ij}]$ is positive definite on the subspace of all vectors of the form $[x_1, x_2, \cdots, x_k, 0, 0, \cdots, 0]$ if and only if the quadratic form $\sum_{i,j=1}^{k} x_i a_{ij} x_j$ is positive definite on $V_k(R)$.

4. A Geometric Interpretation of Equivalence of Quadratic Forms

The equivalence of a quadratic form $Q(\mathbf{X}) = \sum_{i,j=1}^{n} x_i a_{ij} x_j$ to a diagonal form $y_1^2 + \cdots + y_p^2 - y_{p+1}^2 - \cdots - y_r^2$ has a simple interpretation in E_n. An illustration of the ideas in the plane will be of value.

We assume that we have a Cartesian coordinate system in a plane and use the association of points $X(x_1, x_2)$ with vectors $[x_1, x_2]$. The coordinates of $X(x_1, x_2)$ are the components of $[x_1, x_2]$ relative to the natural basis.

Now let us consider those points in the plane for which

$$Q(\mathbf{X}) = [x_1, x_2]\begin{bmatrix} a_{11} & a_{12} \\ a_{21} & a_{22} \end{bmatrix}\begin{bmatrix} x_1 \\ x_2 \end{bmatrix} = 1. \tag{4.1}$$

We have already discussed the fact that the locus of all points satisfying (4.1) will be a conic C. We plot the graph of C in the plane.

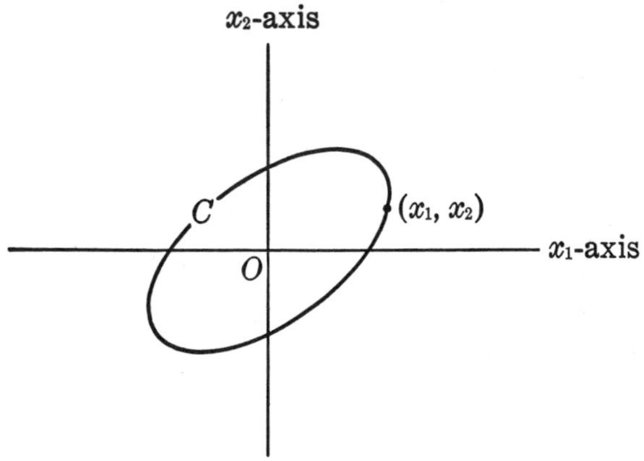

Figure 4.1

If $P = \begin{bmatrix} p_{11} & p_{12} \\ p_{21} & p_{22} \end{bmatrix}$ is the nonsingular matrix such that

$$PAP^{\mathsf{T}} = \text{Diagonal } [d_1, d_2] \quad (\text{where } d_1, d_2 = \pm 1, 0),$$

we let the points (p_{11}, p_{12}) and (p_{21}, p_{22}) be the unit points of a new coordinate system with the origin unchanged. The new coordinates (y_1, y_2) of a point $X(x_1, x_2)$ are obtained from the relation

$$[x_1, x_2] = y_1[p_{11}, p_{12}] + y_2[p_{21}, p_{22}],$$

or

$$[x_1, x_2] = [y_1, y_2] \begin{bmatrix} p_{11} & p_{12} \\ p_{21} & p_{22} \end{bmatrix}.$$

Thus we are looking at the change of variables as an introduction of a new coordinate system in the plane; or, if you wish, as the change of basis

$$\begin{bmatrix} \mathbf{Y}_1 \\ \mathbf{Y}_2 \end{bmatrix} = \begin{bmatrix} p_{11} & p_{12} \\ p_{21} & p_{22} \end{bmatrix} \begin{bmatrix} \mathbf{E}_1 \\ \mathbf{E}_2 \end{bmatrix} \quad \text{of } V_2(R).$$

Graphically, we have the following situation:

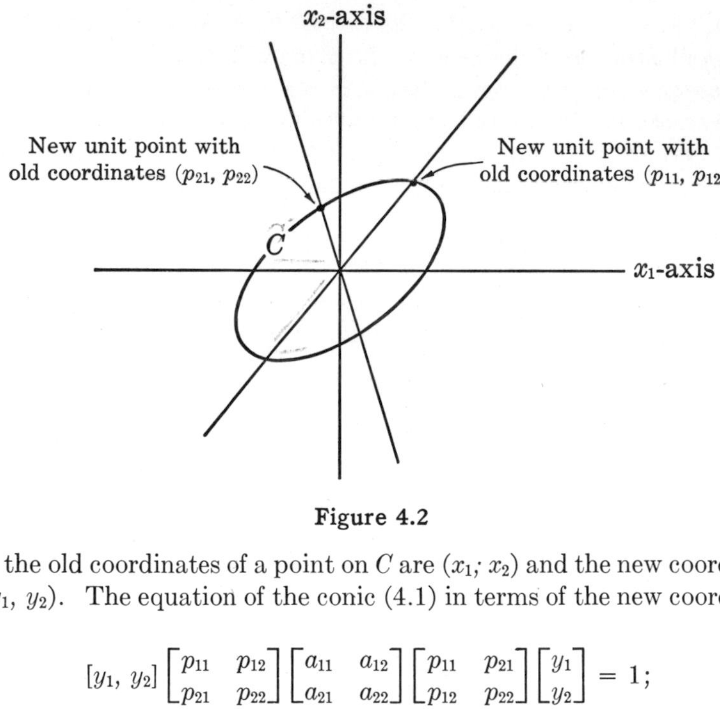

Figure 4.2

Now, the old coordinates of a point on C are (x_1, x_2) and the new coordinates are (y_1, y_2). The equation of the conic (4.1) in terms of the new coordinates is

$$[y_1, y_2] \begin{bmatrix} p_{11} & p_{12} \\ p_{21} & p_{22} \end{bmatrix} \begin{bmatrix} a_{11} & a_{12} \\ a_{21} & a_{22} \end{bmatrix} \begin{bmatrix} p_{11} & p_{21} \\ p_{12} & p_{22} \end{bmatrix} \begin{bmatrix} y_1 \\ y_2 \end{bmatrix} = 1;$$

or

$$[y_1, y_2] \begin{bmatrix} d_1 & 0 \\ 0 & d_2 \end{bmatrix} \begin{bmatrix} y_1 \\ y_2 \end{bmatrix} = 1,$$

where $d_1, d_2 = \pm 1, 0$.

In general, the new coordinate system will not be Cartesian.

The corresponding interpretation of $Q(\mathbf{X}) = \sum_{i,j=1}^{n} x_i a_{ij} x_j$ for $n > 2$ follows the pattern for $n = 2$. We assume that we have a Cartesian coordinate system in E_n and associate the point $(x_1, x_2, \cdots, x_n)$ with the vector $[x_1, x_2, \cdots, x_n]$ and the natural basis $\{\mathbf{E}_1, \mathbf{E}_2, \cdots, \mathbf{E}_n\}$ of $V_n(R)$. If $P = [p_{ij}]$ is the nonsingular matrix such that

$$PAP^{\mathsf{T}} = \text{Diagonal } [d_1, \cdots, d_n],$$

we let $P_i^{(1)} = (p_{i1}, p_{i2}, \cdots, p_{in})$ be the unit points of a new coordinate system for E_n. Here again we are merely using the rows of $P = [p_{ij}]$ as the coordinates of the unit points for the new coordinate system. The relation between the old and new coordinates, $(y_1, y_2, \cdots, y_n)$, of a point $X(x_1, x_2, \cdots, x_n)$ is given by

$$[x_1, x_2, \cdots, x_n] = [y_1, y_2, \cdots, y_n]P.$$

The locus of points whose equation is

$$[x_1, x_2, \cdots, x_n]A \begin{bmatrix} x_1 \\ x_2 \\ \cdot \\ \cdot \\ \cdot \\ x_n \end{bmatrix} = 1$$

in the old coordinate system becomes

$$[y_1, y_2, \cdots, y_n] \begin{bmatrix} d_1 & & & & \\ & d_2 & & & \\ & & \cdot & & \\ & & & \cdot & \\ & & & & \cdot \\ & & & & & d_n \end{bmatrix} \begin{bmatrix} y_1 \\ y_2 \\ \cdot \\ \cdot \\ \cdot \\ y_n \end{bmatrix} = 1,$$

where $d_i = \pm 1, 0$, in the new coordinate system.

The new coordinate system for E_n will not, in general, be a Cartesian coordinate system; that is, the unit points $P_i^{(1)}$ do not lie on mutually perpendicular lines at equal distances from the origin.

The classification of conics in E_n restricts the permissible changes of coordinates to involve only rotations. We shall return to this question in Chapter 10, §4.

5. Geometric Applications of Bilinear and Quadratic Forms

We shall now discuss briefly a point that was mentioned in the introduction to this chapter; that is, possible alternatives for an "inner product" in $V_n(R)$.

Let us consider the bilinear form

$$\text{(5.1)} \qquad \mathrm{B}(\mathbf{X}, \mathbf{Y}) = \sum_{i,j=1}^{n} x_i a_{ij} y_j = (\mathbf{X}A, \mathbf{Y}),$$

where $\mathbf{X} = [x_1, x_2, \cdots, x_n]$, $\mathbf{Y} = [y_1, y_2, \cdots, y_n]$, and A is the $n \times n$ matrix $[a_{ij}]$. As the student may suspect, we are contemplating the use of $\mathrm{B}(\mathbf{X}, \mathbf{Y}) = (\mathbf{X}A, \mathbf{Y})$ as a more general "inner product" of $V_n(R)$. However, we must be sure that $(\mathbf{X}A, \mathbf{Y})$ does indeed satisfy the properties that have been proposed for a general "inner product" in Chapter 3, § 6.

If we are to have $\mathrm{B}(\mathbf{X}, \mathbf{Y}) = \mathrm{B}(\mathbf{Y}, \mathbf{X})$ for all vectors $\mathbf{X}$, $\mathbf{Y}$ of $V_n(R)$, then we must insist that $a_{ij} = a_{ji}$ for $i \neq j$ in the bilinear form of (5.1). Consequently, our first restriction is to the consideration of symmetric bilinear forms as possible generalizations of $(\mathbf{X}, \mathbf{Y})$.

Next, if we are to have $\mathrm{B}(\mathbf{X}, \mathbf{X}) > 0$ for all nonzero vectors $\mathbf{X}$ of $V_n(R)$, we must restrict the quadratic form $\mathrm{Q}(\mathbf{X}) = \mathrm{B}(\mathbf{X}, \mathbf{X})$ to be positive definite on all of $V_n(R)$.

The concept of a positive definite quadratic form is extended to matrices by saying that an $n \times n$ symmetric matrix $A = [a_{ij}]$ is a *positive definite symmetric matrix* if the quadratic form $\mathrm{Q}(\mathbf{X}) = \sum_{i,j=1}^{n} x_i a_{ij} x_j$ is positive definite on $V_n(R)$. We now define a new inner product in the following manner:

DEFINITION 5.1. *Let A be an $n \times n$ positive definite symmetric matrix and define the bilinear form*

$$B(\mathbf{X}, \mathbf{Y}) = \sum_{i,j=1}^{n} x_i a_{ij} y_j = (\mathbf{X}A, \mathbf{Y}),$$

for all vectors $\mathbf{X}$, $\mathbf{Y}$ *of* $V_n(R)$. *We call* $(\mathbf{X}A, \mathbf{Y})$ *the* A-INNER PRODUCT *for* $V_n(R)$.

All the properties desired for an "inner product" are satisfied by the A-inner product of $V_n(R)$. By A-orthogonality we would mean that the vectors $\mathbf{X}$ and $\mathbf{Y}$ are A-orthogonal if $(\mathbf{X}A, \mathbf{Y}) = 0$. Then we could seek an A-orthogonal basis for $V_n(R)$, and its existence could be demonstrated in a straightforward manner (as we shall do in Example 1) or we could provide an A-orthogonal Gram-Schmidt process.

The concept of A-orthogonal subspaces would make sense and we could have a decomposition of $V_n(R)$ into a direct sum of A-orthogonal subspaces.

We could even provide an analogue for the Schwarz inequality in terms of the A-inner product. Thus, we would have

$$(\mathbf{X}A, \mathbf{Y})^2 \leq (\mathbf{X}A, \mathbf{X})(\mathbf{Y}A, \mathbf{Y}),$$

for all vectors $\mathbf{X}$ and $\mathbf{Y}$ of $V_n(R)$. The student will find that practically the same proof is valid here as the one given in Chapter 4, § 3, if he replaces the inner product $(\mathbf{X}, \mathbf{Y})$ by the A-inner product.

Example 1. Let us determine an A-orthogonal basis of $V_3(R)$, where A is the positive definite matrix

$$\begin{bmatrix} 1 & 2 & -1 \\ 2 & 5 & 0 \\ -1 & 0 & 6 \end{bmatrix}$$

of Exercise 10, § 3.

We choose as a first basis vector $\mathbf{X}_1 = [1, 0, 0]$. Now if $\mathbf{X}_2$ and $\mathbf{X}_3$ are to be A-orthogonal to $\mathbf{X}_1$, we must have

$$([1, 0, 0]A, \mathbf{X}_2) = ([1, 0, 0]A, \mathbf{X}_3) = 0;$$

or possibilities for $\mathbf{X}_2$ and $\mathbf{X}_3$ are solutions of

$$([1, 0, 0]A, [x_1, x_2, x_3]) = x_1 + 2x_2 - x_3 = 0.$$

Thus, we choose $\mathbf{X}_2 = [2, -1, 0]$, and then $\mathbf{X}_3 = [x_1, x_2, x_3]$ must satisfy both the equations

$$x_1 + 2x_2 - x_3 = 0$$

$$([2, -1, 0]A, [x_1, x_2, x_3]) = 0 \quad \text{or} \quad -x_2 - 2x_3 = 0.$$

Therefore, we let $\mathbf{X}_3 = [5, -2, 1]$ and we have the A-orthogonal basis

$$[1, 0, 0], \quad [2, -1, 0], \quad [5, -2, 1]$$

of $V_3(R)$.

The concept of A-inner product has useful applications. For example, in the theory of small vibrations it is desirable to simultaneously reduce two quadratic forms (one of them being positive definite) to diagonal form. The reduction will not be given at this time but a solution may be given that involves the concept of A-inner product.

We next consider a new definition of distance which may replace the definition given for E_n. We define the distance between points $X(x_1, x_2, \cdots, x_n)$ and $Y(y_1, y_2, \cdots, y_n)$ to be

$$d_Q(X, Y) = Q(\mathbf{Y} - \mathbf{X})^{1/2},$$

where $Q(\mathbf{X})$ is a positive definite quadratic form.

Two questions occur immediately: (1) Does this definition agree with our intuitive ideas concerning distance? (2) Does this definition of distance really produce a geometry essentially different from the one we have discussed for E_n after assuming that distance is defined by

$$d(X, Y) = (\mathbf{Y} - \mathbf{X}, \mathbf{Y} - \mathbf{X})^{1/2}?$$

To answer question 1, we wish to determine whether $d_Q(X, Y)$ has the following properties:

$$(5.2) \quad \begin{cases} \text{(i) } d_Q(X, Y) > 0 \text{ unless } X = Y, \text{ in which case } d_Q(X, X) = 0. \\ \text{(ii) } d_Q(X, Y) = d_Q(Y, X). \\ \text{(iii) } d_Q(X, Y) + d_Q(Y, Z) \geq d_Q(X, Z). \end{cases}$$

Property (i) is an immediate consequence of the fact that $Q(\mathbf{X})$ is positive definite. Property (ii) is a simple consequence of the fact that $Q(-\mathbf{X}) = Q(\mathbf{X})$. Finally, the verification of (iii) duplicates the proof in Chapter 4 for $d(X, Y)$, using the more general Schwarz inequality of this section.

The answer to the question of whether we have essentially different geometries using $d_Q(X, Y)$ and $d(X, Y)$ is No! It is more a matter of interpretation. Since $Q(\mathbf{X})$ is a positive definite quadratic form, we know that its associated symmetric matrix A is congruent to the identity matrix I. Hence, there is a matrix P such that $PAP^{\mathsf{T}} = I$. If we choose a new coordinate system such that the new coordinates are related to the old coordinates by means of the relation

$$[x_1, x_2, \cdots, x_n] = [x_1{}^*, x_2{}^*, \cdots, x_n{}^*]P,$$

we see that $d_Q(X, Y) = d(X^*, Y^*)$, so that in this sense we have merely chosen the wrong coordinate system for our definition of distance. In the new coordinate system we have our old familiar definition of distance.

Example 2. Let us assume that our coordinate system for E_3 is established with points (0, 0, 0), (1, 0, 0), (0, 1, 0), and (0, 0, 1) as origin and unit points on three lines. Then the coordinates of the point (x_1, x_2, x_3) with respect to this coordinate system are x_1, x_2, and x_3.

Let distance be defined by the positive definite quadratic form

$$Q(\mathbf{X}) = [x_1, x_2, x_3]\begin{bmatrix} 1 & -1 & 2 \\ -1 & 2 & -2 \\ 2 & -2 & 5 \end{bmatrix}\begin{bmatrix} x_1 \\ x_2 \\ x_3 \end{bmatrix}.$$

It is a routine problem to see that

$$\begin{bmatrix} 1 & 0 & 0 \\ 1 & 1 & 0 \\ -2 & 0 & 1 \end{bmatrix}\begin{bmatrix} 1 & -1 & 2 \\ -1 & 2 & -2 \\ 2 & -2 & 5 \end{bmatrix}\begin{bmatrix} 1 & 1 & -2 \\ 0 & 1 & 0 \\ 0 & 0 & 1 \end{bmatrix} = \begin{bmatrix} 1 & 0 & 0 \\ 0 & 1 & 0 \\ 0 & 0 & 1 \end{bmatrix}.$$

Now, let us choose (0, 0, 0), (1, 0, 0), (1, 1, 0), and (− 2, 0, 1) as origin and unit points for a new coordinate system. Then the new coordinates $(x_1{}^*, x_2{}^*, x_3{}^*)$ are obtained from the relation

$$[x_1, x_2, x_3] = x_1{}^*[1, 0, 0] + x_2{}^*[1, 1, 0] + x_3{}^*[-2, 0, 1],$$

or

$$[x_1, x_2, x_3] = [x_1{}^*, x_2{}^*, x_3{}^*]\begin{bmatrix} 1 & 0 & 0 \\ 1 & 1 & 0 \\ -2 & 0 & 1 \end{bmatrix} = [x_1{}^*, x_2{}^*, x_3{}^*]P.$$

The square of the distance from (x_1, x_2, x_3) to (y_1, y_2, y_3),

$$d_Q{}^2(X, Y) = [y_1 - x_1, y_2 - x_2, y_3 - x_3] \begin{bmatrix} 1 & -1 & 2 \\ -1 & 2 & -2 \\ 2 & -2 & 5 \end{bmatrix} \begin{bmatrix} y_1 - x_1 \\ y_2 - x_2 \\ y_3 - x_3 \end{bmatrix},$$

is given in terms of the new coordinates by

$$[y_1{}^* - x_1{}^*, y_2{}^* - x_2{}^*, y_3{}^* - x_3{}^*] P \begin{bmatrix} 1 & -1 & 2 \\ -1 & 2 & -2 \\ 2 & -2 & 5 \end{bmatrix} P^{\mathsf{T}} \begin{bmatrix} y_1{}^* - x_1{}^* \\ y_2{}^* - x_2{}^* \\ y_3{}^* - x_3{}^* \end{bmatrix}$$

$$= \{(y_1{}^* - x_1{}^*)^2 + (y_2{}^* - x_2{}^*)^2 + (y_3{}^* - x_3{}^*)^2\},$$

the distance formula we have assumed for our previous discussion of E_3. In this sense, we have now chosen the correct coordinate system to replace the original one. Of course, it must be realized that relative to the old coordinate system our new coordinate system need not be Cartesian, although the distance formula takes that form.

EXERCISES

1. Determine an A-orthogonal basis for $V_3(R)$, where A is the matrix of Example 1, by the generalized Gram-Schmidt process and the initial basis vectors $\mathbf{X}_1 = \mathbf{E}_1$, $\mathbf{X}_2 = \mathbf{E}_2$, $\mathbf{X}_3 = \mathbf{E}_3$.

2. Prove the statements in (5.2).

3. Find the A-orthogonal subspace to $L\{[1, 2, 0, 0], [1, -1, 0, 0]\}$ in $V_4(R)$, where

$$A = \begin{bmatrix} 1 & -1 & 1 & 1 \\ -1 & 5 & -1 & -1 \\ 1 & -1 & 2 & 0 \\ 1 & -1 & 0 & 3 \end{bmatrix}.$$

4. As in Example 2, let distance be defined by means of the quadratic form

$$Q(\mathbf{X}) = [x_1, x_2, x_3] \begin{bmatrix} 1 & 2 & -1 \\ 2 & 5 & 0 \\ -1 & 0 & 6 \end{bmatrix} \begin{bmatrix} x_1 \\ x_2 \\ x_3 \end{bmatrix}.$$

Determine the coordinates of new unit points in order that distance be given in terms of the new coordinates by

$$\{(y_1{}^* - x_1{}^*)^2 + (y_2{}^* - x_2{}^*)^2 + (y_3{}^* - x_3{}^*)^2\}^{1/2}.$$

5. Prove that a real symmetric matrix A is positive definite if and only if $A = PP^{\mathsf{T}}$, where P is a real nonsingular matrix.

6. If a real symmetric matrix is positive definite, show that $\det A > 0$.

*7. Prove that a real symmetric matrix A is positive definite if and only if the determinants

$$\Delta_k = \det \begin{bmatrix} a_{11} & a_{12} & \cdots & a_{1k} \\ \vdots & \vdots & & \vdots \\ a_{k1} & a_{k2} & \cdots & a_{kk} \end{bmatrix} > 0$$

for $k = 1, 2, 3, \cdots, n$.

*8. Show that there always exists a real number c such that $cI + A$ is positive definite for any real symmetric matrix A.

CHAPTER 9

Complex Number Field, Polynomial Rings

The determination of canonical sets of matrices under the equivalence relation defined by the similarity of matrices ($B = PAP^{-1}$) is of importance in many applications. This problem will involve polynomial equations and their roots. In many cases the real number field is not sufficient to provide the answer. We shall devote this chapter to a discussion of the complex number field and to properties of polynomials needed for the remainder of the text. For many students this chapter will be a review, although the material may be approached from a new point of view.

1. The Complex Number Field C

We have assumed in some of the problems throughout the text that the student is familiar with "complex numbers," $a + bi$, where a and b are real numbers and $i^2 = -1$. In a somewhat vague sense, the complex numbers provide a field containing the real number field and solutions of the equation $x^2 + 1 = 0$. An extension of the real numbers is necessary if a solution of the equation $x^2 + 1 = 0$ is desired; the properties of order for the real numbers imply that there are no elements of R satisfying this equation. In order to make the relationship between complex numbers and real numbers more precise, we shall define the complex number field C in a more formal manner.

Take as elements of the complex number field C ordered pairs of real numbers $[a, b]$. Thus the elements of C have the same notation as the vectors of $V_2(R)$, and we shall retain for the elements of C the definitions of equality and addition that they have as elements of $V_2(R)$. Specifically,

Definition 1.1. Equality. $[a, b] = [c, d]$ *if and only if* $a = c, b = d$.

Definition 1.2. Addition. $[a, b] + [c, d] = [a + c, b + d]$.

Now, in order to obtain a number system satisfying the postulates of a field (Chapter 1, §2), we provide a multiplication of elements of C by means of the following definition:

Definition 1.3. Multiplication. $[a, b] \times [c, d] = [ac - bd, ad + bc]$.

There is nothing to verify for the postulates A1, A2, A3, A4, and A5 because the definitions of equality and addition are those of $V_2(R)$ and we know them to be satisfied. The postulate M1 is satisfied because of the very nature of our definition of multiplication.

We may compute

$$[0, 0] + [a, b] = [a, b] + [0, 0] = [a, b],$$
$$[1, 0] \times [a, b] = [a, b] \times [1, 0] = [a, b],$$

and consequently [0, 0] and [1, 0] play the role in C that 0 and 1 play for the real number field R. We say that [0, 0] is the zero element and [1, 0] is the unity, or identity, element of C.

For M2, let $[a, b]$, $[c, d]$, and $[e, f]$ be three arbitrary elements of C and compute

$$\begin{aligned}
([a, b] \times [c, d]) \times [e, f] & \\
&= [ac - bd, ad + bc] \times [e, f] \\
&= [(ac - bd)e - (ad + bc)f, (ac - bd)f + (ad + bc)e] \\
&= [ace - bde - adf - bcf, acf - bdf + ade + bce]; \\
[a, b] \times ([c, d] \times [e, f]) & \\
&= [a, b] \times [ce - df, cf + de] \\
&= [a(ce - df) - b(cf + de), a(cf + de) + b(ce - df)] \\
&= [ace - adf - bcf - bde, acf + ade + bce - bdf].
\end{aligned}$$

We observe that the final forms of these associations are equal so that postulate M2 is valid for the multiplication of elements of C. It should be noted that the distributive, associative, and commutative laws for real numbers have been used extensively in making the reductions above.

We shall show that every nonzero element $[a, b]$ has an inverse.

For M4, given $[a, b] \neq [0, 0]$, we seek an element $[x, y]$ such that

$$[a, b] \times [x, y] = [1, 0];$$

or, after applying the definition of multiplication, such that

$$[ax - by, ay + bx] = [1, 0].$$

The last equality leads to the system of linear equations

$$\begin{aligned}
ax - by &= 1 \\
bx + ay &= 0.
\end{aligned}$$

Since $[a, b] \neq [0, 0]$, $a^2 + b^2 \neq 0$, and these equations have the unique solution

$$x = \frac{a}{a^2 + b^2}, \quad y = \frac{-b}{a^2 + b^2}.$$

A straightforward computation yields

$$[a, b] \times \left[\frac{a}{a^2 + b^2}, \frac{-b}{a^2 + b^2}\right]$$
$$= \left[\frac{a^2}{a^2 + b^2} + \frac{b^2}{a^2 + b^2}, \frac{-ab}{a^2 + b^2} + \frac{ab}{a^2 + b^2}\right] = [1,0],$$

and we have shown the existence of $[a, b]^{-1}$.

Example 1. We shall illustrate the commutative law of multiplication and the distributive laws. These postulates comprise the unverified portions of the proof of the theorem to follow. Their verification is left to the student.

Let $[3, 2]$, $[1, 4]$, $[-1, 1]$ be elements of C. We calculate

$$\begin{aligned} [3, 2][1, 4] &= [3 - 8, 12 + 2] = [-5, 14] = [1, 4][3, 2]; \\ ([3, 2] + [1, 4])[-1, 1] &= [4, 6][-1, 1] = [-10, -2], \\ ([3, 2] + [1, 4])[-1, 1] &= [3, 2][-1, 1] + [1, 4][-1, 1] \\ &= [-5, 1] + [-5, -3] = [-10, -2]. \end{aligned}$$

Our foregoing discussion leads to the following theorem:

THEOREM 1.1. *The set C of all ordered pairs of real numbers $[a, b]$ together with the definitions of addition (Definition 1.2) and multiplication (Definition 1.3) forms a field which we shall call the complex number field C.*

The elements of C of the form $[a, 0]$ have the following rules of operation:

$$\begin{aligned} [a, 0] + [b, 0] &= [a + b, 0], \\ [a, 0][b, 0] &= [ab, 0]. \end{aligned}$$

Ignoring the second component, 0, we see that the elements of C of the form $[a, 0]$ add and multiply like real numbers. More accurately, if we establish the one-to-one mapping T, defined by $[a, 0] \xrightarrow{T} a$, between the complex numbers of the form $[a, 0]$ and the real numbers, we see that

$$\text{if} \begin{cases} [a, 0] \xrightarrow{T} a, \\ [b, 0] \xrightarrow{T} b, \end{cases} \quad \text{then} \begin{cases} [a, 0] + [b, 0] \xrightarrow{T} a + b, \\ [a, 0][b, 0] \xrightarrow{T} ab. \end{cases}$$

This preservation of algebraic operations under the mapping T is reminiscent of the situation in the case of linear transformations and matrices, and again we speak of the two systems as being isomorphic.

In general, two fields, F (with operations $+$ and $\cdot$) and F^* (with operations $\oplus$ and $\otimes$), are said to be *isomorphic* if there exists a one-to-one mapping T of F onto F^* such that $(a + b)\mathrm{T} = a\mathrm{T} \oplus b\mathrm{T}$, $(ab)\mathrm{T} = a\mathrm{T} \otimes b\mathrm{T}$. It is in this sense that we say (somewhat loosely) that the complex number field C contains the real numbers; actually C contains a subset that is isomorphic to the real number field R.

We see easily that

$$[a, b] = [a, 0] + [b, 0][0, 1],$$
$$[0, 1] \times [0, 1] = [-1, 0],$$

so that, by making the identification of $[a, 0]$ with the real number a, we can write every number of C in the familiar form

$$[a, b] = a + bi,$$

where $i = [0, 1]$ and $i^2 + [1, 0] = [0, 0]$, or i is a solution of the equation $x^2 + 1 = 0$.

When a complex number is written in the form $a + bi$, we refer to a as the real part and to b as the imaginary part of the complex number $a + bi$.

We have observed that complex numbers $[a, b]$ have the same definitions of equality and addition as the vectors of $V_2(R)$, and so it should not be surprising that the vectors in the plane provide a convenient geometric interpretation for complex numbers. We establish a Cartesian coordinate system for the plane and refer to the x_1-axis as the real axis and the x_2-axis as the imaginary axis. We may now associate the complex number $z = a + bi$ with the point (a, b). It should be clear that this establishes a one-to-one mapping between points in the plane and complex numbers.

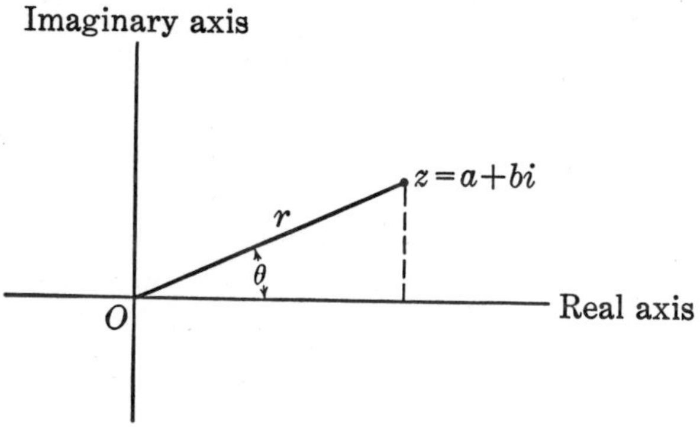

Figure 1.1

The length of the vector $[a, b]$, or, equivalently, the length of the line segment from the origin to the point (a, b), is called the *absolute value*, or *modulus*, of the complex number $z = a + bi$. We denote the absolute value of the complex number $z = a + bi$ by

(1.1) $$|z| = |a + bi| = (a^2 + b^2)^{1/2}$$

and will often refer to the line segment from O to the point (a, b), as well as to the absolute value of $z = a + bi$, by r.

If $z = a + bi$, the complex number $\bar{z} = a - bi$ is called the *conjugate* of z. Note that $z\bar{z} = |z|^2$.

The angle θ from the positive real axis to the line segment r, measured in a counterclockwise direction, is called the *amplitude* of the complex number $z = a + bi$. We see from Figure 1.1 that

$$\theta = \tan^{-1} b/a$$

and that any complex number $z = a + bi$ may be written in the *polar form*

$$z = |z|(\cos \theta + i \sin \theta) = r(\cos \theta + i \sin \theta). \tag{1.2}$$

Example 2. The complex number $z = 1 + \sqrt{3}i$ may be written in the polar form

$$1 + \sqrt{3}i = 2(\cos 60° + i \sin 60°).$$

We have arranged the association of complex numbers with points in the plane so that we can think of the complex number $a + bi$ as corresponding to the vector $[a, b]$. Since the addition of complex numbers corresponds to the addition of vectors, we have already established a geometrical interpretation for complex addition in §2 of Chapter 2. If z_1 and z_2 are complex numbers, this geometrical interpretation of addition in terms of the three sides of a triangle readily establishes the relation

$$|z_1 + z_2| \leq |z_1| + |z_2|.$$

The interesting geometrical interpretation for multiplication is best obtained from the polar form of complex numbers. Thus, if

$$\begin{aligned} z_1 &= |z_1|(\cos \theta + i \sin \theta), \\ z_2 &= |z_2|(\cos \beta + i \sin \beta), \end{aligned}$$

then

$$\begin{aligned} z_1 z_2 &= |z_1||z_2|(\cos \theta + i \sin \theta)(\cos \beta + i \sin \beta) \\ &= |z_1||z_2|[\cos \theta \cos \beta - \sin \theta \sin \beta + i(\cos \theta \sin \beta + \sin \theta \cos \beta)] \\ &= |z_1||z_2|[\cos (\theta + \beta) + i \sin (\theta + \beta)]. \end{aligned} \tag{1.3}$$

Hence the amplitude of the product of two complex numbers is the sum of their amplitudes and the absolute value is the product of their absolute values.

Example 3. Let $z_1 = 1 + \sqrt{3}i$, $z_2 = 1 + i$; then

$$\begin{aligned} z_1 &= 2(\cos 60° + i \sin 60°), \\ z_2 &= \sqrt{2}(\cos 45° + i \sin 45°), \end{aligned}$$

and

$$z_1 z_2 = 2\sqrt{2}(\cos 105° + i \sin 105°).$$

If we take $z_1 = z_2 = z$ in formula (1.3), we obtain

$$z^2 = |z|^2(\cos 2\theta + i \sin 2\theta),$$

and a simple induction argument gives the more general formula

$$z^n = |z|^n(\cos n\theta + i \sin n\theta), \qquad n = 1, 2, \cdots. \tag{1.4}$$

We can use formula (1.4) quite effectively to obtain the nth roots of any complex number. Let $z_0 = r_0(\cos \phi + i \sin \phi)$ and assume that we wish to find those complex numbers z such that

$$z^n = r_0(\cos \phi + i \sin \phi). \tag{1.5}$$

We substitute from (1.4) to obtain the relation

$$|z|^n(\cos n\theta + i \sin n\theta) = r_0(\cos \phi + i \sin \phi),$$

where $r_0 \geq 0$ and, consequently, $|z|$, being positive, must be a real positive nth root of r_0. As is easily seen, the amplitudes of equal complex numbers must be equal and hence

$$|z|^n = r_0, \quad \text{or} \quad |z| = r_0^{1/n}.$$

We must also satisfy the relations

$$\cos n\theta = \cos \phi$$
$$\sin n\theta = \sin \phi.$$

There is no unique solution for θ since

$$\cos n\theta = \cos n\left(\theta + \frac{2k\pi}{n}\right)$$

for any integer k. However, we see that only the following values of θ,

$$\theta = \frac{\phi}{n} + \frac{2k\pi}{n}$$

for $k = 0, 1, \cdots, n - 1$, yield distinct values for z. (Why?) Hence there are precisely n solutions of the equation (1.5), and these nth roots of $z_0 = r_0(\cos \theta + i \sin \theta)$ are

$$z = r_0^{1/n}\left[\cos\left(\frac{\phi}{n} + \frac{2k\pi}{n}\right) + i \sin\left(\frac{\phi}{n} + \frac{2k\pi}{n}\right)\right]$$

for $k = 0, 1, 2, \cdots, n - 1$.

Example 4. Let us solve $z^3 = 1$. We write

$$1 = 1(\cos 0° + i \sin 0°),$$

and then the cube roots of 1 are

$$z_1 = (\cos 0° + i \sin 0°)$$
$$z_2 = (\cos 120° + i \sin 120°)$$
$$z_3 = (\cos 240° + i \sin 240°).$$

EXERCISES

1. Perform the indicated operation on the complex numbers.

(a) $[3, 4] + [1, -2]$ (c) $(3 + 4i) + (1 - 2i)$
(b) $[1, 6][2, -1]$ (d) $(1 + 6i)(2 - i)$

2. Verify the distributive laws for the field of complex numbers.

3. Convert the following complex numbers to polar form:

(a) $1 - i$ (c) $-3i$ (e) $3 + 4i$
(b) $-1 + i$ (d) $\sqrt{3} + i$ (f) $2 - i$

4. Convert the following complex numbers in polar form to the form $a + bi$:

(a) $4(\cos 30° + i \sin 30°)$ (c) $1(\cos 60° + i \sin 60°)$
(b) $2(\cos 90° + i \sin 90°)$ (d) $\sqrt{3}(\cos 45° + i \sin 45°)$

5. Determine a geometrical construction for the product of two complex numbers.

6. Determine a geometrical construction for the quotient of two complex numbers.

7. Give a complete proof for the formula

$$z^n = |z|^n(\cos n\theta + i \sin n\theta), \qquad n = 1, 2, \cdots.$$

(This is commonly known as Demoivre's formula.)

8. Determine the inverse of a complex number $z = r(\cos \theta + i \sin \theta)$ in polar form.

9. What is the formula for $\frac{z_1}{z_2}$ in polar form?

10. Determine the solutions of the following equations:

(a) $x^5 = 1$ (c) $x^4 = 625$ (e) $x^2 = 1 + \sqrt{3}i$
(b) $x^2 = -1 - i$ (d) $x^3 = -27$ (f) $x^3 = -i$

11. Determine an expression for z^{-1} in terms of $|z|$ and the conjugate $\bar{z}$.

12. Show that $z + \bar{z}$ is always real and that $z - \bar{z}$ is a complex number with real part zero.

13. Prove that the complex nth roots of 1 form a group of n elements for any positive integer n, where the group operation is multiplication.

14. If $z = \cos \frac{2\pi}{n} + i \sin \frac{2\pi}{n}$, show that $z^k = 1$ if and only if n divides k.

15. Among the sixth roots of 1, find those complex numbers that are also cube roots of 1; square roots of 1.

16. Those nth roots of 1 which are not at the same time mth roots of 1 for $m < n$ are called primitive nth roots of 1. How many primitive sixth roots of 1 are there?

17. Prove that every nth root of 1 may be expressed as a power of any primitive nth root of 1.

2. Uniqueness of the Complex Number Field C

In §1 we have pointed out that the elements of the complex number field C are the vectors $[a, b]$ of $V_2(R)$. However, it is not quite accurate to think that the complex number field C is obtained by adopting the algebraic structure of the vector space $V_2(R)$ and imposing the multiplication of vectors $[a, b][c, d] = [ac - bd, ad + bc]$. What would $(r[a, b]) \cdot [c, d]$ mean? If we say that $(r[a, b])[c, d] = [ra, rb] \cdot [c, d] = [rac - rdb, rad + rbc]$, we are *assuming* a relation between *scalar* multiplication and complex-number multiplication that was never made. We adopted only the additive structure of $V_2(R)$ for our definition. It is only because of the resulting association of r with the complex number $[r, 0]$ and the fortunate relations $r[a, b] = [ra, rb]$ for scalar multiplication, $[r, 0][a, b] = [ra, rb]$ for vector or complex multiplication, that no difficulty arises in considering the complex numbers as $V_2(R)$ with multiplication. Actually, if scalar multiplication is allowed, a definite relation is imposed between scalar multiplication of vectors and the multiplication of Definition 1.2. Thus,

$$\begin{aligned}(t[a, b]) \cdot (r[c, d]) &= [ta, tb][rc, rd] = [trac - trbd, trad + trbc] \\ &= tr[ac - bd, ad + bc] = (tr)([a, b] \cdot [c, d]).\end{aligned}$$

In terms of vectors of $V_2(R)$, this last relation would be written

$$(t\mathbf{X}) \cdot (r\mathbf{Y}) = (tr)(\mathbf{X} \cdot \mathbf{Y}). \tag{2.1}$$

It would be quite appropriate to say that the complex number field C is obtained from the algebraic structure of $V_2(R)$ by defining our multiplication of vectors to be $[a, b][c, d] = [ac - bd, ad + bc]$ and insisting that (2.1) be a relation between scalar multiplication and our multiplication of vectors. No prior association of r with the complex number $[r, 0]$ need be made.

It is not difficult to define a multiplication of number pairs $[a, b]$ in which (2.1) is violated if the usual scalar multiplication of $V_2(R)$ is permitted. For example, let

$$[a, b] \times [c, d] = [ac, b^2d^2].$$

Then,

$$(3[1, 2]) \times (2[1, -1]) = [3, 6] \times [2, -2] = [6, 144],$$

but

$$(3 \cdot 2)([1, 2] \times [1, -1]) = 6[1, 4] = [6, 24].$$

On the other hand it is equally simple to define multiplications for which (2.1) is valid. We already have one, and $[a, b] \times [c, d] = [ac, bd]$ is another.

Now, it may have occurred to the student that the multiplication $[a, b][c, d] = [ac - bd, ad + bc]$ was defined as it was because we already knew about complex numbers. This is certainly true, and the student might well ask, "Are there other ways to define a multiplication of vectors of $V_2(R)$ so that the resulting system is a field?" The answer is "Yes, but . . ." The following theorem clarifies the situation:

THEOREM 2.1. *Any field F obtained from $V_2(R)$ by imposing a multiplication for vectors that satisfies* (2.1) *is isomorphic to the complex field C.*

Proof. If we are to have a field F as a result of defining a multiplication $\otimes$ for vectors of $V_2(R)$, there must be a unity element. We shall assume that this unity element is $\mathbf{I} = [a, b]$ and then we know that $\mathbf{I} \otimes \mathbf{I} = \mathbf{I}$, $\mathbf{I} \otimes \mathbf{X} = \mathbf{X} \otimes \mathbf{I} = \mathbf{X}$ for all $\mathbf{X}$ of $V_2(R)$. $\mathbf{I}$ is not the vector $[0, 0]$, since this is the zero element and the distributive laws require that $\mathbf{0} \otimes \mathbf{X} = \mathbf{0}$.

Let us select a vector $\mathbf{E} = [c, d]$ such that $\mathbf{I}$ and $\mathbf{E}$ form a basis for $V_2(R)$. The vector $\mathbf{E} \otimes \mathbf{E}$ is again a vector of $V_2(R)$ and must be a linear combination of $\mathbf{I}$ and $\mathbf{E}$. Hence,

$$\mathbf{E} \otimes \mathbf{E} = x\mathbf{I} + y\mathbf{E} \tag{2.2}$$

for real numbers x and y. $\mathbf{E} \otimes \mathbf{E}$ cannot be $[0, 0]$ because the product of nonzero elements of a field must be nonzero. Therefore x and y are not both 0.

We note that

$$\begin{aligned} \left(\mathbf{E} - \frac{y}{2}\mathbf{I}\right) \otimes \left(\mathbf{E} - \frac{y}{2}\mathbf{I}\right) &= \mathbf{E} \otimes \mathbf{E} - y\mathbf{E} + \frac{y^2}{4}\mathbf{I} \\ &= x\mathbf{I} + \frac{y^2}{4}\mathbf{I} = \left(x + \frac{y^2}{4}\right)\mathbf{I}. \end{aligned} \tag{2.3}$$

In this multiplication we have used the postulates of a field and have used (2.1) to justify the behavior of scalars with respect to multiplication of vectors.

If $x + \frac{y^2}{4} \geq 0$, we can take the square root of $x + \frac{y^2}{4}$, and (2.3) can be written in the form

$$\left(\mathbf{E} - \frac{y}{2}\mathbf{I} + \sqrt{x + \frac{y^2}{4}}\,\mathbf{I}\right) \otimes \left(\mathbf{E} - \frac{y}{2}\mathbf{I} - \sqrt{x + \frac{y^2}{4}}\,\mathbf{I}\right) = \mathbf{0}. \tag{2.4}$$

Either

$$\mathbf{E} - \frac{y}{2}\mathbf{I} + \sqrt{x + \frac{y^2}{4}}\,\mathbf{I} = \mathbf{0} \quad \text{or} \quad \mathbf{E} - \frac{y}{2}\mathbf{I} - \sqrt{x + \frac{y^2}{4}}\,\mathbf{I} = \mathbf{0}$$

if (2.4) is true. But this is impossible because $\mathbf{E}$ and $\mathbf{I}$ were chosen to be linearly independent. Hence, $x + \frac{y^2}{4} < 0$.

Now, for convenience, we define a new vector $\mathbf{E}^*$ by the relation

$$\sqrt{-\left(x + \frac{y^2}{4}\right)}\,\mathbf{E}^* = \mathbf{E} - \frac{y}{2}\mathbf{I}.$$

We use (2.3) to obtain the relation

$$\mathbf{E}^* \otimes \mathbf{E}^* = -\,\mathbf{I}. \tag{2.5}$$

We may argue that $\mathbf{E}^*$ and $\mathbf{I}$ are linearly independent because if $\mathbf{E}^* = k\mathbf{I}$, we would have

$$k\mathbf{I} \otimes k\mathbf{I} = -\,\mathbf{I} \quad \text{or} \quad k^2\mathbf{I} = -\,\mathbf{I}.$$

This is impossible because, k being real, $k^2 \geq 0$.

Every vector of $V_2(R)$ can be expressed as a linear combination of $\mathbf{I}$ and $\mathbf{E}^*$. Moreover, if

$$\begin{aligned} \mathbf{X} &= a\mathbf{I} + b\mathbf{E}^* \\ \mathbf{Y} &= c\mathbf{I} + d\mathbf{E}^*, \end{aligned}$$

we have, for multiplication in F,

$$\begin{aligned} \mathbf{X} \otimes \mathbf{Y} &= (a\mathbf{I} + b\mathbf{E}^*) \otimes (c\mathbf{I} + d\mathbf{E}^*) \\ &= (ac - bd)\mathbf{I} + (ad + bc)\mathbf{E}^*. \end{aligned} \tag{2.6}$$

We compare (2.6) with the multiplication of complex numbers when $[a, b]$ is written as $a[1, 0] + b[0, 1]$ and $[c, d]$ is written as $c[1, 0] + d[0, 1]$. Then

$$\begin{aligned} [a, b] \cdot [c, d] &= (a[1, 0] + b[0, 1]) \cdot (c[1, 0] + d[0, 1]) \\ &= (ac - bd)[1, 0] + (ad + bc)[0, 1]. \end{aligned} \tag{2.7}$$

Now if we associate with every vector $\mathbf{X}$ the ordered pair of its components relative to the basis $\mathbf{I}$ and $\mathbf{E}^*$, we have a one-to-one mapping T ($\mathbf{X} \xrightarrow{\mathrm{T}} [a, b]$), from our new field F to the complex number field C. Moreover, if

$$\begin{aligned} \mathbf{X} &\xrightarrow{\mathrm{T}} [a, b] \\ \mathbf{Y} &\xrightarrow{\mathrm{T}} [c, d], \end{aligned}$$

then

$$\begin{aligned} \mathbf{X} + \mathbf{Y} &\xrightarrow{\mathrm{T}} [a, b] + [c, d] \\ \mathbf{X} \otimes \mathbf{Y} &\xrightarrow{\mathrm{T}} [a, b][c, d], \end{aligned}$$

the latter relation being the interpretation of (2.6). These relations show that F and the complex number field C are *isomorphic*.

Example 1. We suggest that the student consider the multiplication

$$[p, q] \otimes [r, s] = [-\,pr - 2qs + 2ps + 2rq,\ -\,pr + ps + rq]$$

and show that the resulting system is a field F. Moreover, it would be of considerable value if the student followed through in detail the arguments of the previous proof for this specific multiplication.

The idea of providing a multiplication for vectors of $V_2(R)$ to obtain a field F presents the interesting prospect that this might be done for any $V_n(R)$ with $n > 2$. Specifically, the question becomes,

"Is it possible to define a multiplication for vectors of $V_n(R)$ $(n \geq 3)$, also satisfying the relation $(t\mathbf{X})(r\mathbf{Y}) = (tr)(\mathbf{X} \cdot \mathbf{Y})$, such that the resulting algebraic system is a field F?"

The answer is No, but unfortunately the proof is far beyond the scope of this text. However, the question itself and the concepts involved allow us to illustrate in a simple way the continually growing nature of mathematics.

An algebraic system which is first a vector space $V_n(R)$ and for which a multiplication of vectors is defined such that $(t\mathbf{X})(r\mathbf{Y}) = (tr)(\mathbf{X} \cdot \mathbf{Y})$ and such that M1 holds as well as both distributive laws is called an *algebra* over the real field R. If we also insist on a unity element 1 and, for any nonzero vector $\mathbf{A}$, on the existence of unique vectors $\mathbf{A}_R$ and $\mathbf{A}_L$ such that

$$\mathbf{A}\mathbf{A}_R = \mathbf{A}_L\mathbf{A} = 1,$$

we say that we have a *division algebra over R*. Note that no assumption of the associative or commutative laws of multiplication is made.

In 1940, it was shown by a Swiss mathematician, H. H. Hopf, that, if it were possible to define a division algebra on $V_n(R)$, n must be of the form 2^k, where k is some integer. It had long been known that for $k = 1$ the complex number field existed. Moreover, in the 1840's an Irish mathematician, W. R. Hamilton, had determined a division algebra for $k = 2$. Later in the same decade, an English mathematician, A. Cayley, succeeded in determining a division algebra for $k = 3$. This was where the problem remained until Hopf's result although a considerable number of mathematicians had attempted to construct other division algebras over the real field R.

Considerable activity has been devoted to an attempt to solve the problem for $k = 4$ and to define a division algebra for $V_{16}(R)$. It was not until 1955 that a Japanese mathematician, H. Toda, showed that there is no division algebra for $V_{16}(R)$. Subsequently, the work of J. F. Adams (English), M. A. Kervaire (Swiss), and R. Bott and J. W. Milnor (American) has led to a proof of the impossibility of constructing a division algebra for $V_{2^k}(R)$ for $k \geq 4$.

We have mentioned before that n-tuples of rational numbers $[x_1, x_2, \cdots, x_n]$ form a vector space over the rational number field. The question of the existence of *rational division algebras*, that is, the possibility of defining a multiplication for rational n-tuples that satisfies (2.1) and in which nonzero vectors have unique inverses, has an entirely different answer. This is illustrated by Exercise 2.

EXERCISES

1. Show that there is no *associative division algebra* (that is, one satisfying M2) definable for $V_3(R)$ by completing the following steps:

(a) Prove that a basis for $V_3(R)$ may always be chosen to consist of the unity element $\mathbf{I}$ for our assumed multiplication and two other elements $\mathbf{E}_1$ and $\mathbf{E}_2$ satisfying $\mathbf{E}_1{}^2 = \mathbf{E}_2{}^2 = -\mathbf{I}$. (One will need here the result that any cubic equation $ax^3 + bx^2 + cx + d = 0$ with real coefficients has a real root.)

(b) Show that $\mathbf{E}_1\mathbf{E}_2 = A\mathbf{I} + b\mathbf{E}_1 + c\mathbf{E}_2$ implies that $b^2 = -1$.

2. Assuming the result from elementary number theory that, for any three rational numbers a, b, c not all zero,

$$4a^3 + 2b^3 + c^3 - 6abc \neq 0,$$

show that a multiplication

$$[a, b, c] \otimes [x, y, z] = [az + by + cx, 2ax + cy + bz, 2bx + 2ay + cz]$$

defined for all rational triples defines a division algebra over the rational field.

3. Show that there is no field F satisfying (2.1) attainable by defining a multiplication for the vectors of $V_2(C)$.

4. The division algebra Q mentioned in this section for $V_4(R)$ may be defined in the following manner: In order to comply with the usual notation we let $\mathbf{E} = \mathbf{E}_1$, $\mathbf{I} = \mathbf{E}_2$, $\mathbf{J} = \mathbf{E}_3$, $\mathbf{K} = \mathbf{E}_4$, where $\{\mathbf{E}_i\}$ are the natural basis vectors of $V_4(R)$. Every element of $V_4(R)$ may then be written

$$\mathbf{X} = a_0\mathbf{E} + a_1\mathbf{I} + a_2\mathbf{J} + a_3\mathbf{K}, \qquad a_i \in R.$$

In order to define the product of $\mathbf{X}$ and

$$\mathbf{Y} = b_0\mathbf{E} + b_1\mathbf{I} + b_2\mathbf{J} + b_3\mathbf{K},$$

merely assume that $\mathbf{E}$, $\mathbf{I}$, $\mathbf{J}$, $\mathbf{K}$ commute with all scalars and that both distributive laws are valid. Next, define $\mathbf{E}$ to be the unit element and let $\mathbf{I}^2 = \mathbf{J}^2 = \mathbf{K}^2 = -\mathbf{E}$, $\mathbf{IJ} = -\mathbf{JI} = \mathbf{K}$, $\mathbf{JK} = -\mathbf{KJ} = \mathbf{I}$, $\mathbf{KI} = -\mathbf{IK} = \mathbf{J}$.

(a) Show that the inverse of the element $\mathbf{X}$ is

$$\frac{a_0\mathbf{E} - a_1\mathbf{I} - a_2\mathbf{J} - a_3\mathbf{K}}{a_0{}^2 + a_1{}^2 + a_2{}^2 + a_3{}^2}.$$

(b) Verify the associative law for this algebra.

(c) Why is this algebra not a field?

This algebra is called the *real quaternion algebra*. The multiplication should be compared with that defined in the sixth example of a group (the quaternion group) in §5 of Chapter 7 (page 208).

3. Polynomial Rings

As in the case of complex numbers, we have assumed that the student is familiar with the addition and multiplication of polynomials, $a_0 + a_1x + a_2x^2 + \cdots + a_nx^n$, with real coefficients. A number of properties of polynomials will find later applications in our discussion of canonical forms for matrices. We now wish to look at polynomials from a somewhat formal point of view. Moreover, with future applications in mind, we will replace the real field R by any subfield F of the complex numbers; besides C itself, the most important subfields for the student to keep in mind are the rational field Ra and the real field R.

Let us consider a set S whose elements are infinite sequences of numbers from a field $F \subseteq C$, $[a_0, a_1, a_2, \cdots]$, such that only a finite number of terms are nonzero. We define equality, addition, scalar multiplication (by a number $t \in F$), and the product of elements of S as follows:

$$(3.1)\quad \begin{cases} \text{(i)}\ [a_0, a_1, a_2, \cdots] = [b_0, b_1, b_2, \cdots] \quad \text{if } a_i = b_i \text{ for } i = 0, 1, 2, \cdots; \\ \text{(ii)}\ [a_0, a_1, a_2, \cdots] + [b_0, b_1, b_2, \cdots] \\ \qquad\qquad = [a_0 + b_0, a_1 + b_1, a_2 + b_2, \cdots]; \\ \text{(iii)}\ t[a_0, a_1, a_2, \cdots] = [ta_0, ta_1, ta_2, \cdots]; \\ \text{(iv)}\ [a_0, a_1, a_2, \cdots][b_0, b_1, b_2, \cdots] = [c_0, c_1, c_2, \cdots], \\ \qquad \text{where } c_i = a_0b_i + a_1b_{i-1} + a_2b_{i-2} + \cdots + a_ib_0 \\ \qquad \text{for } i = 0, 1, 2, \cdots. \end{cases}$$

Different algebraic systems can be formed from the elements of S; thus,

(a) The set S forms a *vector space over* F under the definitions (i), (ii), and (iii) of (3.1) for the elements of S.

(b) The set S forms a *commutative ring with identity* containing a subset isomorphic to F under the definitions (i), (ii), and (iv) of (3.1).

(c) The set S forms an *algebra over* F under the definitions (i), (ii), (iii), and (iv) of (3.1).

The detailed verification of all the postulates for the different algebraic systems defined for S is somewhat lengthy. Fortunately, the proof that the elements of S satisfy postulates A1, A2, A3, A4, and A5 under addition (+) need be done but once for all three algebraic systems. We shall omit this verification as it closely parallels the proof for $V_n(R)$. The element $[0, 0, \cdots, 0, \cdots]$ is the zero element and will be denoted by 0. The negative of an element $[a_0, a_1, a_2, \cdots]$ is, of course, $[-a_0, -a_1, -a_2, \cdots]$.

When S is considered as a *vector space over* F, there still remains the verification of postulates S1, S2, S3, S4, and S5 (Chapter 3, § 1). Again, we shall omit this verification, as it closely parallels a similar proof for $V_n(R)$, and merely point out features that will be useful in our identification of the algebra in (c) with polynomials.

It will be convenient to use the notation

$$[a_0, a_1, \cdots, a_n, 0, 0, \cdots]$$

to denote an element of S whose last nonzero component is a_n. This last nonzero component must certainly exist because there are only a finite number of nonzero components in every element of S.

It is easy to see that

$$(3.2)\quad \begin{aligned}[a_0, a_1, \cdots, a_n, 0, 0, \cdots] &= a_0[1, 0, 0, \cdots] + a_1[0, 1, 0, 0, \cdots] \\ &\quad + \cdots + a_n[0, \cdots, 0, \underset{\substack{\uparrow \\ n\text{TH COMPONENT}}}{1}, 0, 0, \cdots].\end{aligned}$$

An element of S of the form

$$\mathbf{E}_i = [0, \cdots, 0, 1, 0, 0, \cdots],$$

for $i = 1, 2, \cdots$, whose only nonzero component is a 1 in the ith position, is an obvious generalization of a natural basis vector of $V_n(R)$. Any finite number of the $\mathbf{E}_i$ are linearly independent (Why?), and from (3.2) we see that every element of S can be written as a linear combination of the $\{\mathbf{E}_i\}$. These last two sentences comprise the sense in which we say that the $\{\mathbf{E}_i\}$ are a "basis" for S.

For convenience in future computations, we define another infinite set of vectors by

$$\mathbf{X}_i = \mathbf{E}_{i+1},$$

for $i = 0, 1, 2, \cdots$. Then every vector of S can be written

$$(3.2)'\quad [a_0, a_1, \cdots, a_n, 0, 0, \cdots] = a_0\mathbf{X}_0 + a_1\mathbf{X}_1 + \cdots + a_n\mathbf{X}_n.$$

When S is viewed as a *ring*, we do not have scalar multiplication to contend with but we have yet to verify postulates M1, M2, M3, and M5 for products and the distributive laws. The identity element is

$$\mathbf{X}_0 = [1, 0, 0, \cdots].$$

In order to verify closure (postulate M1), we merely note that in the product

$$[a_0, a_1, \cdots, a_n, 0, 0, \cdots][b_0, b_1, \cdots, b_m, 0, 0, \cdots] = [c_0, c_1, c_2, \cdots],$$

c_{m+n} is the last nonzero component. (Why?) Hence the product of two elements of S is again an element of S.

Example 1. For the product

$$\begin{aligned}[1, 2, 3, 0, 0, \cdots][2, -1, 1, 0, 0, \cdots] &= [1\cdot 2, 1(-1) + 2\cdot 2, 1\cdot 1 + 2(-1) + 3\cdot 2, \\ &\quad 1\cdot 0 + 2\cdot 1 + 3(-1) + 0\cdot 2, \\ &\quad 1\cdot 0 + 2\cdot 0 + 3\cdot 1 + 0(-1) + 0\cdot 2, 0, 0, \cdots] \\ &= [2, 3, 5, -1, 3, 0, 0, \cdots],\end{aligned}$$

we see that we have more of a bookkeeping problem than any difficulty.

The verifications that products are associative (postulate M2), commutative (postulate M5), and distributive are being left to the student in the exercises.

We see that

$$(3.3)\qquad \begin{aligned}&[a_0, 0, 0, \cdots][b_0, b_1, \cdots, b_m, 0, 0, \cdots]\\ &\qquad = [a_0b_0, a_0b_1, \cdots, a_0b_m, 0, 0, \cdots],\end{aligned}$$

and in particular

$$[a_0, 0, 0, \cdots][b_0, 0, 0, \cdots] = [a_0b_0, 0, 0, \cdots].$$

Since we also have

$$[a_0, 0, 0, \cdots] + [b_0, 0, 0, \cdots] = [a_0 + b_0, 0, 0, \cdots],$$

it should be clear that the mapping

$$[a, 0, 0, \cdots] \xrightarrow{\mathrm{T}} a$$

establishes an isomorphism between elements of S of the form $[a, 0, 0, \cdots]$ and the field F; that is, the mapping T is one-to-one and preserves sums and products. Henceforth, we shall accept a_i as an abbreviation of $[a_i, 0, 0, \cdots]$, and we can think of the ring S as containing the field F.

When S is considered as an *algebra over* F, we have little left to verify. All the definitions of (3.1) apply and we have merely to check to see that scalar multiplication behaves correctly with respect to products; that is, we must check (2.1) of the preceding section or $(t\mathbf{X}) \cdot (r\mathbf{Y}) = (tr)(\mathbf{X} \cdot \mathbf{Y})$, where $t, r \in F$ and $\mathbf{X}, \mathbf{Y} \in S$. However, we have already identified $[a, 0, 0, \cdots]$ with a, and equation (3.3) can be used to complete this verification.

From now on, we will consider S as an algebra over F. The element $\mathbf{X}_1 = [0, 1, 0, 0, \cdots]$ plays an important role in the products of elements of S. We have,

$$[0, 1, 0, 0, \cdots][0, 1, 0, 0, \cdots] = [0, 0, 1, 0, 0, \cdots] \quad \text{or} \quad \mathbf{X}_1^2 = \mathbf{X}_2.$$

More generally, $\mathbf{X}_1^k = \mathbf{X}_k$, k an integer ≥ 1. Thus, we can rewrite (3.2)′ as

$$[a_0, a_1, \cdots, a_n, 0, 0, \cdots] = a_0 + a_1\mathbf{X}_1 + a_2\mathbf{X}_1^2 + \cdots + a_n\mathbf{X}_1^n.$$

Example 2. Let us repeat the product of Example 1 in the new notation.

$$\begin{aligned}(1 + 2\mathbf{X}_1 + 3\mathbf{X}_1^2)(2 - \mathbf{X}_1 + \mathbf{X}_1^2) = {}& 2 + 4\mathbf{X}_1 + 6\mathbf{X}_1^2\\ & \quad - \mathbf{X}_1 - 2\mathbf{X}_1^2 - 3\mathbf{X}_1^3\\ & \qquad\qquad \mathbf{X}_1^2 + 2\mathbf{X}_1^3 + 3\mathbf{X}_1^4\\ \hline & 2 + 3\mathbf{X}_1 + 5\mathbf{X}_1^2 - \mathbf{X}_1^3 + 3\mathbf{X}_1^4\end{aligned}$$

When the elements of S are written in the form $a_0 + a_1\mathbf{X}_1 + \cdots + a_n\mathbf{X}_1^n$, the student will readily note that the definitions of (3.1) comprise the familiar rules of equality, addition, and multiplication of polynomials with the element $\mathbf{X}_1$ of S playing the role of x in $a_0 + a_1x + a_2x^2 + \cdots + a_nx^n$.

We will now identify the element $\mathbf{X}_1$ of S with x and denote S, as an algebra, by $F[x]$. We call $F[x]$ a *polynomial ring* (or algebra) *over the field* F. The elements of $F[x]$ now appear in the more familiar form as *polynomials*

$$a_0 + a_1x + \cdots + a_nx^n,$$

with the *coefficients* $a_i \in F$. The symbol x is often called an *indeterminate*. Frequently, an abbreviation such as $p(x)$ will be used for an element of $F[x]$.

Example 3. The polynomial $p(x) = 1 + \frac{1}{2}x + 3x^2$ is an element of $Ra[x]$ but $q(x) = \sqrt{2} - x + (3 + \sqrt{2})x^2$ is not. On the other hand, both $p(x)$ and $q(x)$ are in $R[x]$.

EXERCISES

1. The set S of this section, as a vector space, does not have a finite basis. A subset X of S is said to be a basis of S if any finite number of elements from X are linearly independent and every element of S can be written as a linear combination of a finite number of elements from X. Show that $X = \{\mathbf{X}_0, \mathbf{X}_1, \mathbf{X}_2, \cdots\}$ is a basis for S.

2. Show that

$$[1, 2, -1, 1, 0, 0, \cdots][1, 0, 3, 0, 0, \cdots] = [1, 0, 3, 0, 0, \cdots][1, 2, -1, 1, 0, 0, \cdots].$$

3. Prove, in general, that the product of elements of S (as defined by (3.1), (iv)) is commutative.

4. Show that $(\mathbf{AB})\mathbf{C} = \mathbf{A}(\mathbf{BC})$ for the elements $\mathbf{A} = [1, 0, -1, 0, 0, \cdots]$, $\mathbf{B} = [0, 1, 2, 0, 0, \cdots]$, $\mathbf{C} = [1, -1, 2, 0, 0, \cdots]$ of S.

5. Prove, in general, that the product of elements of S is associative. *Hint:* If $\mathbf{A} = [a_0, a_1, a_2, \cdots]$, $\mathbf{B} = [b_0, b_1, b_2, \cdots]$, and $\mathbf{C} = [c_0, c_1, c_2, \cdots]$, then show that the mth component of $(\mathbf{AB})\mathbf{C}$ and $\mathbf{A}(\mathbf{BC})$ is $\left(\sum_{i+j+k=m} a_ib_jc_k\right)$.

6. Verify the distributive laws for S as a ring.

7. How would you show that the relation $p(x)q(x) = 0$ for elements $p(x)$ and $q(x)$ of $F[x]$ implies either $p(x) = 0$ or $q(x) = 0$? Note that the proof for a field in Chapter 1, §4, is not valid. (A proof of this exercise is suggested at the beginning of the next section.)

4. Division Algorithm for Polynomials

We are primarily interested in developing a theory of factorization of polynomials over F (where F is normally the reals or the rationals) comparable to the factoring of an integer into prime factors. We proceed to develop the necessary tools.

The *degree* of the polynomial $p(x) = a_0 + a_1x + \cdots + a_mx^m$ is defined to be m if $m > 0$. If $m = 0$ and $a_0 \neq 0$, the degree is defined as 0. The zero polynomial, $p(x) = 0$, has no degree. We see from (3.1) that if $p(x)$ and $q(x) = b_0 + \cdots + b_nx^n$ have degrees, then so does $p(x) \cdot q(x)$, and the degree of $p(x) \cdot q(x)$ is the sum of the degrees of $p(x)$ and $q(x)$; the coefficient of x^{m+n} in $p(x) \cdot q(x)$ is $a_mb_n \neq 0$. The student should apply this result to show that the product of two nonzero polynomials is nonzero.

The familiar process of dividing one polynomial by another one is formalized in the following theorem:

THEOREM 4.1 (DIVISION ALGORITHM). *Let $f(x)$ and $g(x) \neq 0$ be two polynomials of $F[x]$. We can find two new polynomials of $F[x]$, $q(x)$ (quotient) and $r(x)$ (remainder), such that*

$$f(x) = q(x)g(x) + r(x),$$

where $r(x)$ is either zero or the degree of $r(x)$ is less than the degree of $g(x)$. Moreover, $q(x)$ and $r(x)$ are uniquely determined by $f(x)$ and $g(x)$.

Proof. If the degree of $f(x)$ is less than the degree of $g(x)$ or if $f(x) = 0$, take $q(x) = 0$, $r(x) = f(x)$. If $f(x)$ and $g(x)$ are both of degree zero: $f(x) = a_0$, $g(x) = b_0 \neq 0$; then $q(x) = a_0/b_0$ and $r(x) = 0$.

Now we may proceed by induction. Specifically, if

$$f(x) = a_0 + a_1x + \cdots + a_mx^m, \quad g(x) = b_0 + b_1x + \cdots + b_nx^n,$$

and $m \geq n$, we assume the existence of a unique quotient and remainder for the division of all polynomials $f_1(x)$ of degree less than m by any polynomial $g(x)$. Form the polynomial:

$$f_1(x) = f(x) - a_mb_n^{-1}x^{m-n}g(x). \tag{4.1}$$

The coefficient of x^m in $f_1(x)$ is $a_m - (a_mb_n^{-1})b_n = 0$; no coefficient of x^k for $k > m$ appears in $f_1(x)$; hence $f_1(x)$ has degree less than m. By our induction hypothesis, we may find $q_1(x)$ and $r(x)$ in $F[x]$ such that

$$f_1(x) = q_1(x)g(x) + r(x),$$

where $r(x)$ is zero or of degree less than that of $g(x)$. Now, substituting for $f_1(x)$ in (4.1):

$$q_1(x)g(x) + r(x) = f(x) - a_mb_n^{-1}x^{m-n}g(x),$$

or

$$f(x) = (a_mb_n^{-1}x^{m-n} + q_1(x))g(x) + r(x),$$

and we have shown the existence of at least one polynomial

$$q(x) = (a_mb_n^{-1}x^{m-n} + q_1(x))$$

and a polynomial $r(x)$ satisfying the division algorithm.

Now we need to show the uniqueness of $q(x)$ and $r(x)$. Suppose that we have two results:

$$f(x) = q(x)g(x) + r(x)$$
$$f(x) = q^*(x)g(x) + r^*(x).$$

Subtracting:

$$(q^*(x) - q(x))g(x) = r(x) - r^*(x). \tag{4.2}$$

If $q^*(x) \neq q(x)$, the degree of the polynomial on the left-hand side of (4.2) is at least as great as n since the degree of $q^*(x) - q(x)$ will be at least zero. Since the degree of the right-hand side cannot be as large as n, the result is impossible. Then $q^*(x) - q(x) = 0$; hence $r(x) - r^*(x) = 0$. Therefore the two results are identical; the division algorithm gives a unique result.

Example 1. Let $f(x) = 3 - 2x + 4x^2 - x^3 + 2x^4$, $g(x) = 1 - x + x^2$. Then it is easy to see that

$$(3 - 2x + 4x^2 - x^3 + 2x^4) = (3 + x + x^2)(1 - x + x^2),$$

and the remainder $r(x)$ is zero.

If $f(x)$ and $g(x) \neq 0$ are two polynomials such that upon division of $f(x)$ by $g(x)$ the remainder $r(x) = 0$, we have the relation

$$f(x) = q(x)g(x). \tag{4.3}$$

In this case we say that $f(x)$ is a *multiple* of $g(x)$, or $g(x)$ *divides* $f(x)$, or $g(x)$ is a *divisor* or *factor* of $f(x)$ in $F[x]$.

DEFINITION 4.1. *Let $f_1(x)$ and $f_2(x)$ be two polynomials of $F[x]$ not both zero. A polynomial of $F[x]$ that divides $f_1(x)$ and $f_2(x)$ is called a common divisor of $f_1(x)$ and $f_2(x)$. A polynomial $d(x)$ of $F[x]$ is called a* GREATEST COMMON DIVISOR (GCD) *of $f_1(x)$ and $f_2(x)$ if*

(i) *$d(x)$ is a common divisor of $f_1(x)$ and $f_2(x)$;*
(ii) *every common divisor of $f_1(x)$ and $f_2(x)$ divides $d(x)$.*

It is not clear that a GCD exists for every two polynomials of $F[x]$. We shall demonstrate this fact and leave to the student the generalization of a GCD for any finite number of polynomials.

Let $f_1(x)$ and $f_2(x)$ be two polynomials not both zero and consider the set S^* of all polynomials of the form $p_1(x)f_1(x) + p_2(x)f_2(x)$, where $p_1(x)$ and $p_2(x)$ are arbitrary polynomials of $F[x]$. Certainly the set S^* contains some nonzero polynomials; pick one of least possible degree:

$$d(x) = p_1^*(x)f_1(x) + p_2^*(x)f_2(x). \tag{4.4}$$

We can show that $d(x)$ is a GCD of $f_1(x)$ and $f_2(x)$.

First, $d(x)$ must divide $f_1(x)$, for if not, $f_1(x) = q_1(x)d(x) + r_1(x)$, where $r_1(x)$ is not zero but is of degree less than that of $d(x)$. But

$$\begin{aligned} r_1(x) &= -q_1(x)[p_1^*(x)f_1(x) + p_2^*(x)f_2(x)] + f_1(x) \\ &= [1 - q_1(x)p_1^*(x)]f_1(x) + [-q_1(x)p_2^*(x)]f_2(x), \end{aligned}$$

and thus $r_1(x)$ is in S^*, contradicting the minimality of the degree of $d(x)$.

Similarly it can be shown that $d(x)$ divides $f_2(x)$. We have then satisfied condition (i) of the definition of a GCD.

Next suppose $d_1(x)$ is any common divisor of $f_1(x)$ and $f_2(x)$; in fact, let $f_1(x) = d_1(x)f_1^*(x)$ and $f_2(x) = d_1(x)f_2^*(x)$. Then

$$\begin{aligned} d(x) &= p_1^*(x)d_1(x)f_1^*(x) + p_2^*(x)d_1(x)f_2^*(x) \\ &= d_1(x)[p_1^*(x)f_1^*(x) + p_2^*(x)f_2^*(x)]. \end{aligned}$$

That is, $d(x)$ is a multiple of $d_1(x)$. Thus both conditions for a GCD are fulfilled by $d(x)$.

Of course the GCD of two polynomials is not unique. If $d(x)$ is one GCD, $cd(x)$ is another, where c is an arbitrary element of F. This is the only latitude allowed since, if $d_1(x)$ and $d_2(x)$ are both GCD's of $f_1(x)$ and $f_2(x)$, condition (ii) implies that each divides the other:

$$d_1(x) = m(x)d_2(x); \quad d_2(x) = n(x)d_1(x),$$

or

$$d_1(x) = m(x)n(x)d_1(x), \quad [1 - m(x)n(x)]d_1(x) = 0.$$

Since the product of two nonzero polynomials is nonzero, we conclude that $m(x)n(x) - 1 = 0$ because $d_1(x) \neq 0$ and the assumption that $m(x)n(x) - 1 \neq 0$ would lead to a contradiction. Thus the sum of the degrees of $m(x)$ and $n(x)$ is 0 so the degree of each must be 0; that is, $m(x)$ and $n(x)$ are both elements of F.

Two polynomials which are multiples of one another and, by the argument just given, have a quotient which is an element of F are called *associates*. If $p(x) = a_0 + a_1x + a_2x^2 + \cdots + a_mx^m \neq 0$, there is precisely one associate of $p(x)$ that has 1 as the coefficient of x^m; namely $a_m^{-1}p(x)$. Such a polynomial is called *monic;* there is a unique *monic* GCD of every pair of polynomials that are not both zero. To summarize, we state the following theorem:

THEOREM 4.2. *If $f_1(x)$ and $f_2(x)$ are any two polynomials of $F[x]$ which are not both zero, they have a greatest common divisor. Any two greatest common divisors of $f_1(x)$ and $f_2(x)$ are multiples of each other; their ratio is an element of F. Any greatest common divisor $d(x)$ may be written in the form:*

$$d(x) = p_1^*(x)f_1(x) + p_2^*(x)f_2(x),$$

where $p_1^*(x)$ and $p_2^*(x)$ are polynomials of $F[x]$.

The proof given for Theorem 4.2 is a *nonconstructive existence* proof. The existence of $d(x)$ was demonstrated but no practicable or even possible method was given to find $d(x)$. We cannot really look over the infinite collection of members of S^* and select one of the minimum degree. In special cases it may be possible to select a reasonable-looking member of S^* and then, by other reasoning, *prove* that no smaller degree can arise than that of the selected polynomial; but no general prescription exists.

There is available an alternate proof of the existence of a GCD that is *constructive* in that it provides a method of computing the GCD in a finite number of steps. We shall state the result and leave the formal proof for the exercises.

THEOREM 4.3 (EUCLID'S ALGORITHM). *Let $f_1(x)$ and $f_2(x)$ be two polynomials of $F[x]$ with degree $f_1(x) \geq$ degree $f_2(x) > 0$. Let*

$$\begin{array}{llll} f_1(x) & = q_1(x)f_2(x) + r_2(x), & & 0 < \text{degree } r_2(x) < \text{degree } f_2(x), \\ f_2(x) & = q_2(x)r_2(x) + r_3(x), & & 0 < \text{degree } r_3(x) < \text{degree } r_2(x), \\ r_2(x) & = q_3(x)r_3(x) + r_4(x), & & 0 < \text{degree } r_4(x) < \text{degree } r_3(x), \\ \cdots & \cdots & & \cdots \\ r_{k-2}(x) & = q_{k-1}(x)r_{k-1}(x) + r_k(x), & & 0 \leq \text{degree } r_k(x) < \text{degree } r_{k-1}(x), \\ r_{k-1}(x) & = q_k(x)r_k(x), & & \\ r_{k+1}(x) & = 0. & & \end{array}$$

Then $r_k(x)$ is a GCD of $f_1(x)$ and $f_2(x)$.

Example 2. We will find a GCD of

$$\begin{aligned} f_1(x) &= -2 - 3x + x^2 + 3x^3 + x^4, \\ f_2(x) &= -8 - 4x + 2x^2 + x^3. \end{aligned}$$

Omitting the details, we state for the student the values of $q_i(x)$ and $r_i(x)$ obtained by applying Theorem 4.3.

$$\begin{array}{ll} q_1(x) = (1 + x), & r_2(x) = 6 + 9x + 3x^2; \\ q_2(x) = (-\tfrac{1}{3} + \tfrac{1}{3}x), & r_3(x) = (-6 - 3x); \\ q_3(x) = (-1 - x), & r_4(x) = 0. \end{array}$$

Thus, $(-6 - 3x)$ or the unique monic polynomial $2 + x$ is a GCD of $f_1(x)$ and $f_2(x)$.

By rewriting $f_2(x) = q_2(x)r_2(x) + r_3(x)$ as $r_3(x) = f_2(x) - q_2(x)r_2(x)$ and then substituting $f_1(x) - q_1(x)f_2(x)$ for $r_2(x)$ we have

$$\begin{aligned} r_3(x) &= f_2(x) - q_2(x)[f_1(x) - q_1(x)f_2(x)] \\ &= -q_2(x)f_1(x) + (1 + q_2(x)q_1(x))f_2(x). \end{aligned}$$

Thus we have expressed the GCD of $f_1(x)$ and $f_2(x)$ as stated in Theorem 4.2. A similar reversal of the division steps with proper substitution is possible to obtain the GCD of any two polynomials $f_1(x)$ and $f_2(x)$ as an expression

$$p_1^*(x)f_1(x) + p_2^*(x)f_2(x) = r_k(x) = d(x).$$

EXERCISES

1. Show that the degree of the sum of two nonzero polynomials is equal to or less than the larger of the degrees of the individual summands when the sum is nonzero.

2. Find the quotient and remainder when the division algorithm is applied to the following pairs of polynomials:

(a) $1 + (\sqrt{2} + \sqrt{3})x + x^2$ divided by $x + \sqrt{3}$
(b) $1 - x^n$ divided by $-1 + x$
(c) $1 + x + 2x^2 + 4x^3 - x^4$ divided by $1 - 2x + x^2 + x^3$
(d) $3 - 5x - 5x^2 + 5x^3 + 3x^4$ divided by $-2 + x + x^2$

3. Find the GCD of the following pairs of polynomials:

(a) $1 - x^2$ and $2 + (2 + \sqrt{2})x + \sqrt{2}x^2$
(b) $1 - 4x + 2x^2 - x^3$ and $1 - x^2 + x^4$
(c) $2 + 2x + 3x^2 + x^3 + x^4$ and $-2 - x^2 + 2x^3 + x^5$
(d) $45 - 12x + 2x^2 - 4x^3 + x^4$ and $-12 + 4x - 12x^2 + 4x^3$

4. For each of the parts of Exercise 3, express the GCD in the form $d(x) = p_1(x)f_1(x) + p_2(x)f_2(x)$.

5. In the notation of Theorem 4.3, prove that a GCD of $f_1(x)$ and $f_2(x)$ is a GCD of $f_2(x)$ and $r_2(x)$. Now show that a GCD of $f_2(x)$ and $r_2(x)$ is a GCD of $r_2(x)$ and $r_3(x)$. Finally show (by iterating this procedure) that the process terminates and $r_k(x)$ is a GCD of $f_1(x)$ and $f_2(x)$.

6. Define a GCD of a finite set of polynomials $\{f_1(x), f_2(x), \cdots, f_n(x)\}$, not all zero. Prove that this GCD exists.

Hint: From the set S^* of all polynomials $p_1(x)f_1(x) + \cdots + p_n(x)f_n(x)$ choose one of smallest degree for $d(x)$.

5. Factorization of Polynomials

A polynomial $p(x) \in F[x]$ is said to be *reducible* over F if there exist polynomials $p_1(x)$ and $p_2(x)$ of degree > 0 in $F[x]$ such that $p(x) = p_1(x) \cdot p_2(x)$. Otherwise, $p(x)$ is said to be *irreducible* over F.

The field F plays a dominant role in the reducibility or irreducibility of a polynomial. For example, let $p(x) = 2 - x^2$ be a polynomial viewed first as an element of $R[x]$, then as an element of $Ra[x]$. We have $2 - x^2 = (\sqrt{2} - x)(\sqrt{2} + x)$, but neither $(\sqrt{2} - x)$ nor $(\sqrt{2} + x)$ is a polynomial of $Ra[x]$. Now if we were able to show that this is the only way to express $2 - x^2$ as the product of polynomials of degree 1 in $R[x]$, then we could conclude that $2 - x^2$ is *irreducible* over the rational field Ra. These details will be supplied later (Theorem 5.2); but for the present, note that $2 - x^2$ as a polynomial of $R[x]$ is reducible.

Two polynomials $f_1(x)$ and $f_2(x)$ are said to be *relatively prime* if any GCD of $f_1(x)$ and $f_2(x)$ is an element of F.

Theorem 4.2 asserts that, for relatively prime polynomials $f_1(x)$ and $f_2(x)$, it is possible to find polynomials $p_1(x)$ and $p_2(x)$ of $F[x]$ such that

$$1 = p_1(x)f_1(x) + p_2(x)f_2(x). \tag{5.1}$$

We shall make use of this property in the proof of the following theorem:

THEOREM 5.1. *If $p(x)$ is an irreducible polynomial over F and $p(x)$ divides $r(x) \cdot s(x)$, where $r(x)$ and $s(x)$ are elements of $F[x]$, then $p(x)$ divides either $r(x)$ or $s(x)$.*

Proof. Let us assume that $p(x)$ does not divide $r(x)$. Then $p(x)$ must be relatively prime to $r(x)$ because, if the GCD of $p(x)$ and $r(x)$ were $d(x)$, not an element of F, $p(x) = q(x)d(x)$ and $p(x)$ would be reducible.

Thus, we may apply (5.1) to obtain

$$1 = p_1(x)r(x) + p_2(x)p(x).$$

Now we multiply both sides by $s(x)$ to obtain

$$s(x) = p_1(x)r(x)s(x) + p_2(x)s(x)p(x).$$

Our hypothesis is that for some $q(x)$,

$$r(x) \cdot s(x) = q(x) \cdot p(x);$$

hence

$$s(x) = p_1(x)q(x)p(x) + p_2(x)s(x)p(x) = [p_1(x) \cdot q(x) + p_2(x) \cdot s(x)]p(x),$$

and so $p(x)$ divides $s(x)$.

THEOREM 5.2. *Let $p(x)$ be a polynomial of degree > 0 in $F[x]$. Then $p(x)$ may be expressed as a product*

$$p(x) = ap_1(x)p_2(x) \cdots p_k(x),$$

where $p_i(x)$ are monic irreducible polynomials of $F[x]$ and a is an element of F. Except for the order, these factors are unique.

Proof. We prove our theorem by induction on the degree of $p(x)$. If $p(x)$ is of degree 1, then $p(x) = ax + b = a(x + a^{-1}b)$. The uniqueness of this expression is easily shown.

Now assume that $p(x)$ is of degree m. Our induction hypothesis is that every polynomial of degree $< m$ satisfies the theorem. If $p(x)$ is irreducible, we are through after factoring out the coefficient of the largest power of x as a. Otherwise $p(x)$ is reducible and is the product of two polynomials of lower degree; that is,

$$p(x) = q(x) \cdot q^*(x).$$

By induction

$$q(x) = a_1p_1(x)p_2(x) \cdots p_h(x),$$
$$q^*(x) = a_2p_{h+1}(x) \cdots p_k(x),$$

where a_1 and a_2 are contained in F and the $p_i(x)$ are monic irreducible polynomials. Thus,

$$p(x) = a_1a_2p_1(x)p_2(x) \cdots p_k(x),$$

and we have at least one factorization satisfying the conditions of our theorem.

The uniqueness of the factors remains to be shown. Let us assume that we have two factorizations of $p(x)$ into monic irreducible factors,

$$p(x) = ap_1(x)p_2(x) \cdots p_k(x),$$
$$p(x) = bq_1(x)q_2(x) \cdots q_r(x).$$

First, $a = b$ since each must be the coefficient of the highest power of x occurring in $p(x)$. We then have

$$p_1(x)p_2(x) \cdots p_k(x) = q_1(x)q_2(x) \cdots q_r(x). \tag{5.2}$$

From (5.2), we see that $p_1(x)$ divides $q_1(x)q_2(x) \cdots q_r(x)$, and from Theorem 5.2 we may argue that $p_1(x)$ must divide one of the $q_i(x)$. Actually, since both are monic they must be identical or $q_i(x)$ would be reducible. For convenience (renumbering if necessary) let $p_1(x) = q_1(x)$ so that

$$p_1(x)p_2(x) \cdots p_k(x) = p_1(x)q_2(x) \cdots q_r(x)$$

or

$$p_1(x)[p_2(x)p_3(x) \cdots p_k(x) - q_2(x)q_3(x) \cdots q_r(x)] = 0.$$

In the last expression $p_1(x) \neq 0$, and we may conclude that

$$p_2(x) \cdots p_k(x) = q_2(x) \cdots q_r(x).$$

We iterate the argument and, if $k < r$, we ultimately arrive at the situation

$$1 = q_{k+1}(x) \cdots q_r(x).$$

But then the factors $q_{k+1}(x), \cdots, q_r(x)$ must all be 1, and our proof is complete.

EXERCISE

Let $p(x)$ and $q(x)$ be polynomials of $F[x]$, where F is a proper subfield of C. Show that if $p(x)$ and $q(x)$ are relatively prime in $F[x]$, then they are relatively prime in $C[x]$.

6. Factorization of Polynomials in $C[x]$ and $R[x]$

We have restricted our discussion of polynomial rings to $F[x]$, where F is a subfield of the complex number field C. Our attention will now be directed to the particular cases in which F is either C or the real field R. Here we shall consider polynomials from a more familiar point of view. We replace the symbol x in the polynomial

$$p(x) = a_m x^m + a_{m-1}x^{m-1} + \cdots + a_1 x + a_0$$

of $F[x]$ by any complex number r and form

$$p(r) = a_m r^m + a_{m-1}r^{m-1} + \cdots + a_1 r + a_0.$$

If addition and multiplication are now considered to be those of the complex number field, we may determine the value $p(r)$. Thus, we think of $p(x)$ as a function with independent variable x whose domain of definition is the complex number field C. The change in the order of presenting the polynomial, that is, highest degree on the left, will remind us of this change of concept. It will also provide a slightly more convenient statement of some of the theorems to follow.

A complex number c, such that $p(c) = 0$, is called a *zero* of the polynomial $p(x)$ or a *root* of the algebraic equation

$$p(x) = a_m x^m + a_{m-1}x^{m-1} + \cdots + a_1 x + a_0 = 0.$$

In many texts, the expression "root of a polynomial" occurs. We shall normally use "zero of a polynomial" but "root of an equation."

Example 1. Let $p(x) = x^3 - 3x^2 + 4x - 2$. We find,

$$\begin{aligned} p(1) &= 1^3 - 3\cdot 1^2 + 4\cdot 1 - 2 = 0; \\ p(1+i) &= (1+i)^3 - 3(1+i)^2 + 4(1+i) - 2 \\ &= 1 + 3i - 3 - i - 6i + 4 + 4i - 2 = 0; \\ p(1-i) &= (1-i)^3 - 3(1-i)^2 + 4(1-i) - 2 = 0. \end{aligned}$$

Thus 1, $1 + i$, $1 - i$ are zeros of the polynomial $p(x)$ or roots of the equation $x^3 - 3x^2 + 4x - 2 = 0$.

If the reader were unaware of irrational real numbers, it would seem logical to say that the equation $x^2 - 2 = 0$ has no roots. Likewise, if the real numbers were the extent of the reader's knowledge of fields, the polynomial $p(x) = x^2 + 3$ would appear to have no zeros. In each case, the zeros of the polynomials $p(x) = x^2 - 2$, $p(x) = x^2 + 3$, are in a larger field. A natural question is, "Are there polynomials of $C[x]$ that have no zeros in the complex number field C?" For example, if

$$(6.1)\quad p(x) = (\sqrt{3} + i)x^3 - (2 + i)x - [(7 - 2\sqrt{3}) + (2 - 9\sqrt{3})i],$$

does $p(x)$ have a zero in C? If not, can a larger field be constructed that contains C and in which $p(x)$ will have a zero? The latter question need not be considered; we do not have to go on constructing fields indefinitely. The polynomial of (6.1) does have the zero $(\sqrt{3} - i)$. It illustrates the following theorem:

THEOREM 6.1. *Let $p(x)$ be an arbitrary polynomial of degree ≥ 1 of $C[x]$. Then there exists an element c of C such that $p(c) = 0$.*

This theorem is often given the title, "The Fundamental Theorem of Algebra." Although many proofs of this theorem are available, they involve concepts beyond the scope of this text. Therefore we shall assume its validity without proof. (The interested reader will find a proof of elementary nature in *The American Mathematical Monthly*, Volume 64 (1957), pages 582–585.)

If c is an arbitrary complex number, $p(x)$ a polynomial of $C[x]$, the division algorithm yields

$$p(x) = q(x)(x - c) + r,$$

where the remainder r is in C. We may determine r by setting $x = c$. Thus, $p(c) = q(c)(c - c) + r = r$. We substitute $r = p(c)$ in the equation above to obtain

$$p(x) = q(x)(x - c) + p(c). \tag{6.2}$$

The relation (6.2) is often called the Remainder Theorem. It yields the following information:

A polynomial $p(x)$ is divisible by $(x - c)$ if and only if c is a zero of $p(x)$.

We may use Theorem 6.1 and the observation above to determine the nature of irreducible polynomials of $C[x]$. First, the polynomials of degree 1 are certainly irreducible. Now, if $p(x)$ is a polynomial of degree > 1, it has a zero in C from Theorem 6.1. Hence $p(x)$ is divisible by $(x - c)$ and $p(x)$ is not irreducible. Therefore the only irreducible polynomials of $C[x]$ are the linear polynomials $p(x) = ax + b$.

The factorization of a polynomial as a product of irreducible polynomials (Theorem 5.2) gives the following theorem for polynomials of $C[x]$:

THEOREM 6.2. *Let $p(x) = a_m x^m + a_{m-1}x^{m-1} + \cdots + a_1 x + a_0$ be a polynomial of degree m of $C[x]$. Then $p(x)$ has the unique factorization (except for order of factors)*

$$p(x) = a_m(x - c_1)(x - c_2) \cdots (x - c_m),$$

where $c_1, c_2, \cdots, c_m$ are zeros of $p(x)$.

COROLLARY. *A polynomial of degree m has at most m zeros.*

Proof. The Corollary is verified by observing that if $c \neq c_1, c_2, \cdots, c_m$, $p(c) = a_m(c - c_1)(c - c_2) \cdots (c - c_m)$ is the product of nonzero elements and $p(c) \neq 0$.

An alternate proof of Theorem 6.2 can be given directly by the use of Theorem 6.1, the remark following (6.2), and induction. Thus, let $p(x)$ be an arbitrary polynomial. Since $p(x) = 0$ for some c, we know that $p(x)$ is divisible by $(x - c)$. Hence $p(x) = q(x)(x - c)$. Now use induction on $q(x)$.

Example 2. If we again let $p(x) = x^3 - 3x^2 + 4x - 2$ as in Example 1, we have already determined the zeros of $p(x)$ so that

$$x^3 - 3x^2 + 4x - 2 = (x - 1)[x - (1 + i)][x - (1 - i)].$$

A straightforward multiplication will verify this relation.

Let us now determine the factorization of a polynomial of $R[x]$ into its irreducible factors. The student may recall that if a complex number $a + bi$ is a zero of a polynomial with real coefficients, then the conjugate complex number $a - bi$ is also a zero of $p(x)$. We will demonstrate the validity of this statement in terms of concepts that we have developed. We note that the mapping $a + bi \xrightarrow{T} a - bi$ is a one-to-one mapping of the complex field C onto itself. Under this mapping, a real number maps upon itself. Now, if

$$a + bi \xrightarrow{T} a - bi, \quad c + di \xrightarrow{T} c - di,$$

then

$$\begin{aligned}(a + bi) + (c + di) &= (a + c) + (b + d)i \xrightarrow{T} (a + c) - (b + d)i \\ &= (a - bi) + (c - di); \\ (a + bi)(c + di) &= (ac - bd) + (ad + bc)i \xrightarrow{T} (ac - bd) - (ad + bc)i \\ &= (a - bi)(c - di).\end{aligned}$$

Hence, we have a mapping of C onto itself that preserves sums and products. Any algebraic theorem involving sums and products will be true if, throughout, a complex number is replaced by its conjugate. Thus, the algebraic statement that $p(a + bi) = 0$ implies that $p(a - bi) = 0$, if all coefficients of $p(x)$ are real so that they map upon themselves. Briefly, the mapping $a + bi \xrightarrow{T} a - bi$ is an isomorphism of the complex field C with itself under which the real numbers are mapped upon themselves identically.

Let us consider a polynomial $p(x)$ of $R[x]$ as an element of $C[x]$ and obtain from Theorem 6.2 the factorization

$$p(x) = a_m(x - c_1)(x - c_2) \cdots (x - c_m)$$

in $C[x]$. Unfortunately, if c_i is a complex number and not a real number, the linear factor $(x - c_i)$ is not in $R[x]$. However, we know that the conjugate of c_i is also a root. For convenience, let us assume that $c_1 = a + bi$;

$c_2 = a - bi$, where, of course, a and $b \neq 0$ are in R. We consider the product of the linear factors

$$[x - (a + bi)][x - (a - bi)] = x^2 - 2ax + a^2 + b^2.$$

Certainly $x^2 - 2ax + a^2 + b^2$ is in $R[x]$ and, since its zeros are $a + bi$ and $a - bi$, irreducible over R. (Otherwise it would have a linear factor in $R[x]$ and consequently a real zero.) By the division algorithm, we may write

$$p(x) = q(x)(x^2 - 2ax + a^2 + b^2) + (dx + f), \tag{6.3}$$

where $q(x) \in R[x]$ and $d, f \in R$. Replacing x by $a + bi$ and $a - bi$ in (6.3), we obtain

$$d(a + bi) + f = 0$$
$$d(a - bi) + f = 0.$$

By subtracting the second of these equations from the first we get $2dbi = 0$ and, since $b \neq 0$, $d = 0$. Then $f = 0$ and (6.3) becomes

$$p(x) = q(x)(x^2 - 2ax + a^2 + b^2),$$

with $q(x) \in R[x]$. We complete the proof of the following theorem by mathematical induction.

THEOREM 6.3. *Let* $p(x) = a_m x^m + a_{m-1}x^{m-1} + \cdots + a_1 x + a_0$ *be a polynomial of* $R[x]$ *of degree* m. *Then, over* R, $p(x)$ *may be factored uniquely (except for order of factors) into irreducible factors:*

$$p(x) = a_m(x^2 + r_1 x + s_1) \cdots (x^2 + r_k x + s_k)(x - c_{2k+1}) \cdots (x - c_m),$$

where $x^2 + r_i x + s_i \in R[x]$ *and* $c_{2k+1}, \cdots, c_m$ *are real.*

This theorem states that the only irreducible polynomials of $R[x]$ are either linear or quadratic.

Example 3. For the polynomial $p(x) = x^3 - 3x^2 + 4x - 2$ of Example 1, the irreducible factorization over R would be

$$x^3 - 3x^2 + 4x - 2 = (x - 1)(x^2 - 2x + 2).$$

In the factorization of a polynomial given in Theorem 6.2,

$$p(x) = a_m(x - c_1)(x - c_2) \cdots (x - c_m),$$

the c_i may not be distinct. Let $c_1, c_2, \cdots, c_k$ be the distinct zeros. Then,

$$p(x) = a_m(x - c_1)^{p_1}(x - c_2)^{p_2} \cdots (x - c_k)^{p_k},$$

where p_i is the number of times that the zero c_i is repeated. The p_i are integers ≥ 1, and $p_1 + p_2 + \cdots + p_k = m$.

A zero c_i with $p_i > 1$ is called a *multiple zero* (or multiple root) of $p(x)$, and p_i is the *multiplicity*. A zero with multiplicity 1 is called a *simple zero*. We see that if a zero is counted according to its multiplicity, a polynomial of degree m has exactly m zeros in the complex field C.

Example 4. Let $p(x) = (x - 2)^3(x - 1)^2(x + i)(x - i)$. Then 2 is a zero of multiplicity 3; 1 is a zero of multiplicity 2; i and $-i$ are simple zeros. Counting according to multiplicities, $p(x)$ has 7 zeros of which 4 are distinct.

EXERCISES

1. Give an alternate proof of Theorem 6.2 following the sketch of the text. Furnish complete details.

2. If $2 - 3i$, $2 + 3i$, 1, 5, $1 - i$, and $1 + i$ are the zeros of a polynomial $p(x)$ of degree 6 of $C[x]$, what are the irreducible factors of $p(x)$ in $C[x]$ and in $R[x]$?

3. Prove that a polynomial $p(x)$ of $R[x]$ is divisible by the square of a polynomial $g(x)$ of $R[x]$ if and only if $p(x)$ has multiple zeros. The multiple zeros need not be real.

4. Prove that, if $a_0 \neq 0$ in $p(x) = a_m x^m + a_{m-1}x^{m-1} + \cdots + a_1 x + a_0$, then $q(x) = a_0 x^m + a_1 x^{m-1} + \cdots + a_{m-1}x + a_m$ is a polynomial whose zeros are the reciprocals of those of $p(x)$; that is, if $p(c) = 0$, then $q(1/c) = 0$.

5. Prove that, if $p(x)$ is as in Exercise 4, the product of the zeros of $p(x)$ is $(-1)^m a_0/a_m$ and the sum of the zeros is $-a_1/a_m$.

7. The Practical Determination of Roots of Algebraic Equations

The previous section provides us with no practical way of determining the roots of an arbitrary algebraic equation

$$p(x) = a_m x^m + a_{m-1}x^{m-1} + \cdots + a_1 x + a_0 = 0.$$

We may reduce the problem to that of a polynomial with simple zeros by means of the following theorem:

THEOREM 7.1. *Let $p(x)$ have a zero c of multiplicity $r > 1$. Then the derivative $p'(x)$ has c as a zero of multiplicity $r - 1$. A simple zero of $p(x)$ is not a zero of $p'(x)$.*

Proof. Let $p(x) = q(x)(x - c)^r$, where $q(c) \neq 0$. We know that $(x - c)$ does not divide $q(x)$ or c would be a zero of multiplicity $> r$. Now take the derivative of $p(x)$, thus

$$\begin{aligned} p'(x) &= rq(x)(x - c)^{r-1} + q'(x)(x - c)^r \\ &= [rq(x) + q'(x)(x - c)](x - c)^{r-1}. \end{aligned}$$

Since $rq(c) + q'(c)(c - c) = rq(c) \neq 0$, we see that c is a zero of multiplicity $r - 1$ of $p'(x)$ when $r > 1$ and c is not a zero of $p'(x)$ when c is a simple zero of $p(x)$.

COROLLARY. *Let $d(x)$ be a GCD of $p(x)$ and $p'(x)$. Then $p(x)/d(x)$ has only simple zeros and these zeros are the distinct zeros of $p(x)$.*

Proof. Let the factored form of $p(x)$ in $C[x]$ be

$$p(x) = a_m(x - c_1)^{p_1}(x - c_2)^{p_2} \cdots (x - c_k)^{p_k}(x - c_{k+1}) \cdots (x - c_t),$$

where $p_i > 1$ and $c_1, c_2, \cdots, c_k$ are multiple zeros of $p(x)$. A zero c_i (for $i = 1, 2, \cdots, k$) is a zero of multiplicity $p_i - 1$ of $p'(x)$, and the zero c_j (for $j = k + 1, \cdots, t$) is not a zero of $p'(x)$. Thus,

$$p'(x) = q(x)(x - c_1)^{p_1-1}(x - c_2)^{p_2-1} \cdots (x - c_k)^{p_k-1},$$

where $q(c_i) \neq 0$ for $i = 1, 2, \cdots, t$. It is easy to see that a GCD of $p(x)$ and $p'(x)$ is

$$d(x) = (x - c_1)^{p_1-1}(x - c_2)^{p_2-1} \cdots (x - c_k)^{p_k-1}.$$

Therefore,

$$p(x)/d(x) = a_m(x - c_1)(x - c_2) \cdots (x - c_t).$$

Example 1. Let

$$p(x) = (x - 1)^3(x^2 + 1) = x^5 - 3x^4 + 4x^3 - 4x^2 + 3x - 1,$$

so that 1 is a zero of multiplicity 3 and i, $-i$ are simple zeros of $p(x)$. Now,

$$p'(x) = 5x^4 - 12x^3 + 12x^2 - 8x + 3$$

and $p'(i) = -4 + 4i$, $p'(-i) = -4 - 4i$, so that the simple zeros of $p(x)$ are not zeros of $p'(x)$.

Next we note that $p'(1) = 0$ and that $p'(x)$ is divisible by $(x - 1)$. We compute

$$p'(x) = (5x^3 - 7x^2 + 5x - 3)(x - 1).$$

For $q(x) = 5x^3 - 7x^2 + 5x - 3$, we have $q(1) = 0$ or

$$q(x) = (5x^2 - 2x + 3)(x - 1),$$

and $5 \cdot 1^2 - 2 \cdot 1 + 3 = 6 \neq 0$. Thus,

$$p'(x) = (5x^2 - 2x + 3)(x - 1)^2,$$

and 1 is a zero of multiplicity 2 for $p'(x)$. Moreover, the GCD of $p(x)$ and $p'(x)$ is $(x - 1)^2$ so that

$$p(x)/d(x) = (x - 1)(x^2 + 1) = x^3 - x^2 + x - 1$$

has only simple zeros.

Actually, the removal of multiple zeros from a polynomial may be done without prior knowledge of its zeros. We have merely to find the GCD of $p(x)$ and $p'(x)$ and divide this into $p(x)$ to obtain the required quotient. The process of finding the GCD by Euclid's algorithm involves no knowledge of the zeros.

Example 2. Let us assume that we are given the polynomial of Example 1 in its unfactored form. Then,

$$\begin{aligned} p(x) &= x^5 - 3x^4 + 4x^3 - 4x^2 + 3x - 1, \\ p'(x) &= 5x^4 - 12x^3 + 12x^2 - 8x + 3, \end{aligned}$$

and we have as the first step in Euclid's algorithm

$$\begin{aligned} &(x^5 - 3x^4 + 4x^3 - 4x^2 + 3x - 1) \\ &\quad = (\tfrac{1}{5}x - \tfrac{3}{25})(5x^4 - 12x^3 + 12x^2 - 8x + 3) + \tfrac{4}{25}(x^3 - 6x^2 + 9x - 4). \end{aligned}$$

Certainly, the constant $\frac{4}{25}$ is not going to change the GCD and it may be ignored in the next division,

$$\begin{aligned} &(5x^4 - 12x^3 + 12x^2 - 8x + 3) \\ &\qquad = (5x + 18)(x^3 - 6x^2 + 9x - 4) + 75(x^2 - 2x + 1). \end{aligned}$$

Again, the constant 75 may be ignored so that

$$(x^3 - 6x^2 + 9x - 4) = (x - 4)(x^2 - 2x + 1).$$

The last nonzero remainder is $(x^2 - 2x + 1)$ and this is the GCD of $p(x)$ and $p'(x)$. Now,

$$p(x)/d(x) = x^3 - x^2 + x - 1,$$

and this agrees with the result of Example 1, but this time we used no prior knowledge of the zeros of $p(x)$.

We have reduced the problem of finding the roots of $p(x) = 0$ to that of finding the roots of an equation having simple roots, but our problem is far from solved.

The student is probably familiar with the formula

$$r = \frac{-b \pm \sqrt{b^2 - 4ac}}{2a}$$

that provides the answer to the problem of solving the equation

$$ax^2 + bx + c = 0,$$

where a, b, and c are real. The extension of the result to complex coefficients is in the exercises. Now, we might hope that similar formulas exist for equations of all degrees.

The roots of the equations

$$\begin{aligned} ax^3 + bx^2 + cx + d &= 0, \\ ax^4 + bx^3 + cx^2 + dx + e &= 0 \end{aligned}$$

may be given by formulas involving radicals and the coefficients. Unfortunately, however, it can be shown that beyond the fourth degree such formulas are impossible. A proof of this fact is an important result of the theory of fields. There have been attempts to provide elementary proofs for this result, but they are quite long and require extensive preparation. The more elegant proofs are much more satisfying. They are, however, beyond the scope of this book and we therefore content ourselves with the bare statement of the facts.

Assuming that there is no algebraic formula involving the coefficients that gives the roots of equations of degree larger than 4, how do we find the roots?

Quite frankly, except for special polynomials, there is no other way than to approximate the root as closely as possible. Normally, we would obtain upper and lower bounds for the real roots and then apply various methods to determine intervals on the real axis containing these roots. Then Newton's method, Horner's method, or other methods may be used to approximate the root. With the advent of high-speed computers, many refinements of these methods have become available. These are discussed in texts in numerical analysis.

For our purposes, it will be desirable to establish for the student a method of determining whether a polynomial has integral or rational zeros. Exercises in later chapters will require a determination of zeros of special polynomials, and the following theorem will prove valuable:

THEOREM 7.2. *Let* $p(x) = a_m x^m + a_{m-1}x^{m-1} + \cdots + a_1 x + a_0$ *be a polynomial whose coefficients are integers. A rational zero of* $p(x)$ *must have the form* s/t, *where* s *is an integer that divides* a_0 *and* t *is an integer that divides* a_m.

COROLLARY. *Rational zeros of a monic polynomial* $p(x) = x^m + \cdots + a_0$ *with integral coefficients must be integers which divide* a_0.

Proof of Theorem 7.2. Let the zero $r = s/t$ of $p(x)$ be reduced to lowest terms. Thus, s and t have no common divisors except ± 1. Then,

$$0 = t^m p(s/t) = a_m s^m + a_{m-1}s^{m-1}t + \cdots + a_1 s t^{m-1} + a_0 t^m.$$

Now $-a_m s^m = (a_{m-1}s^{m-1} + \cdots + a_1 s t^{m-2} + a_0 t^{m-1})t$, and t divides $-a_m s^m$.

We now use a theorem for integers analogous to Theorem 5.1 and, since s^m and t have no common divisors except ± 1, t divides a_m.

In a similar manner it can be shown that s divides a_0.

The Corollary is the special case $a_m = 1$.

Example 3. Let $p(x) = 6x^3 - 2x^2 + 3x + 4$. The possible rational zeros s/t must have $s = \pm 1, \pm 2, \pm 4$ and $t = \pm 1, \pm 2, \pm 3, \pm 6$. The distinct possible values are

$$s/t = \pm 1, \pm \tfrac{1}{2}, \pm \tfrac{1}{3}, \pm \tfrac{1}{6}, \pm 2, \pm \tfrac{2}{3}, \pm 4, \pm \tfrac{4}{3}.$$

For all these sixteen values $p(s/t) \neq 0$; hence $p(x)$ has no rational zeros.

EXERCISES

1. Determine a polynomial having as simple zeros the distinct zeros of $p(x) = 4x^4 + 8x^3 + 9x^2 + 5x + 1$.

2. Solve the equation $z^2 = a + bi$ by setting $z = x + iy$ and equating coefficients to obtain

$$\begin{aligned} x^2 - y^2 &= a \\ 2xy &= b. \end{aligned}$$

3. Solve $(2 + i)x^2 + 3x + (-5 + 7i) = 0$ by the quadratic formula and a *correct* application of Exercise 2.

4. Find all rational roots of the following equations. Where possible, solve completely.

(a) $x^3 - 2x^2 + 3x - 6 = 0$
(b) $2x^3 - 9x^2 + 12x - 5 = 0$
(c) $2x^3 + 3x^2 + 9x + 4 = 0$
(d) $x^4 + 4x^2 - 8x + 12 = 0$
(e) $x^4 + 2x^2 + 1 = 0$

5. If $p(x) = a_m x^m + a_{m-1}x^{m-1} + \cdots + a_0$, show that

$$q(x) = a_m x^m - a_{m-1}x^{m-1} + a_{m-2}x^{m-2} + \cdots + (-1)^m a_0$$

has zeros that are the negatives of the zeros of $p(x)$.

6. Show that the equation

$$p(x) = a_m x^m + a_{m-1}x^{m-1} + \cdots + a_0 = 0,$$

with integral coefficients has no integral roots if $p(0)$ and $p(1)$ are both odd integers.

7. Show that the equation $x^m - 1 = 0$ has no multiple roots.

CHAPTER 10

Characteristic Values and Vectors of Linear Transformations

We now return to a consideration of linear transformations and matrices. These will be limited to transformations from a vector space to itself and to square matrices. The principal subject of this chapter is the use of the idea of characteristic vectors and values to achieve a simplification of the form of representation of linear transformations and quadratic forms. We will consider special cases of the similarity of matrices, and, more or less incidentally, some material on vector spaces over the complex field.

1. Characteristic Values and Vectors

We have defined the length of a vector $\mathbf{X}$ of $V_n(R)$ as $(\mathbf{X}, \mathbf{X})^{1/2}$; a direction of $\mathbf{X}$ may be given by specifying the cosines of the angles between $\mathbf{X}$ and the natural basis vectors $\mathbf{E}_1, \mathbf{E}_2, \cdots, \mathbf{E}_n$. Now if T is a linear transformation from $V_n(R)$ to the same space, $\mathbf{X}$T is normally quite different from $\mathbf{X}$ as to both length and direction. For some vectors $\mathbf{X}$, T may act merely to affect the length without changing the direction except possibly for a simple reversal. That is, $\mathbf{X}\mathrm{T} = \lambda\mathbf{X}$, where λ is a real number. The nonzero vectors $\mathbf{X}$ on which T acts in the manner of $\mathbf{X}\mathrm{T} = \lambda\mathbf{X}$ are, in a sense, distinctive or characteristic of the transformation T.

DEFINITION 1.1. *Let* T *be a linear transformation on a real vector space* V. *A real number* λ *is a* CHARACTERISTIC VALUE *of the linear transformation* T *if*

$$\mathbf{X}\mathrm{T} = \lambda\mathbf{X} \tag{1.1}$$

for some nonzero vector $\mathbf{X}$ *of* V. *A nonzero vector* $\mathbf{X}$ *satisfying* (1.1) *is called a* CHARACTERISTIC VECTOR *of* T (*belonging to the characteristic value* λ).

The names "characteristic vector" and "characteristic value" are standard in American mathematical terminology. Many other adjectives are occasionally found in place of "characteristic." The British tend to use "latent," perhaps because, as we shall see, the values and vectors are, in general, difficult to find. Sometimes "proper" is used as a synonym for "characteristic." Physicists and engineers use the peculiar terms *eigenvector* and *eigenvalue,* which reflect a period when most mathematical physics was in German. Mathematicians also use these terms colloquially, for they have the advantage of conciseness.

Example 1. Let T be the linear transformation which multiplies every vector of $V_n(R)$ by 2; $\mathbf{X}\mathrm{T} = 2\mathbf{X}$ for all $\mathbf{X}$ of $V_n(R)$. Every nonzero vector is a characteristic vector and 2 is the only characteristic value. (Why?)

Example 2. In $V_3(R)$, define T by

$$[x_1, x_2, x_3]\mathrm{T} = [x_1, 2x_2, 2x_3].$$

Any vector $[x_1, 0, 0]$ is left unchanged by T. These vectors for $x_1 \neq 0$ are characteristic vectors, and 1 is the associated characteristic value. Similarly any vector, $[0, x_2, x_3]$, is doubled by T. These are again characteristic vectors, and the associated characteristic value is 2.

Example 3. In $V_2(R)$, define T by

$$[x_1, x_2]\mathrm{T} = [x_2, -x_1].$$

We note that the lengths of $\mathbf{X}$ and $\mathbf{X}\mathrm{T}$ are $(x_1^2 + x_2^2)^{1/2}$, and so the length of $\mathbf{X}$ remains unchanged. However, the direction of a nonzero $\mathbf{X}$ is *always* changed. (Why?)

Example 4. In $V_3(R)$, define T by

$$[x_1, x_2, x_3]\mathrm{T} = [-x_2 - 3x_3, 2x_1 + 3x_2 + 3x_3, -2x_1 + x_2 + x_3].$$

We note,

$$\begin{aligned}[a, -a, -a]\mathrm{T} &= 4[a, -a, -a],\\ [a, a, -a]\mathrm{T} &= 2[a, a, -a],\\ [a, -a, a]\mathrm{T} &= -2[a, -a, a].\end{aligned}$$

Thus all nonzero vectors $[a, -a, -a]$, $[a, a, -a]$, $[a, -a, a]$ are characteristic vectors of T with 4, 2, -2 the corresponding characteristic values.

In each of these examples, we see that the addition of the vector $\mathbf{0}$ to the set of characteristic vectors associated with the same characteristic value yields a subspace. We can prove a more general theorem:

THEOREM 1.1. *Let V be a real vector space and* T *a linear transformation on V. The set M_λ of all vectors* $\mathbf{X}$ *such that* $\mathbf{X}\mathrm{T} = \lambda\mathbf{X}$, *for a real number* λ, *forms a subspace of V. Moreover* $M_{\lambda_1} \cap M_{\lambda_2} = \mathbf{0}$ *if* $\lambda_1 \neq \lambda_2$.

Proof. Since $\mathbf{0}\mathrm{T} = \lambda\mathbf{0}$ for all λ, $\mathbf{0} \in M_\lambda$. If λ is not a characteristic value, there are no vectors except $\mathbf{0}$ satisfying $\mathbf{X}\mathrm{T} = \lambda\mathbf{X}$; then $M_\lambda = \{\mathbf{0}\}$.

Now assume that λ is a characteristic value. If $\mathbf{X}\mathrm{T} = \lambda\mathbf{X}$, $\mathbf{Y}\mathrm{T} = \lambda\mathbf{Y}$, then

$$(a\mathbf{X} + b\mathbf{Y})\mathrm{T} = a(\mathbf{X}\mathrm{T}) + b(\mathbf{Y}\mathrm{T}) = a(\lambda\mathbf{X}) + b(\lambda\mathbf{Y}) = \lambda(a\mathbf{X} + b\mathbf{Y})$$

for all real numbers a, b. Again M_λ is a subspace of V.

Finally, if $\mathbf{X} \in M_{\lambda_1}$ and M_{λ_2}, then $\mathbf{X}\mathrm{T} = \lambda_1\mathbf{X} = \lambda_2\mathbf{X}$, or $(\lambda_1 - \lambda_2)\mathbf{X} = \mathbf{0}$. When $\lambda_1 \neq \lambda_2$, this implies $\mathbf{X} = \mathbf{0}$, and therefore we have $M_{\lambda_1} \cap M_{\lambda_2} = \mathbf{0}$.

The exclusion of $\mathbf{0}$ as a characteristic vector often necessitates additional verbiage. This exclusion nevertheless seems to be the better way out of a bad bargain. If $\mathbf{0}$ were allowed as a characteristic vector it would cause at least as much trouble as it cured. For example, unless preventive restrictions were stated, every real number μ would be a characteristic value since $\mathbf{0}\mathrm{T} = \mu\mathbf{0}$.

The number 0 certainly was *not* excluded as a characteristic value. The null space of T consists of $\mathbf{0}$, and, if 0 is a characteristic value, the characteristic vectors belonging to 0. Clearly, for any $\mathbf{X}$ in the null space, $\mathbf{X}\mathrm{T} = \mathbf{0} = 0\mathbf{X}$.

Example 3 illustrates that a linear transformation T may have no characteristic values as defined. In this case $M_\lambda = \mathbf{0}$ for all real λ.

In Examples 1 and 2 it is reasonably clear what answers are to be expected, but in Examples 3 and 4 the answer requires more than a glance. Let us examine the situation more closely. For Example 3, we seek a *real* number λ and a vector $\mathbf{X}$ such that $\mathbf{X}\mathrm{T} = \lambda\mathbf{X}$ or

$$\begin{aligned} [x_1, x_2]\mathrm{T} &= [\lambda x_1, \lambda x_2], \\ [x_2, -x_1] &= [\lambda x_1, \lambda x_2], \\ [-\lambda x_1 + x_2, -\lambda x_2 - x_1] &= \mathbf{0}; \end{aligned}$$

or

$$\begin{aligned} -\lambda x_1 + x_2 &= 0 \\ -x_1 - \lambda x_2 &= 0. \end{aligned}$$

This is a system of two homogeneous equations and it will have a nonzero solution for a real λ if and only if the determinant of the coefficients, $\lambda^2 + 1$, is zero. Clearly no real λ exists satisfying $\lambda^2 + 1 = 0$, and T will have no real characteristic values.

A more favorable situation occurs in Example 4. Here we seek a *real* number λ and a nonzero vector $\mathbf{X}$ such that

$$\begin{aligned} [x_1, x_2, x_3]\mathrm{T} &= [\lambda x_1, \lambda x_2, \lambda x_3], \\ [-x_2 - 3x_3, 2x_1 + 3x_2 + 3x_3, -2x_1 + x_2 + x_3] &= [\lambda x_1, \lambda x_2, \lambda x_3], \\ [-\lambda x_1 - x_2 - 3x_3, 2x_1 + (3 - \lambda)x_2 + 3x_3, -2x_1 + x_2 + (1 - \lambda)x_3] &= \mathbf{0}; \end{aligned}$$

or

$$\begin{aligned} -\lambda x_1 \quad - x_2 \quad - 3x_3 &= 0 \\ 2x_1 + (3 - \lambda)x_2 \quad + 3x_3 &= 0 \\ -2x_1 \quad + x_2 + (1 - \lambda)x_3 &= 0. \end{aligned}$$

This is a system of three homogeneous linear equations. It will have a nonzero solution if and only if the determinant of the coefficients is 0. Thus, we must have

$$\begin{vmatrix} -\lambda & -1 & -3 \\ 2 & 3-\lambda & 3 \\ -2 & 1 & 1-\lambda \end{vmatrix} = 0,$$

or $$-\lambda^3 + 4\lambda^2 + 4\lambda - 16 = -(\lambda - 4)(\lambda - 2)(\lambda + 2) = 0.$$

Hence we will find characteristic vectors if and only if λ is one of $4, 2, -2$. These are the characteristic values of T. If we try $\lambda = 4$:

$$\begin{aligned} -4x_1 - x_2 - 3x_3 &= 0 \\ 2x_1 - x_2 + 3x_3 &= 0 \\ -2x_1 + x_2 - 3x_3 &= 0, \end{aligned}$$

or $x_1 = -x_2 = -x_3$. Thus $[a, -a, -a]$ is a characteristic vector for $\lambda = 4$, and similar results follow for the other characteristic values.

The procedure of the previous examples is perfectly general for any linear transformation of an n-dimensional real vector space V associated with a matrix A relative to a fixed basis. We may, for simplicity, assume that $V = V_n(R)$ and that the fixed basis is the natural basis $\{\mathbf{E}_1, \mathbf{E}_2, \cdots, \mathbf{E}_n\}$, so that, for $\mathbf{X} = [x_1, x_2, \cdots, x_n]$, $\mathbf{X}\mathrm{T} = \mathbf{X}A$. Then if $\mathbf{X}\mathrm{T} = \lambda\mathbf{X}$; $\mathbf{X}A = \lambda\mathbf{X}$,

$$\begin{aligned} \mathbf{X}A &= \mathbf{X}(\lambda I), \\ \mathbf{X}(A - \lambda I) &= \mathbf{0}, \end{aligned}$$

where I is the $n \times n$ identity matrix. Thus for any characteristic value λ the corresponding characteristic vectors are the nonzero elements of the null space of $(A - \lambda I)$. The necessary and sufficient condition that such nonzero vectors exist is that $A - \lambda I$ be singular; that is, $\det(A - \lambda I) = 0$. For such values of λ, the elements of the null space may be found by solving the system of homogeneous equations expressed in matrix form by

$$[x_1, x_2, \cdots, x_n] \begin{bmatrix} a_{11} - \lambda & a_{12} & \cdots & a_{1n} \\ a_{21} & a_{22} - \lambda & \cdots & a_{2n} \\ \vdots & \vdots & & \vdots \\ a_{n1} & a_{n2} & \cdots & a_{nn} - \lambda \end{bmatrix} = \mathbf{0}.$$

Here again the existence of characteristic values of T depends upon the existence of real numbers λ such that $\det(A - \lambda I) = 0$.

We wish to consider the extension of the concepts of characteristic value and characteristic vector to an arbitrary matrix A, where we have no transformation T in mind. In this case, we shall assume that the elements of $A = [a_{ij}]$ are in a subfield F of the complex number field C.

Also, it will be convenient to regard det $(A - \lambda I)$ as a polynomial in $F[\lambda]$. Up to this point we have considered λ, in det $(A - \lambda I)$, to be a definite but unspecified real number. There is a minor difficulty in changing its position to that of an indeterminate since we have in effect only defined determinants of matrices whose elements are from a prescribed field (originally the real field R). The difficulty can be avoided in several ways; for example, the elements appearing in $A - \lambda I$ may be regarded as members of the field of rational functions (quotients of polynomials) in λ. It is easy to see that this is indeed a field and that det $(A - \lambda I)$ will, in this case, actually be an element of $F[\lambda]$. Since the zeros of such a polynomial are, in general, complex, we shall permit the characteristic values of a matrix A to be complex and the characteristic vectors to be from $V_n(C)$. In this manner we will ensure the existence of characteristic values for the matrix A.

DEFINITION 1.2. *If A is an $n \times n$ matrix with elements in a field $F \subseteq C$, then the polynomial $f(\lambda) = det\ (A - \lambda I)$ is called the* CHARACTERISTIC POLYNOMIAL OF A. *The roots of the characteristic equation $f(\lambda) = det\ (A - \lambda I) = 0$ are the* CHARACTERISTIC VALUES OF A. *For such a value λ, $1 \times n$ matrices (vectors $\mathbf{X}$ with components in the complex field C) such that $\mathbf{X}(A - \lambda I) = \mathbf{0}$ are called* CHARACTERISTIC VECTORS OF A.

We note that these definitions are simply a formal analogue of the method we used to obtain the characteristic vectors and values for a linear transformation T.

We conclude this section with an investigation of the relationship of the characteristic polynomials, values, and vectors of similar matrices; that is, of matrices representing the same linear transformation.

THEOREM 1.2. *If $B = PAP^{-1}$ is an $n \times n$ matrix, where P is any $n \times n$ nonsingular matrix, then*

(i) *A and B have the same characteristic polynomial.*

(ii) *A and B have the same characteristic values.*

(iii) *If $\mathbf{X}$ is a characteristic vector of A, $\mathbf{X}P^{-1}$ is a characteristic vector of B for the same characteristic value.*

Proof. (i) and (ii). For each complex number λ,

$$\begin{aligned} \det (B - \lambda I) &= \det (PAP^{-1} - \lambda I) = \det (PAP^{-1} - \lambda PIP^{-1}) \\ &= \det \{P(A - \lambda I)P^{-1}\}. \end{aligned}$$

We now use the fact that det AB = det $A \cdot$ det B to obtain

$$\begin{aligned} \det (B - \lambda I) &= \det P \cdot \det P^{-1} \cdot \det (A - \lambda I) \\ &= \det PP^{-1} \cdot \det (A - \lambda I) = \det (A - \lambda I). \end{aligned}$$

Thus, if the polynomial

$$G(\lambda) = \det (B - \lambda I) - \det (A - \lambda I)$$

were not identically 0, $G(\lambda)$ would have an infinite number of zeros contrary to Theorem 6.2, Chapter 9. Therefore the characteristic polynomials $\det(B - \lambda I)$ and $\det(A - \lambda I)$ are equal (and consequently their zeros are identical).

(iii) If $\mathbf{X}A = \lambda\mathbf{X}$, then $\mathbf{X}P^{-1}PAP^{-1} = \lambda\mathbf{X}P^{-1}$ or $(\mathbf{X}P^{-1})B = \lambda(\mathbf{X}P^{-1})$.

We have seen that matrices A and B are similar if and only if they represent the same linear transformation T. Hence, we say that $f(\lambda) = \det(A - \lambda I)$ is the characteristic polynomial of T if T is associated with A with respect to some basis.

EXERCISES

1. For the linear transformations T of $V_2(R)$ and $V_3(R)$ defined by the following equations, find the characteristic values and vectors of T.

(a) $[x_1, x_2]\mathrm{T} = [x_1, x_2]$
(b) $[x_1, x_2]\mathrm{T} = [x_1, 2x_1 - 3x_2]$
(c) $[x_1, x_2, x_3]\mathrm{T} = [x_2 - x_1, x_3 - x_2, x_1 - x_3]$
(d) $[x_1, x_2, x_3]\mathrm{T} = [x_1, -2x_1 - x_2, x_1 + 3x_2 + 2x_3]$

2. Find the characteristic polynomial, values, and vectors of the following matrices:

(a) $\begin{bmatrix} 1 & 2 \\ 3 & 2 \end{bmatrix}$

(b) $\begin{bmatrix} 2 & -1 & 1 \\ 1 & 0 & 3 \\ 0 & 0 & 2 \end{bmatrix}$

(c) $\begin{bmatrix} 2 & -2 \\ 3 & -2 \end{bmatrix}$. (This will involve complex numbers.)

3. Prove that the characteristic values of any triangular matrix are the diagonal elements.

4. Prove that a matrix and its transpose have the same characteristic values.

5. If λ is a characteristic value of the matrix A and $\mathbf{X}$ a corresponding characteristic vector, show that $\mathbf{X}A^2 = \lambda^2\mathbf{X}$. What does this prove about the characteristic values of the matrix A^2? Without further proof, is it correct to conclude that all the characteristic values of A^2 are the squares of the characteristic values of A?

6. Generalize Exercise 5 and show that a characteristic value of the matrix $a_0I + a_1A + \cdots + a_mA^m$ is $a_0 + a_1\lambda + a_2\lambda^2 + \cdots + a_m\lambda^m$, where λ is a characteristic value of A.

7. Prove that all real characteristic values of an orthogonal matrix are ± 1.

8. Prove that if $A^m = 0$, the only characteristic value of A is 0. Give examples of such *nilpotent* matrices.

9. Prove that two characteristic vectors belonging to distinct characteristic values λ_1 and λ_2 of a linear transformation T of $V_n(R)$ are linearly independent.

10. If A is a nonsingular matrix, prove that AB and BA have the same characteristic values.

2. Similarity and Diagonal Matrices

We have just seen that any matrix similar to A has the same characteristic polynomial and characteristic values as A. The converse is shown to be false by considering the matrices $A = \begin{bmatrix} 1 & 0 \\ 0 & 1 \end{bmatrix}$ and $B = \begin{bmatrix} 1 & 0 \\ 1 & 1 \end{bmatrix}$. Both A and B have the characteristic polynomial $(\lambda - 1)^2$, but $PAP^{-1} = I$ for any nonsingular matrix P. Therefore B cannot be similar to A. There are, however, special circumstances under which the converse is correct and we shall obtain a partial answer.

We begin by considering a real $n \times n$ matrix A which has n distinct characteristic values $\lambda_1, \lambda_2, \cdots, \lambda_n$. In the event that some of these values are complex, our discussion would have to involve $V_n(C)$. We shall avoid this by assuming, for the present, that the λ_i are real. There is an obvious matrix with precisely the same characteristic values as A, the diagonal matrix:

$$B = \text{Diagonal } [\lambda_1, \lambda_2, \cdots, \lambda_n].$$

The question arises, Is B similar to A?

We have seen (Chapter 6, § 9) that the similarity of matrices is an equivalence relation. Hence we may ask the question in a manner analogous to the discussion of quadratic forms: Does each equivalence class of similar matrices containing a matrix with n distinct characteristic values contain a diagonal matrix?

We are going to give an affirmative answer; indeed, we shall answer a somewhat more general question without additional labor. To find this question, let us approach diagonal matrices from a different point of view. Suppose a matrix A is similar to a diagonal matrix D: $A = PDP^{-1}$. The natural basis vectors $\mathbf{E}_i$ are clearly characteristic vectors of a diagonal matrix

$$D = \begin{bmatrix} d_1 & & & & \\ & d_2 & & & \\ & & \cdot & & \\ & & & \cdot & \\ & & & & d_n \end{bmatrix}$$

with characteristic values d_i. Hence, from Theorem 1.2, $\mathbf{E}_i P^{-1}$ are characteristic vectors of A. The vectors $\{\mathbf{E}_i P^{-1}\}$ are linearly independent and form a basis for $V_n(R)$. Thus we have proved the theorem:

THEOREM 2.1. *If an $n \times n$ real matrix A is similar to a real diagonal matrix, its characteristic vectors generate the vector space $V_n(R)$.*

We see that our more general question is, If the characteristic vectors of a matrix A generate $V_n(R)$, is A similar to a diagonal matrix? There are two points to note here. First, not all matrices with real characteristic values have the property that their vectors span $V_n(R)$. For example, vectors of the form $[a, 0]$ are the only characteristic vectors of $B = \begin{bmatrix} 1 & 0 \\ 1 & 1 \end{bmatrix}$. Exercise 2(b) of §1 provides another example. Second, matrices with n distinct real characteristic values are among the matrices whose characteristic vectors span $V_n(R)$. We need only show that n characteristic vectors, one associated with each distinct characteristic value, are linearly independent. Thus suppose, without loss of generality, that $\mathbf{X}_{k+1}$ associated with λ_{k+1} was a linear combination of the characteristic vectors $\mathbf{X}_1$ for λ_1, $\mathbf{X}_2$ for λ_2, $\cdots$, $\mathbf{X}_k$ for λ_k, the latter being linearly independent. Then

$$\mathbf{X}_{k+1} = c_1\mathbf{X}_1 + \cdots + c_k\mathbf{X}_k,$$

where not all $c_i = 0$. Multiplying both sides by the matrix A and remembering that the $\mathbf{X}_i$ are characteristic vectors, we have

$$\mathbf{X}_{k+1}A = c_1\mathbf{X}_1A + \cdots + c_k\mathbf{X}_kA$$

or

$$\lambda_{k+1}\mathbf{X}_{k+1} = \lambda_1c_1\mathbf{X}_1 + \cdots + \lambda_kc_k\mathbf{X}_k.$$

We also have $\lambda_{k+1}\mathbf{X}_{k+1} = \lambda_{k+1}c_1\mathbf{X}_1 + \cdots + \lambda_{k+1}c_k\mathbf{X}_k$; therefore

$$(\lambda_{k+1} - \lambda_1)c_1\mathbf{X}_1 + \cdots + (\lambda_{k+1} - \lambda_k)c_k\mathbf{X}_k = \mathbf{0}.$$

Since $\mathbf{X}_1, \cdots, \mathbf{X}_k$ are linearly independent and $(\lambda_{k+1} - \lambda_i) \neq 0$ for $1 \leq i \leq k$, we have $c_i = 0$ for $1 \leq i \leq k$. But then $\mathbf{X}_{k+1} = \mathbf{0}$, contrary to our assumption that $\mathbf{X}_{k+1}$ is a characteristic vector.

Not all matrices whose characteristic vectors generate $V_n(R)$ have n distinct characteristic values, as the identity matrix I simply illustrates. For the remainder of this section we shall concern ourselves with the set of real matrices whose characteristic vectors generate $V_n(R)$.

From the point of view of linear transformations, the similarity of a matrix A whose characteristic vectors generate $V_n(R)$ to a diagonal matrix is easy to prove. Let T be a linear transformation of $V_n(R)$ represented by A; then the characteristic vectors of T generate $V_n(R)$. We select a basis from these characteristic vectors and represent T by this basis. That is, if $\mathbf{X}_1, \mathbf{X}_2, \cdots, \mathbf{X}_n$ is such a basis, $\mathbf{X}_i\mathrm{T} = \lambda_i\mathbf{X}_i$, where not all the λ_i are necessarily distinct, and the matrix of T with respect to the basis $\{\mathbf{X}_i\}$ is just the matrix

$$D = \text{Diagonal } [\lambda_1, \lambda_2, \cdots, \lambda_n].$$

Now by the Corollary to Theorem 8.3, Chapter 6, $PAP^{-1} = D$, where P is the matrix of the change of basis from that one giving A as a matrix of T to the basis $\{\mathbf{X}_i\}$.

The algebraic details for the reduction of an $n \times n$ real matrix A, whose characteristic vectors generate $V_n(R)$, to diagonal form proceed from the argument given above as follows: Let $A = [a_{ij}]$ and define a linear transformation T of $V_n(R)$ by

$$[x_1, x_2, \cdots, x_n]\mathrm{T} = [x_1, x_2, \cdots, x_n]A.$$

Thus A is the matrix of T relative to the natural basis $\{\mathbf{E}_i\}$. Now let

$$\mathbf{X}_i = [p_{i1}, p_{i2}, \cdots, p_{in}] = p_{i1}\mathbf{E}_1 + p_{i2}\mathbf{E}_2 + \cdots + p_{in}\mathbf{E}_n$$

be characteristic vectors of A, associated with characteristic values λ_i, that generate $V_n(R)$. Then $\mathbf{X}_i\mathrm{T} = \lambda_i\mathbf{X}_i$ or $\mathbf{X}_iA = \lambda_i\mathbf{X}_i$ so that the matrix of T relative to $\{\mathbf{X}_i\}$ is $D = \text{Diagonal } [\lambda_1, \lambda_2, \cdots, \lambda_n]$. On the other hand, the equation

$$\begin{bmatrix} \mathbf{X}_1 \\ \mathbf{X}_2 \\ \cdot \\ \cdot \\ \cdot \\ \mathbf{X}_n \end{bmatrix} = P \begin{bmatrix} \mathbf{E}_1 \\ \mathbf{E}_2 \\ \cdot \\ \cdot \\ \cdot \\ \mathbf{E}_n \end{bmatrix},$$

where $P = [p_{ij}]$ is the matrix whose rows are the characteristic vectors $\mathbf{X}_i$, represents a change of basis from $\{\mathbf{E}_i\}$ to $\{\mathbf{X}_i\}$. Hence

$$PAP^{-1} = D = \text{Diagonal } [\lambda_1, \lambda_2, \cdots, \lambda_n].$$

Alternatively, using the notation established, we have directly

$$PA = \begin{bmatrix} \mathbf{X}_1 \\ \mathbf{X}_2 \\ \cdot \\ \cdot \\ \cdot \\ \mathbf{X}_n \end{bmatrix} A = \begin{bmatrix} \lambda_1\mathbf{X}_1 \\ \lambda_2\mathbf{X}_2 \\ \cdot \\ \cdot \\ \cdot \\ \lambda_n\mathbf{X}_n \end{bmatrix} = \begin{bmatrix} \lambda_1 & & & \\ & \lambda_2 & & \\ & & \ddots & \\ & & & \lambda_n \end{bmatrix} \begin{bmatrix} \mathbf{X}_1 \\ \mathbf{X}_2 \\ \cdot \\ \cdot \\ \cdot \\ \mathbf{X}_n \end{bmatrix}$$

$$= \begin{bmatrix} \lambda_1 & & & \\ & \lambda_2 & & \\ & & \ddots & \\ & & & \lambda_n \end{bmatrix} P,$$

or $PAP^{-1} = \text{Diagonal } [\lambda_1, \lambda_2, \cdots, \lambda_n]$.

The foregoing discussion answers the questions we posed earlier. We then have the following theorem:

THEOREM 2.2. *A real matrix A is similar to a real diagonal matrix D if and only if the characteristic vectors of A generate $V_n(R)$. A real matrix P which performs the similarity transformation $PAP^{-1} = D$ is obtained by writing a matrix whose rows are a basis of $V_n(R)$ consisting of characteristic vectors of A. The characteristic values of A are the elements appearing on the diagonal in D.*

COROLLARY. *A matrix with n distinct real characteristic values is similar to a real diagonal matrix.*

Example 1. Let $A = \begin{bmatrix} 1 & 1 & -1 \\ 0 & 0 & 1 \\ 0 & -2 & -3 \end{bmatrix}$. The characteristic polynomial of A is

$$\det \begin{bmatrix} 1-\lambda & 1 & -1 \\ 0 & -\lambda & 1 \\ 0 & -2 & -3-\lambda \end{bmatrix} = -(\lambda - 1)(\lambda + 1)(\lambda + 2).$$

For the characteristic value 1, we solve $\mathbf{X}A = \mathbf{X}$, or

$$[x_1, x_2, x_3]A = [x_1, x_1 - 2x_3, -x_1 + x_2 - 3x_3] = [x_1, x_2, x_3].$$

This yields the equations

$$\begin{aligned} x_1 - x_2 - 2x_3 &= 0 \\ -x_1 + x_2 - 4x_3 &= 0, \end{aligned}$$

or $x_3 = 0$, $x_1 = x_2$. A particular characteristic vector for the characteristic value 1 could be [1, 1, 0].

For the characteristic value -1, we must have

$$[x_1, x_1 - 2x_3, -x_1 + x_2 - 3x_3] = [-x_1, -x_2, -x_3],$$

or $x_1 = 0$, $x_2 = 2x_3$. Here we could take [0, 2, 1] as a characteristic vector.

For the characteristic value -2,

$$[x_1, x_1 - 2x_3, -x_1 + x_2 - 3x_3] = [-2x_1, -2x_2, -2x_3],$$

or $x_1 = 0$, $x_2 = x_3$. A particular characteristic vector is [0, 1, 1].

In order to reduce A to diagonal form by a similarity transformation, we choose for the rows of P the vectors selected above so that

$$P = \begin{bmatrix} 1 & 1 & 0 \\ 0 & 2 & 1 \\ 0 & 1 & 1 \end{bmatrix}, \qquad P^{-1} = \begin{bmatrix} 1 & -1 & 1 \\ 0 & 1 & -1 \\ 0 & -1 & 2 \end{bmatrix}.$$

Then PAP^{-1} becomes

$$\begin{bmatrix} 1 & 1 & 0 \\ 0 & 2 & 1 \\ 0 & 1 & 1 \end{bmatrix} \begin{bmatrix} 1 & 1 & -1 \\ 0 & 0 & 1 \\ 0 & -2 & -3 \end{bmatrix} \begin{bmatrix} 1 & -1 & 1 \\ 0 & 1 & -1 \\ 0 & -1 & 2 \end{bmatrix} = \begin{bmatrix} 1 & 0 & 0 \\ 0 & -1 & 0 \\ 0 & 0 & -2 \end{bmatrix}.$$

The student should perform a similar calculation with a different choice of characteristic vectors comprising the rows of P. Actually, by simply permuting appropriately the rows of P, we could reduce A to any of the six diagonal forms,

$$\begin{gathered} [1, -1, -2], \quad [-2, 1, -1], \quad [-1, -2, 1], \\ [1, -2, -1], \quad [-2, -1, 1], \quad [-1, 1, -2]. \end{gathered}$$

This example illustrates that an equivalence class of matrices under similarity containing a diagonal matrix may contain many diagonal matrices. The problem of choosing a "canonical" matrix of the class requires some agreement about the order of the diagonal elements. We illustrate how this may be done in Exercise 5.

The results we have obtained for real matrices may, as usual, be extended to other fields. We need only make sure that the field used includes the elements of A and the characteristic values of A. In particular, the theorems extend easily to matrices whose elements are complex numbers. Here P will possibly be complex also.

Example 2. Let $A = \begin{bmatrix} 1 & 2 \\ -1 & -1 \end{bmatrix}$. The characteristic polynomial is $\lambda^2 + 1$. In the complex field the characteristic values are $+ i$, $- i$. Let us consider the case of $\lambda_1 = i$;

$$[x_1, x_2]A = [ix_1, ix_2]; \quad [x_1 - x_2, 2x_1 - x_2] = [ix_1, ix_2]$$

or $(1 - i)x_1 = x_2$.

For $\lambda_2 = - i$,

$$[x_1 - x_2, \ 2x_1 - x_2] = [- ix_1, \ - ix_2]$$

or $(1 + i)x_1 = x_2$. We choose as characteristic vectors $\mathbf{X}_1 = [i, 1 + i]$, $\mathbf{X}_2 = [i, -1 + i]$. Then PAP^{-1} becomes

$$\begin{bmatrix} i & 1+i \\ i & -1+i \end{bmatrix} \begin{bmatrix} 1 & 2 \\ -1 & -1 \end{bmatrix} \begin{bmatrix} \dfrac{1-i}{2i} & \dfrac{1+i}{2i} \\ \dfrac{1}{2} & \dfrac{-1}{2} \end{bmatrix}$$

$$= \begin{bmatrix} -1 & i-1 \\ 1 & i+1 \end{bmatrix} \begin{bmatrix} \dfrac{1-i}{2i} & \dfrac{1+i}{2i} \\ \dfrac{1}{2} & \dfrac{-1}{2} \end{bmatrix} = \begin{bmatrix} i & 0 \\ 0 & -i \end{bmatrix}.$$

EXERCISES

1. Find the diagonal matrices similar to:

$$(a)\ \begin{bmatrix} 0 & 1 \\ 0 & 1 \end{bmatrix} \qquad (b)\ \begin{bmatrix} 1 & -5 & 9 \\ 2 & 0 & -1 \\ 1 & 2 & -4 \end{bmatrix} \qquad (c)\ \begin{bmatrix} -1 & 4 & -2 \\ 0 & 3 & -2 \\ 0 & 4 & -3 \end{bmatrix}$$

2. Show that $\begin{bmatrix} 0 & 5 & -3 \\ 1 & 0 & 1 \\ 2 & -4 & 4 \end{bmatrix}$ is not similar to a diagonal matrix.

3. Using matrices with complex elements if necessary, diagonalize

$$\begin{bmatrix} 1 & -1 \\ 1 & 2 \end{bmatrix}.$$

4. If the characteristic vectors of a matrix A generate $V_n(R)$, show that a basis for $V_n(R)$ consisting of characteristic vectors of A must contain a vector associated with every characteristic value of A.

5. Finish the proof that, for real matrices with real characteristic values of the type considered in this section, the matrix Diagonal $[\lambda_1, \lambda_2, \cdots, \lambda_n]$, such that $\lambda_i \geq \lambda_j$ for $i \geq j$, is "canonical" for similarity transformations. That is, there are not two such diagonal matrices in the same equivalence class.

6. Show that the only matrices which have $\mathbf{E}_1, \mathbf{E}_2, \cdots, \mathbf{E}_n$ as characteristic vectors are the diagonal matrices.

7. If a matrix A is similar to a diagonal matrix, show that the polynomial matrix

$$f(A) = a_m A^m + a_{m-1}A^{m-1} + \cdots + a_1 A + a_0 I$$

has as characteristic values $a_m c^m + a_{m-1}c^{m-1} + \cdots + a_1 c + a_0 c$, where c ranges over the characteristic values of A. (See also Exercise 6, § 1.)

8. What conclusions can you draw from Exercise 7 if the polynomial $f(\lambda) = a_n\lambda^n + a_{n-1}\lambda^{n-1} + \cdots + a_1\lambda + a_0$ used to form $f(A)$ is the characteristic polynomial of A?

3. Orthogonal Reduction of Symmetric Matrices

In the preceding section we considered the circumstances under which a matrix is *similar* to a diagonal matrix; in Chapter 8 we found that every symmetric matrix is *congruent* to a diagonal matrix, in fact to one whose diagonal elements are ± 1 or 0. The concepts of similarity ($B = PAP^{-1}$) and congruence ($B = PAP^{\mathsf{T}}$) overlap in the case that $P^{\mathsf{T}} = P^{-1}$; that is, if P is an orthogonal matrix. We shall now establish the result that any real symmetric matrix is simultaneously similar and congruent to a diagonal matrix.

We begin by proving that all the characteristic values of a real symmetric matrix are real. Let us assume that A is a real symmetric matrix with characteristic value $a + bi$. Now consider the polynomial

$$p(x) = x^2 - 2ax + (a^2 + b^2).$$

We know (Exercise 6, § 1) that the matrix

$$B = A^2 - 2aA + (a^2 + b^2)I = (A - aI)^2 + b^2I$$

will have $p(a + bi) = 0$ as a characteristic value. Hence there exists a nonzero vector $\mathbf{X}$ of $V_n(R)$ such that $\mathbf{X}B = \mathbf{0}$ or $(\mathbf{X}B, \mathbf{X}) = 0$. Thus,

$$0 = (\mathbf{X}B, \mathbf{X}) = \mathbf{X}\{(A - aI)^2 + b^2I\}\mathbf{X}^\mathsf{T} = \mathbf{X}(A - aI)^2\mathbf{X}^\mathsf{T} + b^2\mathbf{X}\mathbf{X}^\mathsf{T}.$$

However, since $A = A^\mathsf{T}$, $\mathbf{X}(A - aI)^2\mathbf{X}^\mathsf{T} = \mathbf{X}(A - aI) \cdot \{\mathbf{X}(A - aI)\}^\mathsf{T}$. Therefore,

$$0 = (\mathbf{X}_1, \mathbf{X}_1) + b^2(\mathbf{X}, \mathbf{X}), \quad \text{where} \quad \mathbf{X}_1 = \mathbf{X}(A - aI).$$

The last equation is impossible if $b \neq 0$ because the inner product $(\mathbf{X}, \mathbf{X})$ is positive. We must conclude that $b = 0$ so that a proof of the following theorem is complete:

THEOREM 3.1. *If A is a real symmetric matrix, the characteristic values of A are real.*

Next we show that if two vectors are characteristic of the real symmetric matrix A for different characteristic values, they are orthogonal.

THEOREM 3.2. *If A is a real symmetric matrix and $\mathbf{X}$ and $\mathbf{Y}$ are characteristic vectors of A such that $\mathbf{X}A = \lambda_1\mathbf{X}$, $\mathbf{Y}A = \lambda_2\mathbf{Y}$ with $\lambda_1 \neq \lambda_2$, then $(\mathbf{X}, \mathbf{Y}) = 0$.*

Proof. Since $A = A^\mathsf{T}$, $(\mathbf{X}A, \mathbf{Y}) = \mathbf{X}A\mathbf{Y}^\mathsf{T} = \mathbf{X}A^\mathsf{T}\mathbf{Y}^\mathsf{T} = \mathbf{X}(\mathbf{Y}A)^\mathsf{T} = (\mathbf{X}, \mathbf{Y}A)$. Therefore, $(\lambda_1\mathbf{X}, \mathbf{Y}) = (\mathbf{X}, \lambda_2\mathbf{Y})$ or $(\lambda_1 - \lambda_2)(\mathbf{X}, \mathbf{Y}) = 0$. We have assumed that $\lambda_1 \neq \lambda_2$, and hence $(\mathbf{X}, \mathbf{Y}) = 0$.

Finally, we prove:

THEOREM 3.3. *If A is a real symmetric matrix, then there is an orthogonal matrix P such that PAP^{-1} is a diagonal matrix.*

Proof. As in two previous instances of a reduction of matrices to diagonal form (Theorem 3.1, Chapter 8, and Exercise 8, § 2, Chapter 7), our proof will be by mathematical induction on the order of A. If $A = [a_{11}]$, A is already diagonal.

Let us assume the theorem proved for $(n - 1) \times (n - 1)$ matrices and let A be an $n \times n$ symmetric matrix. Associate with A the linear transformation T on $V_n(R)$ defined by $\mathbf{X}\mathrm{T} = \mathbf{X}A$; that is, A is the matrix of T with respect to the natural basis $\{\mathbf{E}_1, \mathbf{E}_2, \cdots, \mathbf{E}_n\}$ of $V_n(R)$. Let λ_1 be a characteristic value of A and hence of T (since λ_1 is real by Theorem 3.1). We may, of course, choose a characteristic vector $\mathbf{X}_1$ associated with λ_1 to be a unit vector and

$$\mathbf{X}_1\mathrm{T} = \mathbf{X}_1 A = \lambda_1 \mathbf{X}_1.$$

Denote by V the $(n-1)$-dimensional orthogonal complement of $L\{\mathbf{X}_1\}$ in $V_n(R)$. Let $\mathbf{X}_2, \mathbf{X}_3, \cdots, \mathbf{X}_n$ be an orthonormal basis of V. Every vector $\mathbf{X}$ of V has the form

$$\mathbf{X} = a_2\mathbf{X}_2 + \cdots + a_n\mathbf{X}_n,$$

and

$$\begin{aligned}(\mathbf{X}\mathrm{T}, \mathbf{X}_1) = ((a_2\mathbf{X}_2 + \cdots + a_n\mathbf{X}_n)A, \mathbf{X}_1) &= (a_2\mathbf{X}_2 + \cdots + a_n\mathbf{X}_n, \mathbf{X}_1 A) \\ &= (a_2\mathbf{X}_2 + \cdots + a_n\mathbf{X}_n, \lambda_1\mathbf{X}_1) = 0,\end{aligned}$$

since every vector of V is orthogonal to $\mathbf{X}_1$. Thus, $\mathbf{X}\mathrm{T}$ is orthogonal to $\mathbf{X}_1$ and is contained in V so that $\mathbf{X}\mathrm{T}$ is again a linear combination of $\mathbf{X}_2, \cdots, \mathbf{X}_n$. The preceding remarks apply to the basis vectors $\mathbf{X}_2, \cdots, \mathbf{X}_n$, and if we represent T in terms of the orthonormal basis $\{\mathbf{X}_1, \mathbf{X}_2, \cdots, \mathbf{X}_n\}$ we obtain a matrix

$$B = \begin{bmatrix} \lambda_1 & 0 & \cdots & 0 \\ 0 & & & \\ \vdots & & A^* & \\ 0 & & & \end{bmatrix},$$

where A^* is $(n-1) \times (n-1)$.

The matrix of the change of basis from $\{\mathbf{E}_i\}$ to $\{\mathbf{X}_i\}$ is the orthogonal matrix R whose rows are the elements of the vectors $\{\mathbf{X}_i\}$. Hence by Theorem 8.3, Chapter 6,

$$RAR^{-1} = B,$$

where B and A^* are symmetric matrices since $R^{-1} = R^{\mathsf{T}}$.

By induction, there is an $(n-1) \times (n-1)$ orthogonal matrix Q^* such that $Q^*A^*Q^{*-1} = \text{Diagonal } [\lambda_2, \lambda_3, \cdots, \lambda_n]$. Clearly, the matrix

$$Q = \begin{bmatrix} 1 & 0 & \cdots & 0 \\ 0 & & & \\ \vdots & & Q^* & \\ 0 & & & \end{bmatrix}$$

is an orthogonal matrix and

$$QRAR^{-1}Q^{-1} = QBQ^{-1} = \text{Diagonal } [\lambda_1, \lambda_2, \cdots, \lambda_n].$$

The matrix $QR = P$ is the product of two orthogonal matrices and hence an orthogonal matrix. Thus, PAP^{-1} is diagonal and our proof is complete.

Example 1. We shall illustrate an alternate proof of Theorem 3.3 by finding an orthogonal matrix P that reduces the symmetric matrix

$$A = \begin{bmatrix} 1 & -4 & 2 \\ -4 & 1 & -2 \\ 2 & -2 & -2 \end{bmatrix}$$

to diagonal form under the similarity transformation PAP^{-1}. We shall construct the rows of P from characteristic vectors in the manner of Example 1, §2.

The characteristic polynomial of the matrix A is

$$\det \begin{bmatrix} 1-\lambda & -4 & 2 \\ -4 & 1-\lambda & -2 \\ 2 & -2 & -2-\lambda \end{bmatrix} = -\lambda^3 + 27\lambda + 54 = -(\lambda+3)^2(\lambda-6).$$

For $\lambda = -3$, we find the characteristic vectors belonging to -3 (the subspace M_{-3} of Theorem 1.1) by solving:

$$[x_1, x_2, x_3] \begin{bmatrix} 4 & -4 & 2 \\ -4 & 4 & -2 \\ 2 & -2 & 1 \end{bmatrix} = \mathbf{0}.$$

The only restriction is that $2x_1 - 2x_2 + x_3 = 0$. An orthogonal basis for M_{-3} is $[2, 1, -2]$, $[1, 2, 2]$.

For $\lambda = 6$,

$$[x_1, x_2, x_3] \begin{bmatrix} -5 & -4 & 2 \\ -4 & -5 & -2 \\ 2 & -2 & -8 \end{bmatrix} = \mathbf{0},$$

or

$$\begin{aligned} -5x_1 - 4x_2 + 2x_3 &= 0 \\ -4x_1 - 5x_2 - 2x_3 &= 0 \\ 2x_1 - 2x_2 - 8x_3 &= 0. \end{aligned}$$

The solutions of this system of equations are $x_1 = -x_2 = 2x_3$, and a basis for M_6 is $[2, -2, 1]$.

Note, as an illustration of Theorem 3.2, that the basis vector of M_6 is orthogonal to the basis vectors of M_{-3}. We now use the unit vectors $[\frac{2}{3}, \frac{1}{3}, -\frac{2}{3}]$, $[\frac{1}{3}, \frac{2}{3}, \frac{2}{3}]$, and $[\frac{2}{3}, -\frac{2}{3}, \frac{1}{3}]$ as the rows of the orthogonal matrix P and see that

$$\begin{aligned} PAP^{-1} = PAP^{\mathsf{T}} &= \begin{bmatrix} \frac{2}{3} & \frac{1}{3} & -\frac{2}{3} \\ \frac{1}{3} & \frac{2}{3} & \frac{2}{3} \\ \frac{2}{3} & -\frac{2}{3} & \frac{1}{3} \end{bmatrix} \begin{bmatrix} 1 & -4 & 2 \\ -4 & 1 & -2 \\ 2 & -2 & -2 \end{bmatrix} \begin{bmatrix} \frac{2}{3} & \frac{1}{3} & \frac{2}{3} \\ \frac{1}{3} & \frac{2}{3} & -\frac{2}{3} \\ -\frac{2}{3} & \frac{2}{3} & \frac{1}{3} \end{bmatrix} \\ &= \text{Diagonal } [-3, -3, 6]. \end{aligned}$$

Since we were dealing with a specific matrix, the main difficulty in extending the preceding example to a general proof is obscured. In general, how can one be sure that the sum of the dimensions of the subspaces M_λ, for characteristic values λ of A, is n? If this is always true, we can provide the n mutually orthogonal characteristic vectors to construct P. We shall leave it to the student in the exercises to show that this is always the case.

In practice, the change to diagonal form is carried out in the manner of the example rather than by the inductive method of the proof.

EXERCISES

1. In Example 1, use as a basis for M_{-3} the vectors $[1, 1, 0]$, $[1, -1, -4]$. Now construct a matrix P such that

$$PAP^{-1} = \text{Diagonal } [-3, -3, 6].$$

2. (a) Find a diagonal matrix D orthogonally similar to the matrix

$$A = \begin{bmatrix} 1 & \frac{1}{3} & 0 \\ \frac{1}{3} & 1 & \frac{1}{4} \\ 0 & \frac{1}{4} & 1 \end{bmatrix}.$$

(b) Verify Theorems 3.1 and 3.2 for the matrix A.

(c) Find a matrix P such that $PAP^{-1} = D$.

3. Discuss the question of canonical forms for real symmetric matrices under the equivalence relation of orthogonal similarity; that is, $B = PAP^{-1}$, where $P^{-1} = P^{\mathsf{T}}$.

4. Suppose that the characteristic polynomial of a symmetric matrix A in its factored form is

$$(\lambda - \lambda_1)^{m_1}(\lambda - \lambda_2)^{m_2} \cdots (\lambda - \lambda_k)^{m_k}; \quad m_1 + m_2 + \cdots + m_k = n.$$

Show that the subspace M_{λ_i} of Theorem 1.1 associated with the characteristic value λ_i has dimension m_i.

Hint: Let $PAP^{-1} = \text{Diagonal } [\underbrace{\lambda_1, \lambda_1, \cdots, \lambda_1}_{m_1 \text{ TIMES}};\ \underbrace{\lambda_2, \cdots, \lambda_2}_{m_2 \text{ TIMES}};\ \cdots]$. Now consider the space generated by $\mathbf{E}_s P^{-1}$ for $s = 1, 2, \cdots, m_1$.

4. Quadratic Forms and Generalized Quadratic Surfaces

A geometric interpretation of a change of variables in the real quadratic form

$$Q(\mathbf{X}) = \sum_{i,j=1}^{n} x_i a_{ij} x_j \tag{4.1}$$

was given in Chapter 8, §4. At that time, we permitted any change of variables

$$[y_1, y_2, \cdots, y_n]P = [x_1, x_2, \cdots, x_n], \tag{4.2}$$

where P was a real nonsingular matrix. This change of variables was looked upon as a change to a new coordinate system in E_n. However, such a change usually involves a coordinate system that is not Cartesian.

We now wish to see how far we can reduce a real quadratic form if we permit only orthogonal matrices P in (4.2); that is, if we simply rotate or reflect the axes of E_n.

In texts on plane analytic geometry, the student will find that a rotation of Cartesian axes (Chapter 6, § 1, Example 1) through an angle $\theta = \frac{1}{2} \arctan \dfrac{2b}{a - c}$ will transform the quadratic form

$$[x_1, x_2]\begin{bmatrix} a & b \\ b & c \end{bmatrix}\begin{bmatrix} x_1 \\ x_2 \end{bmatrix} = a{x_1}^2 + 2bx_1x_2 + c{x_2}^2$$

to the form

$$[x_1{}^*, x_2{}^*]\begin{bmatrix} a^* & 0 \\ 0 & c^* \end{bmatrix}\begin{bmatrix} x_1{}^* \\ x_2{}^* \end{bmatrix} = a^*(x_1{}^*)^2 + c^*(x_2{}^*)^2.$$

This is the result we are going to generalize to quadratic forms in n variables. It will simply be an application and interpretation of the results of § 3. Let us illustrate the general theory with an example.

Example 1. Consider the quadratic form

$$Q(\mathbf{X}) = [x_1, x_2, x_3]\begin{bmatrix} -1 & -4 & 2 \\ -4 & 1 & -2 \\ 2 & -2 & -2 \end{bmatrix}\begin{bmatrix} x_1 \\ x_2 \\ x_3 \end{bmatrix} = \mathbf{X}A\mathbf{X}^{\mathsf{T}}.$$

The matrix A is the matrix considered in Example 1, § 3, and we have seen that for the matrix

$$P = \begin{bmatrix} \frac{2}{3} & \frac{1}{3} & -\frac{2}{3} \\ \frac{1}{3} & \frac{2}{3} & \frac{2}{3} \\ \frac{2}{3} & -\frac{2}{3} & \frac{1}{3} \end{bmatrix},$$

$PAP^{\mathsf{T}} = PAP^{-1} = \text{Diagonal}\,[-3, -3, 6]$. Therefore, if in the quadratic form $Q(\mathbf{X})$ we make the change of variables

$$(4.3) \qquad [x_1, x_2, x_3] = [y_1, y_2, y_3]\begin{bmatrix} \frac{2}{3} & \frac{1}{3} & -\frac{2}{3} \\ \frac{1}{3} & \frac{2}{3} & \frac{2}{3} \\ \frac{2}{3} & -\frac{2}{3} & \frac{1}{3} \end{bmatrix},$$

the quadratic form $Q(\mathbf{X})$ is replaced by the quadratic form

$$Q(\mathbf{Y}P) = Q^*(\mathbf{Y}) = \mathbf{Y}PAP^{\mathsf{T}}\mathbf{Y}^{\mathsf{T}} = [y_1, y_2, y_3]\begin{bmatrix} -3 & 0 & 0 \\ 0 & -3 & 0 \\ 0 & 0 & +6 \end{bmatrix}\begin{bmatrix} y_1 \\ y_2 \\ y_3 \end{bmatrix}.$$

Geometrically, we can think of the change of variables described by (4.3) as follows: Let (x_1, x_2, x_3) be the coordinates of a point P relative to a Cartesian coordinate system (Figure 4.1).

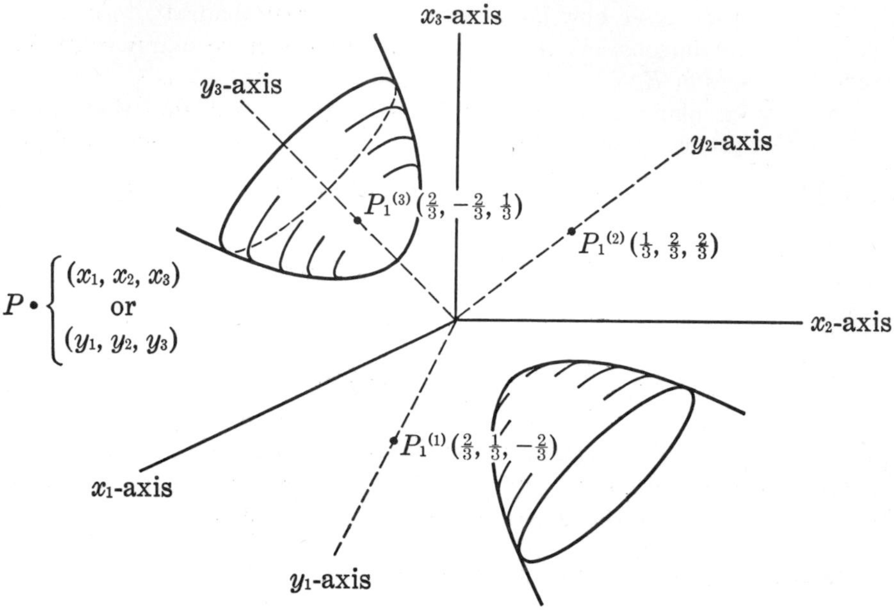

Figure 4.1

We choose the elements of the rows of the matrix P as the coordinates of new unit points $P_1^{(1)}$, $P_1^{(2)}$, $P_1^{(3)}$ for a new coordinate system. For an arbitrary point $P(x_1, x_2, x_3)$ with coordinates (y_1, y_2, y_3) relative to the new coordinate system, we have the following vector relation

$$[x_1, x_2, x_3] = x_1\mathbf{E}_1 + x_2\mathbf{E}_2 + x_3\mathbf{E}_3 = y_1[\tfrac{2}{3}, \tfrac{1}{3}, -\tfrac{2}{3}] + y_2[\tfrac{1}{3}, \tfrac{2}{3}, \tfrac{2}{3}] + y_3[\tfrac{2}{3}, -\tfrac{2}{3}, \tfrac{1}{3}],$$

and the linear relation between coordinates is given by (4.3).

The new unit points are at unit distance from the origin and lie on three mutually perpendicular lines so that we look on this change of variables as a rotation (or reflection) of Cartesian axes.

If, in Figure 4.1, we consider

$$Q(\mathbf{X}) = 1$$

as the equation of a surface in the x_i-coordinate system, then

$$Q^*(\mathbf{Y}) = -3y_1^2 - 3y_2^2 + 6y_3^2 = 1$$

is the equation of the surface in the y_i-coordinate system.

We point out that the coefficients of the y_i^2 are the characteristic values of the matrix A and that $y_3 = 1/\sqrt{6}$ is the point where the surface cuts the y_3-axis. Of course, for the negative characteristic values there is no intersection with the corresponding axis.

It is also of interest to note that, in the original quadratic form $Q(\mathbf{X})$, $Q([\frac{2}{3}, -\frac{2}{3}, \frac{1}{3}]) = 6$. We shall provide an interpretation of this in the general discussion to follow.

Our example may serve as a guide to the general reduction of a real quadratic form by means of a change of variables, $\mathbf{X} = \mathbf{Y}P$, where P is an orthogonal $n \times n$ matrix. The geometric interpretation for quadratic surfaces, $Q(\mathbf{X}) = 1$, in E_n is also parallel to that in the example.

We begin with a real quadratic form in n variables

$$Q(\mathbf{X}) = \sum_{i,j=1}^{n} x_i a_{ij} x_j = \mathbf{X} A \mathbf{X}^{\mathsf{T}}, \tag{4.4}$$

where $\mathbf{X} = [x_1, x_2, \cdots, x_n]$ and $A = [a_{ij}] = A^{\mathsf{T}}$. Now A is a real symmetric matrix and, from Theorem 3.3, there exists an orthogonal matrix P such that $PAP^{\mathsf{T}} = PAP^{-1} = \text{Diagonal } [\lambda_1, \lambda_2, \cdots, \lambda_n]$. Hence, if we make a change of variables

$$\mathbf{X} = \mathbf{Y}P \tag{4.5}$$

in the quadratic form $Q(\mathbf{X})$, we obtain the quadratic form

$$Q(\mathbf{Y}P) = Q^*(\mathbf{Y}) = \mathbf{Y}PAP^{\mathsf{T}}\mathbf{Y}^{\mathsf{T}} = \lambda_1 y_1^2 + \lambda_2 y_2^2 + \cdots + \lambda_n y_n^2, \tag{4.6}$$

where, of course, the λ_i are the characteristic values of the matrix A.

We may think of the change of variables in (4.5) as a rotation (or reflection) of coordinate axes in E_n, where the coordinates of the new unit points in E_n are the elements of the rows of the matrix P (see §6, Chapter 7). If $(x_1, x_2, \cdots, x_n)$ are the coordinates of a point P relative to the natural axes, then $(y_1, y_2, \cdots, y_n)$ are the coordinates of P in the new coordinate system. Thus, a generalized quadratic surface whose equation is

$$Q(\mathbf{X}) = \sum_{i,j=1}^{n} x_i a_{ij} x_j = 1$$

has the equation

$$Q^*(\mathbf{Y}) = \lambda_1 y_1^2 + \lambda_2 y_2^2 + \cdots + \lambda_n y_n^2 = 1 \tag{4.7}$$

in a properly chosen coordinate system.

Geometrically, the new coordinate axes (lines in the direction of the orthogonal vectors forming the rows of the matrix P) used in obtaining the equation (4.7) are called the *principal axes* of the generalized quadratic surface $Q(\mathbf{X}) = 1$. Note that the directions of these principal axes are in the directions of characteristic vectors of the matrix A associated with the characteristic values λ_i.

The line segment of E_n from the origin along one of the principal axes associated with $\lambda_i \neq 0$ and having length $1/\sqrt{|\lambda_i|}$ is called a *semi-axis;* when $\lambda_i > 0$, the end point of this segment will satisfy the equation of the surface. The verification of this is left to the student.

There are several results concerning principal axes which depend on calculus; we shall give an intuitive geometric sketch of them and leave the analytic proofs to the student in the exercises.

As usual, when dealing with points of E_n, we associate with the vector $\mathbf{P} = [p_1, p_2, \cdots, p_n]$ the line segment from the origin to $P(p_1, p_2, \cdots, p_n)$. If $P(p_1, p_2, \cdots, p_n)$ is a point of E_n on the surface

$$Q(\mathbf{X}) = \sum_{i,j=1}^{n} x_i a_{ij} x_j = (\mathbf{X}A, \mathbf{X}) = 1,$$

then $(\mathbf{P}A, \mathbf{P}) = 1$. Let $X(x_1, x_2, \cdots, x_n)$ be any other point not lying on the surface. The vector equation of the line PX is

$$\mathbf{Y} = \mathbf{P} + t(\mathbf{X} - \mathbf{P}).$$

If we insist that the point P be the only point of the line PX on the surface, then it is reasonable to assume that the locus of all such points X is the *tangent hyperplane* to the surface at P. On the other hand, the line $\mathbf{Y} = \mathbf{P} + t(\mathbf{X} - \mathbf{P})$ intersects $Q(\mathbf{X}) = 1$ at those points Y for which

$$Q(\mathbf{Y}) = \{\mathbf{P} + t(\mathbf{X} - \mathbf{P})\}A\{\mathbf{P} + t(\mathbf{X} - \mathbf{P})\}^{\mathsf{T}} = 1,$$

or

$$2t\mathbf{P}A(\mathbf{X} - \mathbf{P})^{\mathsf{T}} + t^2(\mathbf{X} - \mathbf{P})A(\mathbf{X} - \mathbf{P})^{\mathsf{T}} = 0. \tag{4.8}$$

Clearly $t = 0$ is a solution of (4.8), and this will be the only solution if $\mathbf{P}A(\mathbf{X} - \mathbf{P})^{\mathsf{T}} = 0$ and $(\mathbf{X} - \mathbf{P})A(\mathbf{X} - \mathbf{P})^{\mathsf{T}} \neq 0$. Therefore, it is reasonable to call

$$\mathbf{P}A(\mathbf{X} - \mathbf{P})^{\mathsf{T}} = 0 \quad \text{or} \quad \mathbf{P}A\mathbf{X}^{\mathsf{T}} = 1, \tag{4.9}$$

where $\mathbf{X}$ is considered as a variable vector, the equation of the tangent hyperplane to the surface at the point $P(p_1, p_2, \cdots, p_n)$.

Two rather obvious remarks are in order:

1. From (4.9) we see that if $\mathbf{P}$ is a characteristic vector of A, then the tangent hyperplane at $P(p_1, p_2, \cdots, p_n)$ is perpendicular to $\mathbf{P}$. Thus, the tangent hyperplane is perpendicular to the semi-axes (for $\lambda_i > 0$).

2. The distance from the origin to the tangent hyperplane is easily seen to be (Chapter 4, § 3)

$$d^2 = \frac{1}{(\mathbf{P}A, \mathbf{P}A)}.$$

Again, if $\mathbf{P}$ happens to be a characteristic vector of A associated with $\lambda_i > 0$, then

$$d^2 = \frac{1}{\lambda_i(\mathbf{P}A, \mathbf{P})} = \frac{1}{\lambda_i}.$$

If all characteristic values are positive, it may be shown analytically that the shortest distance to the quadratic surface from the origin is along the principal axis associated with the largest characteristic value, and that the longest distance is along the principal axis associated with the smallest characteristic value.

EXERCISES

1. Use the method of this section to find a rotation which will bring $x_1^2 + 8x_1x_2 + 7x_2^2 = 3$ into a form containing no x_1x_2 term. Check your result by the trigonometric formula of plane geometry.

2. Find the principal axes and transform to reduced form:

$$2x_1^2 + 2x_1x_2 + x_2^2 + 2x_3^2 = 1.$$

3. Prove that for positive characteristic values one end of a semi-axis lies on a generalized quadratic surface.

4. Prove (using calculus) that the equation of the tangent plane to the surface $Q(\mathbf{X}) = \mathbf{X}A\mathbf{X}^\mathsf{T} = 1$, at the point $P(p_1, p_2, \cdots, p_n)$ on the surface, is $\mathbf{P}A\mathbf{X}^\mathsf{T} = 1$.

5. Prove analytically that the minimum distance from the origin to the generalized quadratic surface is $1/\sqrt{\lambda_i}$, where λ_i is the maximum characteristic value > 0.

*5. Unitary and Hermitian Matrices

We have avoided any detailed consideration of the complex vector space $V_n(C)$ throughout the text and it has entered in this chapter only to the extent that we desired any real matrix to have characteristic values and characteristic vectors. In this section we shall briefly note some of the distinctive features which arise when vectors with complex components and matrices with complex elements are permitted.

On rereading this book it would be found that most of the theory of vector spaces, linear transformations, and matrices is applicable to $V_n(C)$ (indeed to $V_n(F)$, where F is any field). Some theorems could be improved; for example, Theorem 3.1 of Chapter 8 could be changed to permit the reduction of a symmetric matrix of rank r to a diagonal matrix whose first r diagonal elements are 1 with zeros elsewhere. Trouble will arise whenever properties of the inner product are used which depend, in any sense, on the condition: $(\mathbf{X}, \mathbf{X}) > 0$ unless $\mathbf{X} = \mathbf{0}$. This property is no longer true if we use our original definition of inner product for $V_n(C)$. Consider this inner product, $(\mathbf{X}, \mathbf{X}) = x_1^2 + x_2^2$ for $V_2(C)$, in the cases $\mathbf{X} = [1, i]$, $[0, 1 - i]$, $[i, i]$. The results are 0, $1 - 2i$, -2, respectively. The possibility of an inner product being zero for a nonzero vector will destroy many of our proofs. For example, consider the proof at the beginning of §3 of this chapter that symmetric matrices have real characteristic values; this theorem is valid only for real symmetric matrices.

The correction of our difficulty is relatively simple. We seek a way to define (**X**, **Y**) for vectors of $V_n(C)$ which will give the same answer as the original definition when the components are real but will return positiveness to (**X**, **X**). We recall that the product of a complex number, $a + bi$, and its conjugate, $a - bi$, is $a^2 + b^2 > 0$ unless $a = b = 0$. Therefore we define the inner product for two vectors of $V_n(C)$ as follows:

$$(5.1)\qquad \begin{aligned}(\mathbf{X}, \mathbf{Y}) &= ([x_1, x_2, \cdots, x_n], [y_1, y_2, \cdots, y_n])\\ &= x_1\bar{y}_1 + x_2\bar{y}_2 + \cdots + x_n\bar{y}_n,\end{aligned}$$

where the bar stands, as usual, for complex conjugation.

The inner product for $V_n(C)$ has the following properties:

(i) $(\mathbf{X} + \mathbf{Y}, \mathbf{Z}) = (\mathbf{X}, \mathbf{Z}) + (\mathbf{Y}, \mathbf{Z})$;
(ii) $(\mathbf{X}, \mathbf{Y} + \mathbf{Z}) = (\mathbf{X}, \mathbf{Y}) + (\mathbf{X}, \mathbf{Z})$;
(iii) $(\mathbf{X}, \mathbf{Y}) = \overline{(\mathbf{Y}, \mathbf{X})}$;
(iv) $(a\mathbf{X}, \mathbf{Y}) = a(\mathbf{X}, \mathbf{Y})$;
(v) $(\mathbf{X}, a\mathbf{Y}) = \bar{a}(\mathbf{X}, \mathbf{Y})$;
(vi) $(\mathbf{X}, \mathbf{X}) > 0$ unless $\mathbf{X} = \mathbf{0}$; $(\mathbf{0}, \mathbf{0}) = 0$.

Of these, (iii) and (v) are rather disturbing. We have lost commutativity and have to watch our scalar multiples. It turns out that commutativity was a mere convenience but that positiveness is a necessity.

The new inner product for $V_n(C)$ makes it possible to reformulate practically all the results concerned with inner products, such as the Schwarz inequality, orthogonality, and the Gram-Schmidt process. A simple geometric interpretation is, however, lacking.

In the theory of linear transformations and matrices, the first essential use of the positiveness property of inner products was in the discussion of orthogonal transformations and matrices. However, before proceeding, we must introduce a little new terminology to express our results in matrix terms. Given an $n \times m$ matrix $A = [a_{ij}]$ whose elements are from the complex field C, define the $m \times n$ matrix A^* whose element in the ith row and jth column is $\bar{a}_{ji}$ (complex conjugate) to be the *conjugate transpose* of A. Now it is easy to see that $(AB)^* = B^*A^*$ and that, for $\mathbf{X}, \mathbf{Y} \in V_n(C)$, $(\mathbf{X}, \mathbf{Y}) = \mathbf{X}\mathbf{Y}^*$.

Paralleling our discussion for orthogonal transformations of $V_n(R)$, we may define a *unitary transformation* T of $V_n(C)$ as one for which $(\mathbf{X}\mathrm{T}, \mathbf{X}\mathrm{T}) = (\mathbf{X}, \mathbf{X})$ for all $\mathbf{X} \in V_n(C)$. If A is the matrix such that $\mathbf{X}\mathrm{T} = \mathbf{X}A$, that is, if A is the matrix of T with respect to the natural basis, we have

$$(\mathbf{X}, \mathbf{X}) = (\mathbf{X}\mathrm{T}, \mathbf{X}\mathrm{T}) = (\mathbf{X}A, \mathbf{X}A) = \mathbf{X}A(\mathbf{X}A)^* = \mathbf{X}AA^*\mathbf{X}^*$$

for all $\mathbf{X}$ of $V_n(C)$. It follows that $AA^* = I$, or $A^{-1} = A^*$; such a matrix is called a *unitary matrix*. It is easy to see that unitary transformations are represented by unitary matrices with respect to any orthonormal basis, where orthogonality for $V_n(C)$ is given by an obvious generalization of the definition for $V_n(R)$ in terms of the new inner product.

Unitary transformations form a group as do unitary matrices. The rows and columns of unitary matrices are orthonormal sets of vectors from $V_n(C)$. The determinants of unitary matrices have unit absolute value and, in general, the theory parallels the orthogonal case.

It is clear by now that the complex generalization of a real symmetric matrix is not a complex symmetric matrix but a matrix such that $A = A^*$. Matrices with the latter property are called *Hermitian*. If A is an Hermitian matrix, the form

$$[x_1, x_2, \cdots, x_n]A[x_1, x_2, \cdots, x_n]^*$$

is a generalization of a real quadratic form $Q(\mathbf{X})$ and is called an *Hermitian* form. For example,

$$\begin{bmatrix} 1 & i \\ -i & 1 \end{bmatrix}$$

is an Hermitian matrix, and an associated form is

$$x\bar{x} - iy\bar{x} + ix\bar{y} + y\bar{y}.$$

Hermitian forms have the property of being equal to their own conjugates; hence, for any assignment of values from C to $x_1, x_2, \cdots, x_n$ the result will be a real number.

The student can easily verify that the proof of Theorem 3.1 may be translated to Hermitian matrices. It follows that the characteristic values of any Hermitian matrix are real. The rest of the theory of §3 generalizes readily, and we can prove: An Hermitian matrix is similar under a unitary change of basis to a diagonal matrix

$$\text{Diagonal } [\lambda_1, \lambda_2, \cdots, \lambda_n],$$

where the λ_i are real numbers.

The preceding sketch, in which most of the proofs have been omitted or briefly indicated, must suffice to present the essential details of the theory for the complex case. Hermitian matrices and forms are used extensively in electronics and in modern physics. Proofs have been omitted here not because they are difficult but simply because they would be almost word-for-word repetitions of existing proofs with "conjugate transpose" replacing "transpose" and with a little care for the order of inner products. The student is urged to take a theorem such as the Gram-Schmidt process, Theorem 6.2, Chapter 3, or one of the theorems of §3 of this chapter and carry out the proofs in the complex case.

For complete details, the interested reader should consult other books such as *Finite-Dimensional Vector Spaces* by P. Halmos.

CHAPTER 11

Similarity of Matrices

The basic problems for the similarity of real $n \times n$ matrices whose characteristic vectors generate $V_n(R)$ have been essentially solved in Chapter 10. In this chapter the problems will be investigated both for wider classes of square matrices and for fields other than the real number field. While our primary concern remains with the case where a linear transformation T on $V_n(R)$ is given varying matrix representations by changes of bases for $V_n(R)$, the more general development is of interest both mathematically and for its applications to other fields of study.

Our problems are analogous to those discussed in connection with the congruence of symmetric matrices. We begin with a set of $n \times n$ matrices $\{A, B, \cdots\}$ and a group of nonsingular $n \times n$ matrices $G = \{P, \cdots\}$; then B is similar to A if there is a $P \in G$ such that $B = PAP^{-1}$. Similarity is, as we have seen, an equivalence relation, and we seek:

1. A method of selection of one matrix from each equivalence class; the problem of canonical forms.

2. A list of quantities which are determined by a matrix A, and which are the same for any matrix similar to A (that is, quantities *invariant* under similarity) and such that two matrices are similar if and only if they have the same invariants; the problem of a complete set of invariants.

For those $n \times n$ matrices whose characteristic vectors generate $V_n(R)$ our canonical matrices are diagonal matrices (with a prescribed order for the diagonal elements), and our list of invariants is the set of characteristic values with their multiplicities. We seek substitutes for those cases where the characteristic vectors of a matrix do not generate $V_n(R)$. The concept of invariant subspaces, now to be studied, will provide the substitutes.

1. Invariant Subspaces

We fix our attention and our notation for the next four sections on a given linear transformation on $V_n(R)$ denoted by T, and a matrix representation A of T given by

$$[x_1, x_2, \cdots, x_n]\mathrm{T} = [x_1, x_2, \cdots, x_n]A.$$

Many of our definitions will be given for the linear transformation T with the obvious analogue for the matrix A being omitted.

The student will note that no special properties of the real numbers are used in the first four sections of this chapter so that the real field R could equally well be replaced by any field F; also, applying the isomorphism developed in Chapter 3, he will see that any finite-dimensional vector space may be considered in place of $V_n(R)$.

The subspaces M_λ generated by the characteristic vectors associated with a particular characteristic value λ of a linear transformation T have the property that $(M_\lambda)\mathrm{T} \subseteq M_\lambda$ since $\mathbf{X}\mathrm{T} = \lambda\mathbf{X}$ for any $\mathbf{X} \in M_\lambda$. We generalize these subspaces in the following manner:

DEFINITION 1.1. *A subspace V of $V_n(R)$ is called an* INVARIANT SUBSPACE *of $V_n(R)$ (for T) if $(V)\mathrm{T} \subseteq V$; that is, for each vector $\mathbf{X} \in V$, $\mathbf{X}\mathrm{T} \in V$.*

From a matrix point of view, a subspace V of $V_n(R)$ is an invariant subspace for the matrix A if, for each $\mathbf{X} \in V$, $\mathbf{X}A \in V$. The subspaces M_λ mentioned above are examples of invariant subspaces. We can easily show that these are not the only ones; for example, $\{\mathbf{0}\}$ and $V_n(R)$ itself are certainly invariant subspaces.

Example 1. Let A be the matrix

$$\begin{bmatrix} 3 & -1 & 3 \\ -2 & 2 & -3 \\ -2 & 1 & -2 \end{bmatrix}$$

and define a linear transformation T by $[x_1, x_2, x_3]\mathrm{T} = [x_1, x_2, x_3]A$.

Let $\mathbf{X} = [1, 0, 0]$; then $\mathbf{X}\mathrm{T} = [3, -1, 3]$ and $\mathbf{X}\mathrm{T}^2 = [3, -1, 3]\mathrm{T} = [5, -2, 6] = -[1, 0, 0] + 2[3, -1, 3] = -\mathbf{X} + 2\mathbf{X}\mathrm{T}$. It is now easy to see that $\mathbf{X}\mathrm{T}^i$ for $i = 0, 1, 2, \cdots$ is a linear combination of $\mathbf{X}$ and $\mathbf{X}\mathrm{T}$. For example, $\mathbf{X}\mathrm{T}^3 = (\mathbf{X}\mathrm{T}^2)\mathrm{T} = (-\mathbf{X} + 2\mathbf{X}\mathrm{T})\mathrm{T} = -\mathbf{X}\mathrm{T} + 2\mathbf{X}\mathrm{T}^2 = -\mathbf{X}\mathrm{T} + 2(-\mathbf{X} + 2\mathbf{X}\mathrm{T}) = -2\mathbf{X} + 3\mathbf{X}\mathrm{T}$. It is a simple induction to see that $\mathbf{X}\mathrm{T}^k = -(k-1)\mathbf{X} + k(\mathbf{X}\mathrm{T})$. If we denote $L\{\mathbf{X}, \mathbf{X}\mathrm{T}\}$ by V, we can conclude at once that V is an invariant subspace of $V_3(R)$ for T (or A).

If we are to compute the characteristic values of A in the manner of the last chapter, we must solve:

$$\begin{vmatrix} 3-\lambda & -1 & 3 \\ -2 & 2-\lambda & -3 \\ -2 & 1 & -2-\lambda \end{vmatrix} = 0,$$

or $(1-\lambda)^3 = 0$. The only characteristic value is $\lambda = 1$.

The characteristic vectors may be determined by solving

$$[x_1, x_2, x_3]\begin{bmatrix} 3 & -1 & 3 \\ -2 & 2 & -3 \\ -2 & 1 & -2 \end{bmatrix} = [x_1, x_2, x_3],$$

which reduces to the single equation $x_1 - x_2 - x_3 = 0$. Hence, the vectors [1, 1, 0] and [1, 0, 1] form a basis for the space M_1. It is easy to establish the fact that the vector [1, 0, 0] is not dependent on the vectors [1, 0, 1] and [1, 1, 0] so that $V \neq M_1$.

Note that the characteristic vectors of A do not generate $V_3(R)$.

The use of "invariant" in the phrase "invariant subspace of $V_n(R)$ for the matrix A" differs from the use of the same word in the phrase "complete set of invariants under similarity." In "invariant subspace" attention is being called to the fact that a subspace of $V_n(R)$ is mapped into itself by a linear transformation T associated in a *specific way* with the matrix A. Matrices similar to A but also representing T can, and usually do, yield different invariant subspaces of $V_n(R)$.

Let V be an invariant subspace for the matrix A and let $B = PAP^{-1}$. If $\mathbf{X} \in V$, then $(\mathbf{X}P^{-1})B = \mathbf{X}P^{-1}PAP^{-1} = (\mathbf{X}A)P^{-1} = \mathbf{Y}P^{-1}$, where $\mathbf{Y} = \mathbf{X}A$ is a vector of V since V is an invariant subspace for A. Hence, the subspace $(V)P^{-1}$ is an invariant subspace for the matrix B. In general, the subspace $(V)P^{-1} \neq V$, although equality could conceivably occur. We leave it to the student to show that every invariant subspace for the matrix B is of the form $(W)P^{-1}$, where W is an invariant subspace for the matrix A.

The method used in Example 1 to find an invariant subspace can be generalized to $V_n(R)$. Specifically, let T be a linear transformation on $V_n(R)$ and let $\mathbf{X}$ be an arbitrary vector. Since there are $n + 1$ vectors in the set

$$\{\mathbf{X}, \mathbf{XT}, \mathbf{XT}^2, \cdots, \mathbf{XT}^n\},$$

the vectors are linearly dependent. Let $\mathbf{XT}^k$ be the first vector dependent on the preceding vectors so that

$$\mathbf{XT}^k = a_0\mathbf{X} + a_1(\mathbf{XT}) + \cdots + a_{k-1}(\mathbf{XT}^{k-1}). \tag{1.1}$$

The subspace

$$V = L\{\mathbf{X}, \mathbf{XT}, \cdots, \mathbf{XT}^{k-1}\} \tag{1.2}$$

is an invariant subspace for T. It is only necessary to note that any vector

$$\mathbf{Y} = c_0\mathbf{X} + c_1(\mathbf{XT}) + \cdots + c_{k-1}(\mathbf{XT}^{k-1}) \in V$$

has the image

$$\mathbf{YT} = c_0(\mathbf{XT}) + c_1(\mathbf{XT}^2) + \cdots + c_{k-1}(\mathbf{XT}^k)$$

under T and that equation (1.1) may be used on the last term on the right to express $\mathbf{XT}^k$ as a linear combination of the vectors $\mathbf{X}, \mathbf{XT}, \cdots, \mathbf{XT}^{k-1}$. Hence $\mathbf{YT} \in V$.

DEFINITION 1.2. *An invariant subspace of the form*

$$V = L\{\mathbf{X}, \mathbf{X}\mathrm{T}, \cdots, \mathbf{X}\mathrm{T}^{k-1}\}$$

is called the CYCLIC *subspace of* $V_n(R)$ *generated by* $\mathbf{X}$ (*with respect to* T).

A similar definition for a matrix A would use the notation

$$L\{\mathbf{X}, \mathbf{X}A, \cdots, \mathbf{X}A^{k-1}\}.$$

For brevity, a cyclic subspace will be denoted by $L\{\mathbf{X}\mathrm{T}^i\}$ (or $L\{\mathbf{X}A^i\}$). Note that it is not essential to specify k unless the dimension of the cyclic subspace is of particular interest; $\mathbf{X}\mathrm{T}^m \in V$ for any non-negative integer m by the induction method indicated in Example 1.

Although we have already used the idea of a matrix polynomial, $a_0I + a_1A + \cdots + a_kA^k$ (Chapter 10, § 1, Exercise 6), it will be convenient to formalize the ideas of a *polynomial in a linear transformation* and a *matrix polynomial.*

DEFINITION 1.3. *Let* $p(x)$ *be an element of* $R[x]$,

$$p(x) = a_mx^m + a_{m-1}x^{m-1} + \cdots + a_1x + a_0;$$

let T *be a linear transformation on* $V_n(R)$; *and let* A *be an* $n \times n$ *matrix. By* $p(\mathrm{T})$, *we mean the linear transformation*

$$a_m\mathrm{T}^m + a_{m-1}\mathrm{T}^{m-1} + \cdots + a_1\mathrm{T} + a_0\mathrm{I}$$

on $V_n(R)$. *By* $p(A)$, *we mean the* $n \times n$ *matrix*

$$a_mA^m + a_{m-1}A^{m-1} + \cdots + a_1A + a_0I.$$

It is an exercise for the student to verify that, if $p(x)$ and $q(x) \in R[x]$ and $p(x)q(x) = s(x)$, then

$$(\mathbf{X}p(\mathrm{T}))q(\mathrm{T}) = (\mathbf{X}q(\mathrm{T}))p(\mathrm{T}) = \mathbf{X}s(\mathrm{T}).$$

The result we wish to formulate is that, for any vector $\mathbf{X}$ of $V_n(R)$ and any linear transformation T on $V_n(R)$, there is a unique monic polynomial $m(x)$ of $R[x]$ of minimal degree such that $\mathbf{X}m(\mathrm{T}) = \mathbf{0}$. To see that at least one monic polynomial with this property exists, simply transpose the right-hand side of (1.1) to the left to obtain

$$\mathbf{X}(\mathrm{T}^k - a_{k-1}\mathrm{T}^{k-1} - \cdots - a_1\mathrm{T} - a_0\mathrm{I}) = \mathbf{0}.$$

There is no nonzero polynomial of lower degree with this property since this would imply the linear dependence of $\mathbf{X}, \mathbf{X}\mathrm{T}, \cdots, \mathbf{X}\mathrm{T}^{k-1}$ contrary to the assumption on k in (1.1). (Why?) The student may verify that the same contradiction would arise if there were two distinct monic polynomials of degree k, $m_1(x)$ and $m_2(x)$, such that $\mathbf{X}m_1(\mathrm{T}) = \mathbf{X}m_2(\mathrm{T}) = \mathbf{0}$.

DEFINITION 1.4. *The monic polynomial $m(x)$ of smallest degree such that, for $\mathbf{X} \in V_n(R)$, and* T *a linear transformation on $V_n(R)$, $\mathbf{X}m(\mathrm{T}) = 0$, is called the* RELATIVE MINIMAL POLYNOMIAL *of* $\mathbf{X}$ (*for* T).

If $p(x)$ is a polynomial such that $\mathbf{X}p(\mathrm{T}) = \mathbf{0}$, then $m(x)$ divides $p(x)$. To see this, write the general result of the division of $p(x)$ by $m(x)$:

$$p(x) = q(x)m(x) + r(x),$$

where $r(x)$ has degree less than that of $m(x)$ or is zero. Then, $\mathbf{0} = \mathbf{X}p(\mathrm{T}) = \mathbf{X}(q(\mathrm{T})m(\mathrm{T}) + r(\mathrm{T})) = \mathbf{X}r(\mathrm{T})$. But then $r(x) = 0$ since, as defined above, no polynomial of lower degree than $m(x)$ will have the property that $\mathbf{X}r(\mathrm{T}) = \mathbf{0}$. Therefore $m(x)$ divides $p(x)$ since the remainder is zero.

The discussion following Example 1 may be combined in the following statements:

THEOREM 1.1. *Let* T *be a linear transformation on $V_n(R)$ and* $\mathbf{X}$ *be a vector of $V_n(R)$. Then,*

(i) *$V = L\{\mathbf{X}\mathrm{T}^i\}$ is an invariant subspace for* T.

(ii) *There exists a unique monic polynomial $m(x)$ of minimum degree such that $\mathbf{X}m(\mathrm{T}) = \mathbf{0}$.*

(iii) *The dimension of V and the degree of $m(x)$ are equal.*

(iv) *The polynomial $m(x)$ divides every polynomial $p(x)$ with the property that $\mathbf{X}p(\mathrm{T}) = \mathbf{0}$.*

Example 2. The relative minimal polynomial of [1, 0, 0] with respect to the matrix A of Example 1 is $x^2 - 2x + 1$, as may be seen from the equation $\mathbf{X}\mathrm{T}^2 = -\mathbf{X} + 2\mathbf{X}\mathrm{T}$, given in that example.

Invariant subspaces are to be used in the succeeding sections to replace the spaces M_λ. We know that, if $\lambda_1 \neq \lambda_2$, $M_{\lambda_1} \cap M_{\lambda_2} = \mathbf{0}$ and that, if the characteristic vectors associated with the characteristic values $\lambda_1, \lambda_2, \cdots, \lambda_k$ generate $V_n(R)$,

$$V_n(R) = M_{\lambda_1} \oplus M_{\lambda_2} \oplus \cdots \oplus M_{\lambda_k}.$$

Unfortunately, it is not true that two different invariant subspaces have a zero intersection. In Example 1, $M_1 \cap V = L\{[2, -1, 3]\}$. However, we are going to show that it is possible to find cyclic subspaces, $L\{\mathbf{X}_1\mathrm{T}^i\}, \cdots, L\{\mathbf{X}_s\mathrm{T}^i\}$, for any linear transformation T such that

$$V_n(R) = L\{\mathbf{X}_1\mathrm{T}^i\} \oplus \cdots \oplus L\{\mathbf{X}_s\mathrm{T}^i\}. \tag{1.3}$$

The direct sum decomposition (1.3) and its equivalent for other spaces will enable us to give the answers to the problems of similarity of matrices raised at the beginning of the chapter.

EXERCISES

1. Let A be the matrix

$$\begin{bmatrix} 0 & 2 & -1 \\ -2 & 3 & 0 \\ -2 & 0 & 3 \end{bmatrix}.$$

(a) What is the dimension of the cyclic subspace $V_1 = L\{[1, 0, 0]A^i\}$?
(b) What is the relative minimal polynomial of $[1, 0, 0]$ for A?
(c) What is the dimension of the cyclic subspace $V_2 = L\{[1, -1, 0]A^i\}$?
(d) What is the relative minimal polynomial of $[1, -1, 0]$ for A?
(e) Show that $V_1 \cap V_2 \neq 0$; find a basis of $V_1 \cap V_2$.
(f) Find the relative minimal polynomials of the basis vectors found in (e).
(g) Find the GCD of the answers to (b) and (d) and compare the result with the answer to (f).

2. Show that, if A and B are similar $n \times n$ matrices, every invariant subspace of B is of the form $(W)P^{-1}$, where $B = PAP^{-1}$ and W is an invariant subspace for A.

3. If T is a nonsingular linear transformation, show that any invariant subspace for T is also an invariant subspace for T^{-1}.

4. Show that for any linear transformation T on $V_n(R)$, and any two polynomials $p(x)$ and $q(x)$ of $R[x]$, $p(\mathrm{T})q(\mathrm{T}) = q(\mathrm{T})p(\mathrm{T})$. State and prove the equivalent result for matrices.

5. State results about sums of polynomials which are analogous to the statements of Exercise 4. Were any of these results utilized in the discussion leading to Theorem 1.1?

6. Let $m(x)$ be the relative minimal polynomial of a vector $\mathbf{X}$ of $V_n(R)$ for a linear transformation T. If $\mathbf{X}^* \in L\{\mathbf{X}\mathrm{T}^i\}$, show that the relative minimal polynomial of $\mathbf{X}^*$ divides $m(x)$.

7. Let V_1 and V_2 be invariant subspaces of $V_n(R)$ for the linear transformation T. Show that $V_1 + V_2$ and $V_1 \cap V_2$ are invariant subspaces for T.

2. Cyclic Subspaces

In this section, we shall again use the notation of $V_n(R)$. The student is reminded to observe that our results can readily be phrased in terms of other fields F and of more general vector spaces.

For cyclic spaces, we can go beyond the statement of Exercise 7 of the last section to obtain a theorem leading directly to our goal of expressing $V_n(R)$ as a direct sum of cyclic subspaces.

THEOREM 2.1. *Let* T *be a linear transformation of* $V_n(R)$. *If the relative minimal polynomials of vectors* $\mathbf{X}_1$ *and* $\mathbf{X}_2$ *are* $m_1(x)$ *and* $m_2(x)$ *respectively, where* $m_1(x)$ *and* $m_2(x)$ *are relatively prime, then:*

(i) $L\{\mathbf{X}_1\mathrm{T}^i\} \cap L\{\mathbf{X}_2\mathrm{T}^i\} = \mathbf{0}$.

(ii) *The relative minimal polynomial of* $\mathbf{X} = \mathbf{X}_1 + \mathbf{X}_2$ *is* $m_1(x)m_2(x)$.

(iii) $L\{\mathbf{X}_1\mathrm{T}^i\} \oplus L\{\mathbf{X}_2\mathrm{T}^i\} = L\{\mathbf{X}\mathrm{T}^i\}$.

Conversely, if $\mathbf{X}$ *is a vector of* $V_n(R)$ *whose relative minimal polynomial* $m(x)$ *factors into relatively prime factors* $m_1(x)$ *and* $m_2(x)$, *then:*

(iv) *The relative minimal polynomials of* $\mathbf{X}_1 = \mathbf{X}m_2(\mathrm{T})$ *and* $\mathbf{X}_2 = \mathbf{X}m_1(\mathrm{T})$ *are* $m_1(x)$ *and* $m_2(x)$ *respectively.*

(v) $L\{\mathbf{X}\mathrm{T}^i\} = L\{\mathbf{X}_1\mathrm{T}^i\} \oplus L\{\mathbf{X}_2\mathrm{T}^i\}$.

Proof. (i) Suppose $\mathbf{Y} \in L\{\mathbf{X}_1\mathrm{T}^i\} \cap L\{\mathbf{X}_2\mathrm{T}^i\}$. Then $\mathbf{Y}m_1(\mathrm{T}) = \mathbf{Y}m_2(\mathrm{T}) = \mathbf{0}$ by Exercise 6 of the previous section. Also, by Theorem 4.2, Chapter 9, we may find polynomials $p(x)$ and $q(x)$ such that

$$1 = m_1(x)p(x) + m_2(x)q(x). \tag{2.1}$$

Hence,

$$\mathbf{Y} = \mathbf{Y} \cdot \mathrm{I} = \mathbf{Y}(m_1(\mathrm{T})p(\mathrm{T}) + m_2(\mathrm{T})q(\mathrm{T})) = \mathbf{0},$$

which is the desired conclusion.

(ii) Denote the relative minimal polynomial of $\mathbf{X} = \mathbf{X}_1 + \mathbf{X}_2$ by $m(x)$. Note that $\mathbf{0} = \mathbf{X}m(\mathrm{T}) = \mathbf{X}_1m(\mathrm{T}) + \mathbf{X}_2m(\mathrm{T})$, so that

$$\mathbf{X}_1m(\mathrm{T}) = -\mathbf{X}_2m(\mathrm{T}).$$

The left-hand member of the equation above is an element of $L\{\mathbf{X}_1\mathrm{T}^i\}$, while the vector on the right is an element of $L\{\mathbf{X}_2\mathrm{T}^i\}$. Therefore, from (i), we have

$$\mathbf{X}_1m(\mathrm{T}) = -\mathbf{X}_2m(\mathrm{T}) = \mathbf{0}.$$

Part (iv) of Theorem 1.1 then assures us that $m_1(x)$ and $m_2(x)$ divide $m(x)$. As $m_1(x)$ and $m_2(x)$ are relatively prime, $m_1(x)m_2(x)$ divides $m(x)$. (Why?) On the other hand,

$$\mathbf{X}m_1(\mathrm{T})m_2(\mathrm{T}) = (\mathbf{X}_1m_1(\mathrm{T}))m_2(\mathrm{T}) + (\mathbf{X}_2m_2(\mathrm{T}))m_1(\mathrm{T}) = \mathbf{0} + \mathbf{0} = \mathbf{0},$$

so that $m(x)$ divides $m_1(x)m_2(x)$; or, combining the results, $m(x) = m_1(x)m_2(x)$.

(iii) We again apply (2.1) to obtain

$$\begin{aligned}\mathbf{X} = \mathbf{X} \cdot \mathrm{I} &= \mathbf{X}m_1(\mathrm{T})p(\mathrm{T}) + \mathbf{X}m_2(\mathrm{T})q(\mathrm{T}) \\ &= (\mathbf{X}_1 + \mathbf{X}_2)m_1(\mathrm{T})p(\mathrm{T}) + (\mathbf{X}_1 + \mathbf{X}_2)m_2(\mathrm{T})q(\mathrm{T}) \\ &= \mathbf{X}_2m_1(\mathrm{T})p(\mathrm{T}) + \mathbf{X}_1m_2(\mathrm{T})q(\mathrm{T}).\end{aligned}$$

Thus, $\mathbf{X}$ is the sum of a vector of $L\{\mathbf{X}_2\mathrm{T}^i\}$ and a vector of $L\{\mathbf{X}_1\mathrm{T}^i\}$ so that

$L\{\mathbf{X}T^i\} \subseteq L\{\mathbf{X}_1T^i\} \oplus L\{\mathbf{X}_2T^i\}$. The dimension of $L\{\mathbf{X}T^i\}$ is the degree of $m(x)$ which is the sum of the degrees of $m_1(x)$ and $m_2(x)$. Therefore the dimension of $L\{\mathbf{X}T^i\}$ is the sum of the dimensions of $L\{\mathbf{X}_1T^i\}$ and $L\{\mathbf{X}_2T^i\}$, and

$$L\{\mathbf{X}T^i\} = L\{\mathbf{X}_1T^i\} \oplus L\{\mathbf{X}_2T^i\}.$$

We turn to the converse statements.

(iv) We have $\mathbf{X}_1m_1(T) = \mathbf{X}m_2(T)m_1(T) = \mathbf{0}$ so that the relative minimal polynomial of $\mathbf{X}_1$, say $m_1^*(x)$, divides $m_1(x)$. If $m_1^*(x)$ were of smaller degree than $m_1(x)$ (that is, not $m_1(x)$),

$$\mathbf{X}m_2(T)m_1^*(T) = \mathbf{X}_1m_1^*(T) = \mathbf{0}$$

and $m_2(x)m_1^*(x)$ would be a polynomial of smaller degree than $m(x)$, which annihilates $\mathbf{X}$. This is impossible, and $m_1(x) = m_1^*(x)$.

A precisely similar argument applies to $\mathbf{X}_2$.

(v) $L\{\mathbf{X}_1T^i\} \cap L\{\mathbf{X}_2T^i\} = \mathbf{0}$ by part (i). Since $\mathbf{X}_1$, $\mathbf{X}_2$ are contained in $L\{\mathbf{X}T^i\}$, $L\{\mathbf{X}T^i\} \supseteq L\{\mathbf{X}_1T^i\} \oplus L\{\mathbf{X}_2T^i\}$. The dimension argument given in (iii) may now be used to establish the equality.

Example 1. For a linear transformation T, we choose one whose matrix with respect to the $\{\mathbf{E}_i\}$ basis for $V_4(R)$ is

$$A = \begin{bmatrix} 3 & -1 & -1 & -2 \\ 1 & 1 & -1 & -1 \\ 1 & 0 & 0 & -1 \\ 0 & -1 & 1 & 1 \end{bmatrix}.$$

Let $\mathbf{X}_1 = [1, -1, -1, 0]$; $\mathbf{X}_1A = [1, -2, 0, 0]$, $\mathbf{X}_1A^2 = [1, -3, 1, 0]$. It is easy to see that $\mathbf{X}_1$ and $\mathbf{X}_1A$ are linearly independent and that $\mathbf{X}_1A^2 = 2(\mathbf{X}_1A) - \mathbf{X}_1$ or $\mathbf{X}_1(A^2 - 2A + I) = \mathbf{0}$. The relative minimal polynomial of $\mathbf{X}_1$ is, then, $x^2 - 2x + 1 = (x - 1)^2 = m_1(x)$.

Let $\mathbf{X}_2 = [1, 0, -1, -1]$; then $\mathbf{X}_2A = [2, 0, -2, -2] = 2\mathbf{X}_2$. The relative minimal polynomial of $\mathbf{X}_2$ is $x - 2 = m_2(x)$. Then, for $\mathbf{X} = \mathbf{X}_1 + \mathbf{X}_2 = [2, -1, -2, -1]$, the relative minimal polynomial must be $(x - 1)^2(x - 2) = x^3 - 4x^2 + 5x - 2 = m(x)$.

As a check,

$$\begin{aligned} \mathbf{X}A &= [3, -2, -2, -2] \\ \mathbf{X}A^2 &= [5, -3, -3, -4] \\ \mathbf{X}A^3 &= [9, -4, -6, -8], \end{aligned}$$

and it is a simple matter to establish that $\mathbf{X}$, $\mathbf{X}A$, $\mathbf{X}A^2$ are linearly independent and that

$$\mathbf{X}A^3 = 4\mathbf{X}A^2 - 5\mathbf{X}A + 2\mathbf{X}.$$

The student may wish to check the other statements of Theorem 2.1 for this example.

THEOREM 2.2. *Let* T *be a linear transformation of* $V_n(R)$; *let* V *be an invariant subspace for* T, *and let* $L\{\mathbf{X}\mathrm{T}^i\}$ *be a cyclic subspace of maximum dimension which is contained in* V *(that is,* $\mathbf{X} \in V$*). Then, if* $m(x)$ *is the relative minimal polynomial of* $\mathbf{X}$, $(V)m(\mathrm{T}) = \mathbf{0}$.

Proof. Let a basis for V be $\{\mathbf{X}_1, \mathbf{X}_2, \cdots, \mathbf{X}_r\}$ and denote by $m_i(x)$ the relative minimal polynomial of $\mathbf{X}_i$. We wish to show that $m_i(x)$ divides $m(x)$ for any $i = 1, \cdots, r$.

Let $p_1(x), p_2(x), \cdots, p_t(x)$ be the distinct irreducible polynomials appearing in the factorizations of $m(x)$ and $m_i(x)$ for an arbitrary (but fixed) i. By a modification of the standard representation (Theorem 5.2, Chapter 9), we may write

$$\begin{aligned} m(x) &= p_1(x)^{a_1}p_2(x)^{a_2} \cdots p_t(x)^{a_t} \\ m_i(x) &= p_1(x)^{b_1}p_2(x)^{b_2} \cdots p_t(x)^{b_t}, \end{aligned} \tag{2.2}$$

where $a_j \geq 0$, $b_j \geq 0$, but where the possibility that some of the exponents may actually be zero is not excluded. Further, choose the numbering of the $p_j(x)$ so that $a_j \geq b_j$ for $j = 1, 2, \cdots, k$, and $b_j > a_j$ for $j = k + 1, \cdots, t$. Our problem is to show that $k = t$.

If $k < t$, define $\mathbf{Y}_1$ and $\mathbf{Y}_2$ as follows:

$$\begin{aligned} \mathbf{Y}_1 &= \mathbf{X}p_{k+1}(\mathrm{T})^{a_{k+1}} \cdots p_t(\mathrm{T})^{a_t}; \\ \mathbf{Y}_2 &= \mathbf{X}_i p_1(\mathrm{T})^{b_1} \cdots p_k(\mathrm{T})^{b_k}. \end{aligned}$$

The minimum polynomial of $\mathbf{Y}_1$ is $p(x) = p_1(x)^{a_1} \cdots p_k(x)^{a_k}$ and that of $\mathbf{Y}_2$ is $q(x) = p_{k+1}(x)^{b_{k+1}} \cdots p_t(x)^{b_t}$ by part (v) of Theorem 2.1. Then the minimum polynomial of $\mathbf{Y} = \mathbf{Y}_1 + \mathbf{Y}_2$ is $p(x)q(x)$, which has degree greater than $m(x)$. However, $\mathbf{Y} \in V$ and $L\{\mathbf{Y}\mathrm{T}^i\} \subseteq V$, so that the relative minimal polynomial of $\mathbf{Y}$ cannot be of greater degree than that of $\mathbf{X}$ since $L\{\mathbf{X}\mathrm{T}^i\}$ was of maximal dimension. This contradiction establishes that $k = t$.

COROLLARY 1. *There is a vector* $\mathbf{X} \in V_n(R)$ *such that the relative minimal polynomial* $m(x)$ *of* $\mathbf{X}$ *has the property that* $(V_n(R))m(\mathrm{T}) = \mathbf{0}$; *that is,* $m(\mathrm{T}) = 0$.

Proof. $V_n(R)$ is an invariant subspace for T. Thus the theorem states that it is only necessary to find a vector $\mathbf{X}$ such that $L\{\mathbf{X}\mathrm{T}^i\}$ is of maximum dimension in order to satisfy the corollary.

COROLLARY 2. *If* T *is a linear transformation of* $V_n(R)$, *then there exists a polynomial* $m(x) \in R[x]$ *of minimum degree such that* $m(\mathrm{T}) = 0$, *and for any polynomial* $p(x)$ *such that* $p(\mathrm{T}) = 0$, $m(x)$ *divides* $p(x)$.

The proof of Corollary 2 is left for the student.

DEFINITION 2.1. *The (necessarily unique) monic polynomial of minimum degree such that* $m(\mathrm{T}) = 0$ *for a linear transformation* T *of* $V_n(R)$ *is called the* MINIMUM POLYNOMIAL OF T. *A similar definition applies to an arbitrary matrix* A.

Note that the minimum polynomial for a linear transformation T does not depend on any particular matrix representation of T. Of course, the degree of the minimum polynomial is less than or equal to n.

For an invariant subspace V, the polynomial $m(x)$ described in the statement of Theorem 2.2 may occasionally be called the *relative* (with respect to T) *minimal polynomial* of V as well as of **X**. It is the polynomial $m(x)$ of least degree such that the linear transformation $m(\mathrm{T})$ annihilates V. The minimum polynomial of a linear transformation T is the relative minimal polynomial of $V_n(R)$.

Example 2. Let us find the minimum polynomial for the linear transformation T of Example 1. There we have already found a vector **X** with the relative minimal polynomial of degree 3,

$$m(x) = x^3 - 4x^2 + 5x - 2.$$

If we compute $A^3 - 4A^2 + 5A - 2I$, we obtain the zero matrix. Since $m(A)$ takes every vector of $V_4(R)$ to $\mathbf{0}$, so does $m(\mathrm{T})$, and $m(\mathrm{T}) = 0$. It is easy to see that no polynomial of lower degree will do this.

The student may complain that the vectors $\mathbf{X}_1$ and $\mathbf{X}_2$ and, thus, **X** of Example 1 were given a priori and no way to find a satisfactory vector **X** *ab initio* for Corollary 1 of Theorem 2.2 has been demonstrated. The difficulty is that, with examples of reasonably small dimension, one is almost certain to choose a vector whose relative minimal polynomial is, at the same time, the minimum polynomial of the linear transformation T.

A general prescription for finding a vector **X** such that the cyclic subspace $L\{\mathbf{X}\mathrm{T}^i\}$ has maximal dimension proceeds as follows:

(a) Choose a basis $\{\mathbf{X}_1, \mathbf{X}_2, \cdots, \mathbf{X}_n\}$ of $V_n(R)$.

(b) Compute the relative minimal polynomials of the vectors $\mathbf{X}_i$ for $i = 1, 2, \cdots, n$; that is,

$$m_i(x) = p_1(x)^{b_{i1}}p_2(x)^{b_{i2}} \cdots p_t(x)^{b_{it}},$$

where, as in the proof of Theorem 2.2, some of the b_{ij} may be zero.

(c) For $k = 1, 2, \cdots, t$, let b_k be the largest integer occurring in the set $\{b_{1k}, b_{2k}, \cdots, b_{nk}\}$ and find a vector $\mathbf{Y}_k$ whose relative minimal polynomial is $p_k(x)^{b_k}$. For example, if $b_1 = b_{11}$, then $\mathbf{Y}_1 = \mathbf{X}_1p_2(\mathrm{T})^{b_{12}}p_3(\mathrm{T})^{b_{13}} \cdots p_t(\mathrm{T})^{b_{1t}}$.

(d) Now, $\mathbf{Y} = \mathbf{Y}_1 + \mathbf{Y}_2 + \cdots + \mathbf{Y}_t$ has as its relative minimal polynomial $m_1(x) = p_1(x)^{b_1}p_2(x)^{b_2} \cdots p_k(x)^{b_t}$ and generates a cyclic subspace of maximal dimension.

We leave the proof of (d) for the student in Exercise 7 and illustrate with an example the process described.

Example 3. Again we use the linear transformation T of Example 1. Choose as a basis of $V_4(R)$:

$$\mathbf{X}_1 = [1, -1, 1, 0], \quad \mathbf{X}_2 = [0, 0, 1, 0],$$
$$\mathbf{X}_3 = [1, 0, -1, -1], \quad \mathbf{X}_4 = [0, 0, 0, 1].$$

The relative minimal polynomials of the basis vectors $\mathbf{X}_i$ are:

$$\begin{aligned} m_1(x) &= (x-1)^2 \\ m_2(x) &= (x-1)(x-2) \\ m_3(x) &= (x-2) \\ m_4(x) &= (x-1)^2. \end{aligned}$$

For part (c) of the discussion preceding this example, we let

$$\mathbf{Y}_1 = \mathbf{X}_1, \quad \mathbf{Y}_2 = \mathbf{X}_2(A - I) = [1, 0, -1, -1];$$

then $\mathbf{Y} = \mathbf{Y}_1 + \mathbf{Y}_2 = [2, -1, 0, -1]$ has the relative minimal polynomial $m(x) = (x-1)^2(x-2)$.

We have found a polynomial $m(x)$ such that $m(\mathrm{T})$ annihilates the basis vectors $\mathbf{X}_1, \mathbf{X}_2, \mathbf{X}_3, \mathbf{X}_4$, and hence $m(\mathrm{T}) = 0$; moreover $m(x)$ is the relative minimal polynomial for $\mathbf{Y}$ so that $L\{\mathbf{Y}\mathrm{T}^i\}$ is a cyclic subspace of maximal dimension.

EXERCISES

1. Let a linear transformation T of $V_4(R)$ be defined by $[x_1, x_2, x_3, x_4]\mathrm{T} = [x_1, x_2, x_3, x_4]A$, where

$$A = \begin{bmatrix} -2 & 4 & 1 & 1 \\ 0 & 1 & 0 & 0 \\ 0 & 0 & 1 & 0 \\ -1 & 0 & -1 & 0 \end{bmatrix}.$$

(a) What is the relative minimal polynomial of $\mathbf{E}_1$?

(b) Verify parts (i) and (ii) of Theorem 2.1 for the vectors $\mathbf{X}_1 = [0, 1, 0, 0]$ and $\mathbf{X}_2 = [-3, 4, 1, 1]$.

(c) What is the minimum polynomial of T?

2. Prove Corollary 2 of Theorem 2.2.

3. Find the minimum polynomial for the linear transformation represented by the matrix A of Exercise 1, §1.

4. Show that, if a linear transformation T on $V_n(R)$ has n distinct characteristic values, the minimum polynomial has degree n. What is the minimum polynomial in this case?

5. If the constant term in the minimum polynomial of a linear transformation T is not zero, prove that T is nonsingular. Is the converse true? If so, provide the proof.

6. If $m(x)$ is an arbitrary polynomial of $R[x]$ and $B = PAP^{-1}$, show that $Pm(A)P^{-1} = m(B)$.

Use this result to show directly that the minimum polynomials of similar matrices are equal.

7. Prove that the relative minimal polynomial of any vector $\mathbf{X}$ of $V_n(R)$ is a divisor of the minimum polynomial of T.

8. Prove that, if λ is a characteristic value of a linear transformation T, then $x - \lambda$ divides the minimum polynomial of T.

*9. Let the set of vectors $\{\mathbf{X}_1, \mathbf{X}_2, \cdots, \mathbf{X}_n\}$ be a basis for $V_n(R)$, the relative minimal polynomial of $\mathbf{X}_i$ being $m_i(x)$ for $i = 1, 2, \cdots, n$. Show that the minimum polynomial of T is the least common multiple of all the polynomials $m_i(x)$.

Hint: Modify the proof of Theorem 2.2 for the factorization of the n polynomials $m_i(x)$.

3. Direct Sums of Cyclic Subspaces; Invariant Factors

We continue the study of invariant subspaces in this section and prove that any invariant subspace of a linear transformation can be expressed as a direct sum of cyclic subspaces. This result is quite difficult to prove. However, once it is proved, the theory of canonical forms for matrices under similarity becomes comparatively easy. We have preferred to place the difficulty at one point rather than have recurring special problems to consider later. At first reading, it may be preferable to omit the proofs of Theorems 3.1, 3.2, and 3.3 and return to them after studying their utilization in the next section.

Throughout, it will be assumed that all spaces and polynomials are being considered with respect to a fixed linear transformation T of $V_n(R)$.

We begin with a theorem which is, in effect, the induction step for our principal theorem.

THEOREM 3.1. *Let V be an invariant subspace for a linear transformation* T *and let $L\{\mathbf{X}\mathrm{T}^i\}$ be a cyclic subspace of maximal dimension contained in V. If $V \neq L\{\mathbf{X}\mathrm{T}^i\}$, then there exists an invariant subspace W for* T *such that*

$$V = L\{\mathbf{X}\mathrm{T}^i\} \oplus W.$$

Proof. We know that there are invariant subspaces $W \subseteq V$ such that $L\{\mathbf{X}\mathrm{T}^i\} \cap W = \mathbf{0}$; namely, $W = \{\mathbf{0}\}$. Hence, let W be an invariant subspace in V of maximal dimension for which

$$L\{\mathbf{X}\mathrm{T}^i\} \cap W = \mathbf{0}.$$

If $V = L\{\mathbf{X}\mathrm{T}^i\} \oplus W$, we are through. Therefore we shall assume that $V \neq L\{\mathbf{X}\mathrm{T}^i\} \oplus W$ and show that this leads to a contradiction.

Let $m(x)$ be the relative minimal polynomial of $\mathbf{X}$ and, selecting a $\mathbf{Y} \in V$ but not in $L\{\mathbf{X}\mathrm{T}^i\} \oplus W$, let $n(x)$ be the polynomial of least degree such that $\mathbf{Y}n(\mathrm{T}) \in L\{\mathbf{X}\mathrm{T}^i\} \oplus W$; or

$$\mathbf{Y}n(\mathrm{T}) = \mathbf{X}g(\mathrm{T}) + \mathbf{Z}, \quad \text{where} \quad \mathbf{Z} \in W. \tag{3.1}$$

We show first that $n(x)$ divides any polynomial $p(x)$ such that $\mathbf{Y}p(\mathrm{T}) \in L\{\mathbf{X}\mathrm{T}^i\} \oplus W$. To this end, let

$$p(x) = d(x)n(x) + e(x),$$

where either the degree of $e(x)$ is less than the degree of $n(x)$ or $e(x) = 0$.

Then $\mathbf{Y}p(\mathrm{T}) = \mathbf{Y}n(\mathrm{T})d(\mathrm{T}) + \mathbf{Y}e(\mathrm{T}) \in L\{\mathbf{X}\mathrm{T}^i\} \oplus W$ and, since we know that $\mathbf{Y}n(\mathrm{T}) \in L\{\mathbf{X}\mathrm{T}^i\} \oplus W$, this implies that

$$\mathbf{Y}e(\mathrm{T}) \in L\{\mathbf{X}\mathrm{T}^i\} \oplus W.$$

But then, if $e(x) \neq 0$, $e(x)$ can qualify for consideration as $n(x)$; since $n(x)$ was of minimal degree we must conclude that $e(x) = 0$. In particular, it follows from Theorem 2.2 that

$$\mathbf{0} = \mathbf{Y}m(\mathrm{T}) \in L\{\mathbf{X}\mathrm{T}^i\} \oplus W,$$

and hence $n(x)$ divides $m(x)$; or

$$m(x) = d(x)n(x). \tag{3.2}$$

Now return to equation (3.1) and, for the polynomial $g(x)$ determined there, divide $g(x)$ by $n(x)$ so that

$$g(x) = q(x)n(x) + r(x),$$

where $r(x)$ has smaller degree than $n(x)$ or $r(x) = 0$.

We note that the vector $\mathbf{Y}^* = \mathbf{Y} - \mathbf{X}q(\mathrm{T})$ has the property that

$$\mathbf{Y}^*n(\mathrm{T}) = \mathbf{Y}n(\mathrm{T}) - \mathbf{X}q(\mathrm{T})n(\mathrm{T}) = \mathbf{X}r(\mathrm{T}) + \mathbf{Z}. \tag{3.3}$$

Hence $\mathbf{Y}^*n(\mathrm{T}) \in L\{\mathbf{X}\mathrm{T}^i\} \oplus W$, and no polynomial of smaller degree than $n(x)$ will map $\mathbf{Y}^*$ into $L\{\mathbf{X}\mathrm{T}^i\} \oplus W$ because this would imply that $n(x)$ is not the polynomial of least degree taking $\mathbf{Y}$ into $L\{\mathbf{X}\mathrm{T}^i\} \oplus W$. (Why?)

If we now multiply both sides of (3.3) by $d(\mathrm{T})$, where $d(x)$ is defined as in (3.2), we have

$$\begin{aligned} \mathbf{0} = \mathbf{Y}^*m(\mathrm{T}) = \mathbf{Y}^*n(\mathrm{T})d(\mathrm{T}) &= \mathbf{X}r(\mathrm{T})d(\mathrm{T}) + \mathbf{Z}d(\mathrm{T}), \\ \text{or} \qquad \mathbf{X}r(\mathrm{T})d(\mathrm{T}) &= -\mathbf{Z}d(\mathrm{T}). \end{aligned} \tag{3.4}$$

The left member of (3.4) is in $L\{\mathbf{X}\mathrm{T}^i\}$ and the right member is in W. Since $L\{\mathbf{X}\mathrm{T}^i\} \cap W = \mathbf{0}$, it follows that

$$\mathbf{X}r(\mathrm{T})d(\mathrm{T}) = -\mathbf{Z}d(\mathrm{T}) = \mathbf{0}.$$

If $r(x) \neq 0$, this last equation gives a polynomial of smaller degree than $m(x)$, annihilating $\mathbf{X}$, since $r(x)$ is of smaller degree than $n(x)$ and $m(x) = d(x)n(x)$; hence, we must conclude that $r(x) = 0$ and that $n(x)$ divides $g(x)$ so that $\mathbf{Y}^*n(\mathrm{T}) = \mathbf{Z}$ from (3.3).

Finally, we are prepared to show that

$$L\{\mathbf{X}\mathrm{T}^i\} \cap (W + L\{\mathbf{Y}^*\mathrm{T}^i\}) = \mathbf{0},$$

and this contradicts the assumption that W was an invariant subspace of maximum dimension disjoint from $L\{\mathbf{X}\mathrm{T}^i\}$ so that we must conclude $V = L\{\mathbf{X}\mathrm{T}^i\} \oplus W$. We note that $\mathbf{Y}^*$ is not in W, for if $\mathbf{Y}^*$ were in W, then $\mathbf{Y} - \mathbf{X}q(\mathrm{T}) \in W$ and $\mathbf{Y} \in L\{\mathbf{X}\mathrm{T}^i\} \oplus W$. Hence, the dimension of $W + L\{\mathbf{Y}^*\mathrm{T}^i\}$ is larger than the dimension of W and it is very easy to sec that $W + L\{\mathbf{Y}^*\mathrm{T}^i\}$ is an invariant subspace contained in V.

If $L\{\mathbf{X}T^i\} \cap (W + L\{\mathbf{Y}^*T^i\}) \neq \mathbf{0}$, we would have a relation of the form

$$(3.5) \qquad \mathbf{0} \neq \mathbf{X}f(T) = \mathbf{Z}^* + \mathbf{Y}^*s(T), \quad \text{where} \quad \mathbf{Z}^* \in W.$$

Then, dividing $s(x)$ by $n(x)$, $s(x) = b(x)n(x) + c(x)$, we get

$$\begin{aligned}\mathbf{X}f(T) &= \mathbf{Z}^* + \mathbf{Y}^*(n(T)b(T) + c(T)) \\ &= \mathbf{Z}^* + (\mathbf{Y}^*n(T))b(T) + \mathbf{Y}^*c(T),\end{aligned}$$

or, using $\mathbf{Y}^*n(T) = \mathbf{Z}$,

$$\mathbf{X}f(T) - \mathbf{Z}^* - \mathbf{Z}b(T) = \mathbf{Y}^*c(T).$$

If $c(x) \neq 0$, we contradict the minimality of degree for $n(x)$ since

$$\begin{aligned}\mathbf{Y}c(T) &= \mathbf{Y}^*c(T) + \mathbf{X}c(T)q(T) \\ &= \mathbf{X}f(T) + \mathbf{X}c(T)q(T) - \mathbf{Z}^* - \mathbf{Z}b(T) \in L\{\mathbf{X}T^i\} \oplus W.\end{aligned}$$

But if $c(x) = 0$, (3.5) may be used to show that $\mathbf{X}f(T) \in W$; hence $\mathbf{X}f(T) = \mathbf{0}$ (by $L\{\mathbf{X}T^i\} \cap W = \mathbf{0}$). Thus the contradiction is established; a vector $\mathbf{Y} \in V$, $\mathbf{Y} \notin L\{\mathbf{X}T^i\} \oplus W$ does not exist, and $V = L\{\mathbf{X}T^i\} \oplus W$.

THEOREM 3.2. *Let V be an invariant subspace for a linear transformation T. Then there exist vectors $\mathbf{X}_1, \mathbf{X}_2, \cdots, \mathbf{X}_k \in V$ such that*

(i) $V = L\{\mathbf{X}_1T^i\} \oplus L\{\mathbf{X}_2T^i\} \oplus \cdots \oplus L\{\mathbf{X}_kT^i\}$;

(ii) $L\{\mathbf{X}_jT^i\}$ *is a cyclic subspace of maximal dimension in*

$$V_j = L\{\mathbf{X}_jT^i\} \oplus \cdots \oplus L\{\mathbf{X}_kT^i\} \text{ for } j = 1, 2, \cdots, k;$$

(iii) *If $m_j(x)$ is the relative minimal polynomial of $\mathbf{X}_j$ for $j = 1, 2, \cdots, k$, then $m_{j+1}(x)$ divides $m_j(x)$ for $j = 1, 2, \cdots, k - 1$.*

Proof. We use induction on the dimension of V and merely piece together our previous results. The theorem is certainly true if the dimension of V is 1. Hence, assume that V has dimension greater than 1 and that the theorem is valid for invariant subspaces of smaller dimension.

If $V = L\{\mathbf{X}_1T^i\}$ we are through; otherwise we apply Theorem 3.1 to V to obtain

$$V = L\{\mathbf{X}_1T^i\} \oplus V_2,$$

where $L\{\mathbf{X}_1T^i\}$ is a cyclic subspace of maximal dimension in V and $(V)m_1(T) = \mathbf{0}$ by Theorem 2.2. By induction,

$$V_2 = L\{\mathbf{X}_2T^i\} \oplus \cdots \oplus L\{\mathbf{X}_kT^i\},$$

where the properties of the theorem are satisfied for the $L\{\mathbf{X}_jT^i\}$ and $m_j(x)$ with $j \geq 2$. Hence,

$$V = L\{\mathbf{X}_1T^i\} \oplus L\{\mathbf{X}_2T^i\} \oplus \cdots \oplus L\{\mathbf{X}_kT^i\},$$

and $m_j(x)$ divides $m_1(x)$ for $j \geq 2$ because $\mathbf{X}_jm_1(T) = \mathbf{0}$.

COROLLARY. *If* T *is a linear transformation of* $V_n(R)$, *then*

$$V_n(R) = L\{\mathbf{X}_1\mathrm{T}^i\} \oplus \cdots \oplus L\{\mathbf{X}_k\mathrm{T}^i\},$$

where $L\{\mathbf{X}_j\mathrm{T}^i\}$ *is a cyclic subspace of maximal dimension in*

$$V_j = L\{\mathbf{X}_j\mathrm{T}^i\} \oplus \cdots \oplus L\{\mathbf{X}_k\mathrm{T}^i\}$$

for $j = 1, 2, \cdots, k$.

Example 1. We again use for our illustration the matrix

$$A = \begin{bmatrix} 3 & -1 & -1 & -2 \\ 1 & 1 & -1 & -1 \\ 1 & 0 & 0 & -1 \\ 0 & -1 & 1 & 1 \end{bmatrix}.$$

We know from Example 2 of §2 that the minimum polynomial of A is $x^3 - 4x^2 + 5x - 2 = (x-1)^2(x-2)$. The vectors $\mathbf{X}_1 = [1, 0, 0, 0]$, $\mathbf{X}_1A = [3, -1, -1, -2]$, and $\mathbf{X}_1A^2 = [7, -2, -4, -6]$ are linearly independent so that $L\{\mathbf{X}_1A^i\}$ is a cyclic subspace of maximal dimension in $V_4(R)$ and the relative minimal polynomial of $\mathbf{X}_1$ is $(x-1)^2(x-2)$. The student may wish to verify this assertion.

We wish to find a cyclic subspace $L\{\mathbf{X}_2A^i\}$ such that

$$V = L\{\mathbf{X}_1A^i\} \oplus L\{\mathbf{X}_2A^i\}.$$

The method of the proof of Theorem 3.1 will produce a vector $\mathbf{Y}^*$ such that $L\{\mathbf{X}_1A^i\} \cap L\{\mathbf{Y}^*A^i\} = \mathbf{0}$ if W is not of maximal dimension. Indeed, it is not hard to see that the vector $[0, 0, 0, 1]$ is not in $L\{\mathbf{X}_1A^i\}$ and that

$$[0, 0, 0, 1](A - I) = [0, -1, 1, 0] = [1, 0, 0, 0](-A^2 + 3A - 2).$$

In the notation of the proof of Theorem 3.1, $m(x) = (x-1)^2(x-2)$; $n(x) = x - 1$; and $g(x) = -(x-1)(x-2)$. Hence, according to that proof,

$$\mathbf{Y}^* = \mathbf{X}_2 = [1, -1, -1, -1] = [0, 0, 0, 1] - [1, 0, 0, 0](-A + 2I)$$

has $(x - 1)$ as relative minimal polynomial and

$$L\{\mathbf{X}_1A^i\} \oplus L\{\mathbf{X}_2A^i\} = V_4(R).$$

Sure enough, $[1, -1, -1, -1]A = [1, -1, -1, -1]$, $L\{\mathbf{X}_2A^i\}$ is an invariant subspace for A, and

$$V_4(R) = L\{[1, 0, 0, 0], [3, -1, -1, -2], [7, -2, -4, -6]\} \oplus L\{[1, -1, -1, -1]\}.$$

DEFINITION 3.1. *The relative minimal polynomials,* $m_i(x)$, *of the vectors* $\mathbf{X}_i$ *occurring in the direct sum decomposition of* $V_n(R)$ *in the Corollary to Theorem* 3.2 *are called the* INVARIANT FACTORS *of the linear transformation* T.

Again, a similar definition applies to an $n \times n$ matrix A, when a decomposition of $V_n(R)$ is obtained using a matrix A in place of T in Theorem 3.2 and its Corollary.

The term "invariant factor" needs justification if the definition is to have any intrinsic meaning. The invariant factors, in their construction, might depend on the particular choice of vectors $\mathbf{X}_i$; or, for similar matrices representing T, we might not have the same invariant factors. Neither of these possibilities occurs; the invariant factors are worthy of their name. Indeed, we shall show in the next section that they are a *complete* list of invariants for matrices under similarity and an answer to problem 2 in the introduction to this chapter.

Of the two possibilities of difficulty mentioned above, the question of similar matrices may be regarded as a problem of a choice of vector representatives. Indeed, if $B = PAP^{-1}$, we have noted in § 1 that the behavior of A with respect to an invariant subspace V is identical to that of B on the space $(V)P^{-1}$. For the vectors $\mathbf{X}_i$ considered for A, we may substitute the vectors $\mathbf{X}_iP^{-1}$ for B. It is an extremely simple exercise to show that, if $p(x)$ is a polynomial of $R[x]$, $p(B) = Pp(A)P^{-1}$, and if $\mathbf{X}p(A) = \mathbf{Y}$, $(\mathbf{X}P^{-1})p(B) = (\mathbf{Y}P^{-1})$; in particular, if $\mathbf{X}p(A) = \mathbf{0}$, then $(\mathbf{X}P^{-1})p(B) = \mathbf{0}$.

A justification for the use of the term "invariant factors" for a linear transformation T is stated formally in the following theorem:

THEOREM 3.3. *If an invariant subspace V (relative to a linear transformation* T) *possesses two decompositions satisfying the conditions of Theorem* 3.2,

$$V = L\{\mathbf{X}_1\mathrm{T}^i\} \oplus \cdots \oplus L\{\mathbf{X}_r\mathrm{T}^i\},$$
$$V = L\{\mathbf{X}_1^*\mathrm{T}^i\} \oplus \cdots \oplus L\{\mathbf{X}_s^*\mathrm{T}^i\},$$

where the relative minimal polynomials of $\mathbf{X}_i$ and $\mathbf{X}_i^*$ are $m_i(x)$ and $m_i^*(x)$, then $r = s$ and $m_i(x) = m_i^*(x)$ for $i = 1, 2, \cdots, r$.

Proof. The theorem is obvious if the dimension of V is 1. Moreover, it is easy to see that it is true whatever the dimension of V if $r = 1$; the vectors $\mathbf{X}_1$ and $\mathbf{X}_1^*$ have as relative minimal polynomial the monic polynomial of least degree, $m(x)$, such that $(V)m(\mathrm{T}) = \mathbf{0}$. The degree of $m(x)$ is equal to the dimension of V so that $L\{\mathbf{X}_1^*\mathrm{T}^i\}$ must also be V. In any case, whether $r = 1$ or not, we must have $m_1(x) = m_1^*(x)$. (Why?)

For our induction, let us assume the theorem proved for all invariant subspaces of dimension less than n.

Let $p(x)$ be an irreducible polynomial of $R[x]$ dividing $m_1(x)$. The null space of $p(\mathrm{T})$ acting on V is an invariant subspace of V which does not include all of V except possibly when $m_1(x) = p(x)$. If $m_1(x) = p(x)$, then $m_j(x) = p(x)$ for $j = 1, 2, \cdots, r$, and, since $m_1(x) = m_1^*(x)$, $m_j^*(x) = p(x)$ for $j = 1, 2, \cdots, s$. Now a simple dimension argument yields $r = s$ and we are done. (How?) Otherwise, designate the null space of $p(\mathrm{T})$ contained in V by V', a space of lower dimension than V, and the induction hypothesis holds for V'.

For $\mathbf{Y} \in V'$, $\mathbf{Y} = \mathbf{X}_1p_1(\mathrm{T}) + \mathbf{X}_2p_2(\mathrm{T}) + \cdots + \mathbf{X}_rp_r(\mathrm{T})$,

$$(3.6) \quad \mathbf{0} = \mathbf{Y}p(\mathrm{T}) = \mathbf{X}_1p_1(\mathrm{T})p(\mathrm{T}) + \mathbf{X}_2p_2(\mathrm{T})p(\mathrm{T}) + \cdots + \mathbf{X}_rp_r(\mathrm{T})p(\mathrm{T}).$$

The expression in (3.6) is a decomposition of $\mathbf{0}$ into vectors from the direct summands of V and hence

$$\mathbf{X}_ip_i(\mathrm{T})p(\mathrm{T}) = \mathbf{0} \qquad \text{for } i = 1, 2, \cdots, r.$$

Therefore, $m_i(x)$ divides $p_i(x)p(x)$ since $m_i(x)$ is the relative minimal polynomial of $\mathbf{X}_i$.

Now either $m_i(x)$ divides $p_i(x)$, in which case $\mathbf{X}_ip_i(\mathrm{T})$ was $\mathbf{0}$ to begin with, or $p(x)$ divides $m_i(x)$ and $p_i(x)$ is a multiple of $m_i(x)/p(x) = q_i(x)$; that is,

$$p_i(x) = q_i(x)w_i(x).$$

Certainly if $p(x)$ divides $m_i(x)$, then $p(x)$ divides $m_j(x)$ for $j < i$; let h be the largest number for which $p(x)$ divides $m_h(x)$ and then

$$\mathbf{Y} = \mathbf{X}_1q_1(\mathrm{T})w_1(\mathrm{T}) + \cdots + \mathbf{X}_hq_h(\mathrm{T})w_h(\mathrm{T}).$$

Thus,

$$V' = L\{(\mathbf{X}_1q_1(\mathrm{T}))\mathrm{T}^i\} \oplus \cdots \oplus L\{(\mathbf{X}_hq_h(\mathrm{T}))\mathrm{T}^i\}$$

since every element in the sum is in V' and every element of V' has a representation as a sum of vectors from the indicated spaces.

Similarly

$$V' = L\{(\mathbf{X}_1^*q_1^*(\mathrm{T}))\mathrm{T}^i\} \oplus \cdots \oplus L\{(\mathbf{X}_{h'}^*q_{h'}^*(\mathrm{T}))\mathrm{T}^i\},$$

and we know that $h = h'$ from our induction hypothesis as both decompositions of V' satisfy Theorem 3.2. (The relative minimal polynomials of $\mathbf{X}_iq_i(\mathrm{T})$ and $\mathbf{X}_i^*q_i^*(\mathrm{T})$ are $p(x)$.)

If we choose $p(x)$ as an irreducible divisor of $m_r(x)$, we will have $h = r$ and $h' \leq s$ so that $r \leq s$. If we choose $p(x)$ to divide $m_s^*(x)$, then $h' = s$ and $h \leq r$ so that $s \leq r$. These inequalities give $r = s$.

Next, consider the range of $p(\mathrm{T})$ acting on V. Certainly, by Theorem 2.2, Chapter 6, $(V)p(\mathrm{T})$ is a proper subspace of V since V' is nonzero ($\mathbf{X}_1q_1(\mathrm{T}) \neq 0$ but $\mathbf{X}_1q_1(\mathrm{T})p(\mathrm{T}) = \mathbf{0}$). By an argument similar to that given above

$$\begin{aligned}(V)p(\mathrm{T}) &= L\{\mathbf{X}_1p(\mathrm{T})\} \oplus \cdots \oplus L\{\mathbf{X}_kp(\mathrm{T})\} \\ &= L\{\mathbf{X}_1^*p(\mathrm{T})\} \oplus \cdots \oplus L\{\mathbf{X}_{k'}^*p(\mathrm{T})\},\end{aligned}$$

where k and k' are the indices of the last $m_i(x)$ and $m_i^*(x)$ which differ from $p(x)$. Again, the induction assumption implies $k = k'$, and, further, an easy calculation shows that the relative minimal polynomial of $\mathbf{X}_ip(\mathrm{T})$ is

$q_i(x)$ and that of $\mathbf{X}_i{}^*p(\mathrm{T}) = q_i{}^*(x)$. The induction assumption now shows that $q_i(x) = q_i{}^*(x)$ or

$$m_i(x) = p(x)q_i(x) = p(x)q_i{}^*(x) = m_i{}^*(x).$$

This completes the proof.

COROLLARY. *The invariant factors of an $n \times n$ matrix A are independent of the particular vectors selected in a decomposition of $V_n(R)$ into cyclic subspaces satisfying Theorem 3.2, and are the same for any matrix $B = PAP^{-1}$, where P is a nonsingular $n \times n$ matrix.*

EXERCISES

1. Express $V_4(R)$ as the direct sum of cyclic subspaces satisfying Theorem 3.2 relative to the matrix

$$A = \begin{bmatrix} -2 & 4 & 1 & 1 \\ 0 & 1 & 0 & 0 \\ 0 & 0 & 1 & 0 \\ -1 & 0 & -1 & 0 \end{bmatrix}.$$

2. Verify Theorem 3.3 by finding a second decomposition of $V_4(R)$ for the matrix A in Exercise 1, starting with a different choice for $\mathbf{X}_1$.

3. Prove that, for any $n \times n$ matrix A, a nonsingular $n \times n$ matrix P, and $\mathbf{X}$ an arbitrary vector of $V_n(R)$, the relative minimal polynomials of $\mathbf{X}$ with respect to A and of $\mathbf{X}P^{-1}$ with respect to PAP^{-1} are identical.

4. Jordan Canonical Form for Matrices under Similarity

We begin by showing how a decomposition of $V_n(R)$ into invariant subspaces for a linear transformation T on $V_n(R)$ may lead to a simple matrix representation of T.

Initially, let T be represented by the matrix A with respect to the natural basis $\{\mathbf{E}_i\}$, so that

$$[x_1, x_2, \cdots, x_n]\mathrm{T} = [x_1, x_2, \cdots, x_n]A$$

for any vector $[x_1, x_2, \cdots, x_n]$ of $V_n(R)$. Next, assume that $V_n(R)$ is the direct sum of the invariant spaces V_1 and V_2:

$$V = V_1 \oplus V_2.$$

It follows that, if $\{\mathbf{X}_1, \mathbf{X}_2, \cdots, \mathbf{X}_k\}$ is a basis for V_1 and $\{\mathbf{X}_{k+1}, \mathbf{X}_{k+2}, \cdots, \mathbf{X}_n\}$ is a basis for V_2, $\{\mathbf{X}_1, \mathbf{X}_2, \cdots, \mathbf{X}_n\}$ is a basis for $V_n(R)$. Since V_1 and V_2 are invariant subspaces for T,

$$\begin{aligned} \mathbf{X}_i\mathrm{T} &= b_{i1}\mathbf{X}_1 + \cdots + b_{ik}\mathbf{X}_k, & i &= 1, 2, \cdots, k, \\ \mathbf{X}_j\mathrm{T} &= b_{j,\,k+1}\mathbf{X}_{k+1} + \cdots + b_{jn}\mathbf{X}_n, & j &= k+1, \cdots, n. \end{aligned}$$

Therefore, the matrix representation of T with respect to the $\{\mathbf{X}_i\}$ basis has the form:

$$B = \begin{bmatrix} b_{11} & \cdots & b_{1k} & 0 & \cdot & \cdot & \cdot & 0 \\ \cdot & & \cdot & \cdot & & & & \cdot \\ \cdot & & \cdot & \cdot & & & & \cdot \\ \cdot & & \cdot & \cdot & & & & \cdot \\ b_{k1} & \cdots & b_{kk} & 0 & \cdot & \cdot & \cdot & 0 \\ 0 & \cdots & 0 & b_{k+1,\,k+1} & & \cdots & & b_{k+1,\,n} \\ \cdot & & \cdot & \cdot & & & & \cdot \\ \cdot & & \cdot & \cdot & & & & \cdot \\ \cdot & & \cdot & \cdot & & & & \cdot \\ 0 & \cdots & 0 & b_{n,\,k+1} & & \cdots & & b_{nn} \end{bmatrix},$$

which may be abbreviated by

$$B = \begin{bmatrix} B_1 & 0 \\ 0 & B_2 \end{bmatrix},$$

where B_1 is $k \times k$, B_2 is $(n - k) \times (n - k)$, and the 0 submatrices are $k \times (n - k)$ and $(n - k) \times k$. These 0 matrices reflect the decomposition of $V_n(R)$ into invariant subspaces and the corresponding choice of basis. Finally, if P is the matrix by which the $\{\mathbf{X}_i\}$ basis is given in terms of the $\{\mathbf{E}_i\}$ basis, we know from the Corollary to Theorem 8.3 of Chapter 6 that

$$B = PAP^{-1}.$$

We can extend this procedure in a search for a particularly simple matrix to represent the equivalence class of the matrix A under similarity by utilizing the decomposition of $V_n(R)$ as given in Theorem 3.2:

$$V_n(R) = L\{\mathbf{X}_1\mathrm{T}^i\} \oplus L\{\mathbf{X}_2\mathrm{T}^i\} \oplus \cdots \oplus L\{\mathbf{X}_k\mathrm{T}^i\}. \tag{4.1}$$

Then we choose bases of the individual summands $L\{\mathbf{X}_j\mathrm{T}^i\}$ as follows:

$$\begin{array}{llll} \mathbf{Y}_1, & \mathbf{Y}_2, & \cdots, & \mathbf{Y}_{i_1} \in L\{\mathbf{X}_1\mathrm{T}^i\}, \\ \mathbf{Y}_{i_1+1}, & \mathbf{Y}_{i_1+2}, & \cdots, & \mathbf{Y}_{i_2} \in L\{\mathbf{X}_2\mathrm{T}^i\}, \\ \cdot\ \cdot\ \cdot & \cdot\ \cdot\ \cdot & \cdot\ \cdot\ \cdot & \cdot\ \cdot\ \cdot \\ \mathbf{Y}_{i_{k-1}+1}, & \mathbf{Y}_{i_{k-1}+2}, & \cdots, & \mathbf{Y}_n \in L\{\mathbf{X}_k\mathrm{T}^i\}. \end{array}$$

A simple generalization of our result for two summands shows that the matrix of T with respect to the resulting basis $\{\mathbf{Y}_1, \cdots, \mathbf{Y}_n\}$ of $V_n(R)$ has the form:

$$M = \begin{bmatrix} M_1 & 0 & \cdots & 0 \\ 0 & M_2 & & \cdot \\ \cdot & & \ddots & \cdot \\ \cdot & & & \cdot \\ 0 & \cdot & \cdot & M_k \end{bmatrix}, \tag{4.2}$$

where M_j is a square submatrix of order equal to the dimension of $L\{\mathbf{X}_j\mathrm{T}^i\}$

for $j = 1, \cdots, k$ and the 0 submatrices are of sizes required to fill out M. Again, if Q represents the change of basis from $\{\mathbf{E}_i\}$ to $\{\mathbf{Y}_i\}$,

$$M = QAQ^{-1}.$$

Except for the fact that the submatrices M_j need not be 1×1, we have a "diagonal matrix" similar to A.

What happens to M when we choose a new basis for a particular $L\{\mathbf{X}_j\mathrm{T}^i\}$? Clearly, the submatrix M_j is changed and the remainder of M is not affected at all. Hence, we can confine our attention in further simplifications to selecting bases for the spaces $L\{\mathbf{X}_j\mathrm{T}^i\}$ which will give the M_j a particularly simple form. As we work with each summand we are free to regard T as acting only on that space and to ignore, temporarily, the remainder of $V_n(R)$.

Example 1. We again use the matrix

$$A = \begin{bmatrix} 3 & -1 & -1 & -2 \\ 1 & 1 & -1 & -1 \\ 1 & 0 & 0 & -1 \\ 0 & -1 & 1 & 1 \end{bmatrix}.$$

From Example 1 of §3 we know that

$$V_4(R) = L\{\mathbf{X}_1\mathrm{T}^i\} \oplus L\{\mathbf{X}_2\mathrm{T}^i\},$$

where $\mathbf{X}_1 = [1, 0, 0, 0]$, $\mathbf{X}_2 = [1, -1, -1, -1]$, and the linear transformation T is associated with A by the choice of the $\{\mathbf{E}_i\}$ basis.

A simple computation will show that

$$\{[1, 0, 0, 0], [0, 1, -1, 0], [3, -1, -1, 2]\}$$

is a basis for $L\{\mathbf{X}_1\mathrm{T}^i\}$ and that $\{[1, -1, -1, -1]\}$ is a basis for $L\{\mathbf{X}_2\mathrm{T}^i\}$. Then, if

$$P = \begin{bmatrix} 1 & 0 & 0 & 0 \\ 0 & 1 & -1 & 0 \\ 3 & -1 & -1 & -2 \\ 1 & -1 & -1 & -1 \end{bmatrix},$$

$$P^{-1} = \tfrac{1}{2}\begin{bmatrix} 2 & 0 & 0 & 0 \\ -1 & 1 & 1 & -2 \\ -1 & -1 & 1 & -2 \\ 4 & 0 & -2 & 2 \end{bmatrix} \quad \text{and} \quad PAP^{-1} = \left[\begin{array}{ccc:c} 0 & 0 & 1 & 0 \\ 0 & 1 & 0 & 0 \\ -2 & 1 & 3 & 0 \\ \hdashline 0 & 0 & 0 & 1 \end{array}\right].$$

This is a matrix M as in (4.2). For the selected bases, the effect of T on $L\{\mathbf{X}_1\mathrm{T}^i\}$ may be represented by

$$M_1 = \begin{bmatrix} 0 & 0 & 1 \\ 0 & 1 & 0 \\ -2 & 1 & 3 \end{bmatrix}$$

and on $L\{\mathbf{X}_2\mathrm{T}^i\}$ by $M_2 = [1]$.

We return to our general discussion and proceed to select bases for $L\{\mathbf{X}_j\mathrm{T}^i\}$ in (4.1) that simplify the matrices M_j of (4.2).

Let us select as a basis of $L\{\mathbf{X}_j\mathrm{T}^i\}$ the set of vectors

$$\{\mathbf{X}_j, \mathbf{X}_j\mathrm{T}, \cdots, \mathbf{X}_j\mathrm{T}^{r_j-1}\},$$

where r_j is the degree of the invariant factor $m_j(x)$;

$$m_j(x) = x^{r_j} + a_{j,r_j-1}x^{r_j-1} + \cdots + a_{j,1}x + a_{j,0}.$$

That this set of vectors is indeed a basis for $L\{\mathbf{X}_j\mathrm{T}^i\}$ is almost obvious; the number of vectors is correct and they are independent since any relation of dependence would imply the existence of a polynomial of lower degree than r_j, which annihilates $\mathbf{X}_j$. The effect of T on this basis of $L\{\mathbf{X}_j\mathrm{T}^i\}$ is given by the equations:

$$\begin{aligned}
\mathbf{X}_j\mathrm{T} &= 0\cdot\mathbf{X}_j + 1\cdot(\mathbf{X}_j\mathrm{T}) + 0\cdot(\mathbf{X}_j\mathrm{T}^2) + \cdots + 0\cdot(\mathbf{X}_j\mathrm{T}^{r_j-1}),\\
(\mathbf{X}_j\mathrm{T})\mathrm{T} &= 0\cdot\mathbf{X}_j + 0\cdot(\mathbf{X}_j\mathrm{T}) + 1\cdot(\mathbf{X}_j\mathrm{T}^2) + \cdots + 0\cdot(\mathbf{X}_j\mathrm{T}^{r_j-1}),\\
&\cdots\cdots\cdots\cdots\cdots\cdots\\
(\mathbf{X}_j\mathrm{T}^{r_j-1})\mathrm{T} &= -a_{j,0}\mathbf{X}_j - a_{j,1}(\mathbf{X}_j\mathrm{T}) - \cdots - a_{j,r_j-1}(\mathbf{X}_j\mathrm{T}^{r_j-1}),
\end{aligned}$$

where the last equation is obtained from $\mathbf{X}_jm_j(\mathrm{T}) = \mathbf{0}$ by transposition of all but the leading term $\mathbf{X}_j\mathrm{T}^{r_j}$ to the right-hand side.

The corresponding matrix M_j (relative to the basis $\{\mathbf{X}_j, \cdots, \mathbf{X}_j\mathrm{T}^{r_j-1}\}$) is

$$(4.3) \qquad M_j = \begin{bmatrix} 0 & 1 & 0 & \cdots & 0 \\ 0 & 0 & 1 & \cdots & 0 \\ \vdots & \vdots & \vdots & \ddots & \vdots \\ 0 & 0 & 0 & \cdots & 1 \\ -a_{j,0} & -a_{j,1} & -a_{j,2} & \cdots & -a_{j,r_j-1} \end{bmatrix}.$$

Note that M_j is completely determined by $m_j(x)$; this fact leads to the following definition:

DEFINITION 4.1. *For a monic polynomial $p(x) \in R[x]$,*

$$p(x) = x^n + a_{n-1}x^{n-1} + \cdots + a_1x + a_0,$$

the COMPANION MATRIX $C(p(x))$ *is the* $n \times n$ *matrix*

$$(4.4) \qquad C(p(x)) = \begin{bmatrix} 0 & 1 & 0 & \cdots & 0 \\ 0 & 0 & 1 & \cdots & 0 \\ \vdots & \vdots & \vdots & \ddots & \vdots \\ 0 & 0 & 0 & \cdots & 1 \\ -a_0 & -a_1 & -a_2 & \cdots & -a_{n-1} \end{bmatrix}.$$

We now put together our results on the choice of bases for the subspaces $L\{\mathbf{X}_j\mathrm{T}^i\}$ and see that, with respect to the basis

$$\{\mathbf{X}_1, \mathbf{X}_1\mathrm{T}, \cdots, \mathbf{X}_1\mathrm{T}^{r_1-1}, \mathbf{X}_2, \mathbf{X}_2\mathrm{T}, \cdots, \mathbf{X}_2\mathrm{T}^{r_2-1}, \cdots, \mathbf{X}_k, \cdots, \mathbf{X}_k\mathrm{T}^{r_k-1}\} \tag{4.5}$$

of $V_n(R)$, the matrix associated with the linear transformation T (originally associated with the matrix A) is

$$C = \begin{bmatrix} C(m_1(x)) & & & \\ & C(m_2(x)) & & \\ & & \ddots & \\ & & & C(m_k(x)) \end{bmatrix}. \tag{4.6}$$

Stated otherwise, for any $n \times n$ matrix A there exists a matrix C defined by equations (4.4) and (4.6), where $m_1(x), \cdots, m_k(x)$ are the invariant factors of A, such that for some nonsingular matrix P,

$$C = PAP^{-1}.$$

In particular, P may be taken as the matrix expressing the basis of $V_n(R)$ in (4.5) in terms of the $\{\mathbf{E}_i\}$ basis.

DEFINITION 4.2. *Let A be an $n \times n$ matrix whose invariant factors are $m_1(x), m_2(x), \cdots, m_k(x)$. The matrix C of* (4.6) *is called the* JORDAN CANONICAL FORM *for the equivalence class of the matrix A under similarity. The matrix C is also called the* JORDAN CANONICAL MATRIX *representation of the linear transformation* T *of $V_n(R)$ defined by* $\mathbf{X}\mathrm{T} = \mathbf{X}A$.

There is no complete agreement on nomenclature. The matrix C is frequently called the *rational* cancnical form.

Example 2. To obtain the Jordan canonical form associated with the matrix A of Example 1, we select the basis

$$\{[1, 0, 0, 0], [3, -1, -1, -2], [7, -2, -4, -6], [1, -1, -1, -1]\}$$

of $V_4(R)$, where the first three vectors are $\mathbf{X}_1$, $\mathbf{X}_1\mathrm{T}$, and $\mathbf{X}_1\mathrm{T}^2$ and the last is $\mathbf{X}_2$ in our previous notation. The matrix P is, therefore,

$$P = \begin{bmatrix} 1 & 0 & 0 & 0 \\ 3 & -1 & -1 & -2 \\ 7 & -2 & -4 & -6 \\ 1 & -1 & -1 & -1 \end{bmatrix}, \quad \text{and} \quad P^{-1} = \begin{bmatrix} 1 & 0 & 0 & 0 \\ \frac{1}{2} & -1 & \frac{1}{2} & -1 \\ -\frac{3}{2} & 2 & -\frac{1}{2} & -1 \\ 2 & -1 & 0 & 1 \end{bmatrix}.$$

Then

$$PAP^{-1} = \left[\begin{array}{ccc:c} 0 & 1 & 0 & 0 \\ 0 & 0 & 1 & 0 \\ 2 & -5 & 4 & 0 \\ \hdashline 0 & 0 & 0 & 1 \end{array}\right] = \begin{bmatrix} M_1 & 0 \\ 0 & M_2 \end{bmatrix}.$$

We recall that $m_1(x) = x^3 - 4x^2 + 5x - 2$ (Example 2, §2), so that the elements in the bottom row of M_1 are indeed the appropriate coefficients of $m_1(x)$.

The terminology in our Definition 4.2 is a little premature. It remains to be shown that the Jordan canonical form is really canonical for the equivalence relation of similarity of matrices.

THEOREM 4.1. *An $n \times n$ matrix A is similar to one and only one Jordan canonical form; that is, a matrix of the form* (4.6) *where $m_j(x)$ divides $m_i(x)$ if $j \geq i$.*

Proof. We have already shown that a matrix A is similar to at least one Jordan canonical form; it remains to show that there is only one.

Suppose that A is similar to a Jordan canonical form as described in the hypothesis of the theorem, where, initially, the $m_i(x)$ have no significance aside from their definition by submatrices of C and their divisibility properties. We shall show that the $m_i(x)$ are, in fact, the uniquely determined invariant factors of A.

Specifically, associate a linear transformation T of $V_n(R)$ with A by means of the natural basis $\{\mathbf{E}_i\}$, and let the basis by which T is associated with the similar Jordan matrix $C = PAP^{-1}$ be

$$\{\mathbf{Y}_1, \mathbf{Y}_2, \cdots, \mathbf{Y}_n\}.$$

Note that from the form of $C(m_1(x))$,

$$\mathbf{Y}_1\mathrm{T} = \mathbf{Y}_2,\ \mathbf{Y}_2\mathrm{T} = \mathbf{Y}_3,\ \cdots,\ \mathbf{Y}_{r_1}\mathrm{T} = -a_{10}\mathbf{Y}_1 - a_{11}\mathbf{Y}_2 - \cdots - a_{1,\,r_1-1}\mathbf{Y}_{r_1},$$

where $m_1(x) = x^{r_1} + a_{1,\,r_1-1}x^{r_1-1} + \cdots + a_{11}x + a_{10}$. Hence, if we write $\mathbf{X}_1 = \mathbf{Y}_1$, we see that

$$L\{\mathbf{X}_1\mathrm{T}^i\} = L\{\mathbf{Y}_1, \mathbf{Y}_2, \cdots, \mathbf{Y}_{r_1}\}$$

is a cyclic space for which the relative minimal polynomial of $\mathbf{X}_1$ is $m_1(x)$. We proceed by writing $\mathbf{X}_2 = \mathbf{Y}_{r_1+1}$ and so on. The final result is a decomposition of $V_n(R)$ into cyclic subspaces with the divisibility properties of Theorem 3.2 and therefore, by Theorem 3.3, with the invariant factors $m_i(x)$ for T and consequently for A and C.

Theorem 4.1 offers a direct answer to problem 1 of the introduction to this chapter. The Jordan canonical forms are the selected representatives for each equivalence class of matrices under similarity. Although the answer to problem 2 is also implicit in the statement of the theorem, it is desirable to state it explicitly.

COROLLARY. *Two $n \times n$ matrices A and B are similar if and only if they have the same invariant factors.*

EXERCISES

1. Find the Jordan canonical form of the matrix

$$A = \begin{bmatrix} 1 & 0 & 2 \\ -3 & 1 & 4 \\ -1 & 2 & 2 \end{bmatrix}.$$

2. Find the Jordan canonical form of the matrix

$$A = \begin{bmatrix} -2 & 4 & 1 & 1 \\ 0 & 1 & 0 & 0 \\ 0 & 0 & 1 & 0 \\ -1 & 0 & -1 & 0 \end{bmatrix}.$$

3. Determine a matrix which has one invariant factor,

$$m_1(x) = (x - 1)^2(x + 1)(x + 2).$$

4. Determine a matrix that has the invariant factors

$$m_1(x) = (x - 1)^2(x + 1),\ m_2(x) = (x - 1)(x + 1),\ m_3(x) = (x - 1)(x + 1).$$

5. Determine whether the following matrices are similar and, if so, find a matrix P such that $A = PBP^{-1}$:

$$A = \begin{bmatrix} 2 & 1 & 5 \\ -1 & 3 & 1 \\ 1 & -2 & 0 \end{bmatrix}, \quad B = \begin{bmatrix} 3 & -1 & 1 \\ -2 & 5 & 8 \\ 1 & -2 & -3 \end{bmatrix}.$$

Hint: Reduce both A and B to Jordan canonical form.

6. Suppose that $V_n(R)$ is itself a cyclic space for a matrix A. What is the Jordan canonical form for this matrix?

7. Under what conditions on a matrix A can the Jordan canonical form be a diagonal matrix?

8. Prove the Corollary to Theorem 4.1.

*9. Prove that a matrix A is always similar to A^{T}.

5. Classical Canonical Forms for Matrices

Although the initial goals of this chapter have been achieved through the results of the preceding section, there are other selections of matrices representing a linear transformation or an equivalence class of matrices which have important applications. Classical canonical forms, which we shall proceed to obtain, have a more intimate connection with the characteristic values of a transformation or a matrix than does the Jordan canonical form but, what is more important, they are directly dependent on the field under consideration.

The results so far in this chapter have been phrased in terms of $V_n(R)$ but, as was remarked, are equally applicable to $V_n(F)$, where F is any field. We shall assume in this section that we are working with $V_n(F)$ and its subspaces, where F is a specific subfield of the complex numbers. The change in viewpoint may be illustrated by the remark that the Jordan canonical form of an $n \times n$ matrix A, whose elements are rational numbers, would be the same whether we had considered $V_n(Ra)$, $V_n(R)$, or $V_n(C)$ or any other subfield of C; but the classical form will, in general, be different for different subfields of C.

Our point of departure from the work of §4 is in the factorization of the invariant factors, $m_j(x)$, of Theorem 3.2 into their irreducible factors in $F[x]$. It will be convenient to work with $m_1(x)$ alone; the steps for the other invariant factors for a linear transformation T or a matrix A are identical. Let

$$(5.1) \qquad m_1(x) = p_1(x)^{b_1}p_2(x)^{b_2} \cdots p_r(x)^{b_r},$$

where $p_j(x)$ is irreducible in $F[x]$ and $b_j \geq 1$, $j = 1, 2, \cdots, r$. (This is where the role of F is important in the discussion. Clearly the irreducible polynomials will, in general, depend on the field F.)

We now make a corresponding decomposition of $L\{\mathbf{X}_1\mathrm{T}^i\}$ of Theorem 3.2. If $q_j(x) = m_1(x)/p_j(x)^{b_j}$, then by a simple extension of parts (iv) and (v) of the statement of Theorem 2.1 we see that

$$\mathbf{X}_{1j} = \mathbf{X}_1 q_j(\mathrm{T})$$

has as relative minimal polynomial $p_j(x)^{b_j}$, and that

$$(5.2) \qquad L\{\mathbf{X}_1\mathrm{T}^i\} = L\{\mathbf{X}_{11}\mathrm{T}^i\} \oplus L\{\mathbf{X}_{12}\mathrm{T}^i\} \oplus \cdots \oplus L\{\mathbf{X}_{1r}\mathrm{T}^i\},$$

where each $\mathbf{X}_{1j}$ has as relative minimal polynomial $p_j(x)^{b_j}$ for $j = 1, 2, \cdots, r$. Later we shall group together the spaces pertaining to powers of a particular $p_j(x)$ for all invariant factors but for the present we shall content ourselves with the problem of choosing a suitable basis for each of the subspaces $L\{\mathbf{X}_{1j}\mathrm{T}^i\}$. Again, a consideration of $L\{\mathbf{X}_{11}\mathrm{T}^i\}$ will serve to illustrate the general process.

Let $p_1(x)$ have the form

$$(5.3) \qquad p_1(x) = x^s + a_{s-1}x^{s-1} + \cdots + a_1x + a_0,$$

and write

$$\begin{array}{llll}
\mathbf{Y}_1 = \mathbf{X}_{11}, & \mathbf{Y}_2 = \mathbf{X}_{11}\mathrm{T}, & \cdots, & \mathbf{Y}_s = \mathbf{X}_{11}\mathrm{T}^{s-1} \\
\mathbf{Y}_{s+1} = \mathbf{X}_{11}p_1(\mathrm{T}), & \mathbf{Y}_{s+2} = \mathbf{X}_{11}p_1(\mathrm{T})\mathrm{T}, & \cdots, & \mathbf{Y}_{2s} = \mathbf{X}_{11}p_1(\mathrm{T})\mathrm{T}^{s-1} \\
\mathbf{Y}_{2s+1} = \mathbf{X}_{11}p_1(\mathrm{T})^2, & & \cdots, & \mathbf{Y}_{3s} = \mathbf{X}_{11}p_1(\mathrm{T})^2\mathrm{T}^{s-1} \\
\cdot \quad \cdot \quad \cdot \quad \cdot \quad \cdot & & & \cdot \quad \cdot \quad \cdot \quad \cdot \quad \cdot \\
\mathbf{Y}_{(b_1-1)s+1} = \mathbf{X}_{11}p_1(\mathrm{T})^{b_1-1}, & & \cdots, & \mathbf{Y}_{b_1s} = \mathbf{X}_{11}p_1(\mathrm{T})^{b_1-1}\mathrm{T}^{s-1}.
\end{array}$$

The $\mathbf{Y}_j$'s for $j = 1, 2, \cdots, b_1s$ are independent since a relation of dependence would give a nonzero polynomial of lower degree than b_1s, which would annihilate $\mathbf{X}_{11}$. (Why?) Moreover, there are b_1s of the $\mathbf{Y}_j$'s. This number is the dimension of $L\{\mathbf{X}_{11}\mathrm{T}^i\}$, and hence the set of vectors $\{\mathbf{Y}_i\}$ is a basis for $L\{\mathbf{X}_{11}\mathrm{T}^i\}$.

In order to find the submatrix (relative to the $\{\mathbf{Y}_i\}$ basis) which we will associate with T acting on $L\{\mathbf{X}_{11}\mathrm{T}^i\}$, we observe that until we reach $\mathbf{Y}_s$ we have

$$\mathbf{Y}_i\mathrm{T} = \mathbf{Y}_{i+1}, \qquad i = 1, 2, \cdots, s-1.$$

Now, $\mathbf{Y}_s\mathrm{T} = \mathbf{X}_{11}\mathrm{T}^s$ and $\mathbf{Y}_{s+1} = \mathbf{X}_{11}(\mathrm{T}^s + a_{s-1}\mathrm{T}^{s-1} + \cdots + a_1\mathrm{T} + a_0\mathrm{I})$, or

$$\mathbf{Y}_s\mathrm{T} = \mathbf{X}_{11}\mathrm{T}^s = -a_0\mathbf{Y}_1 - a_1\mathbf{Y}_2 - \cdots - a_{s-1}\mathbf{Y}_s + \mathbf{Y}_{s+1}.$$

Similarly,

$$\mathbf{Y}_{s+k}\mathrm{T} = \mathbf{Y}_{s+k+1}, \qquad k = 1, 2, \cdots, s-1$$

and

$$\mathbf{Y}_{2s}\mathrm{T} = \mathbf{X}_{11}p_1(\mathrm{T})\mathrm{T}^s = \mathbf{Y}_{s+1}\mathrm{T}^s$$

and

$$\mathbf{Y}_{2s+1} = \mathbf{Y}_{s+1}(\mathrm{T}^s + a_{s-1}\mathrm{T}^{s-1} + \cdots + a_1\mathrm{T} + a_0\mathrm{I}),$$

so that

$$\mathbf{Y}_{2s}\mathrm{T} = -a_0\mathbf{Y}_{s+1} - a_1\mathbf{Y}_{s+2} - \cdots - a_{s-1}\mathbf{Y}_{2s} + \mathbf{Y}_{2s+1},$$

and so on.

Thus, a submatrix D_{11} representing T on $L\{\mathbf{X}_{11}\mathrm{T}^i\}$ is of the form

$$\left[\begin{array}{ccccc:ccccc:cccc}
0 & 1 & 0 & \cdots & 0 & 0 & 0 & & \cdots & 0 & & & & \\
0 & 0 & 1 & \cdots & 0 & 0 & 0 & & \cdots & 0 & & & & \\
\vdots & \vdots & \vdots & \ddots & \vdots & \vdots & \vdots & & \ddots & \vdots & & & & \\
0 & 0 & 0 & \cdots & 1 & 0 & 0 & & \cdots & 0 & & & & \\
-a_0 & -a_1 & -a_2 & \cdots & -a_{s-1} & 1 & 0 & & \cdots & 0 & & & & \\
\hdashline
 & & & & & 0 & 1 & 0 & \cdots & 0 & 0 & 0 & \cdots & 0 \\
 & & & & & 0 & 0 & 1 & \cdots & 0 & 0 & 0 & \cdots & 0 \\
 & & & & & \vdots & \vdots & \vdots & \ddots & \vdots & \vdots & \vdots & \ddots & \vdots \\
 & & & & & 0 & 0 & 0 & \cdots & 1 & 0 & 0 & \cdots & 0 \\
 & & & & & -a_0 & -a_1 & -a_2 & \cdots & -a_{s-1} & 1 & 0 & \cdots & 0 \\
\hdashline
 & & & & & & & & & & & & &
\end{array}\right]$$

It will be convenient to have an abbreviation for matrices of the form D_{11}. We shall adopt the notation

$$(5.4)\qquad D(p(x)^b) = \begin{bmatrix} C(p(x)) & P(s) & & & \\ & C(p(x)) & P(s) & & \\ & & \ddots & \ddots & \\ & & & & P(s) \\ & & & & C(p(x)) \end{bmatrix},$$

where $C(p(x))$ is the companion matrix of the irreducible polynomial $p(x)$ and is repeated b times along the diagonal, and where $P(s)$ is the $s \times s$ matrix

$$P(s) = \begin{bmatrix} 0 & 0 & \cdots & 0 \\ 0 & 0 & \cdots & 0 \\ \vdots & \vdots & & \vdots \\ 0 & 0 & \cdots & 0 \\ 1 & 0 & \cdots & 0 \end{bmatrix},$$

having a single 1 in the lower left-hand place with all other elements zero. The matrix $P(s)$ is repeated $b - 1$ times above the diagonal in $D(p(x)^b)$. We see that

$$D_{11} = D(p_1(x)^{b_1}).$$

The submatrix D_{11} has precisely b_1 companion matrices $C(p_1(x))$ along the diagonal because

$$\mathbf{Y}_{b_1s}\mathrm{T} = \mathbf{X}_{11}p_1(\mathrm{T})^{b_1-1}\mathrm{T}^s$$

and

$$\mathbf{0} = \mathbf{X}_{11}p_1(\mathrm{T})^{b-1}(\mathrm{T}^s + a_{s-1}\mathrm{T}^{s-1} + \cdots + a_1\mathrm{T} + a_0\mathrm{I}),$$

so that

$$\mathbf{Y}_{b_1s}\mathrm{T} = -a_0\mathbf{Y}_{(b_1-1)s+1} - a_1\mathbf{Y}_{(b_1-1)s+2} - \cdots - a_{s-1}\mathbf{Y}_{b_1s},$$

and we do not have an added vector $\mathbf{Y}_{b_1s+1}$ yielding another $P(s)$.

If the previously described process is carried out for all the subspaces $L\{\mathbf{X}_{1j}\mathrm{T}^i\}$ of formula (5.2), we obtain a sequence of submatrices D_{1j}, corresponding to the first invariant factor and the jth irreducible polynomial of (5.1) for $j = 1, 2, \cdots, r$, occurring down the diagonal and representing the effect of T on $L\{\mathbf{X}_{1j}\mathrm{T}^i\}$ relative to the selected bases for each of the spaces $L\{\mathbf{X}_{1j}\mathrm{T}^i\}$.

Next, we carry out a similar process for all the remaining subspaces $L\{\mathbf{X}_h\mathrm{T}^i\}$ ($h = 2, 3, \cdots, k$) of Theorem 3.2 and obtain a sequence of submatrices D_{hj} down the diagonal of the matrix representing T. Of course, if the irreducible polynomial $p_j(x)$ is not present in a factorization of $m_h(x)$ (the hth invariant factor), then that particular D_{hj} will not be present; this case is illustrated in Example 1.

We have now selected bases for each of the subspaces $L\{\mathbf{X}_{hj}\mathrm{T}^i\}$ for $h = 1, 2, \cdots, k$ and $j = 1, 2, \cdots, r$, which occur in our decomposition of $V_n(F)$. Finally, to obtain a classical form, we reorder the vectors of these bases so that, in the resulting matrix representation of T, the submatrices $D_{11}, D_{21}, D_{31}, \cdots$, corresponding to the subspaces associated with various powers of $p_1(x)$, occur first down the diagonal; then the submatrices $D_{12}, D_{22}, D_{32}, \cdots$ associated with the subspaces annihilated by various powers of $p_2(x)$; then $D_{13}, D_{23}, D_{33}, \cdots$; and so on. In essence, we are grouping together the subspaces $L\{\mathbf{X}_{hj}\mathrm{T}^i\}$ (with j fixed) that are annihilated by various powers of the irreducible polynomial $p_j(x)$, in place of the original grouping by invariant factors.

Example 1. Let A be a matrix whose invariant factors are factored as follows over the real field R:

$$\begin{aligned} m_1(x) &= (x^2 + x + 1)^2(x - 2)^3, \\ m_2(x) &= (x^2 + x + 1)(x - 2)^2, \\ m_3(x) &= x^2 + x + 1. \end{aligned}$$

In this case,

$$D_{11} = D\{(x^2 + x + 1)^2\} = \begin{bmatrix} 0 & 1 & 0 & 0 \\ -1 & -1 & 1 & 0 \\ 0 & 0 & 0 & 1 \\ 0 & 0 & -1 & -1 \end{bmatrix};$$

$$D_{21} = D_{31} = D\{(x^2 + x + 1)^1\} = \begin{bmatrix} 0 & 1 \\ -1 & -1 \end{bmatrix};$$

$$D_{12} = D\{(x - 2)^3\} = \begin{bmatrix} 2 & 1 & 0 \\ 0 & 2 & 1 \\ 0 & 0 & 2 \end{bmatrix};$$

$$D_{22} = D\{(x - 2)^2\} = \begin{bmatrix} 2 & 1 \\ 0 & 2 \end{bmatrix};$$

and D_{32} does not exist since $(x - 2)$ does not occur in a factorization of $m_3(x)$.

Finally, the selected matrix, similar to the matrix A, would appear as

$$D = \left[\begin{array}{cccc|cc|cc|ccc|cc} 0 & 1 & 0 & 0 & & & & & & & & & \\ -1 & -1 & 1 & 0 & & & & & & & & & \\ 0 & 0 & 0 & 1 & & & & & & & & & \\ 0 & 0 & -1 & -1 & & & & & & & & & \\ \hline & & & & 0 & 1 & & & & & & & \\ & & & & -1 & -1 & & & & & & & \\ \hline & & & & & & 0 & 1 & & & & & \\ & & & & & & -1 & -1 & & & & & \\ \hline & & & & & & & & 2 & 1 & 0 & & \\ & & & & & & & & 0 & 2 & 1 & & \\ & & & & & & & & 0 & 0 & 2 & & \\ \hline & & & & & & & & & & & 2 & 1 \\ & & & & & & & & & & & 0 & 2 \end{array}\right].$$

The 8×8 submatrix of D in the upper left-hand corner of D represents the effect of the linear transformation T, defined by A in terms of the natural basis $\{\mathbf{E}_i\}$, on the selected bases of the subspaces annihilated by powers of $(x^2 + x + 1)$, and the 5×5 lower right submatrix represents the effect of T on the subspaces annihilated by powers of $(x - 2)$. As before, there exists a matrix P such that $D = PAP^{-1}$.

The method used in the general case of a linear transformation T of $V_n(F)$ or a matrix with elements from the field F essentially duplicates our example.

We assume the invariant factors of Theorem 3.2 to be factored in $F[x]$ into irreducible polynomials,

$$(5.5) \qquad m_i(x) = p_1(x)^{b_{i1}} p_2(x)^{b_{i2}} \cdots p_r(x)^{b_{ir}},$$

for $i = 1, 2, \cdots, k$, where $b_{1j} \geq 1$ for all j and $b_{hj} \geq 0$ for all h and all j. (Note that $b_{1j} = b_j$ in (5.1).)

Now let

$$(5.6) \qquad D_j = \begin{bmatrix} D(p_j(x)^{b_{1j}}) & & & \\ & D(p_j(x)^{b_{2j}}) & & \\ & & \ddots & \\ & & & D(p_j(x)^{b_{kj}}) \end{bmatrix},$$

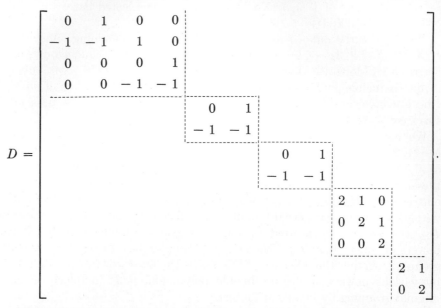

where the $D(p_j(x)^{b_{hj}})$ are defined as in (5.4) and, of course, $b_{rj} \geq b_{sj}$ if $r < s$. The matrix D_j represents the effect of T on the bases selected for the subspaces annihilated by powers of the irreducible polynomial $p_j(x)$ occurring in (5.5). Again, if $b_{hj} = 0$, the corresponding $D(p_j(x)^{b_{hj}})$ is not present. Finally,

$$(5.7) \qquad D = \begin{bmatrix} D_1 & & & & \\ & D_2 & & & \\ & & \cdot & & \\ & & & \cdot & \\ & & & & \cdot \\ & & & & & D_r \end{bmatrix}$$

is a matrix representation of T relative to our selected bases of $L\{\mathbf{X}_{hj}\mathrm{T}^i\}$.

If the linear transformation T is defined on $V_n(F)$ by $\mathbf{X}\mathrm{T} = \mathbf{X}A$, where A is an $n \times n$ matrix with elements in F, then there is a nonsingular matrix P such that

$$D = PAP^{-1}.$$

Example 2. We return to the matrix

$$A = \begin{bmatrix} 3 & -1 & -1 & -2 \\ 1 & 1 & -1 & -1 \\ 1 & 0 & 0 & -1 \\ 0 & -1 & 1 & 1 \end{bmatrix},$$

and consider the elements of A to be from the rational field Ra.

The invariant factors have been determined to be

$$m_1(x) = (x - 1)^2(x - 2) \quad \text{and} \quad m_2(x) = (x - 1)$$

in Example 2, §4. Corresponding to the discussion of this section, we have

$$V_4(R) = L\{\mathbf{X}_1\mathrm{T}^i\} \oplus L\{\mathbf{X}_2\mathrm{T}^i\}$$

where $\mathbf{X}_1 = [1, 0, 0, 0]$ and $\mathbf{X}_2 = [1, -1, -1, -1]$.

Now
$$\begin{aligned} \mathbf{X}_{11} &= [1, 0, 0, 0](A - 2I) = [1, -1, -1, -2], \\ \mathbf{X}_{12} &= [1, 0, 0, 0](A - I)^2 = [2, 0, -2, -2], \\ \mathbf{X}_{21} &= [1, -1, -1, -1], \end{aligned}$$
$\mathbf{X}_{22}$ is not present.

The $\mathbf{Y}$ vectors are

$$\begin{aligned} \mathbf{Y}_1 &= \mathbf{X}_{11} = [1, -1, -1, -2] \\ \mathbf{Y}_2 &= \mathbf{X}_{11}(A - I) = [0, 1, -1, 0] \\ \mathbf{Y}_3 &= \mathbf{X}_{12} = [2, 0, -2, -2] \\ \mathbf{Y}_4 &= \mathbf{X}_{21} = [1, -1, -1, -1]. \end{aligned}$$

We rearrange these vectors for the basis by which we represent T as follows:

$\{[1, -1, -1, -2], [0, 1, -1, 0], [1, -1, -1, -1], [2, 0, -2, -2]\}$.

Now, the matrix P taking the $\{\mathbf{E}_i\}$ basis to the basis listed above is

$$P = \begin{bmatrix} 1 & -1 & -1 & -2 \\ 0 & 1 & -1 & 0 \\ 1 & -1 & -1 & -1 \\ 2 & 0 & -2 & -2 \end{bmatrix};$$

$$P^{-1} = \begin{bmatrix} -1 & -1 & 0 & 1 \\ 0 & 0 & -1 & \frac{1}{2} \\ 0 & -1 & -1 & \frac{1}{2} \\ -1 & 0 & 1 & 0 \end{bmatrix},$$

and the student may check to see that

$$\begin{bmatrix} 1 & -1 & -1 & -2 \\ 0 & 1 & -1 & 0 \\ 1 & -1 & -1 & -1 \\ 2 & 0 & -2 & -2 \end{bmatrix} \begin{bmatrix} 3 & -1 & -1 & -2 \\ 1 & 1 & -1 & -1 \\ 1 & 0 & 0 & -1 \\ 0 & -1 & 1 & 1 \end{bmatrix} \begin{bmatrix} -1 & -1 & 0 & 1 \\ 0 & 0 & -1 & \frac{1}{2} \\ 0 & -1 & -1 & \frac{1}{2} \\ -1 & 0 & 1 & 0 \end{bmatrix} = \begin{bmatrix} 1 & 1 & 0 & 0 \\ 0 & 1 & 0 & 0 \\ 0 & 0 & 1 & 0 \\ 0 & 0 & 0 & 2 \end{bmatrix}$$

is a matrix of the form D in (5.7).

A reordering of the irreducible polynomials $(x - 1)$ and $(x - 2)$ would have yielded the matrix

$$D' = \begin{bmatrix} 2 & 0 & 0 & 0 \\ 0 & 1 & 1 & 0 \\ 0 & 0 & 1 & 0 \\ 0 & 0 & 0 & 1 \end{bmatrix}.$$

Also, note that we would have arrived at the same matrices D and D' even if we had considered the elements of A to be from the real field R. This agreement does not occur in general. (See Exercises 1 and 2.)

DEFINITION 5.1. *The matrices D of the form* (5.7) *in which the submatrices D_j satisfy the restrictions imposed in* (5.6) *are called* CLASSICAL CANONICAL FORMS *for matrices under similarity.*

If D is a matrix of the form (5.7) in which the submatrices D_j satisfy the restrictions imposed in (5.6), we may, by an argument similar to that given in the proof of Theorem 4.1, see that the invariant factors of D are precisely

$$m_i(x) = p_1(x)^{b_{i1}} p_2(x)^{b_{i2}} \cdots p_r(x)^{b_{ir}}.$$

Hence it follows that a matrix A with invariant factors $m_i(x)$ of (5.5) is similar to one such matrix D and, except for the order of the submatrices D_j down the diagonal, this matrix D is unique. With this understanding, the matrices D are indeed canonical forms for the matrices under similarity.

DEFINITION 5.2. *The powers of the irreducible polynomials, $p_j(x)^{b_{hj}}$, occurring in the factorization of the invariant factors $m_h(x)$ of a matrix A are called the* ELEMENTARY DIVISORS *of the matrix A.*

Note that elementary divisors of a matrix depend on the field F, whereas the invariant factors do not. However, given F, the elementary divisors are determined by the invariant factors and conversely.

EXERCISES

1. Determine a matrix D of the form of (5.7) similar to a matrix A with elements in the rational field Ra whose invariant factors are

$$\begin{aligned} m_1(x) &= (x^2 - 2)^3(x + 1)^2(x - 1), \\ m_2(x) &= (x^2 - 2)^2(x + 1). \end{aligned}$$

2. What is the form of a matrix D for Example 1 if the elements of A are considered to be from the real field R?

3. What are the possible sizes of the matrices $P(s)$ for the classical canonical forms over the real field?

4. Find the invariant factors and elementary divisors of the matrices

$$\begin{bmatrix} 0 & 1 & 0 & 0 & & & & \\ -1 & 1 & 1 & 0 & & & & \\ & & 0 & 1 & & & & \\ & & -1 & 1 & & & & \\ & & & & 0 & 1 & & \\ & & & & -1 & 1 & & \\ & & & & & & 3 & 0 \\ & & & & & & 0 & 3 \end{bmatrix}, \quad \begin{bmatrix} 2 & 1 & 0 & & & & & & \\ 0 & 2 & 1 & & & & & & \\ 0 & 0 & 2 & & & & & & \\ & & & 2 & 1 & & & & \\ & & & 0 & 2 & & & & \\ & & & & & 2 & 1 & & \\ & & & & & 0 & 2 & & \\ & & & & & & & & 2 \end{bmatrix}.$$

5. A matrix has the following elementary divisors:

$$(x^2 + 2)^3; \quad (x^2 + 2); \quad (x + 1)^3, (x + 1)^2, (x + 1).$$

What are the invariant factors?

6. Prove that the elementary divisors of a matrix uniquely determine the invariant factors.

6. Classical Canonical Forms for the Complex Field; Hamilton-Cayley Theorem

Perhaps the most useful classical canonical form for matrices under similarity is the one obtained when the linear transformation T is considered as acting on $V_n(C)$ so that the elements of a matrix A are considered to be from the complex field C. In this case, the irreducible polynomials occurring in a factorization of the invariant factors of a linear transformation T (or a matrix A) are linear (Chapter 9, §6). Therefore the elementary divisors (relative to C) are of the form

$$p_j(x) = (x - a)^{b_{hj}},$$

where $a \in C$; the matrices $D(p_j(x)^{b_{hj}})$ of (5.4) take the form

$$D\{(x - a)^{b_{hj}}\} = \begin{bmatrix} a & 1 & 0 & 0 & \cdots & 0 \\ 0 & a & 1 & 0 & \cdots & 0 \\ 0 & 0 & a & 1 & \cdots & 0 \\ \cdot & \cdot & \cdot & \cdot & \cdot & \cdot \\ \cdot & \cdot & \cdot & \cdot & \cdot & \cdot \\ \cdot & \cdot & \cdot & \cdot & \cdot & \cdot \\ 0 & 0 & 0 & 0 & \cdots & 1 \\ 0 & 0 & 0 & 0 & \cdots & a \end{bmatrix}. \tag{6.1}$$

We see in this case that the matrices D_j and D, of (5.6) and (5.7), will be upper triangular matrices.

Example 1. Let A be a matrix whose invariant factors are:

$$\begin{aligned} m_1(x) &= (x^2 + 1)^2(x^2 - 2x + 2) \\ &= (x - i)^2(x + i)^2(x - (1 + i))(x - (1 - i)), \\ m_2(x) &= (x^2 + 1) = (x - i)(x + i). \end{aligned}$$

The form of a matrix D similar to A will be

$$D = \begin{bmatrix} i & 1 & 0 & & & & & \\ 0 & i & 0 & & & & & \\ 0 & 0 & i & & & & & \\ & & & -i & 1 & 0 & & \\ & & & 0 & -i & 0 & & \\ & & & 0 & 0 & -i & & \\ & & & & & & 1 - i & 0 \\ & & & & & & 0 & 1 + i \end{bmatrix}.$$

The matrix D is upper triangular; the zeros of the invariant factors of A occur along the diagonal. The only other elements of D which are not zero are possible chains of ones just above the diagonal. These chains are of length $b_{hj} - 1$ for each elementary divisor occurring.

(The lack of agreement on nomenclature mentioned in §4 has a parallel here. Those who use the term "rational canonical form" frequently call the classical canonical form for the complex field the "Jordan canonical form." The reader must note carefully the definition used in any particular text.)

A diagonal matrix in which equal diagonal elements are arranged together is automatically a classical canonical form. Since these matrices are uniquely defined in an equivalence class up to the order of the elements, it follows that any matrix similar to a diagonal matrix has a diagonal classical form. Therefore we have the interesting result that the matrices similar to a diagonal matrix are precisely those whose invariant factors have only simple zeros so that $b_{hj} = 1$ for all elementary divisors.

Another interesting and important result for matrices that we may obtain easily with the aid of the classical canonical form is contained in the following theorem:

THEOREM 6.1. *If A is an $n \times n$ matrix, the characteristic polynomial of A, ($\det(A - \lambda I)$), is either the product of the invariant factors of A or its negative.*

Proof. The characteristic polynomial of A is the same as the characteristic polynomial of any matrix similar to A (Theorem 1.2, Chapter 10); also the invariant factors of A are identical with those of matrices similar to A.

Thus, using A and the natural basis $\{\mathbf{E}_i\}$ of $V_n(C)$, we define a linear transformation T of $V_n(C)$ and we consider the classical canonical representation D of T given in (5.7). The classical canonical form D of A will be with respect to the complex field. As we have seen, D is upper triangular with the zeros of the invariant factors in the various orders of their multiplicity arranged along the diagonal. That is, if c_j is a zero of $m_i(x)$ of order b_{ij} for $i = 1, 2, \cdots, k$, then the element c_j occurs on the diagonal $b_{1j} + b_{2j} + \cdots + b_{kj}$ times. Therefore $D - \lambda I$ is also upper triangular and the diagonal elements are of the form $c_j - \lambda$. Thus by Theorem 5.2, Chapter 5,

$$\begin{aligned}\det(D - \lambda I) = {} & (c_1 - \lambda)^{b_{11}}(c_1 - \lambda)^{b_{21}} \cdots (c_1 - \lambda)^{b_{k1}} \\ & (c_2 - \lambda)^{b_{12}}(c_2 - \lambda)^{b_{22}} \cdots (c_2 - \lambda)^{b_{k2}} \\ & \quad \vdots \qquad\qquad\qquad\qquad \vdots \\ & (c_r - \lambda)^{b_{1r}}(c_r - \lambda)^{b_{2r}} \cdots (c_r - \lambda)^{b_{kr}}.\end{aligned}$$

But

$$m_i(x) = (x - c_1)^{b_{i1}}(x - c_2)^{b_{i2}} \cdots (x - c_r)^{b_{ir}}, \qquad i = 1, 2, \cdots, k,$$

so that

$$\det(D - \lambda I) = \{\pm m_1(\lambda)\}\{\pm m_2(\lambda)\} \cdots \{\pm m_k(\lambda)\},$$

and this establishes the theorem.

COROLLARY 1. *The minimum polynomial of an $n \times n$ matrix A divides the characteristic polynomial of A.*

COROLLARY 2 (HAMILTON-CAYLEY THEOREM). *Let $f(\lambda) = \det(A - \lambda I)$, the characteristic polynomial of A; then $f(A) = 0$.*

This last corollary is one of the most famous theorems of matrix theory. Coming as it does at the end of a long development and appearing as a mere corollary, the theorem may not appear to the student in its essential difficulty. If this be the case, it is suggested that a proof be attempted without the use of canonical forms. Such proofs may be found, but again the student will observe that considerable preparation and effort are required. For a special case see Exercise 8, §2, Chapter 10.

EXERCISES

1. If the invariant factors of a matrix A are:

$$m_1(x) = (x^2 + 4x + 8)(x^2 + 1), \quad m_2(x) = (x^2 + 1),$$

write a classical canonical form for A with respect to the real field R; to the complex field C.

2. What are the invariant factors and elementary divisors of the matrix

$$D = \begin{bmatrix} i & 1 & 0 & 0 & 0 & 0 \\ 0 & i & 0 & 0 & 0 & 0 \\ 0 & 0 & -i & 1 & 0 & 0 \\ 0 & 0 & 0 & -i & 0 & 0 \\ 0 & 0 & 0 & 0 & 1 & 1 \\ 0 & 0 & 0 & 0 & 0 & 1 \end{bmatrix},$$

with respect to the complex field C? to the real field R?

3. Provide the proof of the Hamilton-Cayley theorem.

4. If the characteristic polynomial of a linear transformation T is $x^4 - 4$, show that this is also the minimum polynomial for T.

5. Generalize Exercise 4 to any linear transformation T whose characteristic polynomial has distinct roots.

6. Use canonical forms to provide a simple proof of Exercise 9, §4.

7. If A is an $n \times n$ matrix and $p(x) \in C[x]$, show that the characteristic values of $p(A)$ are $p(\alpha)$, where α runs through the zeros of the characteristic polynomial of A.

8. Find a polynomial whose zeros are the cubes of the zeros of

$$x^3 - x^2 + x + 1.$$

9. Find the most general matrix that commutes with the matrix $D\{(x - a)^{b_{hj}}\}$ given in (6.1).

10. Prove that the answer to Problem 9 may be written as a polynomial in the matrix $D\{(x - a)^{b_{hj}}\}$.

*11. Generalize Problem 10 as follows: If A is an $n \times n$ matrix having but one invariant factor, show that any matrix that commutes with A must be a polynomial in the matrix A.

Answers to Selected Exercises

CHAPTER 1

§ 1, Page 3

2. (a) Positive integers divisible by 3 but not by 6.
   (b) Those positive integers which are either even or divisible by 3 (or both even and divisible by 3).
   (c) Same as for part (a).
   (d) Same as for part (b).
4. (a) No; yes; no; yes. (b) 16.
5. A set with n elements has 2^n subsets.
10. $(A \cup B) \cap C \subseteq A \cup (B \cap C)$.

§ 2, Page 8

1. (a) 12 (not A3, A4, M4). (b) 14 (not M4). (c) 15.
9. 11; yes.

§ 3, Page 12

2. Yes; yes; into.
3. Single-valued mapping of A into B.
5. Yes; only when A and B have infinitely many elements.
6. Yes; no.
7. 6 mappings; $n!$.
8. Into only.
9. Yes.

CHAPTER 2

§ 1, Page 21

1. (a) $0, 1, \frac{5}{8}, \frac{19}{8}, -\frac{21}{8}, \frac{3}{7}$.
   (b) $-3, 5, 0, 61, -19$.
2. $x' = \dfrac{x+3}{8}$.
5. (a) $(-\frac{1}{2}, 7)$; (b) $(3, 3)$; (c) $(1, 4)$; (d) $(\frac{1}{2}, 0)$; (e) $(-\frac{1}{2}, 1)$.
   (f) $(1, 1)$; (g) $(2, 0)$; (h) $(10, 4)$; (i) $(23, 7)$; (j) $(1, 3)$.
6. $x' = \dfrac{x-y}{2}$, $y' = y$.
7. $2\sqrt{2}$.

§ 2, Page 25

1. $r_1 = 1 + t$, $r_2 = 1 - 2t$, $r_3 = 1 + 2t$; $[r_1, r_2, r_3]$, $[-r_1, -r_2, -r_3]$.
2. $r_1 = 2 + 3t$, $r_2 = 3 - 5t$, $r_3 = -4 + 4t$;
   $[r_1 - 2, r_2 - 3, r_3 + 4]$, $[2 - r_1, 3 - r_2, -4 - r_3]$.
3. (a) $(\frac{3}{2}, 1, 1)$. (b) $(\frac{5}{4}, -\frac{1}{2}, 2)$. (c) $(3, 10, -5)$. (d) $(0, -8, 7)$.
4. $[2, 2, 2]$; $[-1, -1, -2]$; $[1, 1, 0]$.

§ 3, Page 28

1. (a) $[3, 6, 0]$. (b) $[1, 3, 1]$. (c) $[a + b, 2a + 3b, -a + b]$.
3. (a) $\mathbf{R} = [2, 3, -4] + t[3, -5, 4]$. (b) $\mathbf{R} = (1 - t)[1, 1, 1] + t[2, -1, 3]$.
   (c) $\mathbf{R} = [1 + t, -2 + 6t, 3 - 4t]$.
4. $[-1, 1, 0]$; $[\frac{1}{2}, \frac{1}{2}, 0]$.
5. Yes.
6. $[3, 5, -3]$.

§ 4, Page 33

1. Yes.
2. $\mathbf{R} = [p + 3q, 1 - 2p - 3q, - 1 + 2p + 5q]$.
4. Lines through A and C and through A and B respectively.
6. Yes, the $\mathbf{0}$ vector.

§ 5, Page 37

1. If $\mathbf{X}$, $\mathbf{Y}$, and $\mathbf{Z}$ denote the first, second, and third vectors respectively:
   (a) $\mathbf{X} + 3\mathbf{Y} - \mathbf{Z} = \mathbf{0}$.
   (b) Not dependent.
   (c) $3\mathbf{X} + \mathbf{Y} - \mathbf{Z} = \mathbf{0}$.
   (d) Not dependent.
   (e) Not dependent.
2. (a) No solution.
   (b) $x = \frac{5}{2}, y = 1, z = -\frac{1}{2}$.
   (c) $x = \frac{1}{3}, y = \frac{2}{3}, z = \frac{7}{3}$.
   (d) $x = -z, y = -z$, z arbitrary.
   (e) $x = 2 - \frac{3}{7}z, y = 1 - \frac{2}{7}z$, z arbitrary.
   (f) $x = 1, y = 1, z = -1$.
   (g) $x = -t, y = 0, z = 0$, t arbitrary.

§ 6, Page 43

1. $\sqrt{6}$; $\sqrt{10}$; $\sqrt{3a^2 + 2}$.
2. $\cos\theta = \dfrac{18}{\sqrt{374}}$.
4. 5; 8.
5. (a) $(\mathbf{R} - [1, 1, 1], [1, -1, 2]) = 0$.
   (b) $x_1 - x_2 + 2x_3 = 2$.
6. $2x_1 - x_2 - 2x_3 = -4$.
7. $(\mathbf{R}, [-1, 1, 2]) = 9$.

§ 7, Page 47

2. $[-23, -11, -2]$.
3. Linearly dependent.
6. $(\mathbf{X} - [1, -2, 4], [6, 9, -5]) = 0$.
7. $\dfrac{32}{\sqrt{110}}$.
8. (a) Not dependent.
   (b) Dependent.
   (c) Not dependent.

CHAPTER 3

§ 1, Page 52

1. (a) $[4, 7, -1, 3]$. (b) $[5, 7, -3, 16]$. (c) $[2a + b, 3a + 2b, -a, 5a - b]$.
2. The sets in (a) and (b) are vector spaces.
3. (a) Vectors of the form $[a, 0, 0, 0]$ for $a \in R$.
   (b) Vectors of the form $[a, 2a, 0, a + b]$ for $a, b \in R$.
   (c) Vectors of the form $[a + b, a, 0, 0]$ for $a, b \in R$.
5. Yes.
6. All indicated sets are subspaces except (d).

§ 2, Page 60

6. No.
7. Yes.

§ 3, Page 65

1. (a) $\mathbf{A}_3 = 5\mathbf{A}_1 - 3\mathbf{A}_2$. (b) $\mathbf{A}_3 = -\mathbf{A}_1 + 6\mathbf{A}_2$. (c) Independent.
2. $c_1 = c_3, c_2 = -c_3$, c_3 arbitrary.
3. Dependent.
4. $c_1 = \dfrac{26 - 7c_3 - 14c_4}{5}$, $c_2 = \dfrac{2 + c_3 + 2c_4}{5}$, c_3, c_4 arbitrary.

5. Yes.
6. $c_1 = c_2 = c_3 = 0$; independent.
7. $c_1 = -\frac{19}{4}c_4$, $c_2 = -\frac{21}{4}c_4$, $c_3 = -\frac{9}{4}c_4$, c_4 arbitrary.
8. $[\frac{19}{4}, \frac{21}{4}, \frac{9}{4}, -1]$.
9. 1.

§ 4, Page 70

1. (a) No. (b) Yes.
4. All values of k except 0, 1, $-\frac{4}{3}$.
8. (b) $[a + 2b, -a + b, -b, a] \to [a, b]$.

§ 5, Page 75

1. $S \cap T = L\{[1, 2, -1]\}$.
2. Dimensions are 2, 3, 1, 4 respectively.
5. $\mathbf{Y} = [5, 1, -2]$, $\mathbf{Z} = [-1, 0, -1]$.
6. $\mathbf{X} \in T$, $\mathbf{X} \in S$ respectively.
8. $S + T = V_4(R)$; $S \cap T$ consists of all vectors of the form $[2a, b, a, b]$.

§ 6, Page 82

1. (a) -1. (b) 0.
2. $x = \frac{1}{3}, -1$.
3. $\{[1, 2, -1, 0], [\frac{1}{2}, -1, -\frac{3}{2}, 1], [\frac{1}{9}, \frac{1}{9}, \frac{1}{3}, \frac{5}{9}]\}$.
8. $[0, -\frac{8}{5}, \frac{16}{5}, 0]$.

CHAPTER 4

§ 1, Page 89

1. (a) $z_1 = 1 + t$, $z_2 = 2 + 2t$, $z_3 = -1 + 2t$, $z_4 = 3 + 2t$.
   (b) $z_1 = 1 - t$, $z_2 = 4 - t$, $z_3 = -1 - 2t$, $z_4 = 3 - 2t$.
2. Yes; (3, 6, 3, 7).
3. $r_1 = 1 + r_1^*$, $r_2 = 1 + r_4^*$, $r_3 = r_1^* + r_2^* + r_3^*$, $r_4 = r_1^* + r_3^*$.
4. (a) $(2, -2, 2, 0)$. (b) $(2, 1, 5, 2)$.

§ 2, Page 95

1. $(1 + t_1, -1 + 2t_1, t_2, 3 - t_1)$.
4. 2.

§ 3, Page 101

1. (a) $\sqrt{17}$. (b) 5. (c) $2\sqrt{7}$.
2. No.
5. $\dfrac{12}{\sqrt{182}}$.
6. $\dfrac{5}{\sqrt{15}}$.
7. $(\frac{24}{13}, \frac{14}{13}, -\frac{43}{13}, \frac{25}{13})$.
9. 27.

CHAPTER 5

§ 2, Page 108

1. (a) -7. (b) 19. (c) ab.
2. (a) -2. (b) -2. (c) -4.
4. $\Delta(\mathbf{X}_1) = x_1$ where $\mathbf{X}_1 = [x_1]$.

§ 3, Page 112

1. (a) 3 inversions; 3 transpositions.
   (b) 5 inversions; 3 transpositions.
   (c) 9 inversions; 5 transpositions.
   (d) 4 inversions; 2 transpositions.
   (e) 24 inversions; 8 transpositions.
   (f) 25 inversions; 7 transpositions.
   (g) 28 inversions; 4 transpositions.
   (h) 13 inversions; 5 transpositions.

2. (a) $f_P = f_I$; 4 inversions.
   (b) $f_P = -f_I$; 3 inversions.
   (c) $f_P = -f_I$; 3 inversions.
   (d) $f_P = f_I$; 6 inversions.
4. (a) $-$. (b) $+$. (c) $-$. There would be 720 terms.
5. (a) -2. (b) 0.
9. Rules (i) and (iii) are satisfied.

§ 4, Page 119

1. (a) 3. (b) -2. (c) -26. (d) 3.
2. (a) P1. (b) P3. (c) Theorem 4.1. (d) P4. (e) P3.

§ 5, Page 125

1. (a) $-12, -6, -3$. (b) $-12, 6, -3$.
2. (a) -9. (b) 0. (c) -174.
3. (a) $a_{11}a_{22}\cdots a_{nn}$. (b) $(-1)^{\frac{n(n-1)}{2}} a_{1n}a_{2,\,n-1}\cdots a_{n1}$.

§ 6, Page 132

1. (a) Dependent. (b) Dependent. (c) Dependent for all values of x.
4. 5.
10. (a) $y = \frac{14}{11}$. (b) $z = 0$. (c) No unique solution. (d) $x = 1, y = z = t = w = 0$.

CHAPTER 6

§ 1, Page 140

3. Parts (a) and (c) are one-to-one. The image set of (b) is $L\{[1, -1]\}$.
5. Mapped into the point $(1, -1)$.
6. (b), (c), (d) are linear transformations.
8. $[x_1, x_2, x_3] \xrightarrow{\text{T}} [x_1, x_2, -x_3]$; a linear transformation.

§ 2, Page 146

3. $[x_1, x_2, x_3] \xrightarrow{\text{T}} [2x_1 + x_3, x_1 + x_2 + x_3]$. Null space is $L\{[1, 1, -2]\}$. Range is all of $V_2(R)$.
4. Range is $L\{[1, 1, -1], [1, -1, 1]\}$. Null space is $L\{[1, -2, 1]\}$.
5. Range is $L\{[0, 1, 0, 0], [2, 1, 2, 1]\}$. Null space is $L\{[1, 2, -4]\}$.
6. $\mathbf{E}_1\text{T} = 4\mathbf{E}_1' + 4\mathbf{E}_2' + 4\mathbf{E}_3' + 2\mathbf{E}_4'$
   $\mathbf{E}_2\text{T} = -6\mathbf{E}_1' - 8\mathbf{E}_2' - 6\mathbf{E}_3' - 3\mathbf{E}_4'$
   $\mathbf{E}_3\text{T} = -2\mathbf{E}_1' - 3\mathbf{E}_2' - 2\mathbf{E}_3' - \mathbf{E}_4'$.
8. $\mathbf{X}_1\text{T} = 2\mathbf{X}_1 - \mathbf{X}_2 - \mathbf{X}_3$
   $\mathbf{X}_2\text{T} = -\frac{1}{3}\mathbf{X}_1 + \frac{1}{3}\mathbf{X}_2 + \frac{2}{3}\mathbf{X}_3$
   $\mathbf{X}_3\text{T} = -\frac{1}{3}\mathbf{X}_1 - \frac{2}{3}\mathbf{X}_2 + \frac{2}{3}\mathbf{X}_3$.
10. Null space is W. Range is S.

§ 3, Page 152

1. (a) (i) [1, 1, 2]; (ii) [0, 0, 1]; (iii) [3, -1, 2]; (iv) [-1, 3, 1]; (v) [2, 2, 3]; (vi) [-3, 1].
   (b) $[x_1 - 2x_2, x_2, x_1 - x_2]$.
   (c) $[x_2, x_1 - 2x_2, x_1]$.
   (d) $[x_1, x_1, 2x_1 + x_2]$.
   (e) $[x_1 - x_2, x_1 - x_2, 2x_1 - x_2]$.

2\. (a)
$$\begin{aligned} \mathbf{X}_1T_3T_1 &= 2\mathbf{X}_1' - \mathbf{X}_2' + \mathbf{X}_3' \\ \mathbf{X}_2T_3T_1 &= \mathbf{X}_1' + \mathbf{X}_4' \\ \mathbf{X}_3T_3T_1 &= \mathbf{X}_1' + \mathbf{X}_2' + \mathbf{X}_3' + \mathbf{X}_4'. \end{aligned}$$

(b)
$$\begin{aligned} \mathbf{X}_1(T_1 + T_2) &= 2\mathbf{X}_1' - \mathbf{X}_2' + 3\mathbf{X}_3' \\ \mathbf{X}_2(T_1 + T_2) &= 2\mathbf{X}_1' - \mathbf{X}_2' - \mathbf{X}_3' + \mathbf{X}_4' \\ \mathbf{X}_3(T_1 + T_2) &= 2\mathbf{X}_2' + \mathbf{X}_3' + \mathbf{X}_4'. \end{aligned}$$

(c)
$$\begin{aligned} \mathbf{E}_1T_1 &= 2\mathbf{E}_2' - \mathbf{E}_3' + \mathbf{E}_4' \\ \mathbf{E}_2T_1 &= \mathbf{E}_1' + \mathbf{E}_3' \\ \mathbf{E}_3T_1 &= \mathbf{E}_1' - \mathbf{E}_2' + 2\mathbf{E}_3'. \end{aligned}$$

$$\begin{aligned} \mathbf{E}_1T_2 &= -3\mathbf{E}_1' + 7\mathbf{E}_2' + \mathbf{E}_3' + \mathbf{E}_4' \\ \mathbf{E}_2T_2 &= -2\mathbf{E}_1' + 4\mathbf{E}_2' \\ \mathbf{E}_3T_2 &= 3\mathbf{E}_1' - 4\mathbf{E}_2' + \mathbf{E}_3'. \end{aligned}$$

$$\begin{aligned} \mathbf{E}_1T_3 &= 2\mathbf{E}_1 - 3\mathbf{E}_2 \\ \mathbf{E}_2T_3 &= \mathbf{E}_1 - \mathbf{E}_2 \\ \mathbf{E}_3T_3 &= 2\mathbf{E}_2 + 2\mathbf{E}_3. \end{aligned}$$

(d)
$$\begin{aligned} \mathbf{E}_1T_3T_1 &= -3\mathbf{E}_1' + 4\mathbf{E}_2' - 5\mathbf{E}_3' + 2\mathbf{E}_4' \\ \mathbf{E}_2T_3T_1 &= -\mathbf{E}_1' + 2\mathbf{E}_2' - 2\mathbf{E}_3' + \mathbf{E}_4' \\ \mathbf{E}_3T_3T_1 &= 4\mathbf{E}_1' - 2\mathbf{E}_2' + 6\mathbf{E}_3'. \end{aligned}$$

(e)
$$\begin{aligned} \mathbf{E}_1(T_1 + T_2) &= -3\mathbf{E}_1' + 9\mathbf{E}_2' + 2\mathbf{E}_4' \\ \mathbf{E}_2(T_1 + T_2) &= -\mathbf{E}_1' + 4\mathbf{E}_2' + \mathbf{E}_3' \\ \mathbf{E}_3(T_1 + T_2) &= 4\mathbf{E}_1' - 5\mathbf{E}_2' + 3\mathbf{E}_3'. \end{aligned}$$

(f)
$$\begin{aligned} \mathbf{E}_1T_3(T_1 + T_2) &= -3\mathbf{E}_1' + 6\mathbf{E}_2' - 3\mathbf{E}_3' + 4\mathbf{E}_4' \\ \mathbf{E}_2T_3(T_1 + T_2) &= -2\mathbf{E}_1' + 5\mathbf{E}_2' - \mathbf{E}_3' + 2\mathbf{E}_4' \\ \mathbf{E}_3T_3(T_1 + T_2) &= 6\mathbf{E}_1' - 2\mathbf{E}_2' + 8\mathbf{E}_3'. \end{aligned}$$

3\. $\theta_1 = -\theta_2$; $\theta_3 = 0$.

4\.
$$\begin{aligned} &\mathbf{X}_1T_{11} = \mathbf{X}_1'; \quad \mathbf{X}_1T_{12} = \mathbf{0}; \quad \mathbf{X}_1T_{13} = \mathbf{X}_3'; \quad \mathbf{X}_1T_{14} = \mathbf{0}; \\ &\mathbf{X}_2T_{11} = \mathbf{X}_1'; \quad \mathbf{X}_2T_{12} = -\mathbf{X}_2'; \quad \mathbf{X}_2T_{13} = \mathbf{0}; \quad \mathbf{X}_2T_{14} = \mathbf{0}; \\ &\mathbf{X}_3T_{11} = \mathbf{0}; \quad \mathbf{X}_3T_{12} = \mathbf{X}_2'; \quad \mathbf{X}_3T_{13} = \mathbf{0}; \quad \mathbf{X}_3T_{14} = \mathbf{X}_4'. \end{aligned}$$

6\. Parts (i), (ii), (iii) are valid if sum is defined appropriately for mappings.

9\. Respectively: identity transformation, 0, 0, T_1, T_2.

§ 4, Page 158

1\. $\begin{bmatrix} a & 0 & \cdots & 0 \\ 0 & a & \cdots & 0 \\ \cdot & \cdot & & \cdot \\ \cdot & \cdot & & \cdot \\ \cdot & \cdot & & \cdot \\ 0 & 0 & \cdots & a \end{bmatrix}.$ 2. $\begin{bmatrix} ab & 0 & \cdots & 0 \\ 0 & ab & \cdots & 0 \\ \cdot & \cdot & & \cdot \\ \cdot & \cdot & & \cdot \\ \cdot & \cdot & & \cdot \\ 0 & 0 & \cdots & ab \end{bmatrix}.$

3\. $\begin{bmatrix} 1 & 0 \\ a & 1 \end{bmatrix}.$

4\. (a) $[ax_1, x_2]$. (b) $[x_1, x_3, x_2]$. (c) $[ax_1, x_1 + x_2, x_2]$.

5\. (a) $\begin{bmatrix} 1 & 2 \\ 1 & -1 \end{bmatrix}.$ (b) $\begin{bmatrix} 1 & -1 & 1 \\ 0 & 0 & 1 \end{bmatrix}.$

6\. $\mathbf{E}_1T_1T_2 = \mathbf{E}_1' - \mathbf{E}_2' + 3\mathbf{E}_3'$;
$\mathbf{E}_2T_1T_2 = \mathbf{E}_1' - \mathbf{E}_2'$. $\quad T_1T_2 \longrightarrow \begin{bmatrix} 1 & -1 & 3 \\ 1 & -1 & 0 \end{bmatrix}.$

7. (a) $\begin{bmatrix} 1 & 2 & 0 \\ 1 & 0 & 2 \\ -1 & 1 & 1 \end{bmatrix}$. (b) $\begin{bmatrix} 0 & 0 & 1 \\ -1 & 0 & 1 \\ 0 & 0 & 0 \end{bmatrix}$.

8. $\mathbf{E}_1(T_1 + T_2) = [1, 2, 1]$; $\mathbf{E}_1 T_1 T_2 = [-2, 0, 3]$;
$\mathbf{E}_2(T_1 + T_2) = [0, 0, 3]$; $\mathbf{E}_2 T_1 T_2 = [0, 0, 1]$;
$\mathbf{E}_3(T_1 + T_2) = [-1, 1, 1]$; $\mathbf{E}_3 T_1 T_2 = [-1, 0, 0]$.

$$T_1T_2 \longrightarrow \begin{bmatrix} -2 & 0 & 3 \\ 0 & 0 & 1 \\ -1 & 0 & 0 \end{bmatrix}; \qquad T_2T_1 \longrightarrow \begin{bmatrix} -1 & 1 & 1 \\ -2 & -1 & 1 \\ 0 & 0 & 0 \end{bmatrix}.$$

§ 5, Page 163

1. (a) $\begin{bmatrix} 0 & 1 \\ 5 & 1 \end{bmatrix}$.
   (b) $\begin{bmatrix} 2 & 5 & 4 \\ 2 & 5 & 9 \end{bmatrix}$.

4. (a) No answer.
   (b, c) $\begin{bmatrix} 2 & -4 & -3 \\ -1 & 22 & 14 \end{bmatrix}$.
   (d) $\begin{bmatrix} 2 & 5 \\ 5 & 13 \end{bmatrix}$.
   (e) $\begin{bmatrix} 12 & 13 \\ 31 & 34 \end{bmatrix}$.
   (f) $\begin{bmatrix} -3 & -8 \\ 19 & 49 \end{bmatrix}$.
   (g) No answer.
   (h) $\begin{bmatrix} -1 & -4 \\ 8 & 7 \end{bmatrix}$.

5. (a) $[0, 2, -2]$.
   (b) $[0, 2, -2]$.
   (c) $\begin{bmatrix} 2 & 2 & 0 \\ 2 & 0 & 2 \\ 3 & 5 & 1 \end{bmatrix}$.
   (d) $\begin{bmatrix} 2 & 1 & 0 \\ 2 & 2 & 1 \\ 1 & 3 & 2 \end{bmatrix}$.
   (e) $[0, 2, -2]$.

6. $AB = \begin{bmatrix} 0 & 1 \\ 3 & 5 \end{bmatrix}$; $BA = \begin{bmatrix} 5 & 1 \\ 3 & 0 \end{bmatrix}$.

7. Commuting matrices are $\begin{bmatrix} a & b \\ -b & a \end{bmatrix}$ for $\sin\theta \neq 0$.

§ 6, Page 169

1. $[x_1, x_2, x_3]T^{-1} = [x_1 + 2, x_2, x_3 - x_1 - 2]$.

2. $[x_1, x_2]T^{-1} = \left[\dfrac{x_1 + x_2}{2}, \dfrac{x_2 - x_1}{2}\right]$.

3. $[x_1, x_2, x_3]T^{-1} = [x_1 - x_2, x_2 - x_3, x_3]$.

5. $\begin{bmatrix} 1 & 1 \\ -1 & 1 \end{bmatrix}$; $\frac{1}{2}\begin{bmatrix} 1 & -1 \\ 1 & 1 \end{bmatrix}$.

6. $\begin{bmatrix} 1 & 0 & 0 \\ 1 & 1 & 0 \\ 1 & 1 & 1 \end{bmatrix}$; $\begin{bmatrix} 1 & 0 & 0 \\ -1 & 1 & 0 \\ 0 & -1 & 1 \end{bmatrix}$.

8. The first and third.

§ 7, Page 175

1. $\begin{bmatrix} -5 & 3 & 0 & 0 \\ 2 & -1 & 0 & 0 \\ 0 & 0 & 1 & -1 \\ 0 & 0 & -1 & 2 \end{bmatrix}$.

2. (a) $\frac{1}{7}\begin{bmatrix} 3 & -1 \\ 1 & 2 \end{bmatrix}$. (b) $\frac{1}{4}\begin{bmatrix} -3 & 1 & 3 \\ -1 & -1 & 5 \\ 1 & 1 & -1 \end{bmatrix}$. (c) $\begin{bmatrix} 1 & 2 & -1 \\ 0 & 1 & 0 \\ 1 & 5 & -2 \end{bmatrix}$.

4. (a) $\begin{bmatrix} 1 & 1 & 0 \\ 0 & 1 & 1 \\ 1 & 0 & 1 \end{bmatrix}$, $\frac{1}{2}\begin{bmatrix} 1 & -1 & 1 \\ 1 & 1 & -1 \\ -1 & 1 & 1 \end{bmatrix}$.

(b) $\mathbf{Z} = 2\mathbf{Y}_1 - \mathbf{Y}_3$.

(c) $c_1' + c_2' + c_3' = 0$.

5. (a) $\mathbf{Y}_1 = [3, -4, 3, 0]$; $\mathbf{X}_1 = -6\mathbf{Y}_1 + \frac{3}{2}\mathbf{Y}_2 + \frac{7}{2}\mathbf{Y}_3$;
$\mathbf{Y}_2 = [1, 2, 5, 3]$; $\mathbf{X}_2 = 3\mathbf{Y}_1 - \frac{1}{2}\mathbf{Y}_2 - \frac{3}{2}\mathbf{Y}_3$;
$\mathbf{Y}_3 = [5, -8, 3, -1]$; $\mathbf{X}_3 = -\mathbf{Y}_1 + \frac{1}{2}\mathbf{Y}_2 + \frac{1}{2}\mathbf{Y}_3$.

(b) $\mathbf{Z} = 2\mathbf{X}_1 + \mathbf{X}_2 + \mathbf{X}_3 = -10\mathbf{Y}_1 + 3\mathbf{Y}_2 + 6\mathbf{Y}_3$.

§ 8, Page 182

1. $P = \begin{bmatrix} 2 & -1 \\ -1 & 1 \end{bmatrix}$; $Q = \frac{1}{6}\begin{bmatrix} 1 & 1 & 2 \\ 2 & -4 & -2 \\ 3 & 3 & 0 \end{bmatrix}$.

2. $P^{-1} = \begin{bmatrix} 1 & 1 \\ 1 & 2 \end{bmatrix}$; $Q^{-1} = \begin{bmatrix} 1 & 1 & 1 \\ -1 & -1 & 1 \\ 3 & 0 & -1 \end{bmatrix}$.

3. $\begin{bmatrix} -24 & -3 & 10 \\ 14 & 2 & -4 \end{bmatrix}$.

4. $\mathbf{Z} = -13\mathbf{X}_1 + 5\mathbf{X}_2 = -8\mathbf{Y}_1 - 3\mathbf{Y}_2$; $\mathbf{Z}T = [-4, 254, -118]$.

5. $\begin{bmatrix} 1 & 2 \\ \frac{3}{5}, & -\frac{4}{5} \end{bmatrix}$.

6. $\frac{1}{3}\begin{bmatrix} -4 & 5 & -1 \\ -4 & 8 & -1 \\ 8 & -4 & 2 \end{bmatrix}$.

8. $\begin{bmatrix} 0 & 1 & 0 & \cdots & 0 \\ 0 & 0 & 1 & \cdots & 0 \\ \cdot & \cdot & \cdot & & \cdot \\ \cdot & \cdot & \cdot & & \cdot \\ \cdot & \cdot & \cdot & & \cdot \\ 0 & 0 & 0 & \cdots & 1 \\ 1 & 0 & 0 & \cdots & 0 \end{bmatrix}$.

§ 9, Page 187

3. Properties satisfied: (a), (iii); (b), (i), (iii); (c), none; (d), (ii); (e), (i), (ii), (iii); (f), (i), (ii), (iii); (g), (ii).

5. No.

CHAPTER 7

§ 2, Page 197

1. (a) $E = S_{32}(1)$; $AE = B$.

(b) $E = P_{23}$; $EA = B$.

(c) $E = D_1(2)$; $AE = B$.

3. (a) $\frac{1}{20}\begin{bmatrix} -1 & -1 & 6 \\ -13 & 7 & -2 \\ 4 & 4 & -4 \end{bmatrix}$.

(b) $\frac{1}{33}\begin{bmatrix} 8 & 13 & -1 \\ -7 & 1 & 5 \\ -9 & 6 & -3 \end{bmatrix}$.

6. (a) $\frac{1}{6}\begin{bmatrix} 8 & 2 & -6 & 0 \\ -19 & 2 & 3 & 12 \\ -6 & 0 & 0 & 6 \\ -3 & 0 & 3 & 0 \end{bmatrix}$.

(b) $\frac{1}{35}\begin{bmatrix} 25 & -15 & 15 & -5 \\ -7 & 14 & -7 & 7 \\ 9 & -18 & 4 & 1 \\ -6 & 12 & -26 & 11 \end{bmatrix}$.

§ 3, Page 203

1. Ranks are: (a) 3; (b) 2; (c) 3; (d) 3.
3. Rank is 3 unless $h = 3$, $k = 1$; in this case rank is 2.

§ 4, Page 206

1. The first two matrices are equivalent. 2. No solution.

§ 5, Page 209

1. The sets in parts (a), (c), (e), (f) are groups under the indicated operations.
2. In (b) the set of nonsingular lower triangular matrices is a group under multiplication; in (d) the set of nonzero matrices of the type indicated is a group under multiplication.
5. $\{\pm 1, \pm i, \pm j, \pm k\}$, $\{\pm 1, \pm i\}$, $\{\pm 1, \pm j\}$, $\{\pm 1, \pm k\}$, $\{\pm 1\}$, $\{1\}$.

§ 6, Page 215

3. $$\begin{bmatrix} \frac{1}{2} & -\frac{1}{2} & \frac{1}{\sqrt{2}} \\ \frac{5}{6} & \frac{1}{2} & -\frac{1}{3\sqrt{2}} \\ -\frac{1}{3\sqrt{2}} & \frac{1}{\sqrt{2}} & \frac{2}{3} \end{bmatrix}.$$

CHAPTER 8

§ 1, Page 221

1. (a) $[x_1, x_2]\begin{bmatrix} 2 & 3 \\ -4 & 1 \end{bmatrix}[y_1, y_2]^{\mathsf{T}}$.
   (b) $[x_1, x_2]\begin{bmatrix} 5 & 0 \\ -1 & 2 \end{bmatrix}\begin{bmatrix} y_1 \\ y_2 \end{bmatrix}$.
   (c) $[x_1, x_2, x_3]\begin{bmatrix} 1 & 1 & -1 \\ 2 & 0 & -1 \\ 0 & 0 & 0 \end{bmatrix}[y_1, y_2, y_3]^{\mathsf{T}}$.
2. $\begin{bmatrix} 1 & 2 \\ -4 & 3 \end{bmatrix}$.
3. (a) 3; 21.
   (b) $\begin{bmatrix} -1 & 1 \\ -5 & 14 \end{bmatrix}$.
4. Condition $b_{ij} = b_{ji}$ is necessary and sufficient.

§ 2, Page 226

1. (a) $x_1^2 - 6x_1x_2 + 4x_2^2$. (b) $x_1^2 + 4x_2^2 + 5x_3^2 - 4x_1x_2 + 6x_1x_3 + 2x_2x_3$.
2. (a) $[x_1, x_2]\begin{bmatrix} 2 & -4 \\ -4 & 3 \end{bmatrix}\begin{bmatrix} x_1 \\ x_2 \end{bmatrix}$.
   (b) $[x_1, x_2, x_3]\begin{bmatrix} 3 & 3 & 4 \\ 3 & -2 & -2 \\ 4 & -2 & 5 \end{bmatrix}\begin{bmatrix} x_1 \\ x_2 \\ x_3 \end{bmatrix}$.
3. (a) $24y_1^2 + 2y_1y_2 - y_2^2$.
   (b) $\begin{bmatrix} 3 & 1 \\ 2 & -1 \end{bmatrix}\begin{bmatrix} 1 & 2 \\ 2 & 3 \end{bmatrix}\begin{bmatrix} 3 & 2 \\ 1 & -1 \end{bmatrix} = \begin{bmatrix} 24 & 1 \\ 1 & -1 \end{bmatrix}$.
7. $x_2^{*2} - 6x_3^{*2} + 36x_1^*x_2^* + 30x_1^*x_3^* - 6x_2^*x_3^*$.

§ 3, Page 234

1. Both are congruent to $\begin{bmatrix} 1 & 0 & 0 \\ 0 & -1 & 0 \\ 0 & 0 & -1 \end{bmatrix}$.
2. $y_1^2 + y_2^2 - y_3^2$.
4. 10.

§ 5, Page 241

1. $\{[1, 0, 0], [-2, 1, 0], [5, -2, 1]\}$.
3. $L\{[1, 0, -1, 0], [1, 0, 0, -1]\}$.
4. $(1, 0, 0), (-2, 1, 0), (5, -2, 1)$.

CHAPTER 9

§ 1, Page 249

1. (a) $[4, 2]$. (b) $[8, 11]$. (c) $4 + 2i$. (d) $8 + 11i$.
3. (a) $\sqrt{2}\left(\cos\frac{7\pi}{4} + i \sin\frac{7\pi}{4}\right)$. (b) $\sqrt{2}\left(\cos\frac{3\pi}{4} + i \sin\frac{3\pi}{4}\right)$.
   (c) $3\left(\cos\frac{3\pi}{2} + i \sin\frac{3\pi}{2}\right)$. (d) $2\left(\cos\frac{\pi}{6} + i \sin\frac{\pi}{6}\right)$.
   (e) $5\{\cos(\cos^{-1}\frac{3}{5}) + i \sin(\cos^{-1}\frac{3}{5})\}$.
   (f) $\sqrt{5}\{\cos(\tan^{-1}(-\frac{1}{2})) + i \sin(\tan^{-1}(-\frac{1}{2}))\}$.
4. (a) $2\sqrt{3} + 2i$. (b) $2i$. (c) $\frac{1}{2} + \frac{\sqrt{3}}{2}i$. (d) $\frac{\sqrt{3}}{\sqrt{2}} + \frac{\sqrt{3}}{\sqrt{2}}i$.
8. $r^{-1}\{\cos(2\pi - \theta) + i \sin(2\pi - \theta)\}$, or $\frac{1}{r}(\cos\theta - i \sin\theta)$.
9. $\frac{r_1}{r_2}\{\cos(\theta_1 - \theta_2) - i \sin(\theta_1 - \theta_2)\}$.
10. (a) $\cos\frac{2k\pi}{5} + i \sin\frac{2k\pi}{5}$; $k = 0, 1, \cdots, 4$.
    (b) $2^{1/4}\left(\cos\frac{5\pi}{8} + i \sin\frac{5\pi}{8}\right)$, $2^{1/4}\left(\cos\frac{13\pi}{8} + i \sin\frac{13\pi}{8}\right)$.
    (c) $\pm 5, \pm 5i$.
    (d) $-3\left(\cos\frac{2k\pi}{3} + i \sin\frac{2k\pi}{3}\right)$, $k = 0, 1, 2$.
    (e) $\pm\left(\frac{\sqrt{3}}{\sqrt{2}} + \frac{1}{\sqrt{2}}i\right)$.
    (f) $\cos\left(\frac{\pi}{2} + \frac{2k\pi}{3}\right) + i \sin\left(\frac{\pi}{2} + \frac{2k\pi}{3}\right)$, $k = 0, 1, 2$.
11. $z^{-1} = \frac{\bar{z}}{|z|^2}$.
15. $\cos\frac{2\pi}{3} + i \sin\frac{2\pi}{3}$, $\cos\frac{4\pi}{3} + i \sin\frac{4\pi}{3}$, 1 are cube roots of 1; ± 1 are square roots of 1.
16. 2.

§ 4, Page 263

2. (a) $q(x) = x + \sqrt{2}$; $r(x) = 1 - \sqrt{6}$.
   (b) $q(x) = -1 - x - x^2 - \cdots - x^{n-1}$; $r(x) = 0$.
   (c) $q(x) = 5 - x$; $r(x) = -4 + 12x - 5x^2$.
   (d) $q(x) = -1 + 2x + 3x^2$; $r(x) = 1$.

3. (a) $x + 1$. (b) 1. (c) $2 + 2x + 3x^2 + 2x^3 + 2x^4$. (d) $x - 3$.

4. (a) $p_1(x) = \dfrac{\sqrt{2}}{\sqrt{2}+2}$; $p_2(x) = \dfrac{1}{\sqrt{2}+2}$.

(b) $p_1(x) = \frac{1}{14}(-3 - 4x + 2x^2 + 5x^3)$; $p_2(x) = \frac{1}{14}(17 - 8x + 5x^2)$.

(c) $p_1(x) = 1$; $p_2(x) = 0$.

(d) $p_1(x) = \frac{1}{100}(-7 + x)$; $p_2(x) = \frac{1}{400}(-5 + 8x - x^2)$.

§ 6, Page 270

2. In $C[x]$: $(x - 2 + 3i)$, $(x - 2 - 3i)$, $(x - 1)$, $(x - 5)$, $(x - 1 + i)$, $(x - 1 - i)$; in $R[x]$: $(x^2 - 4x + 13)$, $(x^2 - 2x + 2)$, $(x - 1)$, $(x - 5)$.

§ 7, Page 274

1. $2x^3 + 3x^2 + 3x + 1$.

3. $x = 1 - i, \frac{1}{5}(-11 + 8i)$.

4. (a) $2, \pm\sqrt{3}$. (b) $1, 2, \frac{5}{2}$.

(c) $-\frac{1}{2}, \dfrac{-1 \pm i\sqrt{15}}{2}$.

(d) No rational roots. (e) No rational roots, roots are $\pm i$.

CHAPTER 10

§ 1, Page 280

1. (a) Value, 1. Vectors, all nonzero vectors.

(b) Values, $+1, -3$. Vectors, $[2a, a]$, $[0, a]$, $a \neq 0$.

(c) Value, 0. Vectors, $[a, a, a]$, $a \neq 0$.

(d) Values, $\pm 1, 2$. Vectors, $[a, -a, 2a]$, $[0, a, -a]$, $[0, 0, a]$, $a \neq 0$.

2. (a) $\lambda^2 - 3\lambda - 4$; $-1, 4$; $[3a, -2a]$, $[a, a]$, $a \neq 0$.

(b) $-\lambda^3 + 4\lambda^2 - 5\lambda + 2$; $1, 2$; $[a, -a, 2a]$, $[0, 0, a]$, $a \neq 0$.

(c) $\lambda^2 + 2$; $\pm\sqrt{2}i$; $\left[a, \left(\dfrac{-2 + \sqrt{2}i}{3}\right)a\right]$, $\left[a, \left(\dfrac{-2 - \sqrt{2}i}{3}\right)a\right]$, $a \neq 0$.

§ 2, Page 286

1. (a) Diagonal $[1, 0]$. (b) Diagonal $[1, -1, -3]$. (c) Diagonal $[1, -1, -1]$.

2. Characteristic vectors are $[a, -3a, 2a]$ and $[0, -2a, a]$; these do not generate $V_3(R)$.

3. $$\begin{bmatrix} 1 & \dfrac{1+\sqrt{3}i}{2} \\ 1 & \dfrac{1-\sqrt{3}i}{2} \end{bmatrix} \begin{bmatrix} 1 & -1 \\ 1 & 2 \end{bmatrix} \begin{bmatrix} \dfrac{\sqrt{3}+i}{2\sqrt{3}} & \dfrac{\sqrt{3}-i}{2\sqrt{3}} \\ -\dfrac{i}{\sqrt{3}} & \dfrac{i}{\sqrt{3}} \end{bmatrix} = \begin{bmatrix} \dfrac{3+\sqrt{3}i}{2} & 0 \\ 0 & \dfrac{3-\sqrt{3}i}{2} \end{bmatrix}.$$

§ 3, Page 290

1. $$P = \begin{bmatrix} \dfrac{1}{\sqrt{2}} & \dfrac{1}{\sqrt{2}} & 0 \\ \dfrac{1}{3\sqrt{2}} & -\dfrac{1}{3\sqrt{2}} & -\dfrac{4}{3\sqrt{2}} \\ \dfrac{2}{3} & -\dfrac{2}{3} & \dfrac{1}{3} \end{bmatrix}.$$

2. (a) Diagonal $[1, \frac{17}{12}, \frac{7}{12}]$.

(b) $\lambda_1 = 1, \lambda_2 = \frac{17}{12}, \lambda_3 = \frac{7}{12}$; corresponding characteristic vectors are [3, 0, − 4], [4, 5, 3], [4, − 5, 3], which are orthogonal.

(c) $$\begin{bmatrix} \frac{3}{5} & 0 & -\frac{4}{5} \\ \frac{4}{5\sqrt{2}} & \frac{1}{\sqrt{2}} & \frac{3}{5\sqrt{2}} \\ \frac{4}{5\sqrt{2}} & -\frac{1}{\sqrt{2}} & \frac{3}{5\sqrt{2}} \end{bmatrix}.$$

§ 4, Page 295

1. $$[x_1, x_2] = [y_1, y_2]\begin{bmatrix} \frac{1}{\sqrt{5}} & \frac{2}{\sqrt{5}} \\ -\frac{2}{\sqrt{5}} & \frac{1}{\sqrt{5}} \end{bmatrix}.$$

2. Principal axes are in directions indicated by [0, 0, 1], $\left[1, \frac{-1+\sqrt{5}}{2}, 0\right]$, $\left[1, \frac{-1-\sqrt{5}}{2}, 0\right]$. Reduced form is $2y_1^2 + \frac{3+\sqrt{5}}{2}y_2^2 + \frac{3-\sqrt{5}}{2}y_3^2 = 1$.

CHAPTER 11

§ 1, Page 303

1. (a) 2. (b) $x^2 - 3x + 2$. (c) 2. (d) $x^2 - 5x + 6$. (e) $\{[1, -2, 1]\}$. (f) $x - 2$. (g) $x - 2$.

§ 2, Page 308

1. (a) $x^3 + x^2 - x - 1$.

(b) $L\{X_1T^i\} = L\{X_1\}$, $L\{X_2T^i\} = L\{[-3, 4, 1, 1], [5, -8, -3, -3]\}$; $m_1(x) = x - 1$, $m_2(x) = (x+1)^2$. $\mathbf{X} = [-3, 5, 1, 1]$, and the minimum polynomial is $x^3 + x^2 - x - 1$.

(c) $x^3 + x^2 - x - 1$.

3. $x^3 - 6x^2 + 11x - 6$.

§ 3, Page 315

1. $V_4(R) = L\{\mathbf{E}_1A^i\} + L\{\mathbf{E}_3A^i\}$.

§ 4, Page 321

1. $$\begin{bmatrix} 0 & 1 & 0 \\ 0 & 0 & 1 \\ -16 & 1 & 4 \end{bmatrix}.$$

2. $$\begin{bmatrix} 0 & 1 & 0 & 0 \\ 0 & 0 & 1 & 0 \\ 1 & 1 & -1 & 0 \\ 0 & 0 & 0 & 1 \end{bmatrix}.$$

3. $$\begin{bmatrix} 0 & 1 & 0 & 0 \\ 0 & 0 & 1 & 0 \\ 0 & 0 & 0 & 1 \\ -2 & 1 & 3 & -1 \end{bmatrix}.$$

4. $$\begin{bmatrix} 0 & 1 & 0 & 0 & 0 & 0 & 0 \\ 0 & 0 & 1 & 0 & 0 & 0 & 0 \\ -1 & 1 & 1 & 0 & 0 & 0 & 0 \\ 0 & 0 & 0 & 0 & 1 & 0 & 0 \\ 0 & 0 & 0 & 1 & 0 & 0 & 0 \\ 0 & 0 & 0 & 0 & 0 & 0 & 1 \\ 0 & 0 & 0 & 0 & 0 & 1 & 0 \end{bmatrix}.$$

5. Yes.

6. The companion matrix of the minimum polynomial of A.

7. A is scalar.

§ 5, Page 329

1. $$\begin{bmatrix} 0 & 1 & 0 & 0 & & & & & & & & & & & \\ 2 & 0 & 1 & 0 & & & & & & & & & & & \\ & & 0 & 1 & 0 & 0 & & & & & & & & & \\ & & 2 & 0 & 1 & 0 & & & & & & & & & \\ & & & & 0 & 1 & 0 & 0 & & & & & & & \\ & & & & 2 & 0 & 0 & 0 & & & & & & & \\ & & & & & & 0 & 1 & 0 & 0 & & & & & \\ & & & & & & 2 & 0 & 1 & 0 & & & & & \\ & & & & & & & & 0 & 1 & 0 & 0 & & & \\ & & & & & & & & 2 & 0 & 0 & 0 & & & \\ & & & & & & & & & & & -1 & 1 & & \\ & & & & & & & & & & & & -1 & 0 & \\ & & & & & & & & & & & & & -1 & 0 \\ & & & & & & & & & & & & & & 1 \end{bmatrix}.$$

2. $$\begin{bmatrix} \sqrt{2} & 1 & & & & & & & & & & & & \\ & \sqrt{2} & 1 & & & & & & & & & & & \\ & & \sqrt{2} & 0 & & & & & & & & & & \\ & & & \sqrt{2} & 1 & & & & & & & & & \\ & & & & \sqrt{2} & 0 & & & & & & & & \\ & & & & & -\sqrt{2} & 1 & & & & & & & \\ & & & & & & -\sqrt{2} & 1 & & & & & & \\ & & & & & & & -\sqrt{2} & 0 & & & & & \\ & & & & & & & & -\sqrt{2} & 1 & & & & \\ & & & & & & & & & -\sqrt{2} & 0 & & & \\ & & & & & & & & & & -1 & 1 & & \\ & & & & & & & & & & & -1 & 0 & \\ & & & & & & & & & & & & -1 & 0 \\ & & & & & & & & & & & & & 1 \end{bmatrix}.$$

3. 2×2 or 1×1.

4. First matrix: elementary divisors, $(x^2 - x + 1)^2$, $(x^2 - x + 1)$, $(x - 3)$, $(x - 3)$; invariant factors, $(x^2 - x + 1)^2(x - 3)$, $(x^2 - x + 1)(x - 3)$. Second matrix: elementary divisors and invariant factors, $(x - 2)^3$, $(x - 2)^2$, $(x - 2)^2$, $(x - 2)$.

5. $(x^2 + 2)^3(x + 1)^3$, $(x^2 + 2)(x + 1)^2$, $x + 1$.

§ 6, Page 332

1. Real: Complex:

$$\begin{bmatrix} 0 & 1 & 0 & 0 & & \\ -1 & 0 & 0 & 0 & & \\ & & 0 & 1 & 0 & 0 \\ & & -1 & 0 & 0 & 0 \\ & & & & 0 & 1 \\ & & & & -8 & -4 \end{bmatrix}. \qquad \begin{bmatrix} i & 0 & & & & \\ & i & 0 & & & \\ & & -i & 0 & & \\ & & & -i & 0 & \\ & & & & (-2+2i) & 0 \\ & & & & & (-2-2i) \end{bmatrix}.$$

2. Complex: elementary divisors, $(x - i)^2$, $(x + i)^2$, $(x - 1)^2$. Real: elementary divisors, $(x^2 + 1)^2$, $(x - 1)^2$. In either case, the only invariant factor is $(x^2 + 1)^2(x - 1)^2$.

8. $x^3 + 5x^2 + 7x + 1$.

Index

B C D E F G H I J K 0 6 9 8 7 6 5 4 3 2 1

PRINTED IN THE UNITED STATES OF AMERICA